The Radio Amateur's
Satellite Handbook

Martin Davidoff, K2UBC

THE COVER

Clockwise from right:

The mighty new Ariane 5 rocket as it lifted off in October 1997 from Kourou, French Guiana.

Tracking the ham satellites is a pleasant chore with the help of tracking programs such as *WiSP*.

NASA Astronaut Dave Leestma, N5WQC, enjoying a ham contact while in Earth orbit.

Back cover: The *WiSP* setup screen is easy to navigate.

Ariane photo courtesy ESA/CNES
WiSP images courtesy Steve Ford, WB8IMY
Shuttle photo courtesy NASA

Published by
The American Radio Relay League
225 Main Street
Newington, CT 06111

Contents

Foreword

Back in 1984, when the ARRL published the first comprehensive book about the ham satellites, *The Satellite Experimenter's Handbook*, it covered the nine amateur spacecraft then in orbit. How things have changed! As this new book is published, there are 20 (count 'em!) amateur spacecraft available to the amateur community—each a marvel of science, technology and the plain old ham ingenuity that has kept Amateur Radio thriving throughout the 20th century.

Perhaps you enjoyed tracking and using the first of the "Phase 3" amateur spacecraft, OSCAR 10, back in 1984. As this is written, 19 years later, you can still use it! That simple fact speaks volumes for the way the team of volunteers designed and built that particular spacecraft. It also speaks volumes for the way those who contribute to the amateur space program go about their business—with the highest levels of expertise and professionalism. The fact that the overwhelming number are volunteers does not compromise this professionalism one iota.

The ARRL is pleased to have contributed to the amateur satellite program almost from its inception. The new OSCAR 40 spacecraft is by far the most versatile—and expensive—ham satellite to date. It would not have been built without the vision and hard work of hundreds of AMSAT volunteers in Germany, the US and around the world. To help ensure that the amateur space program remains healthy into the next century, ARRL will donate a portion of the proceeds from the sale of this book to AMSAT-NA.

If you're new to the wonders of space communication, this book will get you off the ground. If you're an experienced satellite communicator, you'll find all the reference material and tips you need to get the most out of your pursuit of the amateur birds. Either way, enjoy!

David Sumner, K1ZZ
Executive Vice President
Newington, Connecticut
June 2003

About the Author-Dedication

In the late 1950s, a high school junior in Brooklyn New York passed his first Amateur Radio exam. The new Novice, KN2UBC, had no idea that Amateur Radio would be part of his life over the next half century. The Novice, of course, was me.

My first receiver, a military surplus 6-9 MHz ARC-5 purchased on radio row (Canal Street) in Manhattan, got me on the 40-meter novice band. But the DX bug soon bit so I scraped together the parts for a simple 21-MHz receive converter, a frequency I then regarded as super high. In those years a key element to parts acquisition was walking the streets about 9 PM, prior to garbage collection days, searching for discarded AM radios or the jackpot, a TV.

Sputnik One was launched about six months after my license arrived. The receiving setup just described, and tracking data from W1AW, enabled me to hear its 20-MHz beacon. A few months later I passed the General class exam (on my second try) at the FCC's NYC office—the code was a real struggle. Nowadays I tend to procure parts by other methods, but I still get a thrill from listening to spacecraft, especially on simple equipment that's at least partially homebrew.

Several years later, while an undergraduate physics major at the City University of NY, I applied for an interesting looking part-time job on a weather forecasting project at Columbia University. The job description mentioned computers but the computer turned out to be a mechanical monster known as a Marchant and what they really wanted was a slave for data entry.

About a year later, the academic unit at Columbia University acquired its first real computer—a GE LPG-30 (?). Somehow, I managed to have my boss send me to a short workshop on using it. As I recall, it had a large number of dual triode (tube) flip flops and about 2 K of memory. You had to program in machine language—there weren't any higher-level options.

When I completed my BS the following June, I took a year off from school. My ham radio experience helped me get a job as an electronic technician on Columbia University's deep-sea oceanographic research vessel VEMA. Eight months of on and off seasickness on most of the world's oceans, and a chance to operate as HP9FC/mm and HPFC (the VEMAs commercial call), followed. I figured that there had to be a better way to earn a living.

So, I left the ship and began graduate school in Physics at Syracuse University. My research on transport properties of semiconductors at temperatures near absolute zero provided me with the opportunity to learn FORTRAN and work with some very interesting hardware including giant conventional magnets, early superconducting magnets and microwave klystrons and plumbing at frequencies up to 37 GHz. Our primary conventional magnet, produced by a company in California, had a 4-A, 3000-V constant-current power supply. I always thought it would be the perfect companion for a California kW. One of my more memorable accomplishments was providing an energy source at 74 GHz needed for experiments by designing a coupled cavity frequency doubler using the highest frequency Klystron we had—37 GHz. I even had to grow the crystal used as the nonlinear element. I thought about this for the first time in many years as I recently listened to a recording of AO-40's 24-GHz downlink shortly after it was turned on for initial tests. The quality of the SSB signals was hard to believe—we've clearly come a long way.

While I was living in Syracuse, the FCC changed the rules of the game. Since my main Amateur Radio interest at the time was working CW DX on the HF bands with 50 W and dipoles I needed access to the critical frequencies at the lower edge of the HF bands that the Extra Class ticket provided. By this time, copying code was no longer a problem but writing coherently at 20 WPM was a formidable obstacle.

Obtaining my Ph.D. took more years than I care to remember. The job that followed was in Annapolis, Maryland working for a branch of the Illinois Institute of Technology Research Institute. One of the projects I was involved with focused on the conceptual design of LEO satellite systems. This was in the early 1970s, a year or two after AMSAT was born in the DC area.

I didn't know any of the founders but I attended some meetings, volunteered for a few tasks and did some calculations involving current and future amateur spacecraft that turned out to be as interesting to others as they were to me. A short time later, I switched jobs to accept a position teaching mathematics at a Community College near Baltimore, Maryland where I still work.

Initially I was attracted to AMSAT by a desire to design and construct space hardware. But it soon became apparent that there were other critical tasks that needed attention. And I happened to be in a unique position to work on one— documenting and publicizing the achievements of the Amateur Radio Satellite program. The object was to establish AMSAT's reputation in the professional and academic worlds that would make it easier to get support for future missions.

With this goal in mind, I applied for and received funds from the National Science Foundation and the Smithsonian Air and Space Museum to produce educational materials focusing on AMSAT spacecraft. This led, among other things, to the production in 1977 of a book called Using Satellites in the Classroom: A Guide For Science Educators.

Working with AMSAT was continually exciting. Building and launching satellites was only part of the picture. In 1980, the US boycotted the Moscow Olympics to protest the Soviet invasion of Afghanistan. However, three Soviet gold medals did reach the US that year. They were for RadioSport activities related to the first two Russian amateur satellites, RS-1 and RS-2, which had been launched in 1978. This author received one—for reporting telemetry on one of the first orbits to the Soviet builders. Several years later, I hosted Leo Labutin, UA3CR, on his first trip to the US to attend the 1989 AMSAT-NA convention in Atlanta. I'll never forget the midnight phone call from our hotel room to the cosmonaut command center in Star City, outside Moscow, to make final arrangements for the first Mir-US QSO via Amateur Radio the next day.

When Phase 3A was being built I discussed the possibility of producing a book on the radio amateur satellite program with AMSAT and the ARRL. This led to two editions of the *Satellite Experimenters Handbook* and, several years later, the *ARRL Satellite Handbook*—which you're holding in your hands. Neither of these projects would have been possible without the earlier support from the National Science Foundation and the Smithsonian Air and Space Museum.

I've been following the amateur radio satellite program for over forty years now, and directly involved in it for about thirty. That's a long time—the thing that kept me going was the people I got to work with. I can truly say that some of the finest scientists and engineers I've ever met were through AMSAT activities and one of the great pleasures of my life has been the chance I've had to work with them over the decades. And the opportunities continue. Late in 1996, I spent nearly a month as a Visiting Scientist at the UoSAT Center for Satellite Engineering and Research at the University of Surrey.

Over the years that I've been an active radio amateur I've met a large number of individuals who have devoted a great deal of time and energy to returning something to the "hobby" that has given them so much. They often work with little recognition. They do it simply because they feel it's the right thing to do. This book is my way of showing them my appreciation and saying thanks.

Martin Davidoff, K2UBC, April 2003

Chapter 1

History→1980

1 History: ⇒ 1980

THE DAWN OF THE SPACE AGE

It was October 5, 1957. Shortly after midnight (GMT), at a BBC radio monitoring station located at Tatsfield (just south of London), attention was focused on a strange signal—frequency measurements revealed a slow downward drift having an unusual pattern, and direction finding reports couldn't be reconciled with a terrestrial or airborne source. After eliminating every other conceivable possibility the staff was forced to conclude that the signal was coming from an artificial satellite orbiting the Earth. The Space Age had begun.

At about the same time that the BBC observations were being made public the Soviet news agency, TASS, announced the launch of Sputnik I. The information quickly flashed around the world. Liftoff of Sputnik I had occurred at 19:28:04 GMT on 4 October 1957 from Tyuratam, a village about 150 miles northeast of the Sea of Aral in the USSR.[1] While these events may not sound very spectacular today, they generated tremendous excitement at the time.

Newspapers reported that the world responded with "surprise and elation."[2,3,4] Since the Soviets had been discussing their plans publicly for some time the surprise was mainly due to widespread disbelief in the West that the USSR was capable of such a sophisticated technological feat. The June 1957 issue of *Radio*, a widely distributed Soviet magazine covering practical electronics, had described the forthcoming launch in an article that gave the target date as late September (a remarkably accurate projection) and the beacon frequencies as 20.005 and 40.010 MHz. Details were also made public later that summer at international scientific meetings in Barcelona and Washington.

The prelaunch announcements and the choice of beacon frequencies make it clear that secrecy was not part of the Soviet agenda and that there was, in fact, a strong desire to get the information out. One of the reasons can be inferred from a statement in the *Radio* article, a condensed translation of which was later printed in *QST*: "Since radio amateur observations will be of a mass character they can secure extremely important data on the satellite's flight and the state of the ionosphere."[5]

Tens, perhaps hundreds, of thousands of radio amateurs around the world, fascinated by the idea of listening to signals from space, tuned in the booming 20.005 MHz Sputnik I downlink during the first few days it was in orbit. Because of its strength and proximity to 20 MHz WWV the signal was easy to spot, even using the poorly calibrated general coverage receivers then popular.

THE US ENTERS SPACE

The first successful United States launch took place four months later on 31 January 1958. The spacecraft, Explorer I, contained a scientific instrument package for measuring radiation levels in space designed by a group of physicists under the direction of Dr. James Van Allen of the University of Iowa. When the initial telemetry data arriving at the ground was decoded it indicated that most flight instruments were registering values completely off scale. The scientists first thought that a catastrophic failure had occurred in the satellite electronics. But, after a painstaking but unsuccessful search to identify the failure mode they were forced to conclude that the instruments were actually operating properly. The real "problem" was that the radiation levels encountered were so high that the instruments had been driven into saturation. The now elated scientists began the task of mapping the belts of radiation that would later bear Van Allen's name.[6]

THE IMPACT OF THE SPACE AGE

A considerable amount of money has been invested in space exploration and the development of related technologies over the years since 1957. Unmanned Earth satellites are one area where there has been a clear economic payoff. For more than a quarter century satellites have played a central role in international telecommunications.[7] Daily data provided by spacecraft have revolutionized our ability to forecast weather, predict crop yields, monitor the environment and manage natural resources. Satellites also contribute significantly to terrestrial navigation, scientific exploration and TV broadcasting. And, their unique ability to monitor compliance with arms limitation treaties has contributed to international political stability.[8]

Satellite parking spots in certain desirable regions of the sky are scarce.[9] Perhaps in the 21st century financial support for the United Nations will come from parking meters—leases on communications rights to orbital slots. Meanwhile, radio frequencies suitable for satellite com-

Sputnik Launch Mystery Solved

One day, while preparing a lecture on the occasion of the 25th anniversary of the Space Age, I turned to my files to find the exact time at which Sputnik I had been launched. This basic piece of information seemed to be conspicuously absent from the resources I had on hand. A trip to the library where I spent several hours in front of a microfilm reader checking old copies of *The New York Times*, *Scientific American*, *Science*, *Physics Today*, *Sky and Telescope*, *Science News*, and other magazines, journals and books left me feeling very confused. Only a few of these sources specified a launch time and those that did provided contradictory data which generally lacked information as to source.

A few days later everything seemed to fall into place when I realized what I believe to be the reason for the confusion. In 1957 the cold war was a significant factor in world politics. Knowing Sputnik I's launch time one can trace back along the satellite ground track shown on newspapers worldwide and determine the point of launch. Since the location of the launch site has military significance the Soviets naturally decided to omit this data from their announcements. Statements specifying the launch time coming from a western block country would reveal the extent of western intelligence sources' knowledge of the launch site. Such information was also likely to be withheld. This seemed to explain the lack of information, but how about the contradictory data?

Two estimates that did appear in the contemporary literature were 21:05 GMT, attributed to "western scientists" in *Science News* (Oct. 19, 1957, p 243), and about 21:00 GMT, attributed to astronomers at Bonn University in *Sky & Telescope* (Nov. 1957, p 11). Since these numbers were consistent, appeared to originate from reliable sources (perhaps a single source), and roughly agreed with calculations described in the next paragraph, I was inclined to

accept them. However, because several other sources reported different launch times I didn't feel comfortable endorsing these values until the following scenario occurred to me. Assume that the two estimates mentioned, which had been released by scientists who may have been unaware of the political concerns of the governments involved or who couldn't imagine that their simple, crude calculations could have military significance, had been close to the true launch time. It's possible that western (and/or eastern) intelligence sources purposely released contradictory data to confuse the issue and keep the other side guessing. I therefore, somewhat reluctantly, accepted the 21:00 GMT launch time as being roughly correct.

As to my own calculations. In 1982, when I was researching this question, the launch site was known. This made it possible to use radio amateur satellite tracking techniques and orbital and radio signal acquisition time information available in the *New York Times* the first few days after launch to estimate the actual launch time. Using this approach I felt that the 21:00 Z value was in good agreement with the observations presented.

Several years later, during a lecture at an AMSAT Colloquium at the University of Surrey (England), I discussed this story and my conclusions. Geoff Perry, famous for his observations of the Soviet space program during the period when secrecy was the order of the day, was in the audience. Shortly after I returned home I received a letter from him specifying the launch time as 19:28:04 Z[1] which I now accept as being correct.

The 19:28 Z time is approximately one orbit earlier than I had previously concluded. This may be due to the fact that the low point in the satellite orbit, about 170 km, was occurring near 40° North latitude. Or, it could have been due to the fact that the announced acquisition time was actually the second orbit observed by the BBC and they thought it prudent to conceal their true capabilities. Your turn to speculate.

---

munication have become so valuable that radio amateurs must continually struggle against well financed attempts to evict the Amateur Satellite Service from its assigned bands.

Space satellites have produced major social changes by modifying the way we think about the Earth, the civilizations that inhabit it, and ourselves. Pictures of the Earth taken from space have done more to make us aware of the limits of this planet's resources and force us to recognize the fact that we must work together if we want our spaceship to continue sustaining life, than all the words ever written on the subject.[10] Discussing these effects more than a quarter of a century ago, Isaac Asimov predicted that Earth satellites would produce social changes comparable in magnitude to the creation of speech, writing and printing. These changes, he wrote, would have a profound, positive effect on personal communications between Earth's inhabitants, knitting them together for the first time on a

personal instead of a governmental level.[11]

We now turn to some satellite communications basics and then look at the story of how radio amateurs' fascination with space communications systems, which began with Sputnik I, led them to construct more than 40 spacecraft (1997 totals) which have been launched by the US, the European Space Agency, the CIS (formerly USSR), and the Japanese Space Agency during the past 35 years.

SATELLITE COMMUNICATIONS LINKS

In a vacuum a radio wave travels in a straight line. In such an environment a link involving two stations can only be established if the direct path (also known as the line-of-sight path) between them is clear of obstacles. Most radio links between a *ground station* (station on, or near, the surface of the Earth) and a satellite involve frequencies that require an obstacle-free line-of-sight path. Blockage can be caused by the Earth (due to its overall spherical shape or local irregularities such as mountains), buildings, foliage, or other objects that absorb or reflect the frequency of interest. When studying satellite communication it's convenient to consider the effect of each of these potential obstructions separately.

We begin by observing how the spherical shape of the Earth limits the surface region that a satellite can communicate with. Figure 1.1 pretty much tells the full story. The point on the surface of the Earth directly below the satellite is known as the *subsatellite point*. At any specific time satellite coverage on the surface of the Earth is confined to the region inside a circle (*coverage circle*) around the subsatellite point. The coverage circle is formed by drawing a set of lines from the satellite which just graze the Earth. The set of grazing lines form a *coverage cone*. Of course, the antennas on the satellite may not illuminate the entire coverage area, and other obstructions may act to limit coverage further. These factors will be considered later.

The Satellite Relay

In the mid 1940s[12] Arthur C. Clarke described how terrestrial stations could communicate over long distances by using a satellite relay station employing radio frequencies that easily penetrate the ionosphere (this includes most of the VHF, UHF and microwave spectrum). Although communication over long distances via HF frequencies and ionospheric reflection was an everyday occurrence, satellite relays appeared to have a number of significant advantages for this purpose. These included reliability, predictability, and the ability to handle wide-bandwidth modes such as TV.

Many years later (1955) an independent analysis of the potential value of satellite relays came out of Bell Telephone Laboratories, which was then a world center for state-of-the-art research in communications. The conclusions of the author, a well known physicist named J. R. Pierce, were similar to those of Clarke.[13]

The relay stations proposed by Clarke and Pierce can take a number of different forms. One uses a *linear transponder*, an electronic device that receives, frequency shifts, and amplifies a small slice of the radio frequency spectrum and then retransmits the resulting slice back down to Earth. This is accomplished so quickly (within microseconds) that, insofar as users are concerned, it is instantaneous. The linear transponders used on Amateur Radio satellites can handle a large number of signals of various types at the same time, with the power of each received signal being multiplied by roughly 10^{13} (130 dB) before it's transmitted back to Earth.

A linear transponder permits real-time communication between two or more ground stations as long as the stations are simultaneously within a satellite's coverage circle. For a low altitude spacecraft (altitude about 0.1 to 0.3 Earth radii) the maximum communication distance (the diameter of the coverage circle) is roughly 5000 miles. For a high altitude radio amateur spacecraft (altitude about 6 Earth radii) the maximum communication distance is roughly 11,000 miles or almost halfway around the Earth.

To appreciate the physical meaning of these altitude numbers look at Figure 1.1 and picture the Earth as being a common 12-inch diameter globe. The orbits of the US Space Shuttle and Mir are generally about 0.25 inch above the surface while those of low Earth orbiting (LEO) spacecraft are about 0.5 to 1.5 inches. In contrast, high altitude amateur spacecraft would be found about 3 feet above the surface.

Relay stations can also be designed to receive and store messages (usually in digital form). Each message can then be played back at a later time when the spacecraft passes over a different region of the Earth. Such a device is known as a digital store-and-forward repeater (frequently referred to as a digital repeater). Digital repeaters enable any two ground stations who eventually fall within a satellite coverage circle to communicate by exchanging messages, but this communication is generally not of an immediate nature.

RADIO AMATEURS AND SPACE

Radio amateur interest in signals from space began long before Sputnik I. During the late '30s and early '40s Dr. Grote Reber (W9GFZ) prepared a series of comprehensive radio sky maps using a homebuilt 32-foot diameter parabolic antenna set up in his Wheaton, Illinois, backyard. These maps, showing the location of radio noise sources across the sky, led to the birth of a new branch of basic science now known as radio astronomy.[14] A half century later, in 1985, while radio amateurs around the world were competing to talk to astronaut Tony England, W0ORE, orbiting the Earth on the Spacelab-2 mission, Dr. Reber was still making measurements of signals from space. This time he was working at 1.7 MHz, a frequency that normally doesn't penetrate the ionosphere. A 16 second burn of the

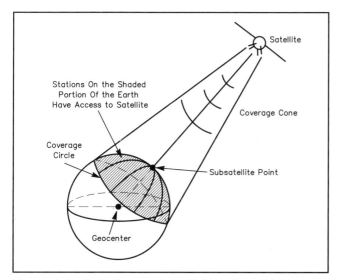

Figure 1.1—Only those terrestrial stations with unobstructed line-of-sight paths to a satellite are in range.

orbital maneuvering rockets aboard Skylab opened a temporary window that provided Reber with a unique opportunity to view cosmic medium frequency signals for nearly four hours.[15]

In 1953 radio amateurs began to explore another arena for space communication when on January 27 Ross Bateman (W4AO) and William L. Smith (W3GKP) beamed radio signals at the moon and succeeded in hearing echos.[16] So, when in the late '50s thousands of radio amateurs monitored signals from early Soviet and American satellites they were following in a long tradition. What would radio amateurs do next?

In April 1959, Don Stoner (W6TNS), a widely known and well-respected electronics experimenter, wrote in *CQ*: "Currently being tested is a solar powered six- to two-meter transistor repeater which could be ballooned over the Southwest. Can anyone come up with a spare rocket for orbiting purposes?"[17] At a point in time when the major governments of the world had only reached the stage of placing beacons in orbit, Stoner was proposing that hams attempt the far more difficult task of building a spacecraft containing a transponder capable of supporting two-way communication. When his proposal was made, construction of the first government/commercial satellite to use a transponder (Telstar I, launched July 1962) hadn't even begun, FM repeaters were virtually unknown in the Amateur Radio community, and most radio amateurs had never had their hands on those newfangled devices called transistors. Although some labeled Stoner's goal science fantasy the proposal was serious and his note provided the spark that led, not many years later, to radio amateurs placing an operational, active relay satellite in orbit.

In 1960, their imaginations fired by the Stoner article, several radio amateurs in Sunnyvale, California, organized the OSCAR Association (Orbiting Satellite Carrying Amateur Radio). The aim of this pioneering group was to build amateur satellites and arrange to have them launched. It wasn't clear which goal would be more difficult. There was reason to believe that a launch might be forthcoming if the US government could be convinced that amateur satellites would serve a useful function in one or more of the following areas: scientific exploration, technical development, disaster communications, or scientific/technical education. As a result, the amateur satellite community has paid serious attention to these areas since its inception, a tradition that continues to this day.

One important factor was to help groups from both the radio amateur and the scientific communities seeking launches. Most large satellites are mated to rockets having excess lift capacity and it's often simpler and cheaper to ballast a rocket with dead weight than to reduce the thrust. As a result, the cost of adding a secondary payload to many missions was relatively modest. Over the years many scientific and amateur satellites have taken advantage of this situation to hitchhike into space as piggyback payloads.

OSCAR I

It took the members of the OSCAR Association less

than two years to build the first radio amateur satellite—OSCAR I—and arrange for its launch. Weighing in at 10 pounds, the spacecraft contained a 140-mW beacon at 145 MHz. The beacon transmitted a simple, repetitive Morse code message (···· ··) at a speed controlled by a sensor responding to the internal spacecraft temperature. Figure 1.2 compares the OSCAR I beacon transmitter to the 10-mW transmitter on Explorer I (the first US satellite) and the transmitter on an early US Vanguard mission. Although OSCAR I did not contain a transponder, it was an important first step toward that goal. The events and emotions surrounding the launch of OSCAR I and its 22-day sojourn in space were beautifully captured in a classic *QST* article by Bill Orr (W6SAI).[18]

OSCAR I was an overwhelming success. More than 570 amateurs in 28 countries made careful measurements of its downlink and forwarded their observations to the Project OSCAR data reduction center. These observations provided important information on radio propagation through the ionosphere, the spacecraft's orbit and satellite thermal design. The OSCAR I mission clearly demonstrated that amateurs are capable of (1) designing and constructing reliable spacecraft, (2) coordinating with government launch agencies, (3) tracking satellites and (4) collecting and processing related scientific and engineering information. Because of its low altitude, OSCAR I only remained in orbit for 22 days before burning up as it reentered the Earth's atmosphere.[19,20]

The launch for OSCAR I was provided by the US Air Force. Since OSCAR I was the first satellite to reach orbit as an auxiliary package ejected from a parent spacecraft, its ejection mechanism was of great interest to scientific groups desiring to place their own free flying satellites in space. When these groups approached the US Air Force for information they were advised to study the OSCAR I design. The ejection mechanism, which had been subjected to detailed stress analysis and careful mechanical and thermal balancing, had been constructed around a $1.15 spring from Sears.[21]

OSCAR II

OSCAR II was successfully launched on June 2, 1962, barely six months after OSCAR I. Structurally and electrically the two spacecraft were initially nearly identical but, despite the extremely short time between the two launches, the design group was able to use results from the first flight to make several improvements in OSCAR II. These improvements included (1) changing the surface thermal coatings to achieve a cooler internal spacecraft environment, (2) modifying the sensing system so the satellite temperature could be measured accurately as the batteries decayed, and (3) lowering the transmitter power output to 100 mW so as to extend the life of the onboard battery. Figure 1.3, which compares the thermal histories of OSCARs I and II, shows the results of the thermal coating modifications. The rapid rise in temperature of OSCAR II in its final orbits was caused by aerodynamic heating (friction from air molecules) as the spacecraft reentered the atmosphere. The

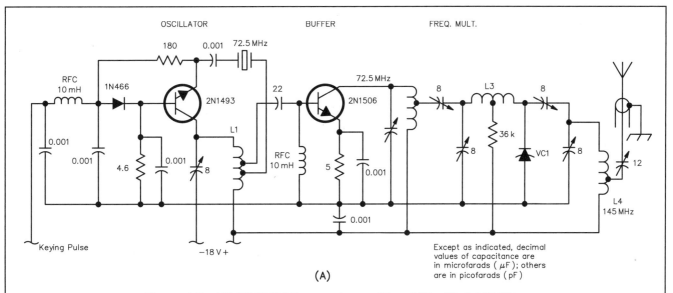

Figure 1.2—(A) OSCAR I Beacon transmitter: 140 mW at 145 MHz.

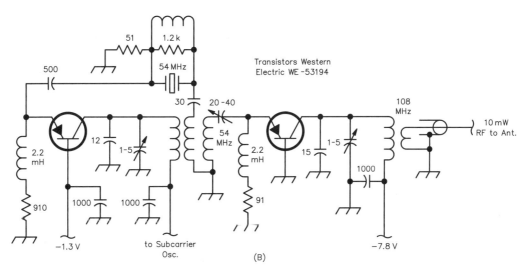

(B) Explorer 1 Beacon transmitter: 10 mW at 108 MHz.

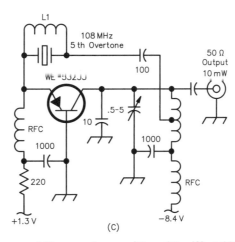

(C) Vanguard Beacon transmitter: 10 mW at 108 MHz.

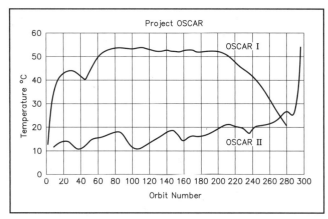

Figure 1.3—A comparison of the OSCAR I and OSCAR II temperature curves as derived from the telemetered data logged by nearly 1000 tracking stations. Modifications to the thermal design of OSCAR II based on the flight of the first satellite provided a relatively constant temperature at a more desirable lower level until the spacecraft began to reenter rapidly.

benefits of an extended battery life were lost due to the early reentry. The final telemetry reports from orbit 295, 18 days after launch, indicated an internal spacecraft temperature of 54°C. The outer shell was probably over 100°C by this time.[22]

OSCAR *

While OSCARs I and II were being built and flown, another more complex spacecraft employing a higher power transmitter and phase-coherent keying was being constructed by Chuck Smallhouse (WA6MGZ) and Orv Dalton (K6VEY). Due to the success of the first two OSCAR launches, it was decided to suspend work on the new spacecraft, OSCAR *, so that the entire OSCAR team could focus their efforts on building the first relay satellite, which would be named OSCAR III.[23]

WHAT PRICE SUCCESS?

The question "What did OSCAR I cost?" was often asked. It's impossible to give a simple answer. The most valuable commodity involved—the technical expertise of the radio amateurs who designed and built the spacecraft—was donated. Major expenses such as travel, long-distance phone calls, machine shop access, key parts, technical books, and so on, were covered by donations or absorbed by the same people volunteering their labor. Tired of repeating this explanation over and over, the OSCAR crew sat down one day and added up the out-of-pocket expenses that immediately came to mind. The figure they came up with was $26 and this number became forever associated with OSCAR I.

As satellites became more complex costs rose precipitously and it became clear that these expenses had to be shared by a larger segment of the radio amateur community if the amateur satellite program was to grow. In April

1962 the OSCAR Association formally incorporated as Project OSCAR, Inc. One of the key goals of the new organization was to help fund the OSCAR program via soliciting donations to and memberships in a national organization that would publish a newsletter focusing on amateur satellite activities.

SPACE COMMUNICATION: PART I

During the early days of the Space Age government engineers considered two promising methods for space communications—satellite-borne active relays (including both linear and store-and-forward technology) and passive reflectors (see Table 1.1). The passive reflectors investigated included natural structures like the moon, artificial structures like those employed in projects ECHO and West Ford, and temporary phenomena like the ionized regions of the ionosphere associated with passing meteorites or space vehicles.

Radio amateurs were quick to realize that passive reflectors could be used by anyone, anywhere without requesting permission from any government agency or launch group. And, having had decades of experience bouncing signals off the passive reflector called the iono-

Chuck Towns, K6LFH, in his own garage workshop with OSCAR II. Though the Amateur Radio Satellite Program had its roots in basements and garages, the strictest professional standards were always maintained for the final spacecraft to pass rigorous testing by the various launch agencies.

Table 1.1

Early Communications Satellites (Comsats)

All carried active, real-time transponders except for SCORE, the ECHO "balloons," Courier 18 and the West Ford needles.

Satellite Launch Date	Perigee/Apogee (Miles)	Comments
SCORE 18 Dec 1958	115/914	Often referred to as first comsat. However, it carried only a taped message for playback. It could *not* be used for relaying signals.
ECHO A-10 13 May 1960		Passive comsat (mylar balloon); failed to orbit (NASA)
ECHO 1 12 Aug 1960	941/1052	First successful passive comsat
Courier 1B 4 Oct 1960	586/767	First successful active comsat; employed store-and-forward message system (non real-time)
Midas 4 21 Oct 1961	2058/2324	West Ford dipoles, failed to disperse
Telstar 1 10 Jul 1962	593/3503	First active real-time comsat (AT&T)
Relay 1 13 Dec 1962	819/4612	(RCA)
Syncom 1 14 Feb 1963	21,195/22,953	Electronics failure (NASA)
Telstar 2 7 May 1963	604/6713	
Classified mission 9 May 1963	2249/2290	West Ford dipoles, successful
Syncom 2 26 Jul 1963	22,062/22,750	First successful comsat in stationary orbit
Relay 2 21 Jan 1964	1298/4606	
ECHO 2 25 Jan 1964	642/816	Last passive comsat; first joint US/USSR program
Syncom 3 19 Aug 1964	22,164/22,312	
LES 1 11 Feb 1965	1726/1744	
OSCAR III 9 Mar 1965	565/585	First radio amateur active real-time comsat
Early Bird 6 Apr 1965	21,748/22,733	First commercial comsat (INTELSAT I)
Molniya 1A 23 Apr 1965	309/24,470	First Soviet comsat
LES 2 6 May 1965	1757/9384	
Molniya 1B 14 Oct 1965	311/24,855	
OSCAR IV 21 Dec 1965	101/20,847	First radio amateur high altitude comsat; partial launch failure

Table 1.2

Radio Amateur EME Milestones

Two-way QSOs except as noted

Date	Band	Stations	Initial QST Reference
Jul 21, 1960	1.2 GHz	W6HB W1BU	Sep 1960, cover, pp 10-11, 62-66, 158
Apr 12, 1964	144 MHz	W6DNG, OH1NL	Jun 1964, p 95
May 20, 1964	430 MHz	W1BU, KP4BPZ	Jul 1964, p 105. 1000 Arecibo 1000 ft. hemispherical dish in use at KP4BPZ
Apr 15, 1967	430 MHz	W2IMU, HB9RG	Jun 1967, pp 92-93
Mar 16, 1970	220 MHz	WB6NMT, W7CNK	May 1970, p 83
Oct 19, 1970	2304 MHz	W3GKP, W4HHK	Dec 1970, pp 92-93
Jul 30, 1972	50 MHz	WA5HNK & W5SXD, K5WVX & W5WAX	Sep 1972, p 91
Apr 5, 1987	3456 MHz	KD5RO & WA5TNY, W7CNK & KA5JPD	Jun 1987, p 61
Apr 24, 1987	5760 MHz	W7CNK & KA5JPD, WA5TNY & KD5RO	May 1988, p 67
Jan 22, 1988	902 MHz	K5JL, WA5ETV	Apr 1988, p 74
Aug 27, 1988	10 GHz	WA5VJB & KF5N WA7CJO & KY7B	Nov 1988, p 64

— **One-Way Reception of Echos** —

Date	Band	Stations	Initial QST Reference
Jan 10 1946	112 MHz	First report of EME echos (nonamateur)	T. Clark, (see note 29)
Jan 27 1953	144 MHz	W3GKP & W4AO	Mar 1953, pp 11-12, 116; Apr 1953, p 56
Early 1963	28 MHz	W6UGL receives echos using 1200 ft antenna at Stanford University	Sep 1963, p 20

sphere, amateurs were willing to try bouncing signals off almost anything—a large balloon, the moon, or the ionized trails left by meteors or artificial satellites.[24]

Project ECHO

We begin by looking at Project ECHO. The aim of this program was to place in orbit a 90 to 125-foot diameter "balloon" having an aluminized Mylar surface capable of reflecting radio signals. The first balloon to reach orbit was ECHO 1 (August 1960). High power commercial and mili-

tary experimenters were able to communicate using it but radio amateur power levels proved inadequate to the task. Radio amateur interest continued because ECHO 2, which was to be larger and lower than its predecessor, looked more promising as a reflector.[25-27] Radio path loss calculations at 144 MHz suggested that communications via ECHO 2 might be possible by amateurs running 1 kW and using large antennas. Its launch, originally planned for 1962, was delayed several times. During the interim both radio amateurs and the US government had a chance to test their first active relay spacecraft. The overwhelming success of the active relay approach led to the demise of Project ECHO, but not before 1964 when ECHO 2 finally reached orbit.

Two amateurs, Bill Conkel (W6DNG) and Claude Maer (WØIC), were able to identify 144 MHz signals bouncing back from ECHO 2 but rapid fading and weak signals prevented two-way communications. Looking back, the ECHO 2 results were remarkable for several reasons. A low altitude satellite is a very rapidly moving target. Keeping a high gain antenna pointed at one was a nearly impossible task back in 1964. Repeating this experiment today with an accurate microcomputer tracking program directly driving an antenna array, up-to-the-minute tracking data off the Internet, and the ultra low noise 144 MHz preamps now available, the results might be very different.

Since NASA (the *National Aeronautics and Space Administration*) began testing inflatable antenna structures deployed from the US Shuttle in mid-1996, an excellent opportunity for amateurs to retest the passive reflector concept may be at hand. For information on the Spartan 207/Inflatable Antenna Experiment carried on STS-77 and similar experiments, check their WWW home page at **http://sspp.gsfc.gov/sp207.html**.

Project West Ford

The goal of Project West Ford was to create an artificial reflecting band around the Earth by injecting hundreds of millions of needle-like copper dipoles into orbit. The experiment was highly controversial. Several scientific organizations suggested that the needles might seriously affect future active satellite relays, the manned space program, radio astronomy and even the weather. However, the program continued. On the first West Ford mission (October 1961) the ejection mechanism jammed and the needles were never released into orbit. A second attempt two years later succeeded. The belt of needles produced did support communication between ground stations but very high power (far above amateur levels) was required. As predicted by the experimenters, the needles decayed from orbit quickly and no permanent harm was done to the near Earth environment. By this time, the advantages of active satellite relays had been demonstrated sufficiently so work on Project West Ford was shelved.

Moonbounce

Radio amateurs have successfully communicated by using the moon, a natural satellite of Earth, as a passive reflector on all amateur bands between 50 MHz and 10 GHz (inclusive). See Table 1.2. Although moonbounce communication, often called EME (Earth-Moon-Earth), has always taken the highest allowable power, large antennas and extremely sensitive receivers, it continues to have a special attraction to radio amateurs. Today, most EME activity is concentrated on 144 MHz and 432 MHz. Signals are weak at best, but continual refinement of all elements of the EME system has resulted in gradual but significant improvement in system performance. On 2 meters, W5UN,

using his 48 Yagi array affectionately known as the MBA (Mighty Big Antenna), was able to contact more than 1000 different stations in 70 countries via the moon within the first three years following its 1985 construction. Several of the stations contacted were running as little as 150 W to a single long-boom Yagi.[28] On 70 cm, DL9KR reports having had QSOs with more than 600 individual stations (1996) and SSB contacts are not uncommon. Both of these big guns, and many others, have earned WAS and WAC via the moon. Cumulative small improvements in station performance related to preamp performance, antenna design, and digital signal processing may one day change EME from a marginal mode to a highly reliable one.[29]

Satellite Scatter

Meanwhile, another, albeit not very well known, space communication medium was being investigated by amateurs. In 1958, Dr. John Kraus (W8JK), director of the Ohio State University Radio Observatory, noted that certain terrestrial HF beacon signals increased in strength and changed in other characteristic ways as low-altitude satellites passed nearby. He attributed the enhancements to reflections off a trail of short-lived ionized particles caused by the passing spacecraft.[30] While this may at first seem similar to meteor scatter communication the physical mechanisms involved are considerably different due to the fact that satellite scatter is taking place at a much higher altitude where ionospheric particle density is orders of magnitude lower.

Capitalizing on satellite scatter, amateurs were able to locate (or confirm the positions of) several silent (nontransmitting) US and Soviet satellites by monitoring signals from WWV.[31] In related work, two electrical engineering students, Perry Klein (W3PK) and Ray Soifer (W2RS), decided to test whether high-frequency satellite scatter could support communication. Calculations suggested that 21 MHz was the optimal amateur frequency for tests. The results were positive and their work received national publicity in various news media.[32,33] But signals using amateur power levels proved only marginal for practical communications purposes.

1963 SPACE CONFERENCE

The OSCAR satellite program nearly came to a screeching halt when the ITU (International Telecommunication Union) convened the 1963 Geneva Space Conference. A motion submitted by the United Kingdom proposed the addition of a footnote in the 144-146 MHz worldwide amateur allocation authorizing amateur space satellites. The USSR delegation emphatically rejected the proposal and stated its opposition to any amateur space activity. Luckily, representatives of the International Amateur Radio Union (IARU) and Project OSCAR present at the meeting were able to mobilize support of delegations sympathetic to amateur satellite activities, notably those of the US, Canada and UK. A *QST* article describing the conference specifically mentions the importance of a report by Bill Orr, W6SAI, representing Project OSCAR, in helping to neutralize the Soviet position. The incident had a happy ending—the proposed footnote authorizing amateur satellite operation in the 144-146 MHz band was adopted. And, amateurs had learned a very important lesson—international regulatory agencies can end the radio amateur satellite program with a stroke of the pen.[34]

OSCAR III

Even as OSCAR II lifted off the launch pad, work was underway on OSCAR III, a far more complex satellite with the communications capabilities Don Stoner had dared speculate about years earlier. OSCAR III carried a 50-kHz wide, 1-W transponder that received radio signals near 146 MHz and retransmitted them, greatly amplified, back to Earth near 144 MHz. The transponder was designed to permit radio amateurs with modest equipment to multiply their effective communications range by a factor of 10 to 20. In addition to the transponder, OSCAR III contained two beacon transmitters. One provided a continuous carrier for tracking and propagation studies, the other conveyed information on the spacecraft primary battery (temperature and terminal voltage) and the transponder's final amplifier (temperature).[35-38]

Because of their low initial orbits, OSCARs I and II remained in space only a short time before reentering the atmosphere and burning up. A simple battery was therefore adequate to power these spacecraft for the expected mission duration. OSCAR III was being placed in a higher orbit where it would remain in space for a much longer time. Since weight constraints severely limited the size of the spacecraft's battery, the designers considered using solar cells for the primary power source on this mission. However, solar cells, which had only been invented in 1954, were extremely expensive and difficult to obtain, and their long term reliability in space was yet to be established.[39] It was therefore decided to approach solar cell use as a test of new technology and limit their function to backing up the battery powering the beacons.

OSCAR III was successfully launched on March 9, 1965. The transponder operated for the next 18 days and about 1000 amateurs in 22 countries were heard through it. A number of long-distance contacts were reported, including Massachusetts to Germany, New Jersey to Spain, and New York to Alaska. The transponder clearly demonstrated that a free-access, multiple-access amateur transponder would work in space. The expression *free access* refers to the fact that anyone licensed by his/her government to operate on the uplink frequency was able to use the spacecraft without charge, and without obtaining permission from or prior notification of any organization or government agency. The expression *multiple access* refers to the fact that a large number of ground stations can use the spacecraft simultaneously if they cooperate in choosing frequencies and limiting power levels. The telemetry beacon, working off its own battery and the solar cells, functioned for several months.[40]

Success brought new challenges. It was clear that future radio amateur satellites would need major changes. First and foremost, operating lifetimes would have to increase by 10 or 100 times to justify the major effort and expense needed to build the sophisticated spacecraft designs being considered. Second, to attract a large user base for future satellites, OSCARs must be simple to use, even if this made them more complex to build. One consequence of experience with OSCAR III was that all future OSCAR transponders would use different bands for uplink and downlink frequencies to reduce the receiver desense problems encountered by ground stations trying to monitor their own downlinks.

OSCAR IV

While OSCAR III was being completed, amateurs were offered a launch aboard a Titan III-C rocket headed for a circular orbit 21,000 miles above the Earth's equator. A spacecraft at this height would see nearly half the planet. Earlier OSCARs had been designed to operate at altitudes under 700 miles. At these low altitudes, transponder power and spacecraft antennas and attitude stabilization are much less critical. Building a high altitude spacecraft is a formi-

OSCAR IV, the only amateur satellite to be designed around a tetrahedral frame. Intended for a 21,000-mile high circular orbit, OSCAR IV was doomed to a short operating life when the top stage of the launch rocket failed, leaving it in an elliptical orbit for which it had not been designed.

dable challenge, even with plenty of time and resources. But time wasn't available: The projected launch date was roughly a year away and the Project OSCAR crew was deeply involved in readying OSCAR III for its flight.

When it appeared that this unique offer might have to be passed up, several members of the TRW (Thompson-Ramo-Woolridge) Radio Club of Redondo Beach, California, decided to undertake the project. (Almost three decades passed before a similar launch opportunity was to materialize with Arsene-OSCAR 24.)

To meet the stringent time schedule, the spacecraft had to be kept as simple as possible—just a transponder, a beacon to be used for tracking and to satisfy Federal Communications Commission identification requirements, and a power system. "Luxuries" such as telemetry and redundant sub-systems, which contribute greatly to reliability and future developments, were omitted. The TRW team chose a crossband 10 kHz wide transponder that received (uplink) on 144 MHz and transmitted (downlink) on 432 MHz. Later called Mode J, this transponder borrowed a number of ideas from a standard ranging transponder NASA used at the time. Power was set at 3 W PEP. The development group opted for a solar power system and designed the spacecraft to a one-year-lifetime goal.

Launch took place on December 21, 1965. On that day radio amateurs were for the first time forced to grapple with the nightmare that constantly haunts satellite builders. The top stage of the launch rocket failed; the spacecraft reached orbit, but one very different from the target. If OSCAR IV had been a commercial satellite it would have been written off as a total failure at this point. However, radio amateurs took stock of what they had, a rapidly tumbling satellite in a highly elliptical orbit, and initiated a salvage operation.

The orbit, which was inclined to the equator at 26° with a high point (*apogee*) 21,000 miles above Earth and the low point (*perigee*) at 100 miles, presented amateurs with a number of serious problems.

Consider tracking, for example. Since ground stations needed high-gain, narrow-beamwidth antennas to access the distant low-power transponder during most of the orbit, tracking information was critical. Had the spacecraft achieved its intended orbit, it would have hung directly over the equator, drifting slowly eastward at just under 30° per day and tracking would have been easy. But, radio amateurs had not yet developed suitable techniques for tracking satellites in the highly elliptical orbit they were presented with. Trying to aim the ground station antenna by peaking received signal strength generally was not effective because the tumbling of the spacecraft caused the signal strength to fluctuate rapidly. But this wasn't the only problem.

The orbit produced large Doppler shifts in the uplink and downlink frequencies. In fact, the Doppler shifts on the uplink were comparable to the transponder bandwidth. When one takes into account the frequency measuring capabilities of most amateurs in 1965 it's difficult to imagine how users even found the transponder uplink band.

Another effect of the unexpected orbit was that the low perigee would cause OSCAR IV to reenter early. But this was actually a minor concern since system failure was likely to occur much sooner due to the fact that the spacecraft was being exposed to a radiation and thermal environment that it was not designed to handle.

Had OSCAR IV operated a sufficient length of time, the rapid tumbling would probably have slowed down and ground stations would have devised methods to overcome the tracking and Doppler shift problems. But the transponder ceased operating after a few weeks. Since the spacecraft didn't have a telemetry system, we can only guess the cause; the two most probable being battery failure from thermal and power supply stresses, or solar cell failure from the radiation levels encountered.

Despite the enormous difficulties faced, several amateurs completed two-way contacts through OSCAR IV. One contact, between a station in the United States and another in the Soviet Union, was the first direct two-way satellite communication between these two nations. And, the mission provided considerable information that would prove valuable in designing future spacecraft.

Although OSCAR IV was, in many ways, a major disappointment, it's important to keep in mind that the key failure occurred in the launch vehicle, a possibility that radio amateurs working with satellites must learn to accept. The OSCAR IV design/construction team did an extraordinary job, and the users whose ingenuity salvaged so much from the mission were a credit to Amateur Radio.[41-43] Finally, the manner in which this group responded to "failure" established a tradition that would help future generations of satellite builders cope with adversity.

THE BALLOON-OSCAR CONNECTION

Many groups interested in producing hardware for OSCAR missions started out by preparing payloads and arranging launches for high altitude balloons. One such group, operating in Germany in the mid-1960s, initiated 18 balloon flights up to 65,000 feet. In addition to testing OSCAR hardware they were interested in training potential users how to operate through a linear transponder. The April 1967 issue of *QST* (p 87) contained an intriguing announcement related to these experiments. A young German engineer, Karl Meinzer (DJ4ZC), was offering to loan, free of charge, the 1-W 2-meter single band linear transponder used on the German flights to an American group interested in organizing balloon launches. Karl reported that "During the first two or three [European] flights a lot of confusion was present, but in later flights skills improved and people in general are now quite capable of making the best of this way of communication. There is still some time until the [next OSCAR] launch, so I think it would be nice to give the American hams an opportunity to train themselves, too." You'll be seeing Karl's name often in the following pages, as he went on to play, and still plays, a key role in OSCAR spacecraft design and construction.

The German balloon launch program actually had a rocky beginning. The German government refused the ini-

Table 1.3

The Introductory Section of AMSAT's Bylaws (as revised in 1989)

BYLAWS of the RADIO AMATEUR SATELLITE CORPORATION

These Bylaws have been adopted pursuant to the Articles of Incorporation, which provide, in part, as follows:

FIRST: The name of the corporation is Radio Amateur Satellite Corporation.

SECOND: The period of duration is perpetual.

THIRD: Said corporation is organized exclusively for scientific purposes, including, for such purposes, the making of distributions to organizations that qualify as exempt organizations under Section 501(c)(3) of the Internal Revenue Code of 1954, as amended (or the corresponding provision of any future United States Internal Revenue Law).

The scientific purposes for which said corporation is organized shall be the carrying on of scientific research in the public interest by the means of:

A. Developing and providing satellite and related equipment and technology used or useful for amateur radio communications throughout the world on a non-discriminatory basis.

B. Encouraging development of skills and the advancement of specialized knowledge in the art and practice of amateur radio communications and space science.

C. Fostering international goodwill and cooperation through joint experimentation and study, and through the wide participation in these activities on a noncommercial basis by radio amateurs of the world.

D. Facilitating communications by amateur satellites in times of emergency.

E. Encouraging the more effective and expanded use of the higher frequency amateur radio frequency bands.

F. Disseminating scientific and technical information derived from such communications and experimentation, and encouraging publication of such information in treatises, theses, publications, technical journals and other public means.

G. Conducting such lawful activities as may be properly incident to or aid in the accomplishment of provisions A-F herein above, and which are consistent with the maintenance of tax-exempt status pursuant to Section 501(c) of the Internal Revenue Code.

tial application requesting permission to launch the transponder payload and turned a deaf ear to appeals to reconsider. Finally, amateurs in Holland volunteered to approach the Dutch government to request the required launch permission. Their request was granted and once a balloon was up, there was no regulation preventing the Germans from using it. After several flights from the Netherlands without incident the German government finally gave the builders permission to launch from Hessel. Over the next several years more than 60 ARTOB flights were undertaken under the direction of Fritz Herbst, DL3YBA.

Over the years balloon flights have continued to play a major role in the Radio Amateur Satellite program as many groups primarily interested in satellite construction begin by undertaking balloon projects. The US currently has several active amateur groups. In addition, the University of Wisconsin is planning a professional launch to 150,000 feet with a one ton payload from the US National Balloon Facility in New Mexico. NASA is considering requests for additional small payloads on this launch. For information contact D. Mullenix, N9LTD, at **djmullen@ facstaff.wisc.edu**. The Proyecto GLOBO [Project balloon] team in Spain also has an extensive program. For information contact Rafael Garcia at **ea4rj @AMSAT.org**. The lessons learned and experience gained from these launches prove invaluable when entering the spacecraft construction arena.

OSCAR 5

The OSCAR 5 story began late in 1965 in Australia. Several students at the University of Melbourne, most undergraduate engineering majors, met to consider the possibility of building an OSCAR satellite. They realized that they faced a number of major obstacles. These included lack of experience designing and constructing spacecraft, lack of information on and access to launch opportunities, lack of access to a suitable environmental testing chamber and lack of cash to support sending a launch operations crew overseas. The students felt that their solid engineering background could overcome the first obstacle. So, when the Project OSCAR team agreed to take care of the three remaining problem areas, the "down under" crew committed to building AO-5 (Australis-OSCAR 5). (Note: With the fifth amateur satellite being readied for flight, amateurs decided to acknowledge the advantage of Arabic numbers over their Roman counterparts—hence OSCAR 5, not OSCAR V.)

Members of the Melbourne group wanted to make a unique and significant contribution to the amateur space program, but they recognized that their isolation and lack of experience dictated a relatively simple spacecraft. The design, finalized in March 1966, showed that their desire and the constraints they were working under could be reconciled.

The design goals for AO-5 included: (1) evaluating the suitability of the 10 meter band as a transponder downlink on future missions; (2) testing a passive magnetic approach to attitude stabilization; and (3) demonstrating the feasibility of controlling an OSCAR spacecraft via uplink commands. The flight hardware to accomplish these goals included telemetry beacons at 144.050 MHz (50 mW) and 29.450 MHz (250 mW at launch), a command receiver and decoder, a seven-channel analog telemetry system and a simple manganese-alkaline battery power supply. The spacecraft did not contain a transponder or use solar cells.

Though technical aspects of the AO-5 project went smoothly, administrative concerns turned out to be a major source of frustration. For example, air-posting a special 50-cent part from the US to Australia might cost $10, and clearing the part through customs could require pages of paperwork and several trips to government offices. Obviously, technical competence isn't enough to build satellites. Management skills and perseverance are also extremely important. Step-by-step, Australian dollar by Australian dollar, AO-5 took shape. On June 1, 1967, 15 months after final plans were okayed, the completed spacecraft was delivered to Project OSCAR in California in time to be prepared for a launch scheduled in early 1968. However, the host mission was delayed several times and then indefinitely postponed and no other suitable launch could be identified.

In January 1969, George Jacobs (W3ASK) was the guest speaker at the COMSAT Amateur Radio Club in Washington, DC. Jacobs discussed the status of AO-5 and suggested that, with the space-related expertise and facilities in the area, the amateur space program might benefit from an East Coast analog of Project OSCAR. As a result, AMSAT (the Radio Amateur Satellite Corporation) was formed. Incorporation took place on March 3, 1969 and the first task the new organization adopted was to arrange for an Australis-OSCAR 5 launch. (Excerpts from the AMSAT bylaws appear in Table 1.3.)

Environmental and vibration tests of AO-5 showed that some minor changes were needed. AMSAT performed the modifications, identified a suitable host mission, and obtained a launch commitment. Finally, on January 23, 1970, AO-5 was orbited on a NASA rocket (previous OSCARs had all flown with the US Air Force). Electronically, the satellite performed nearly flawlessly. One small glitch prevented telemetry data from being sent over the 29-MHz beacon but this problem was minor since the data was available on 144 MHz. The magnetic attitude stabilization system worked well. In less than two weeks the spacecraft's spin rate decreased by a factor of 40—from 4 revolutions per minute to 0.1 revolution per minute. The first successful command of an amateur satellite took place on orbit 61, January 28, 1970 when the 29-MHz beacon was switched off. A network of ground stations later tested their command capabilities by periodically cycling the spacecraft's 29-MHz beacon on/off. The demonstration of the ability to command the spacecraft was to prove very important in obtaining FCC licenses for future missions. And, restricting the beacon to weekend operation helped conserve the limited battery power.

The performance of the 29-MHz beacon confirmed expectations that this band would be suitable as a transponder

downlink for low-altitude spacecraft and led to its use on OSCARs 6,7 and 8 and numerous RS spacecraft. As the battery became depleted, the AO-5 transmitters shut down: The 144-MHz beacon died 23 days into the mission. The 29-MHz beacon, operating at greatly reduced power levels, was usable for propagation studies until day 46.[44-48]

At AMSAT, the project manager responsible for final testing, modification, and integration of AO-5 was a young engineer named Jan King, W3GEY. It's difficult for people not directly involved in a program of this scope to imagine the pressure the project manager is subjected to. But Jan must not have minded too much, as he went on to oversee the design and construction of several additional AMSAT spacecraft over the next quarter century.

AO-5 met its three primary mission objectives. In addition, careful analysis of reports submitted by ground stations monitoring the mission showed that such stations were capable of collecting reliable quantitative data from a relatively complex telemetry format. All in all, AO-5 was a solid success. But radio amateurs wanted a transponder they could use for two-way communication, and five years had passed since the last one had orbited.

SPACE COMMUNICATION II

Deep Space Probes

In the mid-1960s, while waiting for the next active relay satellite to be launched, a few amateurs constructed 2.3-GHz (S-band) microwave receiving stations in order to monitor the Apollo 10, 12, 14 and 15 lunar flights. These activities culminated in amateurs successfully receiving voice transmissions directly from the Command Service Module as it circled the moon during the Apollo 15 mission in August 1971.[49]

Radio Amateur interest in deep space continues to this day. Many amateurs are involved in the Mars Global Surveyor (MGS) program. The MGS spaceship, which was developed by NASA, JPL (Jet Propulsion Laboratory) and Stanford University, contains the Mars Relay, a 1.3 W beacon at 437.1 MHz that will function as the main communication link between MGS and landers placed on the surface of Mars. Many amateurs took part in reception experiments when this beacon was turned on while the MGS was on its way to Mars. For information see the Mars Global Surveyor Home Page on the World Wide Web at **http://mgs-www.jpl.nasa.gov**.

ATS-1

The US government launched ATS-1 (Applications Technology Satellite-1) into a geostationary orbit on December 7, 1966. To an observer on the Earth a geostationary spacecraft appears to remain fixed above a particular spot on the equator. ATS-1 contained an experiment of interest to radio amateurs—a 100-kHz-wide, hard-limiting transponder that received near 149.22 MHz and retransmitted at 135.6 MHz. By monitoring the transponder operation, radio amateurs were able to learn a great deal about link performance to a geostationary satellite near the

144-MHz amateur band and the behavior of hard-limiting transponders similar to those being considered for future amateur missions.[50]

After 20 years of operation ATS-1 ran out of the fuel needed to keep it in position above the equator and was officially retired from regular service. However, as of early 1997, it's still operational and the 137.35 MHz downlink can often be heard being used for special experiments.[51]

But ATS-1 didn't set a record for operating lifetime. The downlink from Relay I, launched in 1962 (see Table 1.1), is still sometimes heard on 136.140 MHz and 136.620 MHz. Today's commercial satellites are being designed with projected lifetimes of more than 10 years. The limiting constraint is usually not electronic failure but the amount of fuel carried for station keeping. While the total cost of some recent amateur spacecraft has been relatively high, the cost per year of operation is a much more important figure to consider. And radio amateurs have demonstrated the ability to keep this cost down by producing long-lived spacecraft. Aiming for lifetimes greater than a decade is not unrealistic; as of 2001 two amateur spacecraft, which have been in orbit for more than 13 years, are in regular use—UoSAT-OSCAR 11 and AMSAT-OSCAR 10. In the future it may be routinely required to shut off functioning older spacecraft so the link frequencies can be used by new satellites. (This was done with Fuji-OSCAR 12.)

Modifying the Ionosphere

Radio amateur interest in projects ECHO and West Ford focused on bouncing radio signals off objects in space. A closely related class of experiments involves changing the radio-reflecting properties of the ionosphere itself. Two approaches have been used to do this. The first method involves the release of chemicals, such as barium, directly into the ionosphere.[52] (The main payload on the ill-fated 1980 AMSAT Phase 3-A mission was a barium-release experiment known as Firewheel.[53]) The second approach is to activate very-high-power, ground-based radio transmitters, operating in the vicinity of 3-10 MHz, to raise the temperature of electrons in localized regions of the ionosphere.[54,55] Experiments using both approaches have been going on since the late 1950s and continue as this is written. In fact, scientific studies of ionospheric heating began many years earlier when it was observed that a very high power European AM broadcast station was inadvertently causing this effect.

Major US facilities for ionospheric heating are located in Colorado, near Platteville, and in Alaska, one station near Fairbanks and a second near Gakona. The Fairbanks site, known as the HIPAS (High Power Auroral Stimulation) Observatory is operated by the UCLA Plasma Physics Laboratory.[56] The unit near Gakona, known as HAARP (High Frequency Active Auroral Research Program), is operated by the US Air Force and Navy but work is not classified; information can be obtained at the World Wide Web site **http://server5550.itd.nrl.navy.mil/haarp.html**.[57]

The "artificial radio auroras" produced by these facilities can have a marked effect on propagation over the range of 20-450 MHz. Though scientific articles suggest that prospective experimenters interested in taking part in these tests should be located within 800 miles of these sites the recommendations refer to terrestrial stations working alone or with other ground stations. When working with satellite radio links the distance limits can be greatly extended.

1971 Space WARC and the Birth of the Amateur Satellite Service

In June 1971, the ITU (International Telecommunication Union) convened a WARC (World Administrative Radio Conference) on Space Telecommunications to review and, if necessary, change the regulations concerning extraterrestrial radio communication, and radio astronomy. This time around, the international radio amateur community was much better organized. They came with a modest set of proposals designed to permit an orderly growth of amateur satellite activities over the next decade. A key element of the proposals was a request that specific frequency bands be allocated for satellite operations. All bands requested were in existing amateur primary or shared allocations and had been carefully selected to minimize the possibility of interference to other services. The amateur proposals were circulated to and discussed with many ITU delegations before the conference began.

As a result of this careful preparatory work, several official ITU members including Argentina, Australia, Brazil, Canada, Federal Republic of Germany, Netherlands, New Zealand, United Kingdom and the United States agreed to sponsor the amateur proposal. With this support and preparation you'd think that the outcome would be assured. It wasn't. Several nations, led by France, intensely opposed any allocation in shared bands. France, in fact, proposed that amateur satellite activities be prohibited from using any frequencies between 146 MHz and 24 GHz!

There was widespread support for the amateur satellite proposals at the conference. However, the nature of the conference requires that official delegations prioritize their objectives and work out compromises. And, Amateur Radio was not near the top of most priority lists. The entire amateur satellite program was again in serious jeopardy. As is often the case, many of the official delegates and advisors at the conference were radio amateurs. These individuals, and a group of observers representing the IARU (International Amateur Radio Union), gathered together an informal team that kept attention focused on the needs of the amateur satellite program. One of these observers was Perry Klein, W3PK, the first president of AMSAT. A quote from another attendee, ZL2AZ, provides some insight into the atmosphere of the conference, "It is surprising how hoarse one can get even though he is supposed to be only an observer!"

One outcome of the 1971 WARC was that amateur satellite frequency allocations were expanded to include all exclusive worldwide amateur bands plus an extremely important segment at 435-438 MHz.[58] From a practical sense, the victory was modest since many of these frequencies are poorly suited to satellite links and requests for key allocations in the 1.2, 5.6 and 10 GHz bands had been denied. In any event, amateurs were no longer officially restricted to 144-146 MHz for space communications; in the near term future they could also look into using 21.0-21.45, 28.0-29.7, and 435-438 MHz, all of which were to see considerable activity.

In addition to the frequency allocation actions the ITU officially recognized and defined the Amateur Satellite Service in the International Radio Regulations. This meant that the *Amateur Service* and *Amateur Satellite Service* now existed as separate legal entities. (In the US an FCC amateur license covers both services.) The implications of this change weren't immediately clear. Some thought that it might, for example, make it more difficult for an amateur group to obtain an STA (special temporary authorization) for important experiments. Twenty-five years later, while preparing for the 1999 WARC, the Board of Directors of AMSAT-NA (AMSAT North America) reviewed this issue and concluded that the benefits of retaining formal separation of the two services outweighed the disadvantages and that we should press to retain the Amateur Satellite Service as a separate entity.

AMSAT-OSCAR 6

Amateur Radio took a giant stride into the future on October 15, 1972 when AMSAT-OSCAR 6 (AO-6) was launched successfully. From this date forward, the Amateur Radio community would always have at least one linear transponder-equipped, low-altitude satellite in operation. Phase 2 of the amateur satellite program, the age of long-lifetime satellites, was underway. While the aggregate operational time of all previous OSCARs amounted to considerably less than one year, AO-6 was to "do its thing" for more than four and a half years.[59]

Although AMSAT-OSCAR 6 was more complex than all previous OSCARs combined, ground stations interested in communicating through its transponder or studying its telemetry found it to be the easiest amateur satellite to work with. AO-6 carried an extremely sensitive 100-kHz-wide transponder with an input near 146 MHz which produced about 1 W output at 29 MHz. Ground stations using as little as 10 W to a groundplane antenna would put through solid signals as long as the transponder wasn't fully loaded, or gain-compressed by users running excessive power. The ease and reliability of communication through the AO-6 transponder were enhanced greatly by the spacecraft's magnetic attitude-stabilization system. The use of 29 MHz for a downlink and magnetic stabilization were both due to experience gathered from experiments on AO-5.

AMSAT-OSCAR 6 was the first amateur satellite to contain a digital store-and-forward message system. The system, called *Codestore*, used discrete logic and had a memory capacity of 256 characters. This is certainly a far cry from today's spacecraft where memory capacity is

measured in megabytes. Suitably equipped ground stations could load messages into Codestore using Morse code (or any other digital code as long as it conformed to FCC regulations) for later replay. Playback could either be continuous (broadcast mode) or in response to a request from a ground station (communication mode). Codestore was often used to relay messages between Canadian and Australian command stations. And, many radio amateurs outside the USA reported that Codestore bulletins proved to be their best source for information relating to the launch of AMSAT-OSCAR 7.

To appreciate the impact of AO-6 one must consider the philosophy underlying its construction. Two beliefs were paramount. First, due to the investment needed in both dollars and effort to produce a spacecraft that could make significant new operational, scientific or engineering contributions to Amateur Radio, the satellite must be designed to operate for at least one year in orbit. Second, constructing a reliable long-life satellite required much more than replacing a battery power supply with a power system consisting of solar cells, rechargeable batteries and related control electronics. Long lifetime could be reasonably assured only if a spacecraft contained (1) a sophisticated telemetry system permitting onboard systems to be monitored, (2) a flexible command system so that specific spacecraft subsystems could be turned on/off as conditions warranted, and (3) redundant critical systems. In addition, the design strategy must attempt to prevent catastrophic failure by anticipating possible failure modes and providing avenues for "soft" failure by, for example, incorporating facilities for isolating and replacing defective subsystems.

AMSAT-OSCAR 6 wasn't the first amateur spacecraft to use solar power and it wasn't the first to include a command and telemetry system. But it took each of these sub-

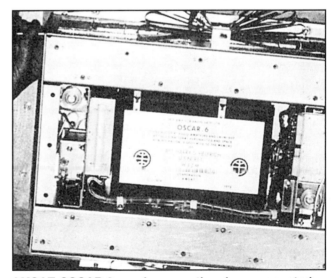

AMSAT-OSCAR 6, as shown on the plaque mounted inside the satellite structure, was dedicated to Capt Harry D. Helfrich, W3ZM, an active AMSAT participant in the OSCAR 6 project who became a Silent Key shortly before the satellite was launched.

systems a quantum step forward. For example, the command system on AO-5 could only turn the 10-meter beacon on/off. AO-6 recognized 35 distinct commands, 21 of which were acted on. The telemetry system on AO-5 included seven analog channels. The system on AO-6 contained 24 channels and a special processing system that translated the analog voltage, temperature and current information into a digital format and then encoded the digital data as Morse code numbers. This greatly simplified the capture and decoding of telemetry by eliminating the need for special ground station equipment. A ground station interested in observing the internal operation of AO-6 only had to copy numbers in Morse code and refer to a set of graphs.[60]

Although AMSAT-OSCAR 6 was an overwhelming success, it did encounter problems. One problem was that the 435 MHz beacon failed after about three months. It lasted long enough, however, to test 435 MHz as a downlink for future low-altitude spacecraft and to enable John Fox (WØLER) and Ron Dunbar (WØPN) to discover an interesting Doppler anomaly.[61] Since all telemetry information was available via the 29-MHz beacon this provides a good example of a soft failure.

A second spacecraft problem had a serious impact on performance during AO-6's early days in orbit. The satellite control system tended to interpret internally generated noise as a command to turn the transponder and other subsystems on or off. Working with AO-6 in those early months was, at times, extremely frustrating. It seemed as if the decoding system would regularly choose the most inopportune times to misinterpret noise as a command to shut down the transponder.

However, amateurs were able to overcome this falsing problem. Although the orbiting spacecraft couldn't be repaired, it was suggested that the operational difficulties would be minimized if ground stations would send a constant stream of commands to the satellite directing it into the correct mode. To accomplish this one had to (1) develop an automated ground command station and (2) identify stations around the world who would volunteer to place such stations on the air. One of the first to feverishly attack the falsing problem was Larry Kayser (then VE3QB). He quickly put a manual command station in operation. His first attempt at automation used an audiotape-recorder control loop. Since his work required that he frequently be out on the road, he connected the automated system to his phone as soon as it was operating fairly reliably. This enabled him to command the satellite by ringing up his home number. As Kayser tells it:

"For the next few weeks, it was not uncommon [for me] to dash for a telephone, dial a number, and hang up. This went on several times in a 10-minute period for each pass, sometimes from Montreal, Toronto, a gas station on the highway, or wherever ... Full automation was certainly a more desirable way to go."

Kayser went on to replace the audiotape setup with a series of much more reliable ones employing digital logic. By August 1973, a system capable of automatically generating 80,000 commands per day was in operation. Compare this to the twice-weekly command schedule used to control the 29-MHz beacon on AO-5.[62]

In addition to keeping AO-6 on a reliable operating schedule, command stations were largely responsible for the spacecraft's 4.5-year lifespan. Without their careful management, it's doubtful that even the original one-year design lifetime of the spacecraft could have been reached. The death of AO-6 occurred when several battery cells failed in a shorted mode.

AMSAT-OSCAR 6 was truly an international project. Subsystems for the spacecraft were built in the US, Australia and West Germany. Ground command stations were activated in Australia, Canada, Great Britain, Hungary, Morocco, New Zealand, the US and West Germany. And, users in well over 100 countries reported two-way communications.[63]

Though AO-6 was awarded a free ride into space for several reasons, its potential value as an educational tool was paramount. The introduction of long-lifetime radio amateur satellites made it feasible for science instructors at all levels to incorporate class demonstrations of satellite reception into regular course activities. To assist teachers pioneering in this work, AMSAT and the American Radio Relay League granted funds to the Talcott Mountain Science Center in Connecticut so that an instruction manual aimed at educators working with grades 1 through 12 could be produced. The result was the well-received *Space Science Involvement* manual, first published in 1974. Thousands of free copies were distributed to teachers over the following six years. In 1978 a follow-up publication geared to college level instruction was published. This publication, *Using Satellites in the Classroom: A Guide for Science Educators*, was produced with the financial assistance of the National Science Foundation and the Smithsonian National Air and Space Museum.[64] Both the ARRL and AMSAT do their best to encourage and support educational activities involving satellites and the manned space program. However, the resources both organizations have to devote to this effort are severely limited. Despite these constraints the ARRL designated an OSCAR Education coordinator who oversaw an ongoing educational program. Over the years this program has included (1) referrals for local assistance, (2) personalized educational bulletins via satellite, (3) special satellite scheduling, (4) the publication of a newsletter for science educators, (5) development of a slide show library and (6) coordinating schedules for NASA's orbit to school radio links from US shuttle flights and (7) the production of the aforementioned *Space Science Involvement* manual.

AMSAT-OSCAR 7

AMSAT-OSCAR 7 (AO-7), launched November 15, 1974 was another success story. For the first time, amateurs had two operating satellites in orbit. While AO-6 represented a quantum leap forward technically, AO-7 was more of an evolutionary step.[65] It contained two transponders, one similar to the unit flown on AO-6, using a 146-MHz uplink and a 29-MHz downlink (known as Mode A),

(2) 3w. eric. ed. gov.

and the second with an uplink at 432 MHz and a downlink at 146 MHz (known as Mode B).

The Mode B transponder was based on a unique design developed by Karl Meinzer (DJ4ZC) and built in West Germany under the sponsorship of AMSAT-Deutschland. It ran 8 W (PEP) and employed a highly efficient method of linear frequency translation that Karl had developed while pursuing his PhD degree in engineering. The Mode B system, which includes the transponder, the link frequencies, the antennas and the magnetic attitude control, provided outstanding performance. Whereas AO-6 demonstrated that simple ground stations could communicate via satellite, AO-7 showed that low-altitude satellites could, under many conditions, provide simple stations with communications capabilities over moderate distances (200-4500 miles) far exceeding any alternative terrestrial or space communications mode available to radio amateurs.

The AMSAT-OSCAR 7 spacecraft carried Codestore and telemetry units nearly identical to those of AO-6. It also contained beacons at 146 MHz, 435 MHz (built in Canada) and 2304 MHz, and a new high-speed, high-accuracy telemetry system (designed by an Australian group) that encoded information in a radioteletype format.

Many experimenters were very interested in the 100-mW, 2304-MHz beacon, which had been contributed by members of the San Bernardino Microwave Society (California, USA). Much has been learned from this beacon, though not in the manner anticipated. Because of international treaty constraints, and strong objections of at least one country, the FCC decided to deny amateurs permission to turn this valuable experiment on, even for short

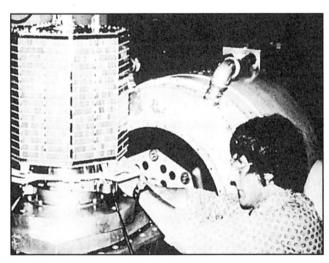

Jan King, W3GEY, adjusts OSCAR 7 on its perch atop a "shake table." All OSCARs must undergo rigorous testing to prove that they will survive the rigors of launch and the hostile space environment without damaging or otherwise affecting the mission of the primary payload. The shake table, a distant relative of your local hardware store's paint shaker, is used for vibration tests in which the structure is subjected to the severe vibrations that will be experienced during launch. Secondary payloads, the "piggyback riders" of the aerospace world, aren't certified for flight until they have passed such tests.

time periods while the spacecraft was over the US. As a result, it was never tested in space.

Several years later, in 1979, at another major World Administrative Radio Conference, the Amateur Satellite Service was finally able to obtain several important new frequency allocations in the microwave portion of the spectrum. Although the events at the 1979 WARC and the legal problems associated with the AO-7 2304-MHz beacon appear, at first glance, unrelated some believe that the responsible, restrained manner in which radio amateurs handled the frustrating but politically sensitive 2304-MHz beacon issue had significantly helped their cause.

Although the 146-MHz spectrum was severely limited it was quickly noted that it was theoretically possible to link 432 MHz to 29 MHz through 146 MHz. For two ground stations to communicate, one would transmit to AO-7 on 432 MHz, having the signals relayed directly to AO-6 on 146 MHz, and then downlinked on 29 MHz. Never before in any radio service, had two terrestrial stations communicated using a direct satellite-to-satellite relay. Amateurs looked forward to the time when the two spacecraft would be close enough to test the performance of such links. Many such contacts were later made.[66,67]

AMSAT-OSCAR 7 operated for more than six and a half years. It died in mid-1981 at the start of a three-week period during which the spacecraft entered the Earth's shadow for up to 20 minutes on each orbit. These eclipses caused the average spacecraft temperature to drop and parts of the spacecraft to experience very rapid large temperature excursions and consequently, severe thermal stresses. It is believed that these stresses caused a battery cell that had previously failed in the open mode (soft failure) to short, placing a very large load across the solar panel output, which effectively shut down all power to the electronics modules.

Flight hardware for the AMSAT-OSCAR 7 satellite was contributed by groups in Australia, Canada, the US and West Germany.

AMSAT-OSCAR 8

Each time a new amateur satellite is placed in orbit, launch-day radio networks provide information on countdown, liftoff, rocket staging and the first user reception reports. AMSAT-OSCAR 8 (AO-8) was orbited successfully at 1754 UTC on March 5, 1978. Minutes later, those monitoring the launch nets heard G2BVN report reception of the 435-MHz beacon confirming that the spacecraft was in orbit and operating. But this report didn't end the suspense. AO-8 carried a novel 10 meter antenna that had to be deployed by ground command before the Mode A transponder could be turned on. Project managers wanted to extend the antenna as soon as possible since it was believed that the reliability of the mechanical deployment mechanism would rapidly decrease in the vacuum of space. But they had to be extremely careful because extending the antenna before the satellite spin decreased to an acceptable level could be catastrophic. Pre-launch speculation was that it might take a week for the spacecraft spin to slow down sufficiently. Roughly seven hours after launch, however, as the satellite was passing over the East Coast of the US, the spin rate looked good and the decision was made to send the antenna deployment command. Hundreds of stations listening to the 80-meter AMSAT-NA net breathed a simultaneous sigh of relief as the antenna extended and the Mode A transponder responded to the "on" command.

Previous launch descriptions would have ended here with the commencement of two-way communications but this time amateurs were being asked to temporarily refrain from transmitting to the spacecraft. This would enable the design team to test the orbit-determination ranging techniques being developed for future missions and evaluate AO-8's engineering performance as quickly and efficiently as possible. Monitoring the engineering tests proved intrinsically interesting. During sensitivity tests, for example, users could witness the true capabilities of the transponder as they listened to a transmitting station announce the power levels being used: "... 10 watts ... 1 watt ... one-tenth watt ...". The unloaded sensitivity of the transponder was remarkable. Two weeks after launch, AO-8 was officially opened for general operation, with all systems in excellent shape.[68]

Let's backtrack a bit to look at some of the events leading to the launch of AO-8. After AO-7 was placed in orbit late in 1974, the AMSAT design team focused their attention on the next major step in the radio amateur space program—building a high-altitude, long-life (Phase 3) spacecraft. Early in 1977, however, when it became clear that AO-6 was nearing the end of its lifespan, AMSAT had to face the prospect that AO-7 might not last until the first Phase 3 satellite was launched. There was a strong desire to provide continuity of service (at least one satellite in orbit) to, and to continue to support Mode A for, the thousands of amateurs and educators who had financially supported the AMSAT satellite program. This was a serious problem; AMSAT simply didn't have the financial resources and experienced volunteers needed to simultaneously build a Phase 3 spacecraft and a follow-on Low Earth Orbit (LEO) spacecraft with Mode A capabilities.

Responding to the problem, the American Radio Relay League (ARRL) offered to donate $50,000 to AMSAT and provide technical support if an interim Phase 2 satellite could be built. It was an offer AMSAT couldn't refuse so plans for a simple spacecraft with a Mode A transponder and a minimal telemetry and command system were drafted.

When JAMSAT (the Japanese affiliate of AMSAT) learned of plans for AO-8, they offered to provide a second transponder for the mission. The JAMSAT transponder (Mode J) would use an uplink at 146 MHz and a downlink at 435 MHz. AMSAT agreed to fly the JAMSAT transponder and to provide the associated antennas and interface circuitry. An interesting feature of the AO-8 spacecraft was that the two transponders could be operated simultaneously when the batteries were sufficiently charged. Since a single uplink signal would then be retransmitted on both downlinks, the performance of the two modes could be directly compared. And if, as expected, Mode J provided significantly better performance, users had an easy upgrade

path; stepping up to Mode J only required adding a 435/28 MHz receiver converter and a 435-MHz antenna to their Mode A station. AO-8 operated flawlessly in orbit from March 1978, through mid-1983. And, the Japanese team that was formed to build the transponder went on to coordinate and construct the Fuji-OSCAR series of LEO spacecraft.

Flight hardware for AO-8 was provided by AMSAT, JAMSAT and Project OSCAR. By prior agreement, the responsibility for operating AO-8 resided with the ARRL.

THE '70s DRAW TO A CLOSE

While most amateurs were using OSCARs 6, 7 and 8 to communicate with each other, a few individuals were engaged in more serious pursuits. One set of experiments focused on evaluating the feasibility of transmitting medical telemetry from isolated locations via linear transponders on low altitude satellites.[69,70] Another set of experiments involved using OSCARs 6 and 7 to validate the concept and viability of the Search and Rescue Satellite system later known as COSPAS/SARSAT.[71] The satellite-aided search and rescue system worked as follows. A low power transmitter is placed aboard every civilian aircraft. In case of sudden impact (i.e., crash) the transmitter is automatically activated. The signal is relayed to a central processing center via a low altitude spacecraft and the Doppler shift signature is analyzed to determine the location of the downed plane. The amateur experiments were a central element in the decision to activate a governmental COSPAS/SARSAT project involving the US, the Soviet Union, Canada and France.[72] According to James Bailey, SARSAT program manager at the US National Oceanic and Atmospheric Administration, COSPAS/SARSAT had saved more than 1150 lives by mid-1988.

As the '70s ended, a major new contributor to the amateur satellite program emerged on the scene. The first two Soviet amateur satellites, RS-1 and RS-2, were successfully launched in October 1978. We'll look at these two spacecraft and the extensive program that was to follow shortly. Meanwhile, AMSAT rushed to complete work on Phase III-A hoping to see it in space before WARC-79 took place. But a series of delays at the European Space Agency pushed the launch back into the '80s. The '70s closed with the amateur scorecard totaling 10 launches by the US and USSR in 19 years and the Amateur Satellite Service facing another WARC.

WARC-79

Most WARCs focus on one part of the radio spectrum or a limited class of users. However, every so often there's a general WARC where everything is laid on the table. WARC-79, which opened Sept 24, 1979, was the first general WARC since 1959.[73] The IARU had prepared extensively for this conference over many years. Their underlying strategy was to have the IARU member societies agree on a set of common goals and then work to generate maximum support for these objectives by the voting members of the ITU. After a great deal of effort four objectives were agreed upon at a series of regional IARU meetings in 1975 and 1976. One of these was to obtain authorization for amateur satellite radio links in sections of each of the amateur bands between 1 and 10 GHz. To an Amateur Radio operator, the social and economic benefits that a country gains from having a healthy Amateur Radio Service seem obvious. However, the value of having a large body of trained, proficient communications specialist wasn't necessarily appreciated by many of the voting WARC delegates who came from countries where Amateur Radio hardly existed. The IARU had to reach and brief as many as possible of these delegates in the time leading up to the WARC.

Most will agree that, on the whole, efforts put into preparing for WARC-79 paid off. The amateur satellite program did obtain access to all bands between 1 and 10 GHz (inclusive). However, there were some restrictions on the links and we didn't always receive the specific allocations requested. Still, the new allocations will one day permit activities that would otherwise be impossible—fast-scan TV across continents and to amateurs aboard space stations, and a worldwide digital data system capable of handling very high data rates in near real time.

Notes

[1]Personal Communication from Geoff Perry dated August 26, 1990 reporting on announcement by M. Tikhonravov at a conference in Baku in 1973. See sidebar for additional information.

[2]G. S. Sponsler, "Sputniks Over Britain," *Physics Today*, Vol 11, no. 7, Jul 1958, pp 16-21. Reprinted in *Kinematics and Dynamics of Satellite Orbits*, American Association of Physics Teachers, 335 East 45th St, NY, NY 10017.

[3]F. L. Whipple and J.A. Hynek, "Observations of Satellite I," *Scientific American*, Vol 197, no. 6, Dec 1957, pp 37-43.

[4]R. Buchheim and Rand Corp Staff, *New Space Handbook* (New York: Vintage Books, 1963), pp 283-312.

[5]V. Vakhnin, "Artificial Earth Satellites," *QST*, Nov 1957, pp 22-24, 188. Condensed translation of June 1957 article in Soviet journal *Radio*.

[6]From a presentation by Dr. Van Allen at a special program commemorating the 20th anniversary of the launch of Explorer I. Held at the National Academy of Sciences, Washington, DC, Feb 1, 1978.

[7]B. I. Edelson, "Global Satellite Communications," *Scientific American*, Vol 236, no. 2, Feb 1977, pp 58-69, 73.

[8]T. R. McDonough, *Space: The Next Twenty-Five Years* (NY: Wiley, 1987), p 64ff. "A Proposal for an International Arms Verification and Study Center" by Jerome Wiesner (Science Advisor to President J. F. Kennedy), MIT, 1986.

[9]W. L. Morgan, "Satellite Utilization of the Geosynchronous Orbit," *COMSAT Technical Review*, Vol 6, no. 1, 1976, pp 195-205.

[10]A. C. Clarke, "Beyond Babel," *UNESCO Courier*, Mar 1970, pp 32, 34-37.

[11]I. Asimov, "The Fourth Revolution," *Saturday Review*, Oct 24, 1970, pp 17-20.

[12]A. C. Clarke, "Extra-Terrestrial Relays," *Wireless World*, Vol 51, no. 303, Oct 1945, Chapter 3.

[13]J. R. Pierce, "Orbital Radio Relays," *Jet Propulsion*, Vol 25, no. 4, Apr 1955, p 153.

[14]A discussion of Dr Reber's work and original references can be found in J. D. Kraus, *Radio Astronomy* (New York: McGraw-Hill, 1966, Chapter 1). Dr Reber is currently living in Bothwell, Tasmania. Dr Kraus, former director of the Ohio State University Radio Observatory, is W8JK.

[15]R. W. Miller, "The Listener," *QST*, Jan 1989, pp 58-59.

[16]E. P. Tilton, "Lunar DX on 144 Mc.," *QST*, Mar 1953, pp 11-12, 116.

[17]D. Stoner, "Semiconductors," *CQ*, Apr 1959, p 84.

[18]W. I. Orr, "Sixty Years of Radio Amateur Communications," *QST*, Feb 1962, pp 11-15, 130, 132.

[19]H. Gabrielson, "The OSCAR Satellite," *QST*, Feb 1962, pp 21-24, 132, 134. Technical description of OSCAR I.

[20]W. I. Orr, "OSCAR I: A Summary of the World's First Radio-Amateur Satellite," *QST*, Sep 1962, pp 46-52, 140.

[21]P. McKnight, "QST Profiles Chuck Towns, K6LFH: 'Let's Fly High,'" *QST*, Jan 1987, pp 68-69.

[22]W. I. Orr, "OSCAR II: A Summation," *QST*, Apr 1963, pp 53-56, 148, 150.

[23]W. I. Orr, "OSCAR II: A Summation," *QST*, Apr 1963, p 56.

[24]R. Soifer, "Space Communication and the Amateur," *QST*, Nov 1961, pp 47-50; "The Mechanisms of Space Communication," *QST*, Dec 1961, pp 22-26, 168, 170. These two references treat basic concepts in a comprehensive manner, and the information contained is still of interest to experimenters involved in radio astronomy and direct reception from lunar and deep space probes.

[25]R. Soifer, "Amateur Participation in ECHO A-12," *QST*, Apr 1962, pp 32-36. Note: ECHO 2 was known as ECHO A-12 before launch.

[26]R. Soifer, "Project ECHO A-12," *QST*, June 1962, pp 22-24.

[27]R. Soifer, "Amateur Radio Satellite Experiments in the Pre-OSCAR Era," *Orbit*, Vol 2, no. 1, Jan/Feb 1981, pp 4-7.

[28]D. Blaschke, "The Evolution of the 'Mighty Big Antenna'," *QST*, Jan 1989, pp 15-19.

[29]For information on the history of EME see: W. Orr, "Project Moon Bounce," *QST*, Sep 1960, pp 62-64, 158; F.S. Harris, "Project Moon Bounce," *QST*, Sep 1960, pp 65-66; H. Brier and W. Orr, *VHF Handbook for Radio Amateurs* (Wilton, CT: Radio Publications, 1974); T. Clark, "How Diana Touched the Moon," *IEEE Spectrum*, May 1980, pp 44-48.

[30]J. D. Kraus, R.C. Higgy and W.R. Crone, "The Satellite Ionization Phenomenon," *Proc IRE*, Vol 48, Apr 1960, pp 672-678.

[31]C. Roberts, P. Kirchner and D. Bray, "Radio Detection of Silent Satellites," *QST*, Aug 1959, pp 34-35.

[32]R. Soifer, "High-Frequency Satellite Scatter," *QST*, Jul 1960, pp 36-37.

[33]R. Soifer, "Satellite Supported Communication at 21 Megacycles," *Proc IRE*, Vol 49, no. 9, Sep 1961.

[34]"The 1963 Geneva Space Conference," *QST*, Jan 1964, pp 60-61, 134.

[35]W. I. Orr, "The OSCAR III V.H.F. Translator Satellite, *QST*, Feb 1963, pp 42-44.

[36]A. M. Walters, "OSCAR III — Technical Description," *QST*, Jun 1964, pp 16-18.

[37]A. M. Walters, "Making Use of the OSCAR III Telemetry Signals," *QST*, Mar 1965, pp 16-18.

[38]W. I. Orr, "OSCAR III Orbits the Earth!," *QST*, May 1965, pp 56-59.

[39]D. M. Chapin, S.S. Fuller and G.L. Pearson, "A New Silicon p-n Junction Photocell for Converting Solar Radiation into Electrical Power," *J. Applied Physics*, Vol 25, May 1954, p 676

[40]H. C. Gabrielson, "OSCAR III Report — Communications Results," *QST*, Dec 1965, pp 84-89.

[41]"OSCAR IV News," *QST*, Dec 1965, p 41.

[42]"OSCAR IV Due Dec 21," *QST*, Jan 1966, p 10.

[43]E. P. Tilton and S. Harris, "The World Above 50 Mc.," *QST*, Feb 1966, pp 80-82.

[44]T. Bellair and S. E. Howard, "Australis-Oscar," *QST*, Jul 1969, pp 58-61.

[45]T. Bellair and S. E. Howard, "Obtaining Data from Australis-Oscar 5," *QST*, Aug 1969, pp 70, 72, 82.

[46]J. A. King, "Proposed Experiments with Australis-Oscar 5," *QST*, Dec 1969, pp 54-55.

[47]R. Soifer, "Australis-Oscar 5 Ionospheric Propagation Results," *QST*, Oct 1970, pp 54-57.

[48]J. A. King, "Australis-Oscar 5 Spacecraft Performance," *QST*, Dec 1970, pp 64-69.

[49]P. M. Wilson and R. T. Knadle, "Houston, This is Apollo ... ," *QST*, Jun 1972, pp 60-65.

[50]K. Nose, "Using the ATS-1 Weather Satellite for Communications," *QST*, Dec 1971, pp 48-51.

[51]*Spacewarn Bulletin*, 25 July, 1996. Prepared by World Data Center A for Rockets and Satellites, Goddard Space Flight Center. For updated information see the World Wide Web at **http://nssdc.gsfc.nasa.gov/spacewarn.html**

[52]O. G. Villard, Jr and R. S. Rich, "Operation Smoke-Puff," *QST*, May 1957, pp 11-15.

[53]M. W. Browne, "June Space Test [Firewheel] to Outdo Moon in Brief Display," *New York Times*, Vol CXXIX, no. 44547, Tues 8 Apr 1980, pp C1, C2.

[54]V. R. Frank, R. B. Fenwick and O. G. Villard, Jr, "Communicating at VHF via Artificial Radio Aurora," *QST*, Nov 1974, pp 27-31, 34.

[55]V. R. Frank, "Scattering Characteristics of Artificial Radio Aurora," *Ham Radio*, Nov 1974, pp 18-24. (Contains an extensive bibliography.)

[56]L. Van Prooyen, "Stimulating the Ionosphere in Alaska," *QST*, Jul 1989, pp 22-26.

[57]E. J. Kennedy, J. Heckscher, "The High Frequency Active Auroral Research Program," *QST*, Sep 1966, pp 33-35.

[58]J. Huntoon, "The 1971 Space Conference," *QST*, Sep 1971, pp 78-81.

[59]J. A. King, "The Sixth Amateur Satellite," Part I, *QST*, Jul 1973, pp 66-71, 101; Part II, *QST*, Aug 1973, pp 69-74, 106. This article is highly recommended for anyone interested in satellite design.

[60]P. I. Klein, J. Goode, P. Hammer and D. Bellair, "Spacecraft Telemetry Systems for the Developing Nations," *1971 IEEE National Telemetering Conference Record*, Apr 1971, pp 118-129.

[61]J. C. Fox and R. R. Dunbar, "Preliminary Report on Inverted Doppler Anomaly," *ARRL Technical Symposium on Space Communications*, Reston, VA, Sep 1973, pp 1-30.

[62]L. Kayser, "SMART — System Multiplexing Amateur Radio Telecommands,"*ARRL Technical Symposium on Space Communications*, Reston, VA, Sep 1973, pp 31-45.

[63]P. I. Klein and J. A. King, "Results of the AMSAT-OSCAR 6 Communications Satellite Experiment," *IEEE National Convention Record*, NYC, Mar 1974.

[64]M. Davidoff, *Using Satellites in the Classroom: A Guide for Science Educators*, 1978, sponsored by the National Science Foundation (SED 75-17333) and Smithsonian Air and Space Museum. Out of Print. Microfiche copies available from ERIC (Educational Resources Information Center), 1-800-443-ERIC. Document ED 162 635. Print copies available through OCLC (national inter-library loan service).

[65]J. Kasser and J. A. King, "OSCAR 7 and Its Capabilities," *QST*, Feb 1974, pp 56-60.

[66]P. Klein and R. Soifer, "Intersatellite Communication Using the AMSAT-OSCAR 6 and AMSAT-OSCAR 7 Radio Amateur Satellites," *Proceedings of the IEEE Letters*, Oct 1975, pp 1526-1527.

[67]M. Davidoff, "Predicting Close Encounters: OSCAR 7 and OSCAR 8," *Ham Radio*, Vol 12, no. 7, Jul 1979, pp 62-67.

[68]P. Klein and J. Kasser, "The AMSAT-OSCAR D [8] Spacecraft," *AMSAT Newsletter*, Vol IX, no. 4, Dec 1977, pp 4-10.

[69]J. P. Kleinman, "OSCAR Medical Data," *QST*, Oct 1976, pp 42-43.

[70]D. Nelson, "Medical Relay by Satellite," *Ham Radio*, Apr 1977, pp 67-73.

[71]D. L. Brandel, P. E. Schmidt and B. J. Trudell, "Improvements in Search and Rescue Distress Alerting and Locating Using Satellites," IEEE WESCON, Sept 1976.

[72]"Four Nations Sign 15-Year Sarsat Pact," *Aviation Week & Space Technology*, Oct 24, 1988, p 41.

[73]R. Baldwin and D. Sumner, "The Geneva Story," *QST*, Feb 1980, pp 52-61.

Chapter 2

History: 1980 ⇒ Future

PHASES 1, 2, 3, 4, 5

AMSAT PHASE 3 PROGRAM

AMSAT Phase 3A
AMSAT-OSCAR 10
AMSAT-OSCAR 13
AMSAT-OSCAR 40

AMSAT PHASE 4 PROGRAM

AMSAT PHASE 5 PROGRAM

UoSAT PROGRAM

UoSAT-OSCAR 9
UoSAT-OSCAR 11
UoSAT-OSCARs 14, 15 and 22
KITSAT-OSCARs 23 and 25
PoSAT-OSCAR 28
TMSAT-OSCAR 31
UoSAT-OSCAR-36
TiungSAT-1 (MO-46)

AMSAT MICROSAT PROGRAM

AMSAT-OSCAR 16 and LUSAT-OSCAR 19
DOVE-OSCAR 17
WEBERSAT-OSCAR 18
ITAMSAT-OSCAR 26
AMRAD-OSCAR 27
Mexico-OSCAR 30

JAPANESE JAS PROGRAM

Fuji-OSCAR 12
Fuji-OSCAR 20
Fuji-OSCAR 29

SOVIET RS PROGRAM

RS-1, RS-2
RS-3 - RS-8
RS-10/11
RS-12/13

RS-14/AO 21
RS-15
ISKRA-2, ISKRA-3
RS-16
RS-17, RS-18
RS-21
RS-20

OTHER AMATEUR PROGRAMS (BY COUNTRY)

France
Arsene-OSCAR 24
SARA
BO-47, BO-48
Israel
TechSat series (1A, TO-31)
Germany
AMSAT-DL Spacecraft
AATIS-OSCAR 49 (AO-49)
Saudi Arabia
SO-41, SO-42
SO-50
South Africa
SUNSAT (SO-35)
US Educational Institutions
SEDSAT (SO-33)
PANSAT (PO-34)
ASUSAT (AO-37)
OPAL (OO-38)
JAWSAT (WO-39)
StenSat, Artemis JAK/Thelma/Louise
Starshine-3 (SO-43)
PCsat (NO-44)
Sapphire (NO-45)

HAMS IN SPACE

US STS
Russian *Mir*
International Space Station

CONSIDERATIONS FOR THE FUTURE

Attracting Volunteer Support
Obtaining Launches
RF Spectrum Access
Financing

2 History: 1980 ⇒ Future

In the early 1970s, when amateurs began working on a radically new satellite capable of providing greatly expanded services, they named it Phase 3A to distinguish it from earlier spacecraft. While criteria for assigning a particular spacecraft to Phase 1 or Phase 2 were never formally specified, certain traits relating to design goals, orbital characteristics, primary mission subsystem, launch date, etc. were generally accepted. By the late 1980s the number and types of spacecraft had outgrown the old classification criteria. As a result, later spacecraft were generally identified as belonging to a particular series or program and it's best to do this if there's any possibility of confusion. Use of the term "Phases" to describe satellites resurfaced, however, as we'll see.

Phase 1 satellites were short-lived and designed to gather information on basic satellite system performance. They appealed mainly to a relatively small number of hard-core radio amateur experimenters—perhaps several thousand.

Phase 2 satellites were characterized by low altitudes (a small fraction of an Earth radius), long lifetimes and communications capabilities. They attracted a significantly larger, new group of operators to the space program, amateurs who shared a vision of the future communications services that satellites would provide and wanted to assist in working toward the success of the amateur space program. Estimates are that by 1983 between 10,000 and 20,000 amateurs had communicated through a Phase 2 satellite.

Phase 3 spacecraft reside in highly elliptical orbits having an apogee of several Earth radii. They contain high power transmitters, gain antennas and complex telemetry and control systems. With Phase 3 spacecraft in operation since 1983 and the introduction of sophisticated digital store-and-forward spacecraft in 1990, amateurs gained access to reliable, predictable long-distance communication capabilities of a type never before available in the amateur service. As a result, the number of radio amateurs engaged in space communications continued to grow.

The term Phase 4 is applied to geostationary spacecraft. Although such spacecraft only exist in the design study stage, the concept has received much attention.

The expression Phase 5 has been applied to spacecraft designed for lunar or Mars missions that have a significant Amateur Radio component.

Table 2.1 shows the "Phase" assignments of past and current spacecraft. Although some placements are not clear cut—for example, where to place OSCAR IV—this does not cause any practical problems.

AMSAT PHASE 3 PROGRAM

Early Phase 3 satellites were designed to provide modestly equipped ground stations with major improvements in the amount, type and quality of communications available via a satellite system. To do this, Phase 3 spacecraft were placed in highly elliptical orbits and outfitted with high-power transmitters, large solar power systems, high-gain directional antennas, attitude sensing/adjusting systems, sophisticated computer control, rocket motors and so on. In their elliptical orbits Phase 3 satellites spend most of their time at high altitudes where they are in view for long periods of time to about 40% of the Earth. For example, AMSAT-OSCAR 13 was accessible by Northern Hemisphere ground stations, on average, more than 10 hours each day during the period 1989-1995. To understand the significance of this figure compare it to a satellite in a circular low Earth orbit such as OSCAR 8 (Phase 2) or a modern counterpart such as Fuji-OSCAR 29. Such spacecraft are only in view of about 10% of the Earth at any given time and accessible to most ground stations for less than two hours each day.

If you don't have any personal experience communicating via a Phase 3 satellite, an effective method for getting a handle on their capabilities is to compare communicating through one to normal terrestrial communications on a familiar HF band—14 MHz is a good choice. A modestly equipped 14-MHz HF station can communicate with any place on Earth by exploiting favorable ionospheric conditions. But, if the station is interested in scheduled communications, either over specific point-to-point paths or involving a multipoint network, reliability is not very high. The unpredictable nature of the 14-MHz band isn't necessarily a negative attribute; in many situations it's a feature that makes the band interesting and exciting—when you turn your HF station on you never know who the next contact might be.

In contrast, Phase 3 spacecraft provide highly reliable, predictable and consistent communications over long paths

Table 2.1

Classification Criteria: Amateur Satellite Phases

Stage	Characteristics	Satellites
Phase 1	experimental, short-lifetime, low-earth-orbit	OSCAR I, OSCAR II, OSCAR III, Australis-OSCAR 5, ISKRA 2, ISKRA 3, RS-17, RS-18
Phase 2 (Early)	developmental and operational, long-lifetime, low earth orbit, analog links	AMSAT-OSCARs 6, 7, 8 RS-1, 2, 3, 4, 5, 6, 7, 8, 10/11, 12/13, 15
Phase 2 (Recent)	developmental and operational, long-lifetime. low earth orbit, digital links	JAS Series: Fuji-OSCARs 12, 20, 29 RS Series: RS-14 UoSAT Series: UoSAT-OSCARs 9, 11, 14, 15, 22 KITSat Series: KITSat-OSCARs 23, 25 MicroSat Series: OSCARs 16, 17, 18, 19, 26, 27, 30 Other: ASUSat, SEDSAT, SUNSAT, TechSAT, etc.
Phase 3	operational, long-lifetime, high altitude elliptical orbit	AMSAT-Phase 3A, AMSAT-OSCAR 10, AMSAT-OSCAR 13, AMSAT-OSCAR 40
Phase 4	Operational, long-lifetime, geostationary or drifting geostaionary orbit	OSCAR IV ARSENE
Phase 5	Lunar or Planetary	P5D

to stations modestly equipped for the VHF and UHF frequencies used by the satellites. With AO-10 and AO-13 downlink signal levels were not very strong but they were sufficient to provide excellent readability. The hope was that AO-40 would provide considerably improved performance. However, serious problems were encountered while positioning AO-40 in its final orbit and, in 2003, it's still unclear as to whether 3-axis stabilization can be achieved. As a result, radio links are better than on previous Phase 3 missions but not to the extent planned. The predictability of Phase 3 spacecraft radio links makes them an invaluable asset when natural disasters occur and in other situations where getting a message through in a timely fashion is of paramount importance. Examples include general bulletins, code practice, phone patches, coordinating DXpeditions or arranging moonbounce schedules.

Satellite links don't have any "skip zone." As a result, nets run more smoothly and efficiently and accidental QRM can be avoided since anyone listening to the downlink will know if a frequency is in use. Although the skip zone can cause problems for 14 MHz HF stations it can also be helpful by, for example, allowing several QSOs to take place on a single frequency with each group unaware of the presence of the others.

This brief comparison of the 14-MHz band and Phase 3 satellite communication links illustrates their complemen-

tary nature. Whatever your primary interests are, don't get caught in the trap of viewing the situation as a competition where one tries to decide whether satellite communication is "better" than HF communication. Satellites provide another dimension to Amateur Radio, they are not meant to replace existing options.

We now look at four spacecraft in the Phase 3 series. Satellites are not assigned a number until after they've been successfully deposited in orbit. The Phase 3D spacecraft, for example, became known as AMSAT-OSCAR 40 once the launch vehicle dropped it off in space.

AMSAT Phase 3A

The launch window opened at 1130 UTC on Friday, May 23, 1980, with AMSAT Phase 3A perched atop an Ariane rocket in Kourou, French Guiana. Following nine years of planning, including four of intensive construction, AMSAT workers around the world listened while Dr. Tom Clark (W3IWI), then president of AMSAT, relayed the countdown as it occurred on the northern coast of South America. Would the tropical weather clear for a liftoff? Would rocket systems remain "go"? Continuous status reports were being broadcast on several HF amateur bands as Phase 3A waited within the cowling of the newly developed European Space Agency (ESA) launch vehicle. The amateur spacecraft had been awarded this prized position in a stiff international competition involving more than 80 applicants. Finally, at approximately 1430 UTC, the liftoff signal was given and the Ariane rose from its pad. For several minutes spirits soared.

Then disaster. Amateurs monitoring the net had their hopes dashed as they heard the words "non-nominal flying . . . problem in one engine . . . rocket is going down . . . splashdown." The first stage of the Ariane rocket had failed and unceremoniously dumped Phase 3A in its final resting place several hundred feet under the Atlantic Ocean.

While many AMSAT members wondered if they had just witnessed the end of the amateur space program, Clark drafted a statement objectively describing the situation. Later that evening it was read over AMSAT post launch nets.

"What we lost on Black Friday was sheet metal, solar cells, batteries, transistors, a lot of sleep and a major portion of our lives for the last few years. What we gained over those same years was knowledge; knowledge that we could make a complicated spacecraft. Knowledge in areas of aerospace technology that none of us had before. Knowledge that we could work as a team, despite national boundaries, differences in our cultures, lifestyles and personalities. Knowledge that, from within the ranks of Amateur Radio, we could draw upon enough resources to attempt a project with a complexity rivaling commercial satellite endeavors funded at levels of tens of millions of dollars. The knowledge is still intact. We even had the forethought to purchase a duplicate set of sheet metal that constitutes the spaceframe. We have a second set of solar panels, batteries and sensors. We have on hand the documentation and art work necessary to replicate all the printed-circuit boards. We have in place and ready to go a network of ground telecommand stations."[1] The situation was bleak but not completely hopeless.

At this point the AMSAT Board of Directors looked to the membership to see if the spirit and confidence to continue existed since a commitment to a follow-on spacecraft required reasonable assurance of financial and moral backing. Over the next several weeks a tidal wave of support arose and, one by one, key volunteers, convinced that Phase 3B was possible, recommitted themselves to the project. As the elements of the jigsaw puzzle settled into place a picture of the satellite emerged. The amateur space program would continue.

We now take a brief look at some of the hardware that was lost. Phase 3A was the first amateur satellite to carry its own propulsion system, a rocket (kick motor) accounting for roughly half the spacecraft's 93 kg launch weight. The kick motor was required for this mission because the initial (transfer) orbit targeted by ESA had a low point (perigee) of only 125 miles. Left here, the orbit would rapidly decay and the spacecraft would reenter the atmosphere and burn up within the year. The kick motor would have enabled AMSAT to (1) prolong the spacecraft's lifetime by increasing the perigee and (2) enhance the spacecraft's utility to Northern Hemisphere ground stations by raising the inclination of the orbit.

It's fair to say that the Phase 3A project was more complex, involved a larger financial investment and reflected a greater total effort than all previous OSCARs combined. The spacecraft contained a 50-W Mode B transponder and an energy supply system capable of supporting the transponder. A computer for flexible control of command, telemetry, Codestore and housekeeping functions, a sophisticated attitude sensing and control system permitting the use of high-gain antennas and two beacons sandwiching the 180-kHz-wide 146-MHz downlink. Building and testing the spacecraft was only part of the Phase 3A project. AMSAT also coordinated the development, construction and deployment of a series of ground telecommand stations and provided a crew to oversee mating of the satellite to the launch rocket in Kourou. The telecommand stations, located around the world, were capable of loading the spacecraft computer, providing real-time orbit determination and attitude control data and reducing the relatively sophisticated telemetry to meaningful values.

Flight hardware for the project was produced in Canada, Hungary, Japan, the US and West Germany. Primary responsibility for spacecraft and ground support systems resided with the US and West Germany. The project was directed by Jan King (W3GEY) and Dr. Karl Meinzer (DJ4ZC). Jan, acting as the senior spacecraft engineer,

oversaw the entire construction project, which began in 1971 when the first highly speculative feasibility studies were completed. Karl was responsible for the overall technical design of the spacecraft and for the design and construction of many of the unique high-technology subsystems developed for it. In recognition of the ESA-sponsored launch and the major contributions to the spacecraft by AMSAT-Deutschland (AMSAT-DL) members, the satellite was licensed as DLØOS.[2,3]

AMSAT-OSCAR 10

On June 16, 1983 AMSAT Phase 3B was successfully launched by a European Space Agency Ariane rocket along with the European Communications Satellite ECS-1. Upon separation from the launcher Phase 3B became known as AMSAT-OSCAR 10 (AO-10). Similar in appearance to Phase 3A it weighed about 40% more primarily due to the fact that it used a new liquid fuel rocket engine.

A great many radio amateurs shared the anxiety of liftoff by monitoring the usual AMSAT coordinated worldwide radio networks. At the announcement of each milestone—attaining orbit, separation of various payloads—you could almost feel a collective sigh of relief. This was followed by a feeling of great elation when the first report of telemetry reception, from New Zealander Ian Ashley (ZL1AOX), arrived.

But the feeling of elation was short-lived as analyses of the telemetry showed that the spacecraft was behaving oddly. The orientation and spin were far from nominal and as a result, the spacecraft was capturing very little solar power and running dangerously cold.

The best way to gauge the competence of a technical team is to observe how they handle the unexpected. The AMSAT crew analyzed the problem, took corrective measures and revised plans for orbit transfer before most radio amateurs realized the serious nature of the situation. It wasn't until weeks later that AMSAT learned the cause of the odd initial behavior. ESA had tested a new procedure for separating the AMSAT satellite from the Ariane rocket's third stage and an unforeseen set of circumstances had caused the third stage to bump into OSCAR 10 twice shortly after separation.[4]

The collision affected the mission in several ways. At least one of the elements of the high gain 2-meter antenna on OSCAR 10 appears to have been damaged. The resulting asymmetry caused a slight reduction in gain, on the order of 2 dB, and a small increase in spin modulation on the 2-meter downlink. The impact also affected the spacecraft initial orientation and spin. As a result, OSCAR 10 was subjected to temperatures considerably below the limits designed for and tested to. It's believed that the low temperatures damaged the plumbing associated with the spacecraft's liquid fuel rocket. Although the rocket ignited for the first burn, which raised the perigee, a leak in a high pressure helium tank prevented operation of the valves needed for reignition. So the second burn, required to adjust the perigee height and orbit inclination, never took place. OSCAR 10 ended up residing in a final orbit having an inclination of 26° (the target was 57°) and a perigee near

4000 km (the target was 1500 km). Superficially, the final orbit doesn't appear to differ too much from the target but a careful analysis shows several major effects including the following. Ground control stations had to adjust the satellite's attitude very often to ensure sufficient solar illumination and had to accept orientations that were far from optimal with respect to antenna pointing. And, it's believed that increased cumulative radiation exposure due to the resulting orbit contributed to reducing the operating life of the spacecraft's control computer. However, the picture wasn't too bleak—early reentry wouldn't be a problem.

Despite the negative aspects just presented, AMSAT-OSCAR 10 was a great success. The Mode B transponder performed superbly, providing amateurs with their first exposure to the communications capabilities of a high altitude Phase 3 satellite. OSCAR 10 was available a great many hours each day, it was where you expected it to be, it was on when the schedule said it would be on and with a little experience you could easily predict link performance before you even switched on your rig.

One of the more interesting uses that OSCAR 10 was put to involved Lothar Baumann, DG5SL, who was wintering over at the German "Georg-Von-Meumayer" Antarctic Station (DP0GVN). In all, Lothar spent more than a year at the station regularly using OSCAR 10 to communicate with amateurs (including DP0SL—the US Shuttle/Space Lab mission) and his family back home in Germany.

Technically, AMSAT-OSCAR 10 was closely patterned after Phase 3A but there were two significant design changes involving the rocket motor and transponder complement. Phase 3A's solid-fuel kick motor had been replaced with a liquid-fuel rocket. A solid rocket can only be ignited once. The new rocket was more powerful and it was designed to support multiple reignition. This enabled AMSAT to target a more desirable final orbit and plan a series of burns to get there, eliminating the dangers associated with certain single burn orbit maneuvers. The liquid fuel motor, valued at 2 million dollars, was donated by the manufacturer, Messerschmitt-Bolkow-Blohm (MBB). It had been a backup for the European Symphonie communications satellite.

The added payload capabilities of the rocket also permitted AMSAT to add a second transponder and extra radiation shielding to the main computer. The new transponder, an 800 kHz wide unit using a 1269 MHz uplink and a 435 MHz downlink was called Mode L. The primary transponder remained Mode B. Plans were to schedule the Mode B transponder most of the time during the early part of the satellite's life and then, when/if crowding became a problem and the number of amateurs with the ability to access Mode L increased, to raise the percentage of the time allocated to the high capacity (wide bandwidth) Mode L unit. These plans had to be curtailed for several reasons. A biasing regulator in the Mode L transponder failed. As a result, users required approximately 10-15 dB more uplink power than anticipated. Also, the need to adjust sun angles so that the satellite would have adequate power in the revised orbit affected the aiming of the spacecraft's highly directional Mode L antenna in an unfavorable manner.

OSCAR 10 was small enough to be carried by two or three people. Solar panels cover most of the surface.

Because of these factors, Mode L remained essentially experimental and it only received a limited amount of operating time. However, when the spacecraft antennas were properly lined up toward Earth and the Mode L transponder was turned on, the small group of amateurs equipped to access it were treated to phenomenal performance. The near total lack of spin modulation, the excellent linearity and an exceptionally high signal-to-noise ratio produced a link that sounded as good as most telephone connections.

OSCAR 10 had an Achilles heel. It was known before launch that the satellite control computer was susceptible to cumulative radiation damage and its projected lifetime, in the aimed-for orbit was at most 5 to 7 years. Everything possible had been done to maximize this figure using the best technology available to AMSAT in late 1982 when the spacecraft was buttoned up. If other subsystems performed as expected this is where catastrophic failure would occur. In May 1986, after approximately 3 years of excellent service, radiation damage began to be observed and by the end of the year the computer on OSCAR 10 was declared dead.

Without the computer the satellites attitude couldn't be controlled, the telemetry system no longer yielded information and command stations couldn't provide a reliable schedule. When the spacecraft orientation caused the solar cells to turn away from the sun, battery power would drop nearly to zero, subsystem temperatures would plummet far below the safe range and the communications systems on OSCAR 10 would cease operating. But, OSCAR 10 refused to die. To the surprise of many, each time conditions improved the spacecraft would recover and, in 2001, it's still operating. When solar illumination is adequate the satellite returns to its default mode with the Mode B transponder on and the low gain omni-directional antenna connected. To prolong the operational life of OSCAR 10, AMSAT requests that amateurs use the transponder only during certain parts of the orbit and at certain times of the year when the sun angles are providing adequate power. For updated information on when operation is permitted, check local AMSAT nets and packet Bulletin Boards.

AMSAT-OSCAR 13

AMSAT-OSCAR 13 (AO-13) was launched June 15,

1988. The launch and the orbital transfer operations that followed went flawlessly. Two burns placed the spacecraft precisely in the desired orbit. AMSAT had, for the first time, demonstrated its ability to take a spacecraft through the series of reorientations, spin-ups, spin-downs and rocket firings, needed for a complex orbit change. All maneuvers were accomplished using Amateur Radio communications equipment and personal computers for ranging, telemetry capture, spacecraft control and orbit and attitude determination.

OSCAR 13 was modeled on OSCAR 10. There were small, evolutionary, changes in some subsystems plus a few major changes and additions. One major change was to the spacecraft computer. Thanks to a donation from Harris Semiconductor of special radiation hardened ICs, radiation damage to key computer circuitry wasn't expected to limit satellite life. When OSCAR 13 was placed in orbit it had no known Achilles heel. New systems on the spacecraft included an experimental Mode S transponder (435 MHz uplink, 2.4 GHz downlink—future Mode S uplinks may use 1.2 GHz) and a special digital transponder, known as RUDAK, with an uplink at 435 MHz and a downlink near 146 MHz. Several changes were made to the Mode L transponder, which traded off some bandwidth for versatility and robustness. A narrow (50 kHz wide) 2-meter secondary input channel was added to Mode L with the output superimposed on the normal 250 kHz wide downlink. When the secondary input channel is operating the mode is designated JL. To provide additional protection against surprise hazards, like those that occurred with OSCAR 10, several key systems were designed and tested over an extended temperature range.

The Mode B transponder, generally activated about 60-75% of each orbit, performed excellently. Subjective reports seem to agree that the OSCAR 13 downlink was slightly (2-3 dB) stronger than that of OSCAR 10 under similar conditions and that spin modulation on OSCAR 13 was less obtrusive. The spin modulation performance was of special interest since Mode B was generally operative when the spacecraft antennas were off-pointed from the Earth due to the fact that the high gain antennas used by Modes L and S permitted their use only when the pointing angle was very favorable.

During the early days of OSCAR 13 the Mode L transponder was used approximately 20% of each orbit. It provided excellent performance; reasonably equipped ground stations could hear the transponder noise floor. A report by Bill McCaa, KØRZ, listed more than 200 stations known to have been active on Mode L during its first three months of operation. On weekends the secondary 2-meter uplink was often activated during the time scheduled for Mode L (now Mode JL). The 2-meter uplink, which was very sensitive, was specifically added to the spacecraft to provide Mode L access to amateurs in countries where operation on the 1.2 GHz uplink is not permitted or equipment is not available. Other amateurs were asked to refrain from using this uplink. Part of the reason was to gather support at future WARCs from developing regions of the world.

The Mode S transponder exhibited some initial prob-

lems, which reduced the sensitivity of the uplink receiver. But some long-distance trouble shooting and software repairs improved the situation. As an experimental system it was initially operated a small percentage of the time. But when, after several years in space, the Mode L transponder failed, interest in Mode S grew rapidly, especially among Mode B users when they realized that all they needed to gain access to this superb transponder was a receive downconverter and antenna.

OSCAR 13 carried a sophisticated digital communications system known as RUDAK but a serious problem prevented its general use. Some rather ingenious long distance trouble-shooting enabled AMSAT-DL to identify the cause of the malfunction, but they were unable to implement a cure.

Although OSCAR 13 had no "known" Achilles heel when it was launched, it did turn out to have a fatal flaw lurking in the background. Initial orbital maneuvers had placed OSCAR 13's perigee (low point) far above the Earth's atmosphere so that atmospheric drag wouldn't directly affect the spacecraft lifetime in orbit. However, after about a year in orbit, observations revealed a very disturbing fact—OSCAR 13's perigee was getting closer and closer to the Earth. A simple least-squares extrapolation of existing data suggested that OSCAR 13 would reenter in mid 1992. Since the height change couldn't be due to atmospheric drag it had to be due to some other physical mechanism. Viktor Kudielka (OE1VKW), an amateur familiar with astrodynamics, surmised that the observations might be due to small forces caused by the sun, moon and Earth's asymmetry. Using a powerful microcomputer and a great deal of ingenuity to study the situation he concluded that these forces were indeed the cause and that OSCAR 13 would reenter but the date was more likely to be closer to 1995.[5]

In an independent analysis, Tom Clark (W3IWI) and Erricos Pavlis arranged to pass the data through GEODYN, a professional orbit prediction program developed at NASA, which ran on a powerful CYBER 205 mainframe computer. They arrived at a similar conclusion: OSCAR 13 was likely to reenter. The graphs they provided showed the time as late 1996. Events nearly seven years later revealed their predictions to be right on target.[6]

James Miller (G3RUH) went on to investigate whether a careful analysis of the physics involved and the choice of mathematical approaches to the problem might enable him to devise a model and program running on a microcomputer with predictive capabilities similar to GEODYN for the case at hand. He provided a very readable account of the situation in 1993 in *The AMSAT Journal*.[7] Continuing this work he predicted, in mid 1994, that reentry would occur at noon December 5, 1996.[8] The prediction was remarkably accurate; the actual date/time turned out to be 0900, December 5, 1996.

All three analyses, using very different mathematical techniques and models had come to the same astonishing conclusion—the shape of OSCAR 13's orbital ellipse was changing and this would cause it to reenter near the end of 1996. Amateurs couldn't do anything but watch as the spacecraft approached its ultimate fate. It continued to perform excellently until November 1996 when atmospheric drag began to seriously affect spacecraft temperature and orientation near perigee. Soon afterward the following telemetry message was heard on the downlink:

*QST de AO-13 *** BIRTH ANNOUNCEMENT *** 1996 Nov 20 0240 EST*

My child, P3D, began "thinking" today when its IHU [Internal Housekeeping Unit = primary computer] was activated. I'm glad I lived long enough to learn of this wonderful event. I wish P3D a long, functional life. Do not grieve for me when I'm gone. I'm only metal, plastic, & sand. My "life" came from enriching the lives of those who built, commanded & utilized me and it's been a good "life." Danke Karl, et al. No regrets. The baton will soon be passed. AO-13 signing off.

The last reported QSO via OSCAR 13 occurred four days later, November 24, 1996. The problem encountered with OSCAR 13 was difficult to foresee. When orbit parameters were being selected for this satellite AMSAT did not have access to the computer resources needed to investigate how changes in the time of launch could affect the long term evolution of the orbit. Had the launch time (a factor AMSAT had no control over) been slightly different OSCAR 13 might still be in orbit and operating. However, the experience has stimulated AMSAT to develop the computer models and tools needed to investigate long-term orbit evolution and we can rest assured that similar problems will not occur with OSCAR 40.[9] In case you've been wondering, OSCAR 10 will remain in orbit for centuries.

AMSAT-OSCAR 40

In the late 1980s and early 1990s there was considerable discussion concerning the next major radio amateur satellite project. Feelings in the US appeared to lean towards building a geostationary (Phase 4) spacecraft while sentiment in Germany was to develop the Phase 3 approach. The reasons for the preferences are discussed in the next section where Phase 4 is introduced. As often happens, a launch opportunity had a major impact on the choice. When it began to appear likely that ESA would offer AMSAT-DL an opportunity to place a satellite on a powerful new Ariane rocket under development amateurs looked at their options, taking into account technical and political considerations. The conclusion was that the most appropriate spacecraft for this launch was a Phase 3 model, but one considerably larger than previous members of the series. By "larger" we mean an increase of a factor of perhaps five in weight and power budget. This was going to be a *large* spacecraft.

The OSCAR 40 physical structure bears little resemblance to earlier Phase 3 satellites. The most noticeable new feature is the solar panels that can be extended out from the spacecraft body. These panels provide the spacecraft with a power budget of about 250 W. Another major change is not immediately visible from pictures. OSCAR 40 is the first amateur spacecraft to include 3-axis stabilization using internal momentum wheels. These momentum wheels, which use magnetic bearings (*no* physical contact) allow the spacecraft to re-orient itself throughout the orbit so that the antennas can always be pointed at the center of the Earth.

The transponder on OSCAR 40 has been totally reengineered. Rather than include a few fixed frequency transponders as on earlier missions the designers decided to fly a large number of independent transmitters and receivers on different bands and arrange to connect them through an IF matrix, which could be configured through the command channel. This makes it possible to experiment with different uplink and downlink combinations once the spacecraft is in orbit. It is possible to test the performance of several downlinks in conjunction with one uplink or several uplinks in conjunction with one downlink, etc. As a result of the high power transmitters and the optimal antenna orientation provided by the 3-axis stabilization, the links on OSCAR 40 were expected to average about 10 dB better than on OSCAR 13.

The IF strip in the transponder merits a special look. It implements the LEILA (LEIstungsLimit Anzeige) concept. LEILA consists of a spectrum analyzer that monitors the transponder passband. If a signal is observed using too much power, a CW message indicating the problem is superimposed on the downlink. If there is no response, the signal is attenuated by a tunable notch. Several notches can be handled simultaneously.

With all the frequency combinations possible the spacecraft naturally has a great many antennas mounted on the surface. For details related to frequency ranges, powers, spacecraft antennas, etc, see Appendix C: Profiles of Current Amateur Satellites.

The orbit selected for OSCAR 40 was again highly elliptical, but it has a number of unique characteristics due to the fact that the design team decided to raise the apogee somewhat so the spacecraft would complete exactly three circuits about the Earth every two days (referred to as the 3/2 orbit). One result is that coverage patterns would repeat every other day. Another is that the spacing between ascending nodes closely matches the locations of the major land masses on the Earth.

After several years of delays AO-40 was treated to a perfect Ariane 5 launch from Kourou on 16 November 2000. The spacecraft was supposed to power up with its 70-cm beacon on, but the transmitter failed and the 2-meter transmitter had to be activated in its place. This was accomplished smoothly within a few hours. Things went well for the next several days as the satellite was checked out and oriented. But then, as the complex sequence of spacecraft orientations and engine firings needed to move AO-40 to its target orbit were initiated, the situation quickly deteriorated. Rocket burns did not produce the expected results, communication with the spacecraft was lost for an extended period and at one point, it appeared that the spacecraft might have been totally lost in a major explosion.

Despite these events, AO-40 was recovered and radio amateurs still have a functioning spacecraft. Although several important subsystems were damaged by an apparent

OSCAR 40 under construction in the clean room on the grounds of the Orlando International Airport. (Left to right: Stan Wood, WA4NFY, and Dick Jansson, WD4FAB. *Photo courtesy Ed Richter, KD4JL and Rod Davis, KC4NEQ*)

explosion, or failed due to other causes, key elements of the spacecraft are still operating. And, most important to the user community, the 70 cm and 23 cm uplinks and 13 cm downlink are daily providing radio amateurs with the best world wide satellite communications links they've ever had access to.

Everyone would have preferred a boring textbook orbit transfer scenario. What we ended up with was a series of events more suspenseful than any novelist could have imagined.[10] The first attempt to fire the high thrust AO-40 engine early in day on December 11 was a total washout—nothing happened. Telemetry suggested that the problem was due to stuck helium valves. Commands, sent to the spacecraft to cycle the valves, appeared to solve the problem. Later in the day the engine was fired but anomalies were observed and the resulting orbit was not as planned. The resulting orbit wasn't a problem; it could be easily corrected in future firings. However, it was critical to understand what was happening on the spacecraft before the engine was re-fired.

On December 13, while again cycling component valves

in the high thrust rocket in order to study the problem, the spacecraft went mute. To quote Robin Haighton, then president of AMSAT-NA...

"Initial thoughts were that the spacecraft was completely dead and that chances of recovery were remote, with the possibility that AO-40 was in multiple pieces."

In short, we didn't know for certain where the spacecraft was or even whether it had exploded. Ground stations around the world repeatedly sent commands to the spacecraft using orbital elements valid prior to the event. But these produced no observable results. Some hope was restored when NORAD reported that radar contact suggested that the spacecraft was in the expected location and in one piece. However, attempts to command the spacecraft continued to prove fruitless.

The main hope of the engineering team was that a reset timer, included on the spacecraft for just such emergencies, would turn the spacecraft back on. But the reset failed to occur on schedule. It was noted that if one of the blind commands sent up by control stations had been received by the spacecraft the onboard timer would have been reset. So, all commanding attempts were terminated and everyone sat and listened. Finally, on Christmas day 2000, the watchdog timer did its job and the spacecraft beacon reappeared.

At this point spacecraft telemetry was extensively analyzed, various systems were checked out, and the current orbit analyzed with respect to long-term stability. Significant spacecraft damage was seen, most likely due to a small explosion. None of the low-gain antennas were operating and several of the transmitters (including the 2-meter unit) had been lost. However, other important RF links remained operational and the control computers were in good condition. A very useful spacecraft still existed, but questions as to whether caustic fuel was still leaking and slowly destroying onboard systems, whether another explosion would occur as soon as a high power transmitter was turned on, or whether the orbit was stable remained. While these concerns still exist, the fact that the spacecraft has been operating for more than two years is a very positive sign.

AO-40's orbit at this point appeared to be marginally stable. Simulations predicted the perigee might get as low as 160 km but the probability of re-entry was extremely low, even if no steps were taken to modify it. However, since the arc-jet engine was available to improve the orbit, and since its activation would provide valuable technical information, the decision was made to fire it using a strategy based on assuring that any conceivable failure mode would not leave AO-40 in an unstable orbit. Here too, AMSAT encountered problems. The arc-jet placed AO-40 in a more desirable orbit but not the one targeted.

Finally, on 5 May 2001, AO-40 was opened for general operation and it has been available every day since. The technical team is constantly working with the spacecraft. Both SCOPE cameras have been activated. The photos they've produced are excellent and have been used to calibrate other attitude sensors on the spacecraft so that the orientation of AO-40 is known very accurately. As a result, the spacecraft's 24-GHZ transmitter and highly directional antenna has been successfully activated. Valuable data collected by the experimental GPS payload has been downlinked and is being used to map the extraterrestrial transmitter radiation pattern produced by the GPS constellation. Experiments with RUDAK have been fruitful and plans are to open a RUDAK channel for general use during 2003.

One very big question remains: should an attempt be made to deploy the spacecraft solar panels? Deployment is a one-way trip; if it's only partially successful, we can't go back. At present, the spacecraft is in a spin-stabilized mode and AMSAT has excellent control over it. If the panels are deployed, we must switch to 3-axis stabilization using the reaction wheels. The reaction wheels appear to be working but there is good reason to be concerned as to whether damage from the onboard explosion could impede full panel deployment. Careful consideration must be given as to whether we could revert to spin stabilization if full deployment is not successful. This topic is still being discussed and studied.

The launch and activation of AO-40 has provided an exiting ride and "it ain't over yet." Long distance troubleshooting of AO-40 and after-the-fact analysis of the problems encountered have provided extremely interesting challenges to those technically inclined. Most of the key problems encountered during the launch and orbit change are now felt to be well understood, and therefore preventable in future missions. The trouble with the high thrust rocket was almost certainly due to a blocked exhaust port on a helium valve affecting fuel system pressure. The problem with losing the command link after the rocket explosion was most probably because the resulting high spacecraft spin rate and unfavorable orientation prevented the reception of a complete command block. On future spacecraft, the command link packet structure will be redesigned to prevent this. And, telemetry suggests that the arc-jet problem was due to a defective "thermal mass flow controller."

AMSAT PHASE 4 PROGRAM

In the mid 1980s, after OSCAR 10 had been in orbit for a few years, several amateurs began to seriously think about the direction the amateur satellite program should take over the next decade. Many felt that the ultimate goal of the amateur community should be the construction of a constellation of three geostationary satellites evenly spaced around the equator. (For a satellite to appear stationary it must be in a circular orbit over the equator at a height of about 3.5 earth radii.) Others felt that this goal was inappropriate. After a period of discussion Jan King coordinated the preparation of a document, called the *Phase Four Technical Study Plan* (J. King et al, Sep 1, 1986) which treated the concept in depth. The plan, summarized in a two part article in *QST*[11] focused on three main points: inherent limitations of current satellite systems, technical details of a proposed Phase 4 system and concerns relating to whether such a system could and should be built. There was general agreement within the amateur community as to the limitations of current systems. The technical proposal was very well received.

However, there was and continues to be debate over the conclusions reached.

We begin by looking at the areas of agreement. First, existing amateur satellite programs have three key inherent limitations; the first two affect the entire worldwide community of radio amateurs, while the third affects society at large.

Limitation 1

All current satellite programs require some specialized knowledge of satellite systems, satellite tracking, satellite scheduling, etc. It's been said of radio amateur satellites that the medium is the message; that is, if you use satellites for communicating you're probably more interested in satellites than in communications. As a result, if we elect to pursue evolutionary improvements in current systems, the size of the amateur satellite user community will show only modest growth since the program will continue to appeal to those primarily interested in space activities.

Limitation 2

The UHF and microwave frequencies allocated to the amateur and amateur satellite service are an extremely valuable resource. Transponders operating with a 1.2 GHz uplink and a 2.4 GHz downlink could provide 10 MHz of spectrum, more than three times the total HF spectrum currently available to radio amateurs. One can associate a monetary value with these frequency allocations by assuming that a commercial entity interested in acquiring a revenue-generating resource is generally willing to invest about six times the revenues the resource can return on an annual basis to purchase it. Viewed this way our UHF and microwave allocations are worth hundreds of millions of dollars per megahertz. Because of Limitation 1 the amateur satellite service, using Phase 3 technology and current communications techniques, may not be able to populate our UHF and microwave allocations to the extent needed to retain them indefinitely. In other words, if we want to keep this extremely valuable resource, something major must be done!

Limitation 3

Although Phase 3 satellites are very appealing to technically inclined radio amateurs, other groups, such as those who wish to use them in times of emergency, on the scene of natural disasters, or for educational activities, find the limited access time, the need to continuously re-aim antennas and the fact that spacecraft are only accessible a limited amount of time, pose an insurmountable barrier to such use.

We now look at some technical details of the Phase 4 study plan. The plan proposed the construction of three geostationary spacecraft positioned over the equator, AMSTAR East at 47° W longitude, AMSTAR West at 145 ° W longitude and AMSTAR Asia. Coverage circles (footprints) for AMSTAR East and West are shown in Figures 2.1 and 2.2.

The proposed power budgets and RF systems are similar to those incorporated on OSCAR 40, meaning that link margins up and down exceed those of OSCAR 10 and 13 by about 10 dB. Each spacecraft would contain several tran-

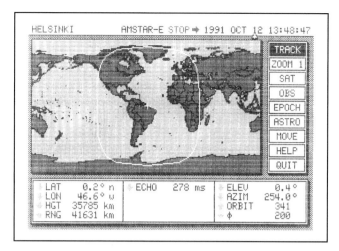

Figure 2.1—Footprint of proposed AMSTAR East satellite (*photo courtesy Silicon Solutions*).

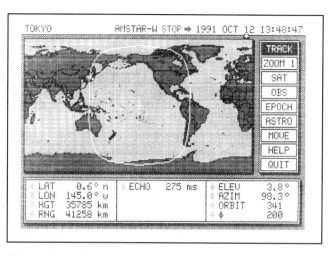

Figure 2.2—Footprint of proposed AMSTAR West satellite (*photo courtesy Silicon Solutions*).

sponders using microwave frequencies capable of providing the wide bandwidth needed to handle high speed digital modes and real time compressed video and VHF and UHF links to satisfy the needs of those in the third world and in case of emergency. The importance of transponder signal processing to control interference from the large number of new users unfamiliar with the operational techniques needed for effective transponder sharing was also emphasized. Many of these design features have been achieved in OSCAR 40 although the specific implementation differs somewhat from that proposed in 1985.

A ground station located inside the footprint of a Phase 4 satellite only has to aim the antenna once, when it's installed. The procedure is very simple: the antenna is pointed in the general direction of the spacecraft, peaked on a downlink beacon and then bolted in position.

Operating schedules could be keyed to local time and very stable. The simplicity and day-to-day consistency of Phase 4 spacecraft schedules would greatly facilitate arranging nets, bulletins, point-to-point communications, classroom demonstrations, etc.

As an example of the type of service one of these spacecraft could provide, imagine the occurrence of a serious earthquake in Central or South America. AMSTAR East could provide around the clock communications between workers and government officials on the scene, UN disaster relief agencies in New York and Red Cross Headquarters in Switzerland.

The design study suggested that terrestrial gateway stations should play a significant role in the Phase 4 program. These gateway stations would enable new users with small hand-held VHF or UHF FM transceivers to engage in continent spanning QSOs.

From a system viewpoint the gateway would operate as follows. One Mode S transponder aboard the spacecraft, capable of simultaneously handling approximately 20 communications channels and one or two command channels, would be optimized for gateway operation. A group of users pools their resources to build a standard gateway station (usually associated with a terrestrial repeater). To initiate

a link a potential user calls up a local repeater using a VHF or UHF FM transceiver and indicates, via tone pad, that access to a specific distant gateway is desired. The transponder command links are used to determine whether the distant gateway is available and if there is an open channel. If the situation permits, a channel is assigned and the connection is opened. From the user point of view most of this is totally transparent. Our potential user just calls up the local repeater and enters five tones, the first to indicate that access to the satellite is desired, the next four to identify the distant gateway. Within a few seconds the local gateway signals whether to "go ahead" or "wait." The signal might consist of synthesized speech, a CW "GA" or "AS" or a simple tone. If used effectively the gateway system has tremendous potential but it requires the user community to participate actively in establishing guidelines on how resources will be allocated.

The Phase 4 Study Plan also addressed a number of concerns and came to several conclusions, some of which are still being debated. These include the following.

Concern 1

Does AMSAT have the technical expertise to design and manage the construction of the proposed spacecraft? AO-40 has proven the contention of the study plan, which stated that AMSAT does have the resources available.

Concern 2

What will Phase 4 cost? At the time the cost of the first Phase 4 spacecraft was estimated at approximately 2 million dollars. Experience with OSCAR 40 shows that 5 million per spacecraft is realistic.

Concern 3

Is it possible to raise this amount of money? The study group concluded that it wasn't possible if the current satellite user community, or even a significantly larger segment of the general amateur community, had to supply the funds. However, it was conceivable if non-amateur groups (Public Service, Education, Disaster Relief, etc.) that will benefit from the new services provided were to take an active rule in sponsoring the project. Those who prepared the plan believed that Phase 4 would provide an entirely new class of service and they thought it reasonable to believe that many of those who would benefit from these services would be willing to help support the program financially. No concrete evidence could be offered to support the hope that such sponsorship would be forthcoming.

Concern 4

Will the amateur community be able to obtain a launch for a Phase 4 spacecraft? This concern was addressed in the conceptual design of the Phase 4 spacecraft. The payload compartment on an Ariane rocket is designed to carry two coaxially mounted large spacecraft into a geostationary transfer orbit. The two spacecraft are joined by a standard connecting ring that is jettisoned in space. The Phase 4 satellite was designed to incorporate this ring as an integral part of its structure. The OSCAR 40 spacecraft adopted and validated this approach. However, the prospects for obtaining an additional, much less two additional, launches of this type at greatly subsidized rates is questionable.

The 1985 design group felt that the only response option the amateur community has that directly addresses all of the previously discussed limitations of existing satellite systems is to construct a constellation of high power, geostationary Phase 4 satellites each carrying several transponders.

While the desirable features of the Phase 4 system have received considerable coverage here and in other places there are significant arguments against viewing the Phase 4 system as the ultimate goal of the amateur satellite program. With Phase 4 one must think in terms of either a regional system (single spacecraft) or a global system (multiple spacecraft).

A single AMSTAR spacecraft only serves about 40% of the Earth. Ground stations in the footprint can only access 40% of the Earth. Compare this to (1) a single Phase 3 spacecraft that is accessible to 100% of the Earth at some time or other and eventually gives users access to about 90% of the Earth and (2) a single low Earth orbit spacecraft such as RS-15 that eventually provides access to about 40% of the Earth. Both systems are, however, only available part of each day while the AMSTAR coverage is available 24 hours. This factor can also be addressed by considering constellations of RS-15 type spacecraft. The single satellite (regional Phase 4 system) system has an extremely high cost per user (financially and in terms of construction effort).

The global Phase 4 system requires three launches and construction programs. While AMSAT has benefited greatly from unique launch opportunities, the possibility of arranging three such scenarios in parallel is difficult to envision. Similarly, while it's possible to imagine finding a nonamateur group to sponsor a single regional spacecraft, finding a sponsor for a global system or finding three such sponsors in different parts of the world seems an almost insurmountable barrier.

While the fact that the Phase 4 systems shield the user from having to understand and deal with satellite concepts has many advantages, it also has a serious downside. One of the key reasons that the satellite program has received the backing of serious experimenters is that most obtain considerable pleasure from exploiting special knowledge to improve station operation and/or take advantage of unusual opportunities for DX via unexpected mutual windows, satellite/satellite links, etc. It's possible that eliminating the challenges will undermine the appeal the program has to its most important supporters. Others argue that the serious experimenters will be able to work on gateway stations. Our crystal ball must remain cloudy here.

Finally, some argue that if system performance and individual station simplicity are our only concerns, then perhaps the communications mode is irrelevant. Amateurs may be able to obtain the communications capabilities of Phase 4 and the associated gateway concept, at far less expense by other means. For example, it's been suggested that radio amateurs rent time on commercial 4/6 GHz geostationary satellite transponders and use these links to interconnect local repeater gateways. This has been tried successfully on a limited scale.

In sum, the conceptual design of the Phase 4 system has been very valuable in that it has led to an in-depth investigation of a number of fundamental questions facing the amateur satellite community and the development of technical systems utilized for the construction of OSCAR 40. Whether the construction of a Phase 4 system should be considered the ultimate goal of the amateur satellite community remains controversial. At present, factors beyond our immediate control such as whether some national government or transnational coordination group adopts the idea and provides the influx of money and/or launch capacity needed to enable it to happen, alleviate our need to make a decision. In any event, OSCAR 40 has shown that technical concerns are not a limiting factor. The ongoing discussions of the utility and desirability of a Phase 4 system will certainly help us make a more informed decision when or if the need arises.

AMSAT PHASE 5 PROGRAM

Radio amateurs' interest in space is not confined to Earth orbit. In the early and mid 1970s unsuccessful attempts were made to convince NASA to have one of the Apollo crews place an amateur built transponder on the moon.

In 1996 NASA and JPL (the Jet Propulsion Laboratory) invited radio amateurs to participate in activities related to the Mars Global Surveyor spacecraft.[12] The spacecraft, launched toward Mars on November 7, 1996, had an RF link near 437.1 MHz designed to be used once the spacecraft was in Mars orbit. The transmitter was activated as the spacecraft traveled toward Mars to enable radio amateurs to experiment with the development of ground stations and tracking and antenna pointing software necessary for reception. A number of radio amateurs took part in prelaunch meetings at the Jet Propulsion Laboratories in California.

In early 1996 Karl Meinzer, whose name should be familiar to you by now, released a proposal to build a spacecraft (Phase 5A) intended to orbit Mars and possibly be used to relay scientific data from probes left on the surface by other spacecraft. P5A would use a P3D-like spaceframe and other technology developed for the Phase 3 program. Because of the time delays and low power levels involved in the RF links between the Earth and Mars it does not appear to be appropriate to include a transponder for general communication as a payload. However, if the amateur community is interested in taking an active part in telemetry capture from onboard cameras, spectrometers, etc. the spacecraft could use RF links on amateur UHF and microwave (2-10 GHz) frequencies. Since P5A would not include a transponder, interest in it is likely to be confined to a small part of the amateur satellite community. However,

this should not be a problem since Dr. Meinzer expects that financial support would be provided by the German government and/or educational sources. As this is written (2003) AMSAT-DL continues to devote significant resources to this project.[13]

UOSAT PROGRAM

We turn now to look at the UoSAT (University of Surrey) satellite program. Situated in Guildford, England, about 40 minutes by rail from London, the operation consists of (1) an academic and research department of the University known as the Centre for Satellite Engineering Research (CSER) which offers MSc, PhD and continuing education training and (2) a wholly owned University Company known as Surrey Satellite Technology Ltd (SSTL) which builds satellites for the commercial market. CSER/SSTL is an acknowledged world leader in the design and construction of microsatellites providing affordable access to space. As of 2003, their activities have resulted in the design, construction and orbital operation of 18 microsatellites with several under development. See Table 2.2. Satellites financed primarily by university grants are assigned UoSAT designations. Contracted spacecraft are named by the sponsor.

The UoSAT project can be traced back to the mid 1970s. Graduate student Martin Sweeting, G3YJO, who was majoring in electrical engineering at the University of Surrey, came to the US to attend preliminary design meetings for the Phase 3 program. He acquired the information needed to set up a command station for OSCARs 6 and 7. In 1979, after completing his PhD, Sweeting proposed that the University initiate a program to investigate cost-effective satellite engineering techniques and demonstrate the feasibility of building inexpensive microsatellites. His arguments must have been convincing because the UoSAT program was funded and he is now the Managing Director and CEO of SSTL and the Deputy Director of CSER. In early 1997 the joint operation moved into a new building which houses more than 150 research staff and advanced level students.

Clearly, the UoSAT program is not an amateur project. However, UoSAT has very deep roots in the radio amateur community and appreciates the major

Table 2.2

CSER/SSTL Spacecraft with Radio Amateur Payloads

All in circular LEO.

All contain imaging subsytems.

All contain open-access transponder except as noted.

Name, aka	Launch date	Status/Notes
UoSAT-1, UoSAT-OSCAR 9, UO-9, UoSAT-A	6/10/81	Re-entered 13/10/89[1]
UoSAT-2, UoSAT-OSCAR 11, UO-11, UoSAT-B	1/3/84	Operational[2]
UoSAT-3, UoSAT-OSCAR 14, UO-14, UoSAT-D, VITASAT, HealthSAT-1	21/1/90	Operational
UoSAT-4, UoSAT-OSCAR 15, UO-15, UoSAT-E	21/1/90	Failed 23/1/90[1]
UoSAT-5, UoSAT-OSCAR 22, UO-22	17/7/91	Operational
KITSAT-1, KITSAT-OSCAR 23, KO-23	10/8/92	Operational
KITSAT-2, KITSAT-OSCAR 25, KO-25	26/9/93	Operational[3]
PoSAT-1, PO-28	26/9/93	Operational[4]
TMSAT, Thai Puht, TO-31	10/7/98	Operational
UoSAT-12, UoSAT-OSCAR 36, UO-36	21/4/99	Operational (?)
TiungSat-1, MO-46	26/9/00	Operational

[1]No open-access transponder
[2]Carries experimental Bulletin board operating on Amateur frequencies. Open downlink but uplink limited to command stations.
[3]KITSAT-2 was built at the Korean Advanced Institute of Science and Technology (KAIST)in South Korea.
[4]Transponder capable of being switched to amateur frequencies.

contributions amateur participation provides to their design and developmental efforts. (The Technical Director of SSTL is Dr Jeff Ward, GØ/K8KA and both organizations contain numerous radio amateurs.) Also there is a great deal of overlap between the UoSAT mission of developing smaller, cheaper, faster [conception to launch] spacecraft and that of the AMSAT program. As a result, there have been a number of cooperative efforts of great benefit to both groups.

To the world radio amateur community UoSAT is best known for providing high speed (9600 baud) store-and-forward transponders for amateur use. Amateur frequency transponders were placed on a number of UoSAT developmental spacecraft and on several contracted spacecraft such as KITSAT. With KITSAT the sponsor recognized the educational value of the subsystem and felt that it complemented their mission objectives and could provide a backup mode on other missions. For example, after the commercial mission was completed the transponder could be switched to amateur frequencies with the sponsor benefiting from ongoing access to telemetry. In addition, many UoSAT produced spacecraft downlink telemetry data of interest to amateurs on amateur frequencies. In return, amateurs using these transponders have helped UoSAT develop and refine the software, procedures and ground station equipment needed to produce a system that could be used by groups not concerned with communications technology. In addition, UoSAT and amateurs have in a large number of instances shared experimental results, information on the reliability of particular electronic and mechanical components used on spacecraft and design data.

We now take a closer look at several of the spacecraft produced by UoSAT paying special attention to subsystems of interest to radio amateurs. Examples include subsystems designed for studying: radio propagation that use beacons operating on amateur bands from 7 MHz to 10 GHz, the radiation environment of space using dedicated charged particle detectors and special software designed to monitor satellite computer operation, the Earth's magnetic field and methods for collecting and downloading high quality images.[14] In all cases where amateur frequencies are used, full information has been provided on capturing and interpreting telemetry.

A brief review of the highlights of the UoSAT program follows. See Appendix C (Satellite Profiles) for more detailed information on operational spacecraft.

UoSAT-OSCAR 9

The first UoSAT spacecraft, UoSAT-OSCAR 9 (UO-9), was launched into a low Earth orbit (LEO) on October 6, 1981 with the Solar Mesosphere Explorer (SME) spacecraft. The payload included a General Data Beacon at 145.825 MHz compatible with standard amateur NBFM receivers, an Engineering Data Beacon at 435.025 MHz, phase-locked HF beacons at 7, 14, 21 and 28 MHz for propagation studies and microwave beacons at 2.4 and 10.47 GHz, also for propagation observations. In addition, the spacecraft carried a CCD camera to send back pictures of the Earth formatted to be viewed on a regular TV after minimal processing. It also carried a 3-axis, wide-range,

flux-gate magnetometer for measurement of the Earth's magnetic field and high-energy particle and radiation detectors. The 146-MHz telemetry beacon could be switched between digital data and a voice synthesizer. Voice synthesized telemetry has a very low data rate but it's excellent for educational demonstrations.

Commanding this complex spacecraft was a real challenge. Each day the satellite would be in range for three brief passes separated by about 1.5 hours and a half a day later, by another set of three similar passes. For the first few months that UoSAT-OSCAR 9 was in orbit a typical day at Surrey would go as follows. During the last orbit of the set collect telemetry. Between sets, study telemetry, plan actions, write and test software on the spacecraft simulator. During the next orbit (about 10 hours later) collect telemetry and check status, transmit commands and new software, verify correct receipt, instruct spacecraft to act on commands and collect telemetry. And finally between orbits, study telemetry, plan actions and so on. Notice that the word sleep isn't mentioned.

While the University of Surrey team perfected the commanding operations (techniques, hardware, software), checked out the spacecraft systems and oriented the spacecraft using the new dynamic magnetorquing system, radio amateurs around the world grew impatient at what appeared to be snails' pace progress. It was a frustrating situation for the Surrey crew who were working till they dropped from exhaustion and for the amateurs who wanted to put the experimental packages aboard UoSAT to practical use. Then disaster struck.

While uplinking commands on April 4, 1982 a software glitch caused both the 2-meter and 70-cm telemetry beacons to be turned on. As a result, satellite command receivers were desensed. When the uplink power at Surrey proved insufficient to overcome the desense problem, Dave Olean, K1WHS, offered the use of his powerful 2-meter EME station for the command link. The 0.5 megawatt EIRP still proved insufficient so a group of amateurs in northern California, under the leadership of Dr. Robert Leonard, KD6DG, obtained permission to reactivate a 150-ft.-dish antenna owned by the Radio Physics Laboratory of Stanford Research Institute (SRI). This dish, when used in conjunction with an amateur 70-cm transmitter, could produce an EIRP of 15 megawatts. The beamwidth was only 0.6 degrees so precise aiming was critical. Returning the Stanford dish to service required several months of work resuscitating drive motors, hydraulic components and control computers. On September 20, 1982, after operating out of control for nearly six months, UoSAT-OSCAR 9 was salvaged and found to be in perfect health. It went on to perform nearly flawlessly until late 1989 when it reentered the Earth's atmosphere and burned up. UoSAT-OSCAR 9 provided solid evidence that projections of 7 to 10 year lifetimes for amateur satellites then being constructed were realistic.

UoSAT-OSCAR 11

In late 1983 the UoSAT team was unexpectedly offered another launch opportunity. But there was a catch—the date was only six months away. Was it possible to design, construct and test a spacecraft in half a year? After evaluating the risk, Martin Sweeting committed the Surrey team to the project. UoSAT-B carried five experimental payloads and several new, or modified, spacecraft engineering systems. The experimental payloads focused on (1) particle-wave detection, (2) Earth imaging, (3) synthesized speech, (4) packet communications and (5) space dust detection. The spacecraft systems' experiments focused on (1) navigation, attitude control and stabilization, (2) computer hardware, software and memory technology and (3) communications systems. Of all the payloads the most interesting to amateurs was the transponder. Although uplinking to the transponder was limited to command stations, these stations arranged to act as gateways so that all amateurs could file messages. The downlink was, of course, open to everyone. Despite the limited access, the relatively low storage capacity of the spacecraft and the modest data rate, this experiment proved very popular and provided a major incentive for the AMSAT MicroSat project.

The Surrey crew completed the spacecraft on time and it was successfully launched on March 1, 1984 and named UoSAT-OSCAR 11 (UO-11). A serious problem quickly arose. On its third orbit of the Earth the spacecraft stopped accepting commands and went into hibernation. Nothing was heard on any of the radio links. The limited amount of data that had been received on the first three orbits did provide some clues. The prevailing theory was that lower than expected spacecraft temperatures following launch, combined with the way in which the spacecraft was tumbling, made it extremely difficult to transfer a complete command block to the satellite.

After attempting to access the spacecraft for several weeks without any success the Surrey crew began to suspect that they might have misdiagnosed the problem and that the situation might be more severe than first thought, perhaps even fatal for OSCAR 11. They devised a plan that would enable them to determine whether the satellite was still alive and confirm the accuracy of their tracking data. The plan involved listening for the extremely weak signal generated by the 1.2 GHz local oscillator in the satellite's command receiver. In order to detect this feeble signal they needed access to a very big antenna so they once again approached Dr. Leonard. This time he suggested using a 100 ft dish at Sondre Stromfjord in Greenland, which already had a 1.2 GHz receiver in place. The station chief in Greenland, Finn Steenstrup, OX3FS, wasted no time. As soon as the proper equipment could be assembled signals were heard from OSCAR 11's local oscillator and the information was relayed back to Surrey. The Surrey crew renewed their control efforts using the updated orbital information and a few days later, on May 14, 1984, they regained control of the bird. In an accident barely six months later, Steenstrup died while working on the Greenland antenna. However, thanks to his efforts UoSAT-OSCAR 11 was returned to life and today, 12 years later it's still performing flawlessly. See Appendix C for additional information.

Reviewing articles that appeared in various radio amateur periodicals between 1981 and 1984 one can't help but notice how the UoSAT saga resembles a script for a soap opera—hopeless predicaments followed by last minute rescues. But radio amateur satellite projects are not immune to the laws of probability, there's no guarantee of a happy ending—Phase 3A met a wet early end, there was a serious launch vehicle failure with OSCAR IV and so on. If there's a message here it's that taking part in the amateur satellite program is not for the faint hearted. Setbacks and barriers will always be part of the picture. And, the most rewarding successes will probably come from employing ingenuity and tenacity to overcome the biggest hurdles.

UoSAT-OSCARs 14, 15 and 22

On January 22, 1990 (UTC), an ESA Ariane rocket launched from Kourou placed seven spacecraft in circular low-Earth orbits, six OSCAR spacecraft (two UoSATs and four AMSAT Microsats) and the commercial satellite SPOT 2. The OSCAR spacecraft provided ESA a chance to test the new Ariane Structure for Auxiliary Payloads (ASAP) which was designed to enable ESA to add several small spacecraft to launches previously dedicated to two large spacecraft.

Once they reached orbit the University of Surrey satellites received the names UoSAT-OSCAR 14 (UO-14) and UoSAT-OSCAR 15 (UO-15). The two spacecraft are structurally similar, they have a number of subsystems in common and they're in nearly identical orbits. They differed mainly in their payloads.

UoSAT-OSCAR 14 was the first spacecraft in the UoSAT series to carry an open access transponder for radio amateurs, a high speed (9600 bps) store-and-forward unit using Mode J frequencies. Funding from AMSAT-UK helped finance its construction. Other payloads on OSCAR 14 focus on studying radiation damage due to high energy particles, experimenting with onboard data handling and improving previous spacecraft attitude control and stabilization systems. OSCAR 14 is operational as this is written. See Appendix C for additional information.

UoSAT-OSCAR 15 carried an improved CCD Camera Imaging Experiment and a set of microcomputers that could be connected together in various ways to study reliability, parallel processing and on-board data manipulation. The spacecraft also carried samples of several solar cell technologies so that the long-term behavior of each type of cell could be observed in a low Earth orbit environment. OSCAR 15 suffered a catastrophic failure in the downlink after about 2 days of operation.

UoSAT-OSCAR 22 (UO-22), launched July 17, 1991, was primarily designed to replace Earth imaging and other experiments lost with OSCAR 15. A store-and-forward transponder similar to the extremely successful unit carried on UO-14 was also included. It is operational as of 1997. See Appendix C for additional information.

KITSAT-OSCARs 23 and 25

KITSAT-OSCARs 23 and 25 (KO-23 and KO-25) were sponsored by the Korean Advanced Institute of Science and Technology (KAIST). Both spacecraft contain Mode J

9600 bps store-and-forward transponders operating on amateur frequencies, high resolution Earth imaging systems and several scientific experiments. The primary command station is located at the Satellite Technology Research Center (SaTReC) in Taejon, South Korea.

KO-23 was built at the University of Surrey by a team consisting of KAIST students and faculty and CSER/SSTL staff and successfully launched on August 10, 1992. Because it has a relatively high orbit for a store-and-forward mission, most users find that it provides considerably longer access times during each pass. This along with a strong downlink and an improved Earth imaging system has made this spacecraft very popular.

KO-25 was built entirely in Korea at KAIST by KAIST staff. It was successfully launched on September 26, 1993, just over a year after KO-23. Although outwardly similar to KO-23, KO-25 contains two cameras, one monochrome and one color and several additional scientific experiments. Both KO-23 and KO-25 are operating as of 2001. See Appendix C for additional information.

Other UoSAT Projects

A number of additional spacecraft have been built by the CSER/SSTL crew at the University of Surrey. Table 2-2 contains information on launch date and operational status. Additional details can be found in Appendix C and at **www.sstl.co.uk/missions/mn_missions.html.**

PoSAT-1 was built for a Portuguese research/educational consortium known as iNETI. When this spacecraft operates on radio amateur frequencies, as it did for several weeks after launch, it is known as PoSAT-OSCAR 28. It remains operational but the owners have not scheduled radio amateur operations since this time.

TMSAT (TO-31) was built for the Mahanakorn University of Technology in Bangkok, Thailand. Its' primary mission is to test new imaging systems. The radio amateur community sincerely appreciates the efforts of the owner/operator, the Thai Microsatellite Company Ltd., to provide information about the imaging system and to make the transponder available to radio amateurs.

TiungSat-1 (MO-46) was a non-commercial project initiated by the Astronautic Technology SDN BHD of Kuala Lumpur, Malaysia. It's instrumented with several experimental packages and a "special" UoSAT store-and-forward digital transponder that can operate at 9.6 kB or 38.4 kB. Radio amateurs have been provided with extensive access to this spacecraft.

UoSAT-12 (UO-36) is SSTLs first minisatellite project. SSTL provided radio amateurs with information about and access to the interesting onboard communications and imaging systems. See Appendix C for details. Last reports of satellite activity were in mid 2001. Current status is not known.

AMSAT MICROSAT PROGRAM

In the mid to late 80s several commercial groups began to realize that small satellites, the size of OSCAR 7, could serve some very practical needs. While AMSAT was pleased that everybody was "discovering" what we knew all along, the impact on our launch opportunities was serious. With a large launch backlog existing in the US and all these groups willing to pay big bucks to get into space, it looked like the plug had been pulled on our hopes for placing a PACSAT (small store-and-forward satellite for packet radio) in low Earth orbit.

Studying the payload envelope of ESA's Ariane rocket, Jan King identified several places where very small satellites could be mounted. One constraint placing a lower limit on the size of a useful spacecraft is that the surface area must be large enough to hold sufficient solar cells to power the mission. Rough calculations showed that if we took advantage of recent advances in solar cell efficiency a PACSAT could be built in a cube roughly 9 inches on edge. AMSAT referred to the resulting spacecraft as a MicroSat. Today, the generic term microsat is generally accepted as referring to any spacecraft weighing under 100 kg.

Jan presented his ideas to a group of AMSAT technical volunteers at the annual meeting in November, 1987. The consensus was that it was the right idea at the right time. In the past, each AMSAT satellite was unique and redundant systems were used to enhance reliability. The MicroSat project introduced fundamental changes. With the premiums on space and power in a MicroSat, AMSAT would approach reliability as a system issue and build multiple spacecraft. Furthermore, to minimize cost and construction time and to make duplication as easy as possible, they would use a modular design. The modules—solar array and power conditioning, master computer, telemetry, command and internal communications—would be constructed to fit a standard structure. This approach would also provide new groups wishing to build amateur spacecraft an excellent entry point—they could design their own mission payload around the basic MicroSat foundation.

Of course, the idea had to be sold to ESA. AMSAT offered to work with ESA to demonstrate how space that was currently being wasted could be marketed to commercial users. ESA liked the idea and went on to develop the Structure for Auxiliary Payloads. Meanwhile, AMSAT started working on MicroSats A, B, C and D; and the University of Surrey began constructing UoSATs D and E. All six were dropped off in circular low Earth orbits on January 22, 1990. AMSAT and UoSAT had to reimburse ESA for direct costs associated with interfacing to the ASAP platform. The charges amounted to approximately $150,000.

Three additional spacecraft employing the basic AMSAT MicroSat satellite platform have been launched since. An overview of these seven spacecraft follows. Our discussion focuses on the primary payloads. Additional details may be found in Appendix C.

AMSAT-OSCAR 16 and LUSAT-OSCAR 19

AMSAT-OSCAR 16 (AO-16) and Lusat-OSCAR 19 (LO-19) contain store-and-forward digital transponders using Mode J frequencies as the primary mission payload. As a result, both of these spacecraft are often referred to as PACSATs (PACket radio SATellites). AO-16 was built by the North American AMSAT group (AMSAT-NA) and

LO-19 by a group from AMSAT Argentina (AMSAT-LU) coordinated by Arturo Carou (LU1AHC).

DOVE-OSCAR 17

DOVE-OSCAR 17 (DO-17) was designed to support educational activities, especially those that encourage young people to become interested in Amateur Radio and the peaceful uses of space. As a result, the primary payload was a powerful 2-meter beacon designed to broadcast audio messages to simple amateur hand-helds and inexpensive scanner radios. The acronym DOVE (Digital Orbiting Space Experiment) refers to the fact that the audio broadcasts are uplinked and stored in a digital format. This allows the spacecraft to transmit natural sounding speech in any language. Plans were to encourage groups of young school children around the world to prepare messages and submit them on audiocassette. DOVE did not contain a transponder but it did contain a 2.3 GHz beacon that was used by amateurs testing receive systems being prepared for AO-40.

DOVE experienced operational problems. While not fatal, they made commanding the spacecraft and uploading messages very difficult and time consuming. However, the broadcasting features inspired by DOVE have been successfully implemented on other spacecraft such as RS-14/AO-21 and SUNSAT-OSCAR 35 and many messages submitted by school children for broadcast on DOVE were later placed on these spacecraft. DOVE was retired from service in late 1998.

The DOVE concept and the leadership needed to bring it to fruition were provided by Junior DeCastro (PY2BJO). The spacecraft was constructed with the aid of AMSAT Brazil (BRAMSAT).

WEBERSAT-OSCAR 18

Webersat-OSCAR 18 (WO-18) was sponsored by Weber State University in Utah. It contains a transponder. However, since the primary goal of the spacecraft is educational, the transponder is generally configured to downlink pictures from an onboard CCD camera or telemetry from onboard experiments. As a result, it is not available for two way communication. Pictures captured by WO-18 are encoded in normal AX.25 packet frames so that they can be received by radio amateurs using packet radio equipment. The last reported operation of WO-18 was in 2000.

ITAMSAT-OSCAR 26

ITAMSAT-OSCAR 26 (IO-26) was successfully launched along with KITSAT-OSCAR 25 and AMRAD-OSCAR 27 on September 26, 1993. Its primary payload is a transponder similar to the one flown on AO-16 and AO-19. It was built by members of AMSAT-Italy under the direction of Alberto Zagni, I2KBD, and Luca Bertagnolio, IK2OVV. One of its primary functions was to provide the AMSAT-Italy group with experience building and commanding a spacecraft.

AMRAD-OSCAR 27

AO-27 was successfully launched along with KITSAT-OSCAR 25 and Italy-OSCAR 26. The spacecraft itself is actually a commercial project more properly known as EYESAT-1, which was closely modeled after the AMSAT MicroSat platform. It carries an Amateur Radio module, known as AMRAD-OSCAR 27, built by the Amateur Radio Research and Development Corporation (AMRAD) based in McLean, Virginia. The transponder, which uses 2 meters up and 70 cm down, can be commanded to operate in a number of configurations. It can, for example, emulate terrestrial 1200 bps systems so that transmissions from the spacecraft can be received using a standard TNC in the KISS mode or it can support 9600 bps packet as employed on UoSAT spacecraft. In addition, it can be operated as a single channel repeater with ground stations using ordinary VHF and UHF FM Amateur Radios. Please note that EYESAT-1 operations have priority so AO-27 will not be available on a continuous basis and the operating schedule is subject to change. The best place for up to the minute schedule information is the AMSAT Bulletin Board on the Internet. The FM repeater configuration is very popular and the spacecraft is often in this mode for daylight passes over the US. When using this mode it is extremely important to listen before *and* during transmissions, use brief calls and frequent breaks and keep QSOs short. When users cooperate all it takes is omnidirectional antennas and 25 W for a QSO.

UNAMSAT-OSCAR 30

UNAMSAT-OSCAR 30 (MO-30) is the second of two nearly identical spacecraft constructed at the Autonomous University of Mexico (Universidad Nacional Autonoma de Mexico or UNAM) by students and staff under the direction of David Liberman, XE1TU. The first, UNAMSAT-A was destroyed on March 28, 1995, when the launch vehicle it was mounted on failed to reach orbit. MO-30 was successfully launched on September 5, 1996. The spacecraft used the basic MicroSat platform. The primary payload was a long-pulse radar transmitter and a receiver and DSP processor.[15] The radar transmitter operated on 40.997 MHz with a 70 W peak power. Due to unforeseen

AMRAD-OSCAR 27. (*photo by Paul Rinaldo, W4RI*)

circumstances, MO-30 wasn't released from the launch vehicle for several hours. As a result, the spacecraft temperature dropped to −30°C. The extreme cold apparently caused the crystal controlled local oscillator in the satellite's uplink receiver to fail. This left the satellite totally deaf and it ran out of power as the batteries drained down. All attempts to revive the spacecraft have been unsuccessful.

OSCAR-ECHO

In early 2003, work was well underway on a modernized Microsat known as Echo which, if all goes as planned, will be launched before the end of the year. Echo will feature major updates to most Microsat technology and will include both digital and analog (FM) transponders with VHF uplinks and UHF downlinks. In addition, it will carry several experimental systems focusing on RF communications. As an AMSAT-funded spacecraft all operation will be in the Amateur Satellite Service and all systems will be available to radio amateurs.

In order to build Echo in a very short time, AMSAT-NA has contracted with SpaceQuest, Ltd, a small company with construction facilities located in Fairfax, Virginia, to oversee fabrication. Two hams with considerable amateur satellite experience direct SpaceQuest: Mark Kanawati, N4TPY and Dr Dino Lorenzini, KC4YMG. Mark and Dino worked with the Saudi Arabian University as prime contractors for the construction of SO-41 and SO-42. In the past similar partnerships between AMSAT groups and commercial/educations entities, like that with the University of Surrey, have proved extremely beneficial to the Amateur Satellite Service. There is every reason to assume that this cooperative effort will follow a similar pattern.

The Echo design team has demonstrated a real commitment to providing information about the spacecraft. Nearly every recent issue of the AMSAT Journal has discussed the approaches and subsystems being considered for this mission. When the design is finalized, full technical details will be placed on AMSAT web sites. This should occur well before launch.

JAPANESE JAS PROGRAM

Japanese involvement in the production of space hardware for radio amateur missions can be traced back to the late '70s when JAMSAT (Japan AMSAT) constructed the Mode J transponder flown on AMSAT-OSCAR 8 and built subsystems for OSCAR 10. Encouraged by Harry Yoneda, JA1ANG, a longtime member of the AMSAT Board of Directors, JAMSAT went on to coordinate the construction of several complete spacecraft (JAS Series), all of which were launched on Japanese rockets, and the design and development of the Earth imaging experiment flown on AO-40.

FUJI-OSCAR 12

The first satellite in the JAS series (JAS-1a) was placed in a low Earth orbit on August 12, 1986 by a two stage H-1 rocket of the Japanese Space Development Agency, NASDA. The payload included two transponders, one analog and one digital. Since congestion makes the 2-meter band almost useless

as a satellite downlink in Japan both transponders employed Mode J frequencies (146 MHz uplink, 435 MHz downlink). The construction of this spacecraft was jointly sponsored by JAMSAT, JARL (Japan Amateur Radio League), NEC Corporation and NASDA (National Aerospace Development Agency).

Fuji-OSCAR 12 (FO-12) was a complex spacecraft for a first effort. Most systems worked well but difficulties were encountered in three areas: (1) spacecraft management, (2) uplinking digital data and (3) power budget. As the UoSAT crew had learned earlier, it's easy to underestimate the time it takes to learn how to write, test and upload control programs for a complex low Earth-orbit spacecraft. In addition, the spacecraft's marginal power budget required a great deal of experimentation with operating schedules.

Back when satellite operators only had a single spacecraft to work with they were willing to put up with the frustrations of not knowing which, if any, transponder would be operating on the next pass. Readers who remember how OSCAR 6 would continually shut down at the most inopportune times during its early days in space, know what I mean. But in 1986 amateurs had a choice of several spacecraft. So, even though the transponders aboard FO-12 provided first class performance when they were available, lack of access to a stable, reliable operating schedule caused many amateurs to focus their operating elsewhere. As FO-12 aged, the solar cells and storage batteries deteriorated and the power budget problem became more acute. On November 5, 1989, having exceeded its three-year design lifetime, FO-12 became the first amateur spacecraft to be withdrawn from service. In spite of the difficulties encountered, JAMSAT reports that more than 300 stations sent packets through FO-12's digital transponder, an impressive achievement for the late 1980s.

FUJI-OSCAR 20

The next satellite in the series (JAS-1b), placed in orbit by the Japanese National Space Agency on February 7, 1990, was called Fuji-OSCAR 20 (FO-20). JAMSAT mission planners requested that NASDA use fuel reserves to raise the apogee of the 900 km circular orbit. NASDA complied and the apogee was increased to about 1700 km. As a result of the elliptical nature of the orbit the total amount of time that the spacecraft is eclipsed by the Earth is greatly reduced during certain parts of the year. This significantly increases the average power available for transponder operation. Although the new spacecraft is very similar to FO-12 it is significantly more user friendly. FO-20 is operational as this is written in 2003.

FUJI-OSCAR 29

For their next major project the JAMSAT team designed a new spacecraft known as JAS-2, which was successfully launched on August 17, 1996 and named Fuji-OSCAR 29 (FO-29). Like its predecessors, FO-29 contains digital and analog transponders. The digital transponder can support the UoSAT 9600 bps standard as well as the MicroSat 1200 bps standard and it works in conjunction with a Digi-talker. When it's in the Digi-talker mode a ground station can receive the natural sounding speech broadcasts on a small hand-held transceiver. So, don't be surprised to hear

JAS-2 is a 50-kg 26-sided polyhedron.

"Koshira wa JAS-2 desu ... " [This is JAS-2]. All FO-29 systems are operational as this is written (1997). For additional details on FO-20 and FO-29 see Appendix C and the JARL JAS-2 Web site **www.jarl.or.jp/English/5_Fuji/ejasmenu.htm**.

SOVIET RS PROGRAM

In the early 1970s US and Soviet engineers and scientists began to plan for the Apollo-Soyuz program, which would involve the first linkup of US astronauts and Soviet cosmonauts in space. As part of the program several Soviet engineers, some of whom were radio amateurs, visited NASA facilities in the US. Their itinerary included Goddard Space Flight Center in Greenbelt, Maryland, an area where several AMSAT designers lived. During these visits the Soviet radio amateurs and the AMSAT crew met, as hams are apt to do and discussed the technical and operational aspects of the OSCAR program. At these meetings, it became clear that the Soviet amateurs were interested in producing their own radio amateur satellites. In fact, a Soviet satellite coordinating group had already been formed and construction of prototype equipment was underway.

Time passed—the Apollo-Soyuz linkup in space succeeded in July 1975—but not much was heard of Soviet amateur satellite plans. Then, in the October 1975 issue of *RADIO*,[16] a very widely read Soviet electronics magazine, the awaited article appeared. It focused on experiments with terrestrial linear Mode A type transponders in Moscow and Kiev and discussed, for the first time in the Soviet press, the OSCAR program. Several US amateurs were able to directly monitor the 29 MHz output of the 1 W transponder mounted on the Moscow rooftop whenever 10 meters was open. Although no mention was made of Soviet radio amateur satellites in the *RADIO* article, some Soviet hams were clearly laying the groundwork. Speculation as to Soviet plans was officially confirmed in July 1977 when the USSR filed a notice with the International Frequency Registration Board (IFRB) of the International Telecommunication Union announcing that a series of satellites in the amateur-satellite service would be launched.[17] This was followed by several articles in *RADIO* discussing the RS spacecraft.[18]

RS-1 and RS-2

Finally, on October 26, 1978, a rocket lifted Cosmos 1045 and two radio amateur satellites, Radio-1 and Radio-2 (RS-1 and RS-2), into low Earth orbit. Each spacecraft carried a Mode A transponder. Since Soviet radio amateurs are limited to 5 W in the 145-MHz uplink band, the transponders contained very sensitive receivers optimized for low-power terrestrial stations. Automatic shutdown circuitry protected them from excessive power drain. In operation, the protective circuits, acting like a time-delay fuse, would shut the transponder off when ground stations used too much uplink power for more than a few seconds. Unfortunately, the fuse could only be reset when the spacecraft passed near a Russian command station. Although the Soviets appeared to make every reasonable effort to keep the satellites on and available to the rest of the world, the transponders were often off over the Western Hemisphere because of the actions of a few inconsiderate high-power amateur ground stations.

The Soviet approach to improving reliability through redundancy merits note; when possible, launch two spacecraft at the same time. In addition to a transponder, each satellite contained a telemetry and command system, a Codestore-like device and a power system using solar cells. The primary telemetry system used Morse code letters and numbers that identified the parameter being measured, encoded the most recent value of that parameter and indicated the status (on/off) of the transponder. Specific decoding information was provided by the Soviets about a month after launch. One of the spacecraft also contained an infrequently used high-speed digital telemetry system described as an experimental prototype.

During the first few weeks that RS-1 and RS-2 were in orbit observers noted where and when operating status changes (except for transponder shut down) occurred. The pattern strongly suggested that command of the spacecraft was confined to Moscow and limited to normal working hours. Further observations indicated that two additional ground command stations were soon activated, one in eastern Asia and another in central Asia. The Soviets later announced that the primary command station was in Moscow, a secondary command station was in Arsen'yev (44.1° N, 133.1° E) near Vladivostok and that a third command station, which was portable (Novosibirsk?) had been tested.

RS-1 and RS-2 had passive temperature control systems similar to those employed on OSCARs 1-8. RS-2 also included a quasi-active thermal regulating system employing a heat bridge connecting the interior of the spacecraft with a heat exchanger on the outer surface. The bridge would automatically turn on whenever the internal temperature exceeded a predetermined level.

The transponders aboard RS-1 and RS-2 could be kept operating for only a few months before power supply (battery) problems disabled both spacecraft. Reception of a weak telemetry signal on 29.401 MHz signing a number group, often 5015 or 5501, is still sometimes reported. The source is believed to be RS-1. RS-1 and RS-2 were certainly an impressive and successful first step.[19] As later RS satellites demonstrate, the Soviets used the results of the first mission to design spacecraft with significantly longer operational lifetimes.

RS-3 - RS-8

On December 17, 1981, six new Soviet amateur satellites, RS-3 through RS-8, were placed in low Earth orbit. The launch had been expected for several reasons. First, an engineering prototype of one of the spacecraft was exhibited at TELECOM-79, a large international telecommunications conference held in Geneva in 1979. Second, the club station at the University of Moscow, RS3A, had been testing many of the spacecraft RF subsystems on the 10-meter band during 1980. Almost all the devices observed being tested, including a Mode A transponder, a Codestore device, a Morse code telemetry system and a CW autotransponder (called ROBOT), were flown. Although the launch was expected the number of spacecraft was a pleasant surprise. The ROBOT repeaters, carried on RS-5 and RS-7, were very popular. To use a ROBOT one calls the satellite on CW at the ROBOT uplink frequency. If your call is received by the satellite the spacecraft acknowledges with your call letters and a QSO number (both logged in spacecraft memory) and a short message. The longest lived members of the group, RS-5 and RS-7 ceased operating reliably in 1988 after providing nearly seven years of service.

RS-10/11

On June 23, 1987 RS-10/11 was successfully launched. The unusual designation is due to the fact that the amateur payload consists of two independent units integrated with the commercial spacecraft COSMOS 1861, which provides power and a stable mounting platform. Generally one of the units is operated and the other is kept in reserve. RS-10/11 was capable of operating in several new modes due to the fact that it could receive on the 21 MHz and 146 MHz bands and transmit on the 29 MHz and 146 MHz bands and the receivers and transmitters could be configured in several ways. Mode A remained very popular. However, Mode K (ground stations uplink on 21 MHz and receive on 29 MHz) also proved extremely popular, especially to newcomers, since it enabled radio amateurs to communicate by satellite using only HF equipment. The spacecraft also includes a ROBOT autotransponder. The 29 MHz downlink can run up to 5 W so signals are relatively strong for a Phase 2 low Earth-orbit satellite. Unfortunately, RS-10/11 is no longer operational.

RS-12/13

RS-12/13, launched February 5, 1991, is another dual

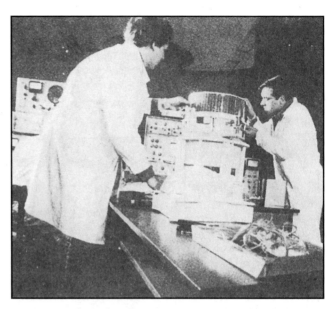

Two technicians assemble the Radio-2 artificial satellite. With Radio-1, this satellite provided communications for more than 700 Amateur Radio operators from 70 countries on all continents. Its communication range was 8000 km (5000 miles). (*Photo courtesy Novosti, provided by the Embassy of the USSR*)

satellite mounted on the commercial spacecraft COSMOS 2123. Its specifications are similar to those of RS-10/11. RS-12/13 was built at the Tsiolkovskiy Museum for the History of Cosmonautics in Kaluga, an industrial center 180 km southwest of Moscow. Tsiolkovskiy, a school teacher, is very famous in Russia due to his having written, in the early 1900s, a number of extremely influential articles discussing the future of rocketry, space satellites and manned space stations. The chief engineers for the RS-12/13 project were Aleksandr Papkov and Victor Samkov. RS-12/13 is no longer operational.

RS-14 / AMSAT-OSCAR 21

RS-14 / AMSAT-OSCAR 21 and RS-14/AO-21 was a cooperative project between amateurs from Russia (AMSAT-U-ORBITA) and amateurs from Germany (AMSAT-DL). The construction agreement refers to the spacecraft as RADIO-M1. The AMSAT-DL group provided a digital transponder known as RUDAK-2. The AMSAT-U-ORBITA crew provided redundant Mode B linear transponders and most other spacecraft systems and handled launch arrangements.

The spacecraft, launched on January 29, 1991, was basically a flying test bed for systems being considered for use on Phase 3D. The RUDAK 2 digipeater was an improved version of the RUDAK 1 system, which flew on OSCAR 13 but malfunctioned. RUDAK 2 was modified to enhance mailbox and store-and-forward operations suitable to the low orbit and it supported a large number of different speeds and modulation schemes.

RS-14 could be operated in various modes: general communications, employing a Mode B linear transponder or using DSP techniques to emulate an FM voice repeater; experimental digital modes; and a broadcast mode using synthesized speech. When the broadcast mode (the RUDAK-RTX Digital Signal Processing unit) was first placed in service on February 24, 1992, listeners were surprised to hear the words "I'm completely operational and all my circuits are functioning perfectly" on the downlink.

The command team encountered several problems with RS-14 while putting it through its commissioning tests. These included a malfunction in the command system, a DC/DC converter with a limit fuse set too low, a possible bus overvoltage and a receiver preamp that under certain switching conditions went into self-oscillation. It took a great deal of effort but Peter Guelzow, DB2OS, Gerhard Metz, DG2CV and other members of AMSAT-DL were able to diagnose, fix and work around the various problems. Their accomplishments were a testimony to the amazing flexibility of the spacecraft and the ingenuity of the design/command team. There was one additional problem encountered that delayed full recovery of the spacecraft for several months. As a result of the rapid political changes taking place, the Russian workers at the General Command Center (GCU) who were responsible for commanding the INFORMATOR-1 mother spacecraft hadn't been paid in months so they went on strike. To resolve this problem AMSAT-U had to sign a separate contract with the GCU.

When the usefulness of the primary spacecraft was exhausted the owners, citing maintenance costs, elected to shut the mother spacecraft down and Radio M1 lost its power source. As a result, on September 16, 1994, the amateur community lost a valuable asset, a fully functioning spacecraft.[20,21]

RS-15

RS-15 was launched on December 16, 1994. It's a relatively simple spacecraft somewhat similar operationally to RS-5 and RS-7. The main payload is a Mode A transponder. Although RS-15 is categorized as being in low Earth orbit (LEO) it actually has a significantly higher orbit than most other LEO spacecraft. As a result, it is available for more time each day, passes have a longer duration and it supports communication over longer distances. However, downlink signals are relatively weak and ground stations need somewhat more power than when using other spacecraft supporting Mode A. Though it is possible to access this bird with as little as 5 W to an omnidirectional antenna on CW, 100 W EIRP is much more reliable. The key to receiving this satellite is to place a preamp with a decent noise figure and at least 15 dB gain *directly at the antenna*. Using a simple 10-meter dipole, inverted V, groundplane, etc., downlink signals are never very loud but certainly adequate. Although this spacecraft is a little more difficult to work than other LEO RS birds it has developed a small but devoted following of excellent operators attracted to its DX potential, making it a real pleasure to operate. RS-15 is currently operational. See Appendix C for details.

ISKRA-2 and ISKRA-3

Soviet radio amateurs have produced another class

of satellites that go by the name ISKRA (*spark* in Russian). Two amateur ISKRA satellites were placed in orbit from the Salyut 7 space station. They're simple spacecraft, of an experimental nature, designed to operate for a short time before they burn up on reentry.

ISKRA-2 (the first in the series) was launched May 17, 1982. (There was an ISKRA-1 but it had no connection to Amateur Radio.) Real-time TV coverage of the event was provided to viewers in Russia and adjacent countries. As a result, students at the Moscow Aviation Institute had a chance to watch the birth of the satellite they helped build. According to *TASS*, solar-cell-powered ISKRA-2 contained a transponder, beacon, command channel, telemetry system and bulletin board (Codestore) facility. The novel 21 MHz up, 28 MHz down transponder (Mode K) was intended to increase radio amateurs' store of practical information on the performance of a new combination of link frequencies. Mode K was later included on several RS spacecraft. The transponder bandwidth was 40 kHz centered at 21.250 and 29.600 MHz and a beacon was placed at 29.578 MHz. Because of a malfunction, apparently associated with the command system receiver/decoder, the transponder was never activated in range of the US. During the 7 weeks that the spacecraft was in orbit it provided interesting telemetry.[22] Reentry occurred on July 9, 1982.

ISKRA-3 was placed in orbit November 18, 1982. Like ISKRA-2 it carried a Mode K transponder. The telemetry beacon was on 29.583 MHz. A serious overheating problem severely curtailed operation. ISKRA-3 was the last one of the series to be launched and no new ISKRAs have been announced for the future, perhaps because the short lifetimes of satellites in the resulting orbit provide a poor payoff for the effort involved in constructing a conventional communication spacecraft.

Soviet radio amateurs directing the RS program have always attempted to provide information about RS spacecraft, coordinate frequencies with OSCAR satellites and make RS spacecraft available to radio amateurs around the world. In addition, they have been the only provider of Mode A service since OSCAR 8 ceased functioning in mid 1983. The international radio amateur community sincerely appreciates the contributions they have made to the Amateur Satellite Service.

RS-16

RS-16, launched in March 1997, contained a Mode A linear transponder and beacons on 10 m and 70 cm. The relatively high power and low orbit of this spacecraft promised a very strong 2m downlink but, unfortunately, command stations were never able to activate the transponder. Telemetry signals from the 70 cm beacon were received until the spacecraft re-entered in Oct 1999.

RS-17 and RS-18

RS-17 and RS-18 (also known as Sputnik-40 and Sputnik 41) were two small spacecraft hand launched from Mir in November 1997 and November 1998. Both contained beacons and were powered entirely by primary cells and, as a result, had brief operational lifetimes. Neither spacecraft carried a transponder.

Sputnik 40 was a 1/3-scale model of the original (1957) Sputnik. It was conceived as a joint French/Russian educational project to celebrate the 40th anniversary of the satellite age. The spacecraft, built by Russian high school students in Naltchik, carried a 2 m transmitter built by French high school students from la Reunion Island that provided telemetry for approximately 8 weeks.

When Sputnik 40 was delivered to Mir a backup spacecraft accompanied it. Discussions between the Russian Aeronautical Federation (the group that initiated the Sputnik-40 project) and AMSAT-France (which designed and funded the spacecraft electronics) led to the idea of retrofitting the backup with a new electronics module that would broadcast voice messages in addition to telemetry information. The Aero Club of France agreed to provide funding for the project. The result, known as RS-18 (Sputnik 41), proved very popular during the 4 weeks it operated before re-entering.

RS-21

RS-21 (also known as Kolibri-2000) was injected into orbit by being released from a Progress M1-7 capsule at the conclusion of a resupply mission to the International Space Station in March 2002. The technology, research and educational groups responsible for RS-21's construction describe it as the first in a series of sophisticated Microsats. Its deployable solar panels and gravity gradient boom make it a complex spacecraft.

RS-21 re-entered on 3 May 2002. The design team is considering various approaches to including an on-board propulsion system for future spacecraft in this series so that the Progress M1-7 launch route can be used for long-term missions.

RS-21 did not carry a transponder but the educational objectives appear to be an important component of the mission. And, amateur radio references, including specific mention of the RS-10/11 and RS-12/13 transponders, are prominent in the design documents. It therefore seems reasonable to expect that future missions will contain transponders. See Appendix C for details.

RS-20

RS-20 is the name of the Radio Amateur payload on the Russian Mozhayets spacecraft. The Mozhayets, launched in late November 2002, is a test bed for developing navigation systems. The RS-20 radio amateur payload was constructed by a new group in St. Petersburg consisting of students and personnel of the Mozhaisky Military space Academy. This spacecraft does not contain a transponder but it does contain beacons on 2 meters and 70 cm and the telemetry format is consistent with other Russian Radio Amateur Spacecraft. See Appendix C for details.

RS-Future

Currently, there appear to be a number of groups of Russian radio amateurs involved in ongoing RS satellite programs. Even back in the darkest days of the Cold War these groups always attempted to provide information about RS spacecraft, coordinate frequencies with OSCAR satellites and make RS spacecraft available to radio ama-

teurs around the world. It is also important to note that they have been the only provider of Mode A linear transponder service since OSCAR 8 ceased functioning in mid 1983.

RS satellites have been a significant part of the radio amateur satellite program over the years and the international radio amateur community sincerely appreciates the contributions they have made to the amateur satellite service.

OTHER SATELLITE PROGRAMS (BY COUNTRY)
Argentina

VOXSAT

A group of Argentinean radio amateurs, including many of those who actively participated in the design and construction of LUSAT-OSCAR 19, have joined together to build the first all Argentinean-made radio amateur satellite known as VOXSAT (Voice Experiment in Space). Like several recent RS spacecraft it will be mounted on a large Russian satellite that will provide power. VOXSAT will carry a digital voice experiment using a 145.825 MHz downlink and a beacon transmitter at 145.995 MHz. A digital transponder using MicroSat 1200 bps protocols will be included. The uplink is on 435.100 MHz.[23]

CHILE

CESAR-1

In January 1993, AMSAT-CE (AMSAT-Chile) signed an agreement with AMSAT-NA permitting the Chilean group, like AMSATs Brazil, Italy and Mexico, to use MicroSat technology to construct a spacecraft in the AMSAT MicroSat series. The satellite is called CESAR-1 (CE Satélite para Aficionado a las Radiocomunicaciones). Planned payload includes a digital Mode J transponder operating at 9600 bps (G3RUH protocol), a synthesized voice broadcast module, a 23 cm up / 13 cm down transponder and a GPS receiver. An engineering module is currently under construction. AMSAT-CE realizes that progress will be slow due to the country's lack of an extensive electronics aerospace industry infrastructure and requests that the international amateur community have patience.[24]

FINLAND

HUTSAT

In 1992 faculty and students at the Helsinki University of Technology, many of whom were involved in designing microwave payloads for the Phase 3D spacecraft, committed to building a Microsat (HUTSAT). An engineering model constructed in 1994 reveals a 3-axis stabilized platform somewhat similar to the UoSAT series, which is not surprising since the spacecraft is designed for an Ariane ASAP launch. The amateur communications payload consists of a digital transponder using an uplink at 1.3 GHz and a downlink at 2.4 GHz and supporting baud rates ranging from 1.2 to 38 kbits/s. The main scientific instrument is a particle detector system consisting of three instruments, an Ion Drift Meter/Retarding Potential Analyzer, a Hemispherical Electrostatic Analyzer and a High-Energy Particle Dosimeter. At present, the group does not have a launch commitment or funding for producing a flight model. For additional information see Web site **avasun.hut.fi/Projects/project10.html**.

FRANCE

ARSENE-OSCAR 24

In late 1978 a group of French radio amateurs who had been closely observing the construction of the Phase 3A spacecraft contacted the directors of CNES (Centre National d'Etudes Spatiales – French National Center for the Study of Space) to discuss the possibility of developing a French radio amateur satellite. CNES responded that it would look favorably on a proposal if the primary focus was on education and if leading French educational institutions (Grandes Ecoles) training the future leaders of the French space program agreed to assume a central role in the project.

Once the support of the educational system was obtained a proposal was submitted and CNES agreed to back the program by providing leftover parts and equipment from prior programs, permitting its employees to participate in the project, making available preflight testing facilities and providing a launch. A number of industrial enterprises also agreed to assist in various ways. The radio amateurs involved in the project grouped together as RACE (Radio-Amateur Club de l'Espace), a legal association that serves much the same function as AMSAT. The French national association of radio amateurs, the REF (Reseau des Emetteurs Francais) participated in the project through membership in RACE.

The spacecraft was named ARSENE (Ariane Radio amateur Satellite pour l'ENseignement de l'Espace – Ariane Amateur Radio Satellite for Space Education). Since the educational aspects of the project had a higher priority than actually putting hardware in space the launch of ARSENE did not take place until May 1993.

ARSENE was a complex spacecraft designed to operate in a high altitude elliptical orbit with very low inclination. The launch weight was approximately 150 kg. An apogee kick motor accounted for nearly half of this, 72 kg including 55 kg of fuel. The kick motor had the power needed to propel ARSENE to its final orbit from the geostationary transfer orbit where it would be dropped off. The attitude control system, using nitrogen gas, was very similar to that used on the commercial Symphonie satellite. Orbital transfer, attitude control and telemetry capture were to be coordinated by ENSAE (Ecole Nationale Supérieure de l'Aéronautique et de l'Espace – National University for Aeronautics and Space) located in Toulouse.

ARSENE carried two payloads of great interest to radio amateurs. One was a 1200 bps FM packet digipeater with three 70-cm uplink channels and a single 2-meter downlink. The digipeater used the standard AX.25 terrestrial format so

that ground stations already operating packet did not need any special software or modems. When the system was initially designed (about 1980) it was felt that this transponder would be able to provide long-distance PBBS mail forwarding and live, keyboard-to-keyboard QSO capabilities. However, by launch time many were giving serious thought to methods for managing severe overcrowding. The second payload was a 16-kHz wide linear transponder with an uplink on 70 cm and a downlink at 13 cm.

The satellite was successfully launched on May 13, 1993. A problem with the 2-meter downlink was immediately observed, however, controllers were able to switch the spacecraft to the 13-cm downlink. On May 17, 1993 the kick motor was fired and ARSENE was placed in an orbit with an apogee at 40,000 km and a perigee near 16,000 km. The events surrounding the orbital transfer maneuvers make for entertaining reading.[23] Because of the problem with the 2-meter downlink, the digital transponder was never activated; however, the Mode S linear transponder was very popular during the months it was in operation. On September 9, 1993 it too ceased functioning and recovery efforts proved unsuccessful. The international radio amateur community is deeply indebted to Dr Bernard Pidoux who, for a great many years has assumed responsibility for providing information on the ARSENE program to the "outside" world in addition to his technical work on the ARSENE project.

SARA

The SARA (Satellite for Amateur Radio Astronmy) spacecraft was designed and built by college students at the Ecole Superieure d'Ingeniur en Electrotechnique et Electronique, Noisy le Grand, France and launched in July 1991. It was designed to monitor naturally occurring radio emissions from Jupitar in order to better understand the planet's magnetosphere. The spacecraft malfunctioned and no useful data was returned.

BO-47/48

The BreizhSat-OSCAR 47/48 mission includes two autonomous but similar shoe box sized spacecraft permanently mounted to the top stage of ESA's Ariane launch vehicle. The goal of this mission was to determine whether the Ariane top stage, which is often abandoned in a stable LEO orbit, could be used as a platform for a long lifetime radio amateur payload. [24]

The IDEFIX (BO-47/48) project was officially proposed on 28 January 2002. Ten weeks later (8/9 April 2002) BO-47 and BO-48 were attached to the Ariane third stage. Launch took place on 4 May 2002 This amazing construction schedule was achieved by a small group of radio amateurs from the region of western France known as Bretagne (Breizh means Bretagne in the Breton language). They accomplished it by eliminating all subsystems not critical to the essential mission and modifying equipment previously developed for the Russian RS-19 spacecraft and for another French satellite being developed as part of the SATEDU project. The resulting spacecraft were powered entirely by primary cells and did not include transponders.

BO-47 and BO-48 both worked well until their batteries were depleted (four weeks for the lower power BO-47 and two weeks for BO-48). Telemetry systems provided detailed data on thermal behavior, solar illumination, and antenna shielding that a payload mounted on the Ariane third stage would encounter. The results are encouraging. They suggest that using the third stage as a platform for long lifetime communications payloads is feasible and that doing so can reduce mission design and integration time and costs. For additional information see Appendix C.

ISRAEL

Gurwin-TechSAT Series

Israel radio amateurs and the Technion (Israel Institute of Technology) are currently engaged in an ongoing academic project known as Gurwin-1-TechSAT whose aim is to develop a series of technically innovative microsatellites for low earth orbit.

A key design goal of these satellites is to produce a 3-axis stabilized platform with 0.1 degree nadir pointing accuracy. Momentum wheels and magnetotorquers will do the pointing using information provided by magnetometers and horizon sensors.

The platform will carry a wide range of amateur and scientific payloads including store-and-forward transponders and CCD cameras. TechSat-1a was launched on 28 March 1995 but the launch vehicle failed so both it and UNAMSAT-A, which was on the same flight, were destroyed.

Gurwin-OSCAR 32 was successfully launched July 10, 1998. This spacecraft is currently operating but it has only seen limited radio amateur service. Details of its design may be found on the Internet at **www.technion.ac.il/pub/ projects/techsat/techsat1.html**. A summary is included in Appendix C.

GERMANY

AMSAT-DL Spacecraft

For the last quarter century AMSAT-DL has played a central role in the radio amateur satellite program. Starting with the contribution of the Mode B transponder on AO-7 launched in November 1974 and still operating, they partnered with AMSAT-NA in developing P3A, AO-10 and AO-13 and accepted leadership responsibilities for AO-40. These efforts have been described in detail earlier in this chapter. AMSAT-DL is currently working on two new spacecraft. One is a Phase III series (P3E) communications spacecraft modeled after AO-13 which is scheduled to be ready for launch in 2004. The other is a Phase V Mars mission. Updated information on both these missions can be found on the AMSAT-DL Web site.

AATis-OSCAR 49 (AO-49)

AATis-OSCAR 49 is the name given the SAFIR-M radio amateur communications payload aboard the RUBIN-2 spacecraft. The payload was designed and built

as part of an educational program at the University of Applied Sciences, Phorzheim Germany. The project was directed by the "Arbeitskreis Amateurfunk & Telekomunikation in der Schule e.V." (AATis) which loosely translates to "Working Group for Amateur Radio and Telecommunications in Schools."

The spacecraft was successfully launched into a low earth orbit in December 2002. It main system is a digital transponder which is intended for digital messaging and the broadcast of voice messages uplinked by the command station. Additional information can be found in Appendix C.

SAUDI ARABIA

SO-41, SO-42, SO-50

SaudiSat-OSCARs 41, 42 and 50 are small spacecraft loosely modeled after the AMSAT Microsat series but incorporating updated technology. All have been successfully injected into low earth orbit. SO-41 and 42 were launched in September 2000, SO-50 went up in December 2002. These spacecraft were designed and built by the Space Research Institute at the King Abdulaziz City for Science and Technology, Riyadh, Kingdom of Saudi Arabia. The three SaudiSats are currently reported to be operating. Amateur radio operators have been given extensive access to SO-41 and SO-50. See Appendix C for additional details.

SOUTH AFRICA

SUNSAT-OSCAR 35

SUNSAT is a 60 kg micro satellite containing both amateur and commercial payloads. It was built by faculty and students of the Department of Electrical and Electronic Engineering at Stellenbosch University in South Africa. Work on the project began in earnest in January 1992 and the spacecraft was successfully launched into a low Earth orbit in February 1999.

One of the prime payloads on SO-35 was a CCD camera and a complex attitude sensor/control system to provide high accuracy nadir pointing. The control devices included a gravity gradient boom, reaction wheels, and torquing coils. The amateur radio payload on the spacecraft was a digital store-and-forward transponder with multiple receivers and transmitters on 2 meters and 70 cm which could be configured to provide Mode J and Mode B operation. The transponder supported 1200 bps AFSK compatible with terrestrial systems, 9600 bps compatible with G3RUH (UoSAT) protocols, and a novel 2 m Parrot mode. In the Parrot mode the transponder records all uplink signals for a specified time period such as 60 seconds and then plays them back on the same frequency. The spacecraft also contained a high speed uplink at 1.2 GHz and a relatively high power (5 W EIRP) downlink at 2.4 GHz.

SO-35 provided nearly two years of excellent service before it ceased operating in January 2001. For detailed technical information see Appendix C and the AMSAT-SA Web pages at **sunsat.ee.sun.ac.za.**

US EDUCATIONAL INSTITUTIONS

Many US educational institutions have recently constructed, or are currently constructing, small spacecraft that combine radio amateur and scientific payloads and have a strong educational component. Several of these are outlined below. Most have Web pages giving detailed up-to-date information. Coverage here is limited to spacecraft that have already been launched.

SEDSAT (SO-33)

In the late 1980s a student group at the University of Huntsville (UAH), Alabama known as SEDS (*Students for the Exploration and Development of Space*) initiated a program that eventually led to the construction and launch of SEDSAT-1. Originally designed to be released from the Space Shuttle as part of NASA's Hitchhiker program SO-33 was eventually placed in orbit in October 1998 by a US Delta launcher.

The original SEDSAT design called for two scientific packages: SEASIS (*SEDS, Earth, Atmosphere and Space Imaging System*) and a three-axis acceleration measurement system designed to provide information on the dynamics of an end mass deployed via a tether. However, the spacecraft had to undergo several major design revisions as launch opportunities changed.

The radio amateur payload on SEDSAT consisted of a Mode A (145.915-145.975 MHz uplink, 29.350-29.410 MHz downlink) linear transponder and a Mode L (1,268.213 MHz uplink, 437.907 MHz downlink) digital transponder using UoSAT compatible protocols at 9600 bps and higher experimental frequencies. Unfortunately, the operations group was never able to activate SO-33. The SEDSAT-1 program was extensively documented on the Internet during its construction. Although the original site is no longer active, historical information can be found at **www.seds.org/pub/seds/SEDSAT/updates/.** See Appendix C for a summary.

PANSAT (PO-34)

The *Petite Amateur Navy Satellite* (PANSAT) is a small (65 kg) communications spacecraft developed as an educational project by students at the Naval Postgraduate School, Monterey, California. It carries an experimental digital spread spectrum transponder optimized for store-and-forward communications. PANSAT doe not have any attitude control system—the spacecraft design accommodates to the tumbling motion that's expected as a result of the ejection mechanism.

PANSAT was designed to be launched from the Space Shuttle as part of the NASA Hitchhiker Program. It was placed in orbit in October 1998. The primary objective of PANSAT was to demonstrate the capabilities of packetized, spread spectrum store-and-forward packet communication and to provide serious amateur radio experimenters with the opportunity to test direct sequence spread spectrum modulation techniques. Uplink and downlink are centered at 436.5 MHz. PANSAT is believed to be operational but is not being used at the present time. See Appendix C for additional information.

ASUSat-1 (AO-37)

AO-37 is a nanosatellite built by students and faculty at Arizona State University in response to a launch opportunity aboard a Pegasus rocket. (The term "nanosat" is used to refer to spacecraft having a mass under 10 kg). While most recent small radio amateur spacecraft designed for low earth orbit have been based on the MicroSat or UoSAT platforms (aluminum boxes bolted together), the structure of ASUSat-1 was an entirely new design based on low-cost, lightweight carbon fiber composites. The payload consisted of both scientific and radio amateur packages.[25]

The primary payload consisted of four cameras and an attitude control system based on gravity gradient techniques using a boom and an experimental damping system. The amateur payload consisted of two single channel Mode J FM repeaters (uplink 145.820 MHz, downlink 436.500 MHz), one for 9600-baud digital store-and-forward operations and the other for voice broadcasts.

AO-37 was successfully launched into low earth orbit as part of the JAWSAT mission in January 2000. The payload only operated for one day due to discharge of the primary battery. Additional details can be found in Appendix C and at the detailed ASUSat Web site: **enws229.eas.asu.edu/asusat/asusat.html.**

OPAL (OO-38)

Stanford University's department of Aeronautics and Astronautics has introduced the SQUIRT (*Satellite QUIck Research Testbed*) program to produce and launch student-engineered microsatellites carrying state-of-the-art research and educational payloads (including Amateur Radio applications) on a yearly basis. Plans are to standardize on 145.945 MHz uplinks and 437.100 MHz downlinks (Mode J). The data downlink will utilize AX.25 packet protocols and operate at 1200 baud employing either terrestrial AFSK or AMSAT MicroSat modulation formats.[26]

OPAL (Orbiting Picosat Automatic Launcher) is a 24 kg spacecraft containing command, control, telemetry and transponder systems and equipped with four trays designed to release microsats in orbit. Each tray can hold one 1 x 3 x 8-inch spacecraft or two 1 x 3 x 4-inch spacecraft. OO-38 was launched January 2000 as part of the JAWSAT MPA mission. Once in orbit it released four additional amateur spacecraft: Artemis JAK, Artemis Thelma, Artemis Louise and StenSat. Telemetry system operated sporadically for several years after launch. For additional Information on OPAL see Appendix C.

JAWSAT (WO-39)

The term JAWSAT MPA is used to describe the "Joint Air Force Academy Weber State University Satellite Multi-Payload Adapter." It's a complete autonomous spacecraft that has the capability of releasing several smaller satellites in orbit. JAWSAT is of interest to radio amateurs because it carries a communications payload operating on amateur frequencies and because two of the spacecraft it released in space, AO-37 and OO-38, also contained amateur payloads. In fact, counting the four small spacecraft ejected from OPAL, this mission accounted for seven autonomous amateur spacecraft.

JAWSAT was launched in January 2000 and performed its primary mission of demonstrating that a single launch opportunity could be used to place a cluster of spacecraft constructed by independent remotely located groups in orbit. However, the communications performance of the various spacecraft involved was a disappointment to radio amateurs. JAWSAT telemetry has been heard intermittently for several years. For additional information see Appendix C.

StenSat, Artemis JAK/Thelma/Louise

These four picosats (each weighing less than one pound) were released from OPAL in February 2000. The Artemis series—JAK, Thelma, and Louise—were designed and built by individual students working in the Remote Extreme Environment laboratory at Santa Clara University in California. JAK was a beacon experiment. Thelma and Louse had sensors to measure the VLF EM energy generated by lightening storms. All were designed to downlink information on radio amateur frequencies using amateur protocols and to cease operating after approximately one month when their primary cells were depleted.

To the radio amateur community the most interesting picosat in the group was StenSat, designed and built by a small group of hams located in the Washington, DC area. StenSat was essentially a solar-powered single-channel FM voice repeater similar in operation to AO-27, but at reduced power. See Appendix C for additional information.

No confirmed reports of signals being received from any of these four picosats have ever been filed.

Starshine-3 (SO-43)

Starshine-3 launched in September 2001 was a key element in a K-12 educational program. The spacecraft had a spherical shape just under a meter in diameter that was covered by approximately 1500 optically reflective mirrors. Students in more than 1000 schools in 30 countries had polished these mirrors. It also carried a 2-meterm beacon powered by solar cells that enabled it to transmit 9600 baud data packets for several months. Starshine-3 reentered in January 2003. For additional information see Appendix C.

PCsat (NO-44)

PCsat is a unique 12 kg satellite constructed at the U.S. Naval Academy as part of a Small Satellite program designed to provide aerospace majors hands on experience in satellite design and operations. All systems are open to radio amateurs around the world.

Built using commercial off-the-shelf components and launched into low earth orbit in September 2001 it has already far exceeded its design operational lifetime. NO-44 continues to give radio amateurs access to a dedicated satellite operating as part of an Automatic Position Reporting System that provides worldwide real-time message and position/status data exchange. As a result of the success of this project several additional spacecraft are being constructed at the Naval Academy. PCsat is extensively documented on the Internet. For additional information see Appendix C.

Sapphire (NO-45)

Sapphire is another small spacecraft designed for low earth orbit. Constructed over a period of several years as an ongoing student project at Stanford University it contains a number of technology experiments and a digital Mode B transponder. Launch occurred in September 2001. The transponder has operated on an intermittent basis for several years.[27] See Appendix C for additional information.

US HAMS IN SPACE

In 1972 Dr Owen Garriott was selected to fly aboard the experimental US space station known as Skylab. Dr. Garriott, who held the call W5LFL, was a strong advocate for a proposal to NASA to allow limited Amateur Radio operation from space. NASA turned down the Skylab request but the text of the rejection made it clear that it was based on time constraints and other important but tangential concerns and that serious consideration would be given to future proposals. So Garriott's July 28 to September 25, 1973 sojourn in space was the Ham-in-Space mission that might have been.[28]

Ten years later Garriott was again selected as a crew member, this time for a Space Transportation System (STS) mission. The flight was aboard the US Space Shuttle Columbia. This time NASA accepted a proposal for experiments involving Amateur Radio to take place during free time periods allocated to the shuttle crew. The STS-9 Spacelab-1 mission occurred from November 28 to December 8, 1983. During the flight Dr Garriott contacted in excess of 250 amateurs using 2-meter FM simplex. His sons, Robert and Richard operating from W5RRR, the club station at Johnson Space Center (JSC), were at the far end of one of these QSOs. The equipment on the shuttle consisted of a modified Motorola hand-held transceiver and a dipole antenna taped to a window. Operation was entirely on the hand-held's internal batteries and independent of Skylab's power system.

Three important objectives of the Amateur Radio experiment were (1) demonstrating that Amateur Radio can operate on the space shuttle without interference to primary mission tasks, (2) directly involving segments of the general public in US space activities and (3) demonstrating Amateur Radio's capabilities as a potential backup means of communication. All three were successfully attained.[29]

Another opportunity for operation from space arose in 1985 when Dr. Tony England, W0ORE, Dr John Bartoe, W4NYZ and Commander Gordon Fullerton, ex WN7RQR, were assigned to Spacelab-2 on shuttle Challenger mission STS-51F. This time NASA granted amateurs permission to undertake a more ambitious set of tests known as SAREX (Shuttle Amateur Radio EXperiment). During this mission the emphasis was on communicating with groups of school children and on demonstrating the capabilities of slow-scan TV for uplinking and downlinking pictorial information. All operation was on 2 meters.

The experiment was again a solid success. Images from

Aboard Discovery—STS-56, Steven Oswald, KC5UAC, talks to Amateur Radio operators on Earth via the Shuttle Amateur Radio Experiment (SAREX). (*photo courtesy NASA*)

the spacecraft were sent directly to classrooms. For the first time, pictures were transmitted from the ground to an orbiting spacecraft. Amateurs also demonstrated their ability to comply with safety procedures that allowed them to connect to the spacecraft power buss and other shuttle equipment. Jess Moore, an associate administrator of NASA stated "I was watching the video of the Mission Control Center in Houston and actually saw the [pictorial] data that was being transmitted up. I was very impressed that we were able to do this using Amateur Radio . . . "

Preparing the SAREX proposal for this flight and coordinating the construction and testing of the equipment used was a mammoth job. Most of the work was handled by a group of amateurs at Johnson Space Center (JSC). Key were Louis McFadin, W5DID, president of the JSC Amateur Radio Club, who led the efforts to design and test the equipment and Chuck Biggs, KC5RG, chief public affairs officer at JSC, who saw to it that the SAREX proposal and activities received needed support and recognition.[30]

Barely three months later another Ham-In-Space mission took place. This time (October 30 to November 6, 1985) the Shuttle *Columbia* carried the European Space Agency's Spacelab mission D1. Three hams were aboard: Dr. Reinhard Furrer, DD6CF, Dr. Ernst Messerschmidt, DG2KM and Dr. Wubbo Ockels, PE1LFO. All used the special call sign DPØSL, which had been assigned for the mission. The equipment on Spacelab consisted of a cross band FM transceiver, which required ground stations to use the Mode B frequency combination of 435 MHz uplink and 145 MHz downlink.[31]

On January 28, 1986, a great many young school children all over the United States gathered around TV sets to observe the launch of the Shuttle *Challenger* and the start of the Teacher in Space Program. As they watched, a critical system aboard the launch vehicle failed and the rocket and shuttle disintegrated, killing all 7 crew members. The shuttle program ground to a halt for two and a half years.

The next radio amateur operation from space was to take place from *Mir* (see next section). During the interregnum, the ARRL established (mid 1987) the SAREX Committee, which was charged with finding ways to take maximum advantage of ham-in-space opportunities. The committee included representatives of the ARRL, The Johnson Space Center Amateur Radio Club, which had been instrumental in preparing and testing hardware for previous flights, and AMSAT-NA. The Committee was backed by a large ad hoc operations team of volunteers committed to the project. With this support, US ham-in-space activities resumed with amateur operations from STS-35 (first packet computer-to-computer link) in December 1990 and STS-37 in 1991 (first fast scan video uplink). Looking back we refer to the first eight years (five flights) as the experimental phase (Phase I) of the SAREX program.

By 1991 NASA and many of the astronauts directly involved in the educational aspects of the US space program were very pleased with the results of SAREX and were actively encouraging amateur operation from space when appropriate. This means focusing on missions where primary activities allow astronauts the time to take part, where the astronauts involved have shown an interest and where the shuttle orbital inclination doesn't restrict ground station participation to latitudes less than 40°. The SAREX program now switched into its operational, or frequent-flier, mode (Phase II) which resulted in three flights in 1992, four in each of 1993, 1994 and 1995 and five in 1996. The transition was made possible by the generation of generic SAREX payload integration paperwork for several specific SAREX configurations, the development of a formalized Crew Training Plan and a concerted effort to license the space shuttle astronauts. A flight summary is provided in Appendix B.

To justify the Hams-in-Space program to NASA, amateurs must ensure that SAREX will support several of the following functions: (1) serve as an educational tool, (2) be an outreach to the general public, (3) allow a method for crews to maintain contact with family and friends while on orbit (psychological factors), (4) provide an experimental communications test bed, (5) offer a back up communications link for emergencies and (6) provide information to the grass-roots public. As a result, during the short duration missions of Phase I and Phase II, astronauts had little time for recreational amateur operation (random QSOs). However, a packet radio Bulletin Board on the shuttle, which used terrestrial standards, provided a great many amateurs with an opportunity for direct shuttle communications.

The late 1990s witnessed the start of SAREX Phase III as the US changed its focus from short, intense Space Shuttle missions to long duration US habitation on *Mir* and finally to a permanent human presence in space on the *International Space Station* (ISS). For example, during a six-month stint in 1996, Shannon Lucid used ham radio to keep in touch with her family. Although radio amateur operation from space will never be commonplace, the ISS should substantially reduce its rarity. Past events, such as the positive reception of ham radio at isolated Antarctic scientific stations, may give us some idea of what to expect. And, in a CNN interview, the astronaut John Blaha praised ham radio for enabling him to keep up with the Rangers and

Cowboys latest scores during his 1996/97 stay on *Mir*.

The Ham-In-Space program also included other experiments aboard the US space shuttle and *Mir* that used Amateur Radio frequencies. One early experiment, known as MARCE (The Marshall Amateur Radio Club Experiment), involved a GAS-Can (Get-Away-Special Canister) payload on the shuttle. Initial sponsors were the Alabama Space and Rocket Center and the Alabama Section of the Institute of Aeronautics and Astronautics. The Marshall Space Flight Center Amateur Radio Club later joined in to provide the downlink telemetry system and coordinate the launch. The GAS-Can contained four experiments, three provided by University of Alabama students plus the communications/telemetry system. The student experiments focused on alloy solidification, plant physiology and crystal growth. AMSAT was particularly interested in the communications experiment because, at the time, consideration was being given to flying a PACSAT as a Get-Away-Special. The downlink employed a 70 cm FM transmitter running 6 W to a dipole mounted directly on the GAS-Can. A voice synthesizer signing WA4NZD spoke the telemetry. Of special interest to AMSAT was the possibility of relaying the MARCE shuttle downlink via the Mode B transponder on AO-10. This would model, in a modest way, the TDRS (Telemetry Data Relay Satellite) employed by NASA to relay shuttle data.

MARCE was flown on STS-41G, launched October 5, 1984, but nothing was heard. It was later learned that, due to a procedural error, the experiment had never been activated. It was re-flown on STS-61C launched January 12, 1986.

GAS-Can payloads are placed in the shuttle cargo bay and exposed to space by opening the bay doors. The shuttle *Columbia* flight plan called for the cargo bay to be Earth facing, a good orientation for direct reception of the 70-cm telemetry at the ground but one that would make a relay by AO-10 highly unlikely. The first report of direct 70-cm telemetry reception was by Junior De Castro, PY2BJO, of Sao Paulo. Part way through the 6 day mission *Columbia* had to be reoriented to warm a cold Auxiliary Power Unit. The new attitude greatly improved the 70 cm link between the shuttle and AO-10 enabling several ground stations to obtain relayed telemetry. KG6DX provided an excellent tape illustrating system capabilities under conditions where the Mode B transponder on AO-10 was lightly loaded. The project coordinator for MARCE, the person who brought it all together, was Ed Stluka, W4QAU.[33]

RUSSIAN HAMS IN SPACE

Rusian Hams-In-Space activities took a first step in 1982 when cosmonauts started tossing ISKRAs from the Salyut 7 space station. But the program began in earnest in 1988 when cosmonauts Musa Manarov, Vladimir Titov and Valery Polyakov qualified for amateur licenses while resident aboard the MIR space station.

Leo Labutin, UA3CR is credited with being instrumental in arranging for the cosmonauts to receive their licenses, coordinating efforts to permit amateur operation from *Mir* and in obtaining the equipment. Manarov, the primary operator and the cosmonaut who initiated the amateur activity,

had the call U2MIR. Titov, being first in command, was assigned U1MIR and Polyakov received U3MIR. Operation on 145.5 MHz FM voice began on November 6, 1988, with the initial test producing a QSO with UA3CR in Moscow.

At the time that all this was occurring UA3CR received permission to make his first trip to the US to attend the AMSAT-NA Annual Conference, which was being held in Atlanta. He arrived in the US a few days after the first *Mir* QSO. To inject a personal note; I had the pleasure of meeting Leo's Aeroflot flight at Dulles airport (near Washington, DC) and hosting him during his stay in the Baltimore/Washington area and for the trip down to Atlanta. One of my most vivid memories of the conference was trying to charge a midnight phone call from our hotel room to Star City, near Moscow to confirm plans to attempt a QSO between *Mir* and an amateur station at the convention. The phone call went through and U2MIR's first US QSO took place the following day with W4BIH/M (UA3CR at the mike) located in the parking lot just outside the hotel where the AMSAT conference was being held. For a detailed story of events leading to Amateur Radio activity from *Mir,* see the reference at the end of this chapter.[34]

The first amateur station aboard *Mir* consisted of an off-the-shelf Japanese 2-meter transceiver (Yaesu FT290R contributed by Valery Agabekov, UA6HZA) feeding a $^1/_4$ wavelength groundplane mounted outside *Mir* by Manarov during an EVA. A number of rumors about how the transceiver came to be delivered on the regularly scheduled resupply ship Progress-37 have circulated but it appears that we'll have to wait until the principal players retire before the definitive version gets told. About six weeks after operations commenced Manarov and Titov returned to Earth having set a record for continuous time in orbit—just over one year. The replacement crew carried up a new 10-W 2-meter transceiver. During the period late 1988 to late 1990 11 Soviet cosmonauts engaged in 2-meter voice communications using this equipment.

Meanwhile, back on the ground Musa Manarov became convinced of the value of packet radio and helped arrange for the January 1991 launch of packet equipment to *Mir*. The equipment, consisting of a PacComm Handi Packet and ICOM IC-228A 2-meter transceiver and a laptop computer, was placed on the air within weeks. By February 1, 1991, you could contact Manarov on 145.55 MHz using simplex FM voice, digipeater (c U2MIR) or Personal Message System (c U2MIR-1). Months later, Helen Sharman (GB1MIR) became the first of many foreign visitors to *Mir* to put the amateur station on the air.

Before 1991 came to a close a guest cosmonaut from Austria, Franz Viehbock (OEØMIR), carried up additional amateur equipment referred to as AREMIR (Austrian Amateur Radio Experiment Aboard *Mir*). Key components were a modified Alinco DJ 120 2-meter transceiver, TNC and CW generator and laptop computer. In March 1992, German guest cosmonaut Klaus Flade, DP1MIR carried up a Digital Voice Memory module to add to the current transceiver.

The next big change in the *Mir* shack occurred in November 1995, when several new pieces of equipment were added—

a Kenwood TM-733 dual band (2 m/70 cm) transceiver, a dual band antenna and a PacComm 9600 bps modem.

In May 1996, a major new structure called Piroda was permanently docked to *Mir*. Piroda contained its own complete amateur station known as SAFEX II. SAFEX II was the result of a joint German/Soviet effort begun in 1992 by DP1MIR after he returned to Earth. The Piroda station has its own call sign, RRØDL, which reflects its collaborative heritage. The SAFEX unit contained the following modules built around a heavily modified ICOM 4020 repeater.

Mode-1 (Repeater mode): Supported QSOs between two or more terrestrial stations—uplink 435.750 MHz and CTCSS; downlink 437.950 MHz

Mode-2 (Packet mode): 9600 baud, echoed every packet—uplink 435.775 MHz (CTCSS not required); downlink 437.975 MHz

Mode-3 (direct QSO): Supported QSOs between *Mir*'s crew and other stations—uplink 435.725 MHz + CTCSS / 437.925 MHz.

The SAFEX II unit was configured so that future modules including a 10 MHz wide linear transponder (1.265 GHz / 2.410 GHz) can be installed and SSTV and ATV capabilities added. For information on SAFEX II see the reference at the end of this chapter.[35] Over the years the Russians have given serious attention to the psychological aspects of long duration space flight, especially the effects of monotony, boredom and isolation. In a February 1989 *Scientific American* article the American astronaut Sally Ride who had spent considerable time with her Soviet counterparts reported that cosmonauts are routinely sent videotapes, books and other personal items on resupply missions.[36] It's safe to assume that Amateur Radio equipment was initially added to this list as a test and that the results have been evaluated as being positive. Before *Mir* finally deorbited in 2001, more than 50 Russian cosmonauts and 10 visitors to *Mir* from Germany, Austria, England, France and the US had been involved in direct links to Earth by Amateur Radio.[37]

International Space Station

In November 1996 Amateur Radio delegates from eight countries—Russia, Japan, Germany, Great Britain, Italy, Canada, France and the US—met at the NASA Johnson Space Center in Houston, Texas to lay plans for a permanent ham radio station aboard the ISS. Henceforth, the project would be known as ARISS for *Amateur Radio on the International Space Station*. These international coordinating activities continue on a regular basis.

Advance planning for the ISS was extremely important. One of the lessons amateurs learned from the W5LFL, W0ORE and later Shuttle missions is that small details such as the existence of a bulkhead feedthrough for antenna lines, or the availability of a power outlet and operating position, could be a determining factor when the decision is made on whether or not to permit amateur radio activity from space. As plans for the ISS firmed up Frank Bauer, KA3HDO, (AMSAT VP for Manned Space Programs) and Matt Bordelon, KC5BTL, (SAREX Principal Investigator, NASA JSC) spent endless hours coordinating the efforts of a large number of amateurs and educators to provide input

to space station designers so that the infrastructure needed to support a wide variety of radio amateur activities from the space station would exist. These efforts were extremely successful. Radio amateur operation from the ISS began in November 2000 and continues on a regular basis. See Appendix B for additional information.

On February 1, 2003 the Space Shuttle Columbia disintegrated as it was returning to Earth at the end of mission STS-107. Three of the seven crew members that perished were radio amateurs: David Brown, KC5ZTC, Kalpana Chawla, KD5ESI and Laurel Clark, KC5ZSU. Kalpana had worked closely with the ARISS team for several years as our astronaut liaison.

Successes in space exploration in recent years have made it easy to forget how dangerous these activities are. A tragedy like the STS-107 mission reminds us of how truly privileged radio amateurs are to be part of this endeavor. Note that it was the Shuttle Columbia that hosted the first ham activity from space way back in 1983 when Owen Garriot made more than 250 QSOs on STS-9.

CONSIDERATIONS FOR THE FUTURE

Every few years the amateur satellite community is faced with the question "Where do we go from here?" Do we continue to update the current Phase 2 and Phase 3 spacecraft, do we focus efforts and resources on the original Phase 4 plan or a simplified Phase 4 strategy, or should we start thinking in terms of constellations of spacecraft?

Our ability to maintain a successful amateur satellite program depends on the answer. Such a program must satisfy four critical needs—obtaining (1) volunteer technical and administrative workers, (2) launches, (3) RF spectrum access and (4) financing.

Attracting volunteer support

In the past, the technical challenges inherent in the Radio Amateur Satellite Program have proven to be extremely successful lures for attracting excellent technical help to the project. As long as the program wrestles with interesting problems and investigates new and innovative solutions it should continue to attract new blood. Administrative support is a different matter. Administrative tasks aren't as glamorous or as intrinsically satisfying as technical ones. As a satellite project becomes more complex the administrative tasks increase faster than the technical work. As a result, recruiting skilled administrative staff capable of managing large projects is going to be a continuing challenge. Without dedicated, competent and creative people representing AMSAT to government agencies and handling fund raising, parts acquisition, information dissemination and coordination there won't be any future spacecraft.

Obtaining Launches

Launch opportunities are another key concern. It's very important that we position ourselves so that we can react quickly to changing world situations. For example, in the early to mid 1980s when it appeared that most US launches would be by the space shuttle, AMSAT actively investigated different types of rocket engines that could take us from shuttle orbit to Phase 3 orbit.

A few years ago, at about the same time the US expendable launcher program was being reborn, several government agencies and large corporations became interested in small satellites similar (in size) to early AMSAT Phase 2 satellites. In a short time a launch backlog developed and it was clear that our chances of obtaining US launches were quickly approaching zero so AMSAT worked with the European Space Agency to develop the ASAP adapter, which allowed the Ariane rocket to carry several microsats as secondary payloads.

To launch OSCAR 40 AMSAT again worked with ESA, this time to exploit a niche that was previously overlooked—using the adapter ring between two larger spacecraft as the frame for an additional payload.

We don't have any guaranteed rides. Several new commercial US launch vehicles are approaching flight readiness (AMSAT might be able to trade some of the technology developed for OSCAR systems for launches). Finally, several foreign countries such as the CIS, Ukraine and China interested in gaining a foothold in the rapidly growing microsat and minisat launching business may be interested in working with AMSAT during their developmental stages.[38,39]

RF Spectrum Access

As has been mentioned several times, frequency allocations made at international conferences have a very great impact on the Amateur Satellite Service. Where would we be today if the only band available for amateur satellite activities was 2 meters as was officially the case from 1963 to 1971? The Amateur Satellite Service has planned for and participated in several General and Space WARCs (now called WRCs). It's critically important that these activities continue in the future. Adequate planning is extremely important. Not many amateurs realize all the factors that affect our WRC position. For example, the MicroSat program makes it much easier for small groups of radio amateurs around the world to become actively engaged in satellite construction. The prestige associated with these activities can have a major impact on the WRC delegations of these countries.

It should be apparent that WRC preparation requires more than writing papers and talking to delegates and other government officials. These activities are extremely important but we must also design satellite systems not only for amateur communications but to justify our existence as an internationally recognized service.

It can be argued that some of the activities proposed for Phase 4 are really not Amateur Radio. If we use a Mode S video transponder to relay pictures from the space shuttle directly to school classrooms on a regular basis aren't we changing the nature of Amateur Radio and, in reality, giving up our frequencies? Yes and no. Yes, such activities are a significant expansion in the type of public service Amateur Radio provides and some of the rules and regulations governing the amateur service may have to be changed. But the world isn't a static place. Rules are always changing in response to new technologies. The question is whether we're to actively pursue changes we see as beneficial or sit back and let other groups impose their desires on us. I do not believe the proposed activities amount to giving up frequencies. Historically, amateurs have often been allocated spectrum that wasn't felt to be of much use. When the value was finally realized (often as a result of amateur experimentation) groups with financial clout would attempt to retrieve it. To a certain extent I believe that many governments initially viewed the UHF and microwave bands allocated to amateurs as being of little value and later, when the value became obvious, as strategic reserves. Such reserves are much easier to reclaim if amateurs aren't using them. By expanding the definition of a legitimate Amateur Radio application we are in effect electing to "share" frequencies by making them available for educational and emergency activities. However, we retain access and control and acquire powerful supporters when questions concerning frequency allocations arise.

Financing

Last and certainly not least, is the matter of financing the Amateur Satellite Program. In the old days of OSCARs I and II when satellites were relatively simple, most flight hardware was donated. Out-of-pocket expenses incurred in building and launching a spacecraft were generally picked up by the same people doing the volunteer work. As amateur satellites grew more complex and expensive it became necessary to seek additional donations to help finance the program. In 1962 the informal OSCAR Association incorporated as Project OSCAR and invited hams all over the world interested in the amateur space program to help support the program financially by signing on as members. Insofar as possible, dues were used to pay for flight hardware and an inexpensive newsletter supplying information about the satellite program to members. In the late 1960s, the hub of amateur satellite construction activities shifted from southern California to Washington, DC, and AMSAT. By the late 1970s groups around the world began building amateur spacecraft and financing became an international concern.

We now take a brief look at the factors contributing to the cost of a satellite and actual cost figures for various amateur spacecraft.

Costs

The direct expenses involved in placing a spacecraft in orbit include the following:

1) Launch fees
2) Technical expertise (engineering design)
3) Flight hardware (satellite parts)
4) Ground hardware (special test instruments, prototype subsystems, etc.)
5) Construction (salaries or contracted costs for machining, wiring, testing, etc.)
6) Administrative (parts procurement, required technical documentation, user documentation, bookkeeping, etc.)
7) Travel, shipping, customs, communication (telephone, telex, postage)

8) Miscellaneous (launch insurance, liability insurance, etc.)

9) Launch and post launch operations

Note that this list contains only spacecraft-related expenses; the very sizable costs of operating an organization such as AMSAT, publishing a newsletter or providing membership services have not been included.

The largest single expense associated with placing a large commercial satellite in position is the launch, which costs hundreds of millions of dollars, to geostationary transfer orbit. Early OSCAR spacecraft were launched for free by the US Air Force and then by NASA and later by the European Space Agency, NASDA and the USSR in recognition of their potential benefit to society in the areas of disaster communications, educational applications and scientific investigations. Later, as launching became more a commercial and less a governmental activity, we were asked to pay the additional costs the launch agency incurred in providing us with a ride. With OSCAR 40 these costs amounted to approximately $1,000,000. NASA, ESA and other government sponsored launchers are likely to continue to make some provisions for noncommercial (scientific, educational, humanitarian) payloads in the future and we may be required to pay the going rate for this class of passenger unless we have something of value to barter in return or we volunteer for high risk missions involving new rocket systems.

Technical expertise for amateur satellite projects has been almost entirely provided by committed volunteers. Many companies in the aerospace industry knowingly contributed to the program in diverse ways such as donating hardware, authorizing computer time, granting access to facilities for vibration and environmental testing, etc. Costs for ground stations used to control and monitor spacecraft have been borne by the person or group directly involved. However, as the Amateur Satellite Program matures and gains momentum, more and more expenses have to be picked up by the organization. There are bills for parts, plane tickets, telephone calls, insurance and launch integration costs that must be paid.

Notes

[1]T. Clark and J. Kasser, "Ariane Launch Vehicle Malfunctions, Phase III-A Spacecraft Lost!" *Orbit*, Vol. 1, no. 2, June/July 1980, pp 5-9.

[2]J.A. King, "Phase III: Toward the Ultimate Amateur Satellite,"
Part I, *QST*, June 1977, pp 11-14;
Part II, *QST*, July 1977, pp 52-55;
Part III, *QST*, Aug 1977, pp 11-13.

[3]J. A. King, "The Third Generation,"
Part I, *Orbit*, Vol. 1, no. 3, Sept/Oct 1980, pp 12-18;
Part II, *Orbit*, Vol. 1, no. 4, Nov/Dec 1980, pp 12-18.

[4]J. Eberhart, "Satellite Hit By Its Own Rocket," *Science News*, Vol. 124, Aug. 6, 1983, p 87.

[5]V. Kudielka, "Long term Predictions for Highly Elliptic Satellite Orbits," *Amsat-DL Journal*, Jun 1990, pp 5-7 [in German].

[6]T. Clark & E. Pavlis, "The Orbital Evolution of AMSAT-OSCAR 13," *Oscar News*, no. 84, August 1990, supplementary insert.

[7]J. Miller, "May the Force Be With You," *The AMSAT Journal*, Jan/Feb 1993, pp 16-19.

[8]J. Miller, "The Re-Entry of OSCAR-13," *Proceedings of the 12th AMSAT-NA Space Symposium*, 1994, pp 36-39.

[9]S. Eckart (DL2MDL), "Orbit Stability," Proceedings 2nd P3D Experimenters Meeting, Marburg, Germany, May 1991.

[10]R. Lindquist, N1RL, "AO-40 Fails to Phone Home," *QST*, Feb 2001, p 90, "AO-40 Project Leader 'Optimistic'," *QST*, March 2001, p 68, "AMSAT Details Likely AO-40 Failure Scenario," *QST*, May 2002, pp 81-83. Karl Meinzer DJ4ZC et al., "AO-40 Log, 16 Nov 2000 – 01 Jan 2001," *The AMSAT Journal*, Jan/Feb 2001, pp 16 – 22. R. Haighton, VE3FRH, "AO-40 News," *The AMSAT Journal*, Jan/Feb 2001, p2. S. Mills W4SM, P Guelzow DB2OS, "Letter," *The AMSAT Journal*, Sept/Oct 2001, pp 29,30.

[11]J. King, V. Riportella, R. Wallio, "OSCAR at 25: The Amateur Space Program Comes of Age," *QST*, Dec. 1986, pp 15-18, "OSCAR at 25: Beginning of a New Era," *QST*, Jan. 1987, pp 41-45.

[12]M. Owen and J. Callas, "DXing enroute to the Red Planet," *QST*, Jan 1996, pp 44-45.

[13]K. Meinzer DJ4ZC, "To Mars with P5-A," AMSAT-DL International Satellite Workshop, Marburg, Nov 2001. English PDF version available. See "With P5A to Mars!" at http://www.amsat-dl.org/p5a/index.htm
K. Baker and D. Jansson, "Mars Mission Proposed," *The AMSAT Journal*, Sept./Oct. 1996, p 26; M. Davidoff, "Comments on Proposed AMSAT MARS-A Experiment," *Proceedings of the 9th AMSAT-NA Space Symposium*, 1991, pp 6-10.

[14]M. Sweeting, "The AMSAT Amateur Scientific and Educational Spacecraft — UoSAT," *Orbit*, Vol. 2, no. 2, March/April 1981, pp 13-17. Also see: *The Radio and Electronic Engineer*, Journal of the Institute of Electronic and Radio Engineers (England), Aug./Sept. 1982, Vol. 52, no. 8/9, Special issue on: "UoSAT — The University of Surrey's Satellite." This issue is highly recommended for anyone seriously interested in satellite design.

[15]D. Liberman, "UNAMSAT-1 Experiment Module TSFR," *AMSAT Journal*, May/June 1994, pp 4-5. D. Liberman, "UNAMSAT-1: An Operations Guide," *Proceedings of the AMSAT-NA 12th Space Symposium*, 1994, pp 77-79.

[16]S. Budin and F. Fekhel, "Amateur VHF/UHF Repeaters," *RADIO*, no. 10, Oct. 1975, pp 14-15.

[17]Special Section No. SPA-AA/159/1273 annexed to International Frequency Registration Board Circular No. 1273 dated 12 July 1977, submitted by USSR Ministry of Posts and Telecommunications.

[18]V. Dobrozhanskiy, "Radioamateur Satellites; The Repeater: How is it Used?" *RADIO*, no. 9, Sept. 1977, pp 23-25. Also, see July, Oct. and Nov. issues of *RADIO* for additional information.

[19]L. Labutin, "The USSR 'Radio' Satellites — Preliminary Results," *RADIO*, no. 5, May 1979, pp 7-8. For a summary of this article in English see: *Telecommunications Journal*, Vol. 46, no. X, Oct. 1979, pp 638-639.

[20]P. Guelzow, "RUDAK-2 on AMSAT OSCAR-21, Full System Overview, Current Activities and Future Planning," *Proceedings of the 10th AMSAT-NA Symposium*, 1992; reprinted in *The AMSAT Journal*, March/April, 1993 pp 14-16, 23-25.

[21]The *AMSAT-DL Journal*, Nr. Jg. 16, Marz/Mai 90 contains an in-depth description of RADIO-M1 and RUDAK-2. AMSAT-DL made available an English language version of this issue thanks to translations by Don Moe, DJ0HC/KE6MN.

[22]*ASR*, no. 34, May 31, 1982.

[23]B. Pidoux, F6BVP, in *OSCAR Satellite Report*, June 1, 1993.

[24]G. Ruy, F1HDD/ON1RG, "The IDEFIX Project," The AMSAT Journal, Sept/Oct 2002, pp 10-14. (Originally presented at AMSAT-UK Colloquium, July/Aug 2002)

[25]S. Ferring, J. Rademacher, H. Reed and J. Puig-Suari, "ASUSat-1: A Low-Cost AMSAT Nanosatellite," *Proceedings of AMSAT-NA 14th Space Symposium*, 1996, pp 58-65.

[26]C. Kitts and R. Lu, "The Stanford SQUIRT Micro Satellite Program," *Proceedings of the 12th AMSAT-NA Space Symposium*, 1994, pp 84-90.

[27]C. Kitts, "SAPPHIRE, A University Student Built Satellite for Space Experimentation," *The AMSAT Journal*, Nov/Dec 1995, pp 17-19.

[28]Happenings of the Month, *QST*, March 1972, pp. 75-76.

[29]P. O'Dell and B. Glassmeyer, "Well Done, W5LFL!," *QST*, Feb. 1984, pp. 11-14.

[30]P. Courson, "W0ORE/Challenger: Picture Perfect from Space," *QST*, Oct. 1985, pp. 47-49.

[31]*ASR* 109, Sept. 14, 1985, pp. 3-4.

[32]Y. Clearwater, "A Human Place in Outer Space," *Psychology Today*, July 1985, pp 35-39, 42-43.

[33]*ASR* 113/114, Dec 12, 1985; *ASR* 115/116, Jan 16, 1986; *QST*, March 84 p 91.

[34]V. Konratko (UV3DQE) and J. Kasser (G3ZCZ), "CQ EARTH, This is MIR Calling," *The AMSAT Journal*, May 1990, pp 1, 4-5.

[35]T. Kieselbach, DL2MDE (translated by J Bubbers, W1GYU), "The Amateur Radio Space Experiment SAFEX II," *The AMSAT Journal*, Nov/Dec 1995, pp 14-15.

[36]P. Banks and S. Ride, "Soviets in Space," *Scientific American*, Feb. 1989, pp 2, 32-40.

[37]G. Carpignano, "MIR: Five Years of a Permanent Packet Radio Space Station," *Proceedings of the 14th AMSAT-NA Space Symposium*, 1996, pp 80-86.

[38]P. Chien, "Launch Opportunities Beyond Phase 3D," *Proceedings of the AMSAT-NA 12th Space Symposium*, 1994, pp 30-35; reprinted in *The AMSAT Journal*, March/April 1995, pp 17-21.

[39]G. Smith, "AMSAT Satellites and ESA Launches," *Proceedings of the AMSAT-NA 14th Space Symposium*, 1996, pp 102-118.

Getting Started

3 Getting Started

Before you commit to setting up a ground station for satellite communications you should give some serious thought to whether satellite operation is really for you. As with HF DXing, contesting and becoming a brain surgeon, success at space communications requires a serious investment of time, effort and often cash. However, the result may be worth the effort. Many old-time HF operators report that their first satellite QSO rates a special place in memory right up there with their premier HF contact. An impressive number of first-class HF DXers, tired of the rat race, have found a new home on the birds.

With more than 18,000 amateurs currently participating in the Amateur Satellite Service[1] it shouldn't be too difficult to locate a few local hams who have had some experience with space communications. Ask them how they feel about it. Some will probably see satellites as the most exciting new dimension of Amateur Radio since the discovery, back in the early '20s, that "useless" shortwaves could propagate across the Atlantic. Others may firmly believe that satellite relays are as exciting as the telephone. Talk to advocates of both viewpoints. If at all possible, visit an active satellite user during a pass. Observing a ground station in operation first-hand is the best way to get a feel for what's involved. If the bug still has you in its clutches at this point, you may as well give in and start making plans to set up your own ground station.

Even though the International Telecommunication Union recognizes the Amateur Satellite Service as being distinct from the Amateur Service, amateurs in the US (and most other countries) do not have to pass any special test or request special permission to use satellites. Your Amateur Radio license is your ticket to satellite operating.

The term satellite operation includes a great many forms of communications. Some satellites carry linear transponders designed to support CW and SSB. The frequencies used vary from HF (21 MHz) to microwave (24 GHz). These satellites generally have separate telemetry beacons. Satellites carrying linear transponders are listed in Table 3.1.

Other spacecraft carry transponders designed to handle digital communication modes. These vary in speed, in the modulation techniques employed and in intended purpose. The main digital applications include: telemetry, store-and-forward communications, real-time communications, and Automatic position Reporting and messaging (APRS). When digital modes are used the transponder downlink is generally time shared between communications and telemetry.

Satellites available for digital communications are listed in Table 3.2. Since each spacecraft is designed (hardware and software) with a special objective in mind it is important to note and comply with the intended function. Attempting to use a system designed for store-and-forward communications for real-time communications can, for example, cause serious disruption ranging from denial of service to most users to automatic spacecraft shutdown due to power shortage.

In addition to these general modes there are several special satellite transponders available. Some operate much like terrestrial FM repeaters (inband or crossband), others provide automated CW QSOs (ROBOT) with the satellite and there's even a PARROT that records about 60 seconds of audio, which is then broadcast in the following 60 second time slot on the same frequency. These special transponders are listed in Table 3.3.

FIRST STEPS

Once you decide to set up a ground station you'll find that the project involves several stages. The first step is to identify a goal—a communications mode (digital or analog) and spacecraft. The analog modes (CW and SSB) are the most popular. More than 75% of those currently set up for satellite operation are equipped for CW or SSB. This is in part due to the fact that most amateurs have found these modes the most effective.

The second step is to gather up-to-date information on which spacecraft are currently available and their operating schedules. Be sure to check sources such as newsletters, radio amateur nets and packet networks and the Internet. Publishing timelines for books (including this one) and glossy magazines limit their ability to provide this information in a timely manner.

Step three is to learn something about tracking and ground station design. Key ground station factors are transmit power requirements, receive system design and appropriate antennas. Investing some time in planning is especially worthwhile if you're considering purchasing new equipment. Make sure the new hardware will be useful if you want to upgrade to other frequencies and spacecraft.

Step four is to set up your receive system (receiver, con-

Table 3.1
Satellites for CW/SSB Communications

AO-7	This LEO satellite carries two linear transponders. One operates 2-meter/10-meter (mode A), the other 70-cm/2-meter (Mode B). The schedule is erratic but one of the transponders is generally on when the spacecraft is in sunlight.
RS-15	This LEO satellite carries a linear 2-meter/10-meter transponder. As a result of a relatively high orbit it provides wide area coverage and long access times. Not recommended for beginners because of relatively weak downlink but very popular with experienced satellite operators. May only be operating in daylight due to battery problems.
FO-20	This LEO satellite carries a linear 2-meter/70-cm transponder. Not recommended for beginners because of relatively weak downlink but very popular with experienced satellite operators.
FO-29	This LEO satellite carries a linear 2-meter/70-cm transponder. See comments under FO-20.
AO-40	This high altitude, high power satellite has a linear transponder that includes links at 2 meters, 70 cm, 23 cm, 13 cm and 1.5 cm. The most popular link is 70-cm/13-cm. Although setting up a ground station for OSCAR 40 may be slightly more difficult than for a LEO satellite, the payback in coverage and available access time may make the effort very worthwhile.
AO-10	After more than 13 years in orbit the 70-cm/2-meter transponder on this brain dead high altitude satellite continues to provide good service when the spacecraft's solar panels are receiving adequate sunlight. Not recommended for beginners due to quirky operation but very popular with experienced operators.

Notes
1. Many of the spacecraft operate on a limited schedule.
2. Updated information is posted weekly in AMSAT News Service (ANS) bulletins available (free) via the Internet. See the AMSAT-NA Web site at **www.amsat.org**.
3. Additional details are contained in Chapter 4 and in Appendix C.

verter, preamps, antenna, feed lines, etc) and get it operating satisfactorily. Spend some time listening to the downlinks to familiarize yourself with satellite operating procedures and tracking techniques.

Step five is to put your uplink in operation—Let the communications begin! Remember, this chapter is designed to help you choose where to start. It does not tell you everything you need to know once you've made the decision. This book should provide you with most of the background information needed to set up a station. You needn't stop and study everything in it just now. Many readers find it more efficient to skim large sections so that later, when access to specific material is needed, they know where to find it. In addition to the information in this book you'll also need to know what satellites are currently available (new spacecraft may have been launched and others may have been put out to pasture since this book went to press) and you'll have to obtain some recent tracking data.

If you've read Chapters 1 and 2 on the history of the Amateur Satellite Program you already know a great deal about satellite communication systems, including the different capabilities of Phase 2 (low Earth orbit) and Phase 3 (high altitude) spacecraft. Your initial ground station setup will probably be designed to give you access to a particular type of operation (digital or analog) and a particular set of

uplink and downlink frequencies (or a specific satellite). Mode and satellite selection are so closely related that they should be chosen together.

THE BASIC GROUND STATION

A satellite ground station has a great deal in common with an HF or VHF station designed for regular terrestrial communication (either direct or via repeater). Both require a transmitter, a transmitting antenna, a receiver and a receiving antenna. Figure 3.1 shows a satellite ground station for CW/SSB communications. For digital modes one would have to add appropriate modems, a TNC (terminal node controller) and a computer. Block diagrams of digital ground stations are shown in Chapter 5. In the following sections we'll look at the frequencies used at the ground station, the power levels required, the types of modulations employed and so on. Naturally, there are also many differences between a satellite ground station and a station for terrestrial work, some subtle, some obvious. As we focus on these differences don't forget the basic, underlying similarity.

To operate all analog transponders on all satellites currently in orbit, or about to be launched, a ground station would need receiving equipment for 29, 145, 435 MHz and 2.4, 10 and 24 GHz, transmitting equipment for 21, 146, 435

Table 3.2

Satellites for Digital Communications

Spacecraft	Primary Activity	Primary Frequencies/ Modulation
UO-11	telemetry broadcasts	2-meter, 1200-baud AFSK
AO-16	store-and-forward	2-meter/70-cm, 1200 baud Manchester FSK
UO-22	store-and-forward	2-meter/70-cm, 9600 baud FSK
IO-26	store-and-forward	2-meter/70-cm, 1200 baud Manchester FSK
NO-44	APRS, instant messaging	2-meter/2-meter, 1200 baud FSK
MO-46	store-and-forward	2-meter/70-cm, 9600 baud FSK
AO-49	experimental	uplink: 70 cm 1200 baud AFSK downlink: 9600 baud FSK
AO-40	real-time communications	70 cm/13 cm, 9600 baud FSK RUDAK
ARISS	experimental	2-meter/2-meter, 1200 baud FSK
RS-20	telemetry broadcasts	2-meter & 70-cm CW

Notes
1. Updated information is posted weekly in AMSAT News Service (ANS) bulletins available (free) vis the Internet. See the AMSAT-NA Web site at **www.amsat.org**.
2. Additional details are contained in Chapter 5 and in Appendix C.
3. Several other spacecraft are operational on an intermittent basis.
4. Plans are to open RUDAK to general communication in late 2003.
5. Communications downlinks are ofetn time shared with telemetry data.

Table 3.3

Satellites for FM Voice

Satellite	Uplink/Downlink
UO-14	2-meter/70-cm
AO-27	2-meter/70-cm
SO-41	2-meter/70-cm
SO-50	2-meter/70-cm

Notes

1. All of these spacecraft operate on a limited schedule.

2. Updated information is posted weekly in AMSAT News Service (ANS) bulletins available (free) via the Internet. See the AMSAT-NA Web site at **www.amsat.org**.

3. Additional details are contained in Chapter 4 and in Appendix C.

4. SO-42 is similar to SO-41 but it has not been operated on a regular basis.

MHz and 1.27. 2.4 and 5.7 GHz and antennas for all of these frequencies. For your starter station you'll only need access to one band for transmitting and one band for receiving.

As most current and planned satellite transponders are designed for cross-band operation, separate receive and transmit antennas will be required. For several reasons, which we'll discuss later, satellite CW/SSB operation also requires that you use a separate receiver and transmitter at your ground station. If you currently own an HF or VHF transceiver it can be used to satisfy (partially or completely) the receive or transmit requirements for your ground station, but not both.

THE SATELLITE TRANSPONDER

A satellite transponder is generally designed to handle either CW and SSB, FM voice, or digital modes. Analog transponders are discussed in detail in Chapter 4. Digital transponders are discussed in Chapter 5. Since most beginners use CW and SSB, a brief sketch of linear transponder operation is given here.

From the user's point of view a linear transponder receives a slice of one amateur band and shifts the entire slice to a different band (or, much less frequently, a different section of the same band) where it's amplified and retransmitted. The "entire slice" really does mean everything present on the uplink—CW, SSB, FM, digital, noise, licensed stations, illegal stations, etc. Slices having widths from 40 kHz to 250 kHz are common on amateur spacecraft.

When describing a transponder the uplink frequency (or wavelength) is always given first. For example, ground stations communicating via a satellite carrying a 146 MHz/ 29 MHz transponder (one that shifts a slice of the spectrum

near 146 MHz down to the 29 MHz region) will all transmit near 146 MHz and listen near 29 MHz. This transponder frequency combination can also be labeled 2 meter/ 10 meter or referred to as Mode A. While the letter designations were very convenient in the early days of the satellite program the growth in the number of new combinations and the use of multiple uplinks or downlinks on a given transponder sometimes makes them a bit confusing. A detailed list of the names used for various frequency combinations can be found in Chapter 4.

CRITICAL DECISION POINTS

Although selecting one's initial goal involves a great

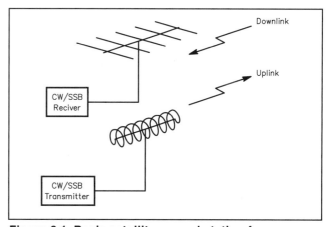

Figure 3.1–Basic satellite ground station for operating through a linear transponder.

many choices three are very important. There are (1) choosing between CW/SSB, FM voice, and digital modes, (2) selecting transmitting and receiving frequencies and (3) electing to use a high or a low altitude spacecraft. In practice, the choice of frequencies and spacecraft are related.

ANALOG VERSUS DIGITAL

The simplest decision point involves the choice between CW/SSB, FM voice and digital modes. The majority of newcomers opt for the CW/SSB route. FM voice is also a popular approach, especially for those who already have the required equipment, however it is very limited with respect to future applications and operational flexibility. The digital modes are not nearly a popular srarting point, except to those already very familiar with digital communications techniques.

FREQUENCIES

Whether you opt for CW/SSB, FM voice or digital operation you're going to need a transmitter on the transponder uplink frequency and a receiver on the downlink frequency. For CW/SSB communications you must be able to transmit and receive at the same time (in order to monitor your downlink) so a single transceiver cannot staisfy both requirements. Obvoiusly, it's desirable to choose frequencies that you already have equipment for, or for which equipment is relatively inexpensive. This is why operators find the 10-meter link on AO-7 especially appealing. However, this link only operates part of the time and the schedule is erratic. For most of the most past two decades Russian RS spacecraft have provided strong HF links but currently (mid 2003) the only Russian HF transponder operating is on RS-15 and it is weak and erratic. Check updated listings to determine if a new RS transponder is available.

It may involve a bit more effort to use satellites that carry 2-meter links but CW/SSB equipment for this band is also readily available. We'll shortly see how it's possible to temporarily improvise equipment for this band. In general, with the technology available today, the higher you go in frequency the greater the effort required to set up transmitting and receiving equipment. However, it's also true that link performance tends to improve with frequency. These are some of the considerations that satellite designers must take into account when selecting transponder frequencies.

HIGH ALTITUDE VERSUS LOW ALTITUDE

In the past, low Earth orbit (LEO) satellites tended to be easier to use for several reasons. First, they could be accessed with low power and simple antennas. Second, they generally used lower frequencies for which transmitting and receiving equipment is widely available. However, the coverage provided by LEO spacecraft is modest. They're generally only in range for 4 to 6 brief (usually less than 20 minutes) passes per day and maximum communications distance is limited (generally under 5000 miles). Finally, because the frequencies used are affected by ionospheric conditions, the radio links are not very reliable.

In the past, high altitude satellites tended to be more

difficult to use. Because the average distance between the satellite and ground station was much greater than with LEO spacecraft the path loss was much larger. As a result, ground stations needed higher power, beam antennas and very sensitive receivers. These obstacles were compounded by the fact that the frequencies in use tended to be higher. High altitude satellites were preferred by experienced, committed operators because they were accessible many more hours each day, had significantly better coverage (communications distances up to 11,500 miles are possible) and provided more reliable link performance. Since OSCAR 40 has considerably more power than any previous high altitude amateur spacecraft, and command stations have better control over the pointing of its high gain antennas, ground station requirements have been simplified.

OSCAR 40 should be given serious consideration for your first goal as a beginner. The higher frequency links may be a stumbling block but the rewards in terms of total Earth coverage and daily access time may make the extra effort worthwhile.

MAKING THE CHOICE

OPTION I: CW/SSB LEO

From 1974-2001 the most popular beginners route to satellite communications was via a low earth orbit (LEO) satellite carrying a linear transponder that used at least one HF band. During this "golden age" several reliable long lifetime spacecraft including AMSAT-OSCARs 6, 7 and 8 and RSs 5, 6, 7, 8, 10/11, 12/13, and 15 were often available at the same time. RS-12/13, with its sensitive receivers, loud downlinks, and the opportunities it offered to use HF for uplinks and downlinks, was extremely popular throughout its ten-year lifetime (it ceased operating in 2001). Unfortunately, the only currently operating spacecraft in this category (LEO and linear transponder with at least one HF link) are AO-7 and RS-15. Both have uplinks at 2-meters and downlinks at 10-meters. However, both spacecraft operate only in sunlight and on an intermittent basis.

While the attractiveness of Option I is somewhat diminished at present it's important to understand the factors that made these satellites so appealing since it's likely that spacecraft with similar capabilities may be launched in the near future. Common frequency combinations employed in the past include mode A (2m up / 10m down), mode K (15m / 10m), mode T (15m / 2m), mode KA (15m & 2m / 10m), and mode KT (15m / 10m & 2m). Many articles have appeared outlining how to use these "Easy Sats" to get started.[1,2,3]

Ground station equipment requirements for accessing these satellites are modest. Most use 2-meter uplinks. A ground station with a 25 watt multimode 2m rig feeding a groundplane antenna generally produces a decent uplink signal. Many operators report that they completed their initial Mode A contacts by keying the push-to-talk line on an FM transmitter with the mike disconnected. A small directional antenna or a little more power will improve your signal but too much power overloads the satellite and causes problems. RS-10/11 and RS-12/13 also monitored a 15-

meter uplink. A ground station could easily access this link with 50 W to a dipole or groundplane antenna. For receiving signals from a spacecraft 10-meter downlink most ground stations used a dipole or groundplane. When a sensitive receiver and low loss feedline were employed this produced good results.

A ground station requires a separate receiver and transmitter so that the downlink frequency and strength can be monitored. As a result, an HF transceiver must be dedicated to either the uplink or downlink chain – it can't be used for both.

The transponders on LEO RS spacecraft tended to be 40 kHz wide while those on AMSAT spacecraft usually had a 100 kHz bandwidth so that they could be used by a great many ground stations at the same time. Actual frequencies for operating transponders are given in Appendix C. By general agreement the downlink passband is informally divided as follows: upper third SSB, lower third CW, middle third mixed CW and SSB.

Satellite transponders using links employing some combination of 15 m, 10 m, and 2m are generally non-inverting. This means that when a ground station changes transmitting frequency the downlink frequency changes an equal amount in the same direction. It also means that when using SSB the downlink sideband matches the uplink sideband. Upper sideband is recommended for all satellite downlinks so ground stations should transmit upper sideband when using non-inverting transponders. (Exceptions may be made in special situations).

If you transmit at the center of the transponder uplink passband your downlink signal will appear near the center of the downlink passband. The difference, which may amount to +/- a couple of kHz, is due to a phenomena called Doppler shift. Doppler shift results from the fact that the distance between the spacecraft and your ground station is changing. It's similar to the effect that causes the pitch of a train whistle to decrease as it approaches and passes you. One result of Doppler shift is that stations may appear to drift several kHz during a QSO requiring that the receiver be frequently adjusted to keep the other station tuned in. To minimize QRM from QSO's drifting onto each other, it's best to try and keep the lower frequency link constant (10 m on mode A, 15 m on mode K). Doppler shift is discussed in detail elsewhere in this book. At this point it's only important to be aware of its existence so that you'll expect and understand the apparent downlink frequency creep.

Always keep in mind that a transponder is a shared resource. Anyone using more than their fair share of the spacecraft power and/or bandwidth will not be very popular. Being told you have the loudest signal on the band may be a compliment on HF but it may a hint to reduce power when you're using a linear satellite transponder. You should always monitor your downlink and, if necessary, arrange to control uplink power so your signal will never be stronger than the adjacent beacon.

Although it's relatively easy to get on 21 MHz and 29 MHz these frequencies are not very well suited for satellite links which must pass through the ionosphere. When the sun is very active, 10 m and 15 m satellite links become unreliable and unpredictable; signals may be excellent one minute and fade completely out of the picture a few minutes later. This is because the same conditions that provide 10 m and 15 m HF operators with excellent world wide skip near peaks in the sunspot cycle can make the ionosphere nearly opaque to satellite radio links. During these times, unusual propagation is often observed— one might hear solid downlink signals when the spacecraft is far out of normal range. Of course, many experienced operators using the HF satellite links find the unpredictable nature of these links an appealing attribute.

If you forgo the requirement that the LEO spacecraft you choose employ at least one HF link you can consider one that uses links at 2-meters and 70-cm. There are several currently in orbit including FO-20 and FO-29 which have uplinks at 2-meters (mode J) and AO-7 which has an uplink at 70-cm (mode B). If you possess the transmitting/receiving equipment needed these spacecraft are easy to access and they provide good performance. As little as ten watts to a small Yagi (3-el on 2-meters, 7-el on 70 cm) work well. The robust 2-meter downlink on AO-7 provides good results with a 3-el beam, even a simple groundplane produces a decent signal. The 70-cm downlinks from FO-20 and FO-29 require a larger beam – a 12-el Yagi being common – and a good low noise preamp. These UHF/VHF satellite links provide good performance – compared to HF links their main disadvantage is the added complexity of antenna aiming. Again, it should be noted that all three of these spacecraft are old and operate on a limited basis when in sunlight. Also, when AO-7 is on it may turn up in either mode A or B since it is not being regularly commanded.

OPTION II: OSCAR 40

OSCAR 40 deserves serious consideration for your initial attempt at satellite communication. Although it encountered numerous problems during its early days in orbit it is now operating very reliably. The most popular OSCAR 40 transponder combination couples the 70-cm uplink to the 2.4 GHz downlink. The transponder is working well and daily providing world wide DX to a great many modestly equipped ground stations. This link was very popular on OSCAR 13 and it will be used on a new Phase 3 spacecraft being constructed by AMSAT-DL so the effort and expensive you devote to setting up for it should be a good investment. Note that at 2.4 GHz an unobstructed path from ground station antenna to the spacecraft is needed so check your location and make sure you have a decent window (free of trees) to a significant portion of the OSCAR 40 orbit before committing to this option.

As with any satellite operation your first goal should be to monitor the downlink. Although receiving 2.4 GHz signals may appear to be a formidable challenge it actually turns out to be relatively simple and inexpensive thanks to the availability of commercial MDDS (Multipoint Microwave Distribution System) converters that have the stability and sensitivity needed for use with OSCAR 40. The input circuits on these converters are generally designed to cover the entire 2.1 – 2.6 GHz range which includes the 2.4 GHz frequencies used on the spacecraft. The output is generally optimized for 220 – 410 MHz. In some cases it's possible to monitor OSCAR 40 by feeding the output from an unmodified unit directly into a general coverage receiver operating near 123 MHz. The more common approach is to modify the converter to provide output on the 2-meter ham band. The 70-cm band can also be used as an IF but this is not a good choice if you're planning on using a 70-cm uplink. LNA's for use with these units are also available, an MDDS converter and LNA can often be obtained for well under $100. An inquiry posted on the AMSAT-BB via the Internet will provide an updated list of sources (and possibly some direct offers). Conversion information is available from links on the AMSAT-NA, AMSAT-UK, and AMSAT-DL web sites.

Once the signal is down to VHF (or UHF) it can be fed into a multimode transceiver or into a 2-meter converter feeding an HF receiver. It's even possible to feed the VHF signal into the front end of a 2 m FM transceiver and then "borrow" a little signal from the IF stages (before the limiter) to feed into a general coverage HF CW/SSB receiver. Just check the 2-meter transceiver instruction manual to find the IF frequency. Next, connect a short piece of coax to the HF receiver antenna terminal and wind a small coil at the far end. Tune the 2-meter FM rig to a signal — any local FM signal will do. Tune the HF receiver to the IF frequency, set the rf gain to maximum, and experiment with positioning the pickup coil near the 2 meter transceiver receiver board until you hear a signal coming through. The procedure also works with 70 cm FM transceivers. The point here is that a CW/SSB receiver for 2.4 GHz can be set up at modest cost. For more detailed instructions see Chapter 11.

The most common 2.4 GHz receiving antenna is a parabolic dish and appropriate feed. Dishes produced for the MMDS and DDS (Direct-to-home Digital Satellite TV) industries are often available at extremely low cost at swap meets or from dealers unloading used or outdated systems. A 60 cm dish is useable with a very low noise receiving system, an 80 cm dish will generally provide significantly better results, and a 1m dish can be counted on to give good results with any decent receiver. You'll probably construct your own dish feed – usually a helix or patch. Mounting the down converter or a preamp directly at the feed can make a big difference in performance. Extensive details can be found in the following articles and on the Internet.[4,5,6] Background information is contained in Chapter 10

The 70-cm and 23-cm uplinks on OSCAR 40 are generally operated simultaneously. Most new users have an easier time gaining access to the equipment needed for transmitting at 70-cm. Informal user surveys show that a transmitter providing 20 to 50 watts and an antenna with about 13 dB gain (2 12-el Yagis) produces good results. At these frequencies low loss coax and short cable runs are important. Old land mobile UHF FM units, available for next to nothing these days, can often be easily converted to CW transmitters for the uplink.

OPTION III: DIGITAL COMMUNICATIONS

A 1996 survey reported that only 25% of those then involved in satellite communications are equipped for digital modes.[7] Of these, about 18% operated 9600 baud FSK and 7% operated 1200 baud PSK. Estimates are that these numbers have not changed greatly over the intervening years.

If the past provides clues to the future the great majority of new satellite users will opt for CW/SSB communications but there will be a small group of beginners who find it easier to set up for one of the digital modes. (Most new stations that show up on the digital satellites have had considerable experience working with analog transponders).

Newcomers to satellite communications who opt for the digital route are generally highly experienced in digital communications. Many are already operating 9600 baud using 70 cm terrestrial repeaters or digipeating at 1200 baud on 2 m. If you're in this group you may already have all the equipment you need to access the 2m/70cm digital repeaters on the LEO satellites, on the International Space Station, or on the OSCAR 40 RUDAK transponder (which should be available for general use by the time you read this). "All" you need is a list of frequencies (see Appendix C), information on tracking (see Chapter 7) and scheduling, software designed expressly to support digital satellite communications (The package called WiSP will provide everything required), background information on digital satellite techniques (Chapter 5), a box of modems and a lot of perseverance.

Actually, the situation is not nearly as daunting as it first appears. This is because WiSP contains a lot of the information needed and anyone going this route probably has access to the AMSAT Internet Bulletin Board where answers to questions are readily available. Also, a number of recent developments such as the fact that most new microcomputers now include sound cards that enable one to emulate modems in software and excellent free software for this purpose now exists have also reduced the difficulty of this approach.

Interest in spacecraft focusing on digital communications was given a big boost by the September 2001 launch of OSCAR 44 which was expressly designed to support the Automatic Position Reporting System and instant messaging applications. This gave amateurs already set up for terrestrial APRS an easy path to satellite operation. Several other LEO satellites are now supporting these operations and additional spacecraft are close to launch. APRS activities and spacecraft are very well documented on the Internet. See the section on NO-44 in Appendix C for detailed references.

OPTION IV: LEO FM VOICE REPEATERS

The transponders on UO-14, AO-27, SO-41, and SO-SO are very different from the linear ones described under Option I. They're crossband (2 meter/70 cm) single channel FM repeaters. Anyone wit a 70-cm H-T can listen in on the action.

A ground station using a 10 W 2-m mobile or base unit feeding a ground plane antenna can put a good signal through one of these spacecraft. The emphasis here is on the word "can". If the repeater is being captured by a high power user a low power ground station will not be heard. With a single channel and a coverage area that often includes the entire

Table 3.4

Radio Amateur Satellite Downlink Frequencies in the 10-Meter Band (May 2003)

Frequency (MHz)	S/C	(T)ransponder (B)eacon (R)obot	Comment
29.353	RS-15	B	Mode A
29.354-29.394	RS-15	T	Mode A
29.399	RS-15	B	Mode A

Table 3.5

Radio Amateur Satellite Downlink Frequencies in the 2-Meter Band (May 2003)

Frequency (MHz)	S/C	(T)ransponder (B)eacon (R)obot	Comment
145.810	AO-10	B	Mode B
145.825	UO-11	B	1200 baud PSK, voice
145.825-145.975	AO-10	T	Mode B
145.987	AO-10	B	Mode B engineering, usually off

continental U.S. it's clear that these spacecraft were not designed as a place for rag chewers to congregate. Keep your contacts very short.

Although these single channel FM repeater spacecraft are very easy to monitor and access they're also very limited with respect to practical applications. If you have the transmitting and receiving equipment on hand give them a try. They're definitely fun the first few times you use them and they're excellent for simple demonstrations that are guaranteed to draw lots of attention. They also provide an operating focus if you're first learning about satellite tracking. But these spacecraft offer little to sustain on going interest so they're best thought of as a stepping stone to some other aspect of satellite operation. Because of power budget constraints all except UO-22 operate on a part time basis. AO-27 is generally only turned on during daylight passes over the U.S. SO-50 requires a CTCSS tone for activation. Additional details are contained in Appendix C.

OPTION V: FOCUS ON MONITORING

A small but significant number of technically inclined radio amateurs may be more concerned with monitoring satellite downlinks than in actually communicating through a transponder. Amateurs in this category may be interested in studying aspects of radio propagation through the ionosphere or in using information about such propagation to infer activities taking place in the ionosphere. They may also be interested in using satellite telemetry to study the performance of spacecraft systems. This information can then be used to perfect the design of future missions, or even to sug-

gest activities that can be used to enhance the performance of ongoing missions. For example, temperature data might suggest that turning on a little used subsystem might change the thermal distribution in the spacecraft is a manor that improves the operation of a more important subsystem. If scientific and technical concerns like these fascinate you give some though to monitoring satellite downlinks as a goal.

If monitoring is your primary objective please see the comments in Options I-IV concerning the strength of various spacecraft downlinks and the receiving equipment and antennas needed to access them as these will not be repeated here.

STARTING OUT: FOUR CASE STUDIES

(The following scenarios were inspired by real people and real events but some details have been changed to take into account spacecraft, equipment and software currently available.)

HAM A

[This profile was initially prepared in the late 1990's. Although RS-12/13 is no longer operational and radio amateurs do not currently have access to a reliable spacecraft with a 10-meter downlink this section is being retained because the situation it describes is important and may apply to future missions.]

Subject A is an experienced HF operator with broad operating interests that include DXing, contesting and lots of casual ragchewing. He splits his time about 50/50 between SSB and CW and operates all bands from 80 meters to 10 meters using a 100 W transceiver and a collection of dipoles and groundplanes. The shack also contains a 25 W 2-meter FM rig.

Subject A is interested in trying something new but he doesn't want to spend much money. While he's not really into building equipment he isn't afraid of taking the cover off a complex rig and making small modifications.

Subject A decides to try Mode A. He acquires some simple public domain tracking software for his computer so that he can predict when RS-12/13 will be in range. He connects his HF transceiver to his regular 10-meter groundplane antenna and tunes the RS-12 10-meter downlink band while the satellite is predicted to be in range. Many solid signals, both CW and SSB, are heard. Some are engaged in brief contest-like QSOs while others are ragchewing.

After listening in for a few passes and liking what he hears he decides to try uplinking. He unplugs the mike from his 2-meter rig, turns the mike gain down to zero and using alligator clip leads wires the push-to-talk line to an old straight key. The usual 2-meter antenna is a large Yagi but he knows that operating gets pretty hectic during a pass and that he'll have enough to handle without trying to keep the beam aimed at the spacecraft. So he runs a spare cable out the window to the 2-meter groundplane on his car (an omni-directional antenna) which is sitting in the driveway. While waiting for the pass he sets his transmitter frequency slightly below the middle of the uplink passband. As soon as the satellite comes in range he starts transmitting dits and adjusts the receiver frequency about the middle of the downlink while listening for his return signal. Sure enough he finds it. A quick CQ and he makes his first contact. Three more QSOs follow before the end of the pass. He thinks to himself—46 more states and I've got WAS.

HAM B

C LIFF !

Subject B is addicted to the technical side of computers and ham radio. He's currently set up for terrestrial VHF/UHF packet operations using 1200 baud AFSK and 9600 baud FSK. He owns late model FM transceivers for 2 meter and 70 cm and his shack is "littered" with terminals, computers, modems and TNCs.

There's no question about what aspect of satellite communications appeals to Subject B. Having just received a demonstration of packet satellite operation from a satellite operator he met on a local voice repeater and having learned that several low altitude PACSATs are in orbit and operating 24 hours per day, it's 9600 baud Mode JD (2 meter/70 cm) here I come. He orders a software package direct from AMSAT to make sure he's got the latest version. The package, *WiSP*, handles all aspects of tracking, ground station frequency control and Doppler compensation and digital communications (See Chapter 5). Since he frequently writes software he appreciates the effort that goes into producing quality work so he's pleased to make the requested contribution, especially since he knows it will go, in large part, to pay for future PACSATs. For initial testing he disconnects his 2-meter and 70-cm beams and replaces them (temporarily) with simple groundplanes.

It takes a while to get everything connected up and working together. When things appear to be operating correctly he tunes to the downlink on the next pass and immediately starts copying broadcast packets. The following pass he tries transmitting. Actually he tells his software to try uplinking since everything is under software control. Things don't go quite right and the satellite never acknowledges his request to enter the uplink queue. Between passes he reviews the situation and figures out why box A isn't talking to box B. Next time he tries, everything works perfectly. As a test he requests a short file, which is successfully captured.

Whereas most hams would be ready to sit down and pat themselves on the back at this point Subject B is already planning to replace the groundplane antennas with his beams and interface the rotators to his tracking program for automatic tracking.

HAM C

Subject C enjoys RF construction projects and operating CW. Subject C hates spending money. In truth, money is actually a secondary issue—he really believes that one of the great pleasures of ham radio is the chance to solve problems by improvising, scrounging and using ingenuity. Much of his vacuum tube vintage equipment, which covers the HF bands and 2 meter and 70 cm FM, is reaching the age where its value is actually increasing each year. He has nothing against solid state equipment, it's just that "you can get your hands on a lot of excellent tube gear for next to nothing." After watching an OSCAR 10 Mode B demonstration at his club's Field Day station he decides that he wants to get on Mode B CW.

He sets up a 2-meter FM receiver RF deck for 145.89 MHz and then experiments with coupling RF from the 2-meter receiver's mixer and first IF over to his HF receiver. The 2-meter FM receiver is essentially being used as a converter. (See Chapter 11 for more information.) When everything appears to be working well, he connects the receive chain to a groundplane to listen for Mode B on AO-10.

At this point he wakes up to the fact that he needs tracking information. Being much more interested in radio communications than computers, the delay and hassle involved in acquiring and installing a software package are not very appealing. So he gets on the local 2-meter repeater and asks for some help in tracking. The only one on frequency who knows what's going on doesn't have current orbital elements for AO-10 but he is able to provide the Internet address of a tracking site. Our subject then asks his pre-teen daughter if she can check out the site and obtain the needed info. A few minutes later she has the data in hand. When he tries to thank her, she responds that the job was trivial and that she can even show him how to do it for himself. He smiles, thinks about the joys of parenthood for a few moments and returns to the shack.

When AO-10 finally comes into range the results are disappointing—he can only hear a few very weak signals. He decides to splurge on a cheap preamp on Mode B. There's not much to gain by trying to get below a 1.0 dB noise figure. He connects it in front of the receiver and it hardly makes any difference. Next he tries moving it to the antenna end of the feed line. This results in a noticeable improvement but signals are still quite weak, so a beam antenna appears necessary. He knows his small linearly polarized Yagi is not optimal but he decides to give it a try. Since his wallet won't bear the shock of a second rotator for elevation control he just raises the antenna boom to a point about 25° above the horizon. Received signals are now pretty decent. You wouldn't call them booming but most stations are solid R5. He notes that no one change to the receiving setup had an overwhelming effect on performance but that, in total, they produced a significant improvement. Now on to the transmitter.

Subject C checks his resources (junkbox) and finds a 10 W 430 MHz RF strip that he purchased as a backup for his old commercial 70-cm FM transceiver. He decides to swap it with the 20 W strip that's currently in the transceiver so he can use the higher power unit for Mode B. He knows that the power rating is for CCS (continuous commercial service) so he decides to run it using ICAS (Intermittent Commercial/Amateur Service) ratings with an ac power supply that will give him close to 40 W. For the transmitting antenna he uses a small Yagi mounted, like the 2-meter Yagi, at a fixed elevation. He has some higher gain antennas around but he figures that with the fixed elevation mount and the 2-meter antenna he's using, going to higher gain at 70 cm would likely reduce, rather than increase, his access time to AO-10. It takes a little experimentation to obtain a clean signal when keying the transmitter. Finally he adds a varactor across the capacitor, which trims the crystal to frequency. This allows him to easily vary the frequency of the crystal controlled transmitter ± 15 kHz, which is adequate.

The setup works fine. Sometimes he wishes he had an elevation rotator or circularly polarized antennas but he figures that these improvements would only increase his solid access time by about 20% and the extra time to implement this is not worth the effort. He looks over his station and feels rather pleased. The tube technology may be 30+ years old and take up lots of room on the bench but the equipment is reliable and it performs well. One change he does consider is replacing the new 2-meter preamp with an old nuvistor unit so he can print up some special satellite QSLs stating that his station is 100% tube—0 % solid state.

HAM D

Subject D is a high school biology teacher. She's an active amateur but she has never worked with OSCAR satellites. It's January 15 and her school has just received a small $300 grant. This will enable the science faculty, students in the sciences, Amateur Radio and other clubs, to design and build a temporary exhibit for the city's Museum of Science and Technology. The exhibit will be on display during July and August. At a meeting called to set design objectives she suggests the "Peaceful Uses Of Space" as a theme. The idea is accepted and the group decides to focus on Earth satellites used for communications, environmental monitoring and special applications. To illustrate these classes of satellites the group selects weather, Earth resources and Amateur Radio satellites.

Guidelines for the museum display suggest including both static and dynamic/interactive sections. The static section generally consists of posters, pictures, models, etc. The dynamic/interactive component is the main area of concern. One student suggests a design focusing on four spacecraft that would require about 12 computer displays. Three displays would be allocated to each spacecraft; one showing the ground track, the second showing the view of the Earth as seen from the spacecraft and the third having a running commentary on the satellite system (in the case of weather satellites, showing a file of weather satellite images). While everyone agrees that this would make a very impressive exhibit and the group has the expertise to build such a display, they feel that the proposal is a little too big to handle considering the time and budget available. The elements of the suggestion are, however, incorporated in the plan chosen.

The final design relies heavily on Amateur Radio for the dynamic/interactive element. Microcomputer software developed for tracking amateur spacecraft will be used to provide a graphic display of the real time positions of the various satellites described in the static part of the exhibit. The computer produced image will be projected on a large screen using a multicolor LCD view projector. This is the system used in the high school when a teacher wishes to display microcomputer output for a class.

Two receivers will be employed. One, a UHF scanner will monitor the voice downlinks used by AO-27 and UO-14. The second will be used to listen to SSB activity between 145.800 and 146.000 MHz. Subject D will be responsible for designing the RF sections of the display and obtaining equipment on loan when possible.

The RF design is complicated by several considerations. Consider the 2-meter SSB receiver first. A modern multimode 2-meter transceiver that can be tuned by buttons on the mike is appealing because it probably would be easy to rig a remote tuning control on the front of the display using a couple of push switches. But, money isn't available to purchase one and if one were borrowed the possibility of damage would be a serious and constant concern. The solution is to invest $70 in a good 2-meter converter and borrow an old amateur band only tube receiver. With the help of the president of a local Amateur Radio club, a member with a spare receiver is located. The individual readily agrees to loan it. In return, a notice about the club's fall Novice class will be prominently displayed at the science museum exhibit. Although the 1960 vintage 60 pound plus receiver greatly reduces concern about theft or damage the group designing the display feels it's in the best interests of all concerned to agree on a value for the receiver ahead of time just in case a problem occurs—a dollar a pound seems reasonable.

The receiver will be placed behind a large sheet of plywood that forms the front of the display. Strategically placed cutouts will provide viewers with access to the volume control and main tuning dial only. The approach is not very hightech but it's cheap and reliable. The antenna will be a simple turnstile with reflector pointing straight up. A high quality preamp (borrowed) mounted directly at the antenna will be used.

The scanner receiver will be permanently set to *Mir* and shuttle frequencies and connected to a simple groundplane. Only one special piece of electronic equipment, referred to as the kludge box, needs to be designed and constructed for the display. It will monitor the squelch line on the scanner receiver. When a spacecraft comes into range and the scanner locks on it, the box will switch on a blinking red light and mute the communications receiver.

The exhibit, finished on time and under budget, turns out to be very popular. The 2-meter converter, the only major piece of equipment purchased for the display, is donated to the high school radio club. Subject D and several members of the high school radio club, become very interested in the OSCAR satellite program.

Notes

[1]R. Soifer, W2RS, "The Amateur Satellite Service in 1996," *The AMSAT Journal*, Sep/Oct 1996, pp 5-8.

[2]W. Daniel, KE3HP, "Getting Started with RS-10," *QST*, Aug 1993, pp 53-56. Reprinted in *The ARRL Satellite Anthology*, 4/Ed., 1996, pp 30-33.

[3]S. Ford, WB8IMY, "Working the EasySats," *QST*, Sep 1992, pp 30-34.

[4]R. Capon, WA3ULH, "Working RS-12 — The Ultimate Satellite Primer," *QST*, Feb 1994, pp 58-60, 64.

[5]S. Ford, WB8IMY, "Phase 3D: The Ultimate EasySat," *QST*, May 1995, pp 21-23.

Chapter 4

Satellite Analog Communications Plus (SSB/FM/PARROT/CW/ROBOT)

4 Satellite Analog Communications Plus SSB/FM/Packet/CW/Robot

USING A LINEAR TRANSPONDER

If you're going to be using linear transponders for CW/SSB communications, it helps to know something about them. In this chapter we'll look at the linear transponder from a user's point of view. We'll also take a brief look at how some other specialized transponders are used. Transponder design is treated in Chapter 14.

INTRODUCTION

Basic Function

A linear transponder receives a slice of the radio frequency spectrum that is centered about a particular frequency, amplifies the entire slice and retransmits it centered about a different frequency. For example, the incoming slice might be a 100-kHz-wide segment centered about 145.950 MHz containing dozens of SSB and CW signals. The slice is amplified, perhaps a million-million times, then retransmitted as a 100-kHz-wide segment centered about 29.450 MHz.

Philosophy: Sharing

Today no one questions the idea of using linear transponders to support communications in the amateur satellite service. But the fundamental idea is rather mind boggling. The amateurs who built the linear transponder for OSCAR III more than 30 years ago had to assume that thousands of inexperienced, untrained users who didn't know each other would somehow cooperate in sharing the available power and bandwidth so that all could benefit. There were many who believed that chaos would result. We now know that the linear transponder concept can work, but, cooperation and the reasons for it, must be continuously stressed so that newcomers will understand the situation. The sharing theme will resurface in many of the following sections, usually as justification for suggested operating procedures.

The Consensus Principle

Amateur satellite operation is based on consensus. The technical crew generally tries to explain what can be done and outline the consequences of various actions. Decisions as to proper operating procedures are then made by consen-

sus among those actually operating on the spacecraft. When necessary, the technical team will act to protect the health of the spacecraft.

Types of Signals Handled

An ideal linear transponder can handle any type of signal—CW, SSB, FM, digital, video, etc. Each signal is retransmitted in its original format, but shifted in frequency and greatly amplified. There are, however, technical *and* practical reasons for limiting usage to CW and SSB with special exceptions that are discussed later.

First, no transponder is ideal—signals do experience some distortion as they pass through. With digital signals the distortion may be a problem, with others (CW and SSB) it can hardly be perceived.

Second, we want to use the available power and spectrum most efficiently. If we compare two downlink signals from a transponder, a 2 W PEP SSB signal and a 2 W FM voice signal, the SSB signal uses, on average, 15% of the power of the FM signal and about 20% of the bandwidth.

The conclusion is clear—unless there are compelling reasons to do otherwise, use SSB and CW for general operation.

Duplex Operation

One very big difference between HF operation and satellite operation is that with satellites you can hear your downlink and know how your signal sounds to others who are listening. Duplex operation (the ability to listen to the downlink while you transmit) is not an option; it's a necessity. If your ground station isn't set up for duplex operation you'll never know where your downlink frequency is and you'll likely spend most of your operating time causing needless QRM to QSOs in progress. You won't know whether your signal is so strong that it's overloading the satellite, or so weak that it can't be heard.

When you operate duplex on SSB it's important to prevent your receiver output from feeding back into your transmitter microphone. Significant feedback leads to horrendous howls. A small amount of feedback may not be immediately noticeable to the transmitting station but others might report severely garbled audio. Attempting to use a speaker with your receiver will leave you continuously lunging for the audio gain control to search for the nonexistent level-setting that will provide feedback-free listening. The sooner you find a comfortable set of headphones the happier you'll be.

TRANSPONDER CHARACTERISTICS

Dynamic Range, Linearity, Phase Shift, Time-Delay

A linear transponder can be characterized by its efficiency, dynamic range, time-delay, linearity and phase delay vs frequency characteristics. What do these terms mean to the user? Efficiency directly affects the power each user is allocated on the downlink. Other parameters held constant, a more efficient transponder produces stronger downlink signals. Dynamic range affects the ability of weak signals to get through when high power users are in the passband. The time delay between a signal entering and leaving a transponder is real and measurable. However, it's so small compared to the travel time for the uplink and the downlink signals that it can be ignored in communications applications. Of course, if you're doing ranging experiments it has to be considered. Linearity and phase delay effect the distortion that signals acquire as they pass through the transponder.

Unfortunately improving one characteristic often degrades another. For example, a transponder can be made more efficient if we're willing to accept a little distortion at a level that would be unobservable to most SSB stations. However, the same distortion could have a severe impact on the modulation of digital signals. To date, transponders have been optimized for CW and SSB operation, with efficiency and dynamic range given priority. As a result, while the ideal linear transponder can be used to support real-time digital communications, most of today's transponders are poor performers in this regard. This situation may change. In the future, some linear transponders may be optimized to support real-time digital communications.

Hardwired vs Matrix

Early linear transponders were hardwired with a fixed input (uplink) frequency range and a fixed output (downlink) frequency range. Some time later amateurs began to experiment with using two frequency ranges on one of the links. For example, a transponder could be designed with a single uplink (2 meter) and two downlinks (10 meter and 70 cm). Such a transponder would be immediately accessible to casual users already set up for the 2-meter/10-meter mode used on many earlier satellites and would serve the needs of serious users willing to equip for the more reliable 70-cm uplink. Most satellites carry at least two transponders in case one fails and to provide options with respect to frequency usage. With each transponder having multiple links the number of receivers and transmitters on each spacecraft was growing.

Evaluating the situation, the P3D design team decided to abandon the hardwired transponder concept and build separate transmitters and receivers for several bands. By agreeing to a standard interface (frequency and signal levels) all units could be interconnected through an IF matrix so that a wide variety of uplink and downlink frequency combinations could be selected. This approach also facilitates decentralized engineering enabling small groups of radio amateurs around the world to participate in the P3D project by constructing specific RF units. Although the matrix concept has proven very effective for P3D, in the future, small spacecraft may find it more efficient to continue the individual transponder approach.

LEILA

The builders of OSCAR 40 were worried that the ease of use and the capabilities of this spacecraft would attract a great many new satellite users with no experience using a shared resource. The possibility of chaos resulting is real. So they evaluated potential preventive measures. Old suggestions revolving around the idea of dividing the passband into discrete segments, each with its own AGC, were considered but the team decided on a new approach—LEILA (LEIstungsLimit Anzeige). LEILA is essentially a sophisticated spectrum analyzer under computer control. It continually monitors the transponder IF section looking for signals using more than their fair share of the downlink power. When such a signal is observed a gentle CW reminder is transmitted on frequency requesting the station to decrease power. If this isn't successful, a selective notch filter can be employed.

Inverting/Noninverting

When a transponder is designed the builder has to decide whether to make it noninverting (the entire slice is transmitted as received; see Figure 4.1A) or inverting (the slice is flipped in frequency before it's retransmitted; see Figure 4.1B). With a noninverting transponder a signal with a frequency near the high end of the uplink passband comes back down near the *high* frequency end of the downlink. With an inverting transponder a signal with a frequency near the high end of the uplink passband comes back down near the *low* frequency end of the downlink. Although frequency inversion may appear to be an unnecessary complication, it has an important function—it reduces the magnitude of observed Doppler shifts. (We'll be discussing Doppler effects shortly.) Noninverting transponders are used mainly for Mode A (2 meter/10 meter) since the Doppler shift on this mode is small. Other modes generally use inverting transponders.

With a noninverting transponder an upper sideband signal on the uplink is returned as an upper sideband signal on the downlink. With an inverting transponder a lower sideband uplink returns as an upper sideband downlink. The usual practice is to select the uplink sideband so that the downlink will be upper sideband.

Determining Downlink Frequency

It helps to understand exactly how uplink and downlink frequencies are related when you're searching for your downlink, or trying to determine what frequency to set your

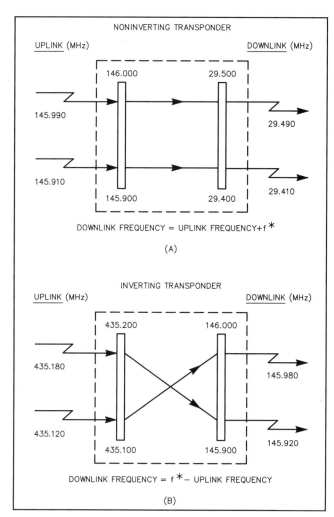

Figure 4.1—A noninverting transponder is shown in A. An inverting transponder is shown in B. Values of F* for each transponder currently in orbit are included in Appendix C.

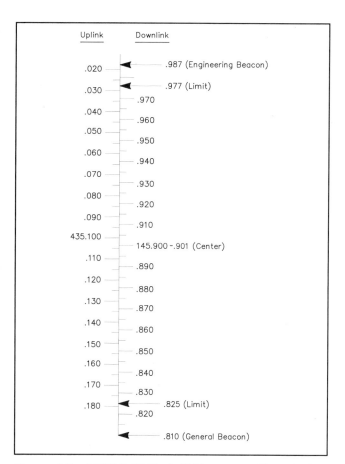

Figure 4.2—OSCAR 10 Mode B Frequency Translation Chart

transmitter to in order to respond to a CQ. The mathematical relation depends on whether the transponder is inverting or non-inverting. A simple formula (called the translation equation) can be written that predicts the approximate downlink frequency, f_{down}, corresponding to a particular uplink frequency, f_{up}, for each type of transponder.

For an inverting transponder (For example: Modes B, J, L)

$$f_{down} = f^* - f_{up} \qquad \text{(Eq 4.1)}$$

For a non inverting transponder (For example: Mode A)

$$f_{down} = f^* + f_{up} \qquad \text{(Eq 4.2)}$$

The constant, f*, associated with each hardwired transponder is listed in the *Spacecraft Profiles* Appendix. Many amateurs find it easier to use Eqs 4.1 and 4.2 to construct frequency translation charts (like the one shown in Figure 4.2) for each transponder they work with than to use the equations themselves while operating.

Eqs 4.1 and 4.2 can easily be rearranged to solve for the uplink frequency or presented in other formats. For example, the following statements accurately describe the

situation: the sum of the uplink and downlink frequencies is constant for an inverting transponder, the difference between uplink and downlink frequencies is constant for a noninverting transponder. Since the translation constant may be defined differently when using different equations it's important to make sure the constant being used is appropriate to the format.

The downlink frequencies predicted by Eqs 4.1 and 4.2 were referred to as approximate because they don't take Doppler shift into account. The maximum Doppler shifts observed on transponders aboard amateur satellites are approximately, ± 4 kHz on Mode A (2 meter/70 cm), ± 7 kHz on Mode B (70 cm/2 meter), ± 7 kHz on Mode J (2 meter/ 70 cm) and ± 22 kHz on Mode L (23 cm/70 cm). For spacecraft in circular low Earth orbits the maximums only occur on orbits where the spacecraft passes nearly overhead. For satellites in highly elliptical orbits (Phase 3) the maximums occur near perigee.

Many computer tracking programs will compute total Doppler shift through a transponder for you. In order to use this feature you have to specify either (1) link frequencies (passband center frequencies are fine) and whether the transponder is inverting or noninverting or (2) a single frequency that should be the difference between uplink and downlink for an inverting transponder or the sum of the uplink and downlink for noninverting transponders. Procedures for dealing with Doppler shift are discussed elsewhere in this chapter. The physics of Doppler shift is discussed in Chapter 8, Satellite Radio Links.

One can construct a variation of the frequency translation chart that takes Doppler shift into account. The design shown in Figure 4.3 is for LEO orbits only. When the inner circle, which can rotate, is set at the appropriate point—start of pass, middle of pass, or end of pass—the chart will provide a very good estimate of the downlink frequency corresponding to a particular uplink.

If you use Eqs 4.1 and 4.2 (or one of the equivalent charts) while operating, you'll be able to quickly locate your downlink since you'll only have to search a few kHz.

USER OPERATION

Ground Station Power Levels

Whenever you began a satellite operating session and periodically in the course of each session, you should check your downlink signal level. Although procedures may vary from satellite to satellite there are a couple of general guidelines for setting power levels. The first is to keep your level below the strength of the satellite beacon that marks the edge of most transponders. The second is not to exceed the general level of other signals on the downlink. The third is to keep within the recommended radiated power guidelines suggested by the satellite builders. Finally, if your signal appears to be depressing the background noise level or interacting with nearby signals, you're way over the limit! On HF being told you have the strongest signal on the band is a complement; with satellite operation it *should*

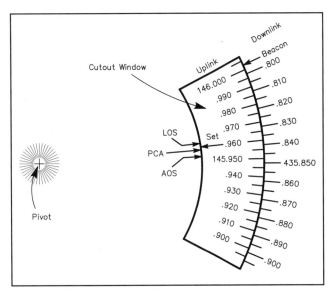

Figure 4.3—Frequency Translation Operating Aid: Fuji-OSCAR 29 Mode J. For overhead pass set overlay to AOS at start of pass, PCA near midpoint, and LOS near end of pass. For grazing pass set overlay midway between AOS and PCA at start of pass, PCA near midpoint, and midway between LOS and PCA near end of pass. (PCA=Point of Closest Approach)

be an extreme embarrassment.

If you hear stations whose downlink is louder than the beacon mention the fact politely. A responsible operator will appreciate the information. If all downlinks, including your own, sound weak you're going to be tempted to turn up the power. However, the problem is more likely to be with your receiving system. When setting up a ground station concentrate your efforts on developing first class receiving capabilities.

Band Plans

Amateurs have voluntarily adopted guidelines regarding the use of different types of modulation on amateur satellites. SSB and CW are preferred because of their efficient use of transponder power and bandwidth. More than a quarter of a century ago satellite users realized that the adoption of a band plan specifying where various modes should congregate could help reduce unnecessary QRM. The plan selected is shown in Figure 4.4. Note that only the downlink is considered; the band plan is independent of whether the transponder is inverting or noninverting and it applies to transponders of any width. Keep in mind that the band plan is only a suggestion; if a crystal controlled CW Field Day station is stuck at the lower end of the passband an SSB response can easily be rationalized.

Finding Your Downlink

Never transmit on a transponder uplink frequency unless you're able to monitor the downlink. Be sure to check your downlink frequency before calling CQ. When calling CQ or when responding to another station don't sent "dits" or croon "heelloo" up and down the band searching for your downlink. You'll almost always have to do some hunting to find your signal but, if you use Eqs 4.1 or 4.2, or a frequency translation chart, the hunt should be very short and only involve a small part of the passband.

The following procedure is recommended for locating your downlink. It's been selected to minimize QRM. Set your receiver to the desired frequency and leave it there. Set your transmitter dial to the computed uplink frequency. Adjust the transmitter frequency while sending some slow CW dits until you hear yourself.

Although any procedure that brings to mind VFOs swishing across a band may cause considerate operators to cringe, the suggested approach really does minimize the effects of interference. Consider: If you use the proposed technique anyone experiencing QRM shouldn't be exposed to more than a few dits. The alternative, transmitting on a fixed frequency and hunting with the receiver, often produces extremely disruptive QRM to a QSO in progress. Remember, good dial calibration, a little experience and a frequency translation chart will minimize the all too familiar clatter of background dits.

Operating: General

Operating with a transponder is much like operating on the HF bands with the added fact that you'll be monitoring your downlink. Because DX windows for LEO satellites

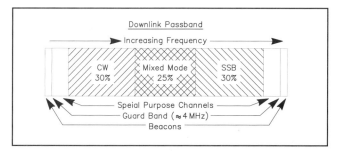

Figure 4.4—Linear Transponder Band Plan: General downlink band plan for OSCAR satellites. The special service channels (SSCs) are meant to be used in a coordinated manner for special activities such as bulletins by national societies, code practice, emergency communications and computer networking. Channels are designated H1, H2,...(high end), L1, L2, ...(low end);with H1 and L1 being closest to the beacons.

are very brief, you'll note a lot of contest-style short exchanges taking place in the passband. Nevertheless, ragchewing is also common: The choice is yours. On Phase 3 satellites you'll find that breaking into a QSO to collect a new DX preface is considered rude. Follow the lead of the DX station. If they want to chat allow them to do so. Most will periodically run a string of contest like QSOs to accommodate those who wish to log the contact. Satellite operation has a well deserved reputation for being a lot less of a rat race than HF. Let's try and keep it that way.

Modulation Restrictions

Recall that guidelines concerning how the transponders on amateur satellites are used are expected to evolve through consensus. As a result, it's only natural that they change from time to time for various reasons. For example, in the early days of satellite operation the use of slow scan TV was discouraged. (This does not refer to special experiments as discussed below.) The reason was that SSTV has a high duty cycle. As a result, the average power used by an SSTV signal is about five times that of an SSB signal with the same PEP. However, when amateurs began to realize that most SSTV operation tends to occur in a round table format involving many listeners and one transmitting station, attitudes changed. From a technical viewpoint one can say that the proper way of evaluating whether the fair share principal is being violated is to divide the power being used to transmit the SSTV signal by the total number participating in the roundtable. By this criteria, SSTV appears quite acceptable. In any event, in the late 1980s, following a series of educational programs on AO-13 that involved SSTV, the old policy changed and it appears that SSTV will continue to be acceptable.

FM voice operation has also been strongly discouraged because it uses excessive power and bandwidth. However, this policy too may have to be reconsidered in special situations. It has been suggested that allocating a small amount of time on P3D to FM communications might be desirable

since such a move would enable a large number of radio amateurs who have never tried satellite communications to gain some experience in the area. This should contribute to a healthy growth of the amateur satellite community. The constraints on what we put through a linear transponder depend more on the goals of the radio amateur satellite community than on technical limitations of transponder technology.

SSB users should avoid speech processing. If all users were to adopt speech processing the average power per user would remain the same while the intelligibility of each signal would decrease. Even if speech processing temporarily increases your share of the available power the results might not be what you expect. SSB experiments on 432-MHz EME have convinced most operators that any type of speech processing reduces signal intelligibility. When working with weak signal modes a clean SSB signal yields the best results.

Finally, restrictions and guidelines refer to general operations. AMSAT has always encouraged the use of satellite resources for serious experimentation as long as due regard is given to concerns of the user community. This basically means that experiments should be discussed in advance with AMSAT officers or technical personnel and with the user community so that potential problems, real or imagined, can be avoided.

Mode Naming

This section focuses on the names given to various transponders. I considered calling it "the name game" or "how did we get into this mess?" but better judgment prevailed.

In the beginning there was OSCAR III. The transponder on OSCAR III (2 meter/2 meter) didn't have a name. The fact that both links were in the same band gave OSCAR III the hardware equivalent of a migraine. As a result, amateurs have never again used a single band linear transponder. The transponder on OSCAR IV (2 meter/70 cm) was called "the OSCAR IV transponder."

With OSCAR 6 the advocates of alphabetical order took control and we had Mode A (2 meter/10 meter). Their rule continued through OSCAR 7 that brought us Mode B (70 cm/2 meter) but their power was waning and users in Germany and other regions of Europe were often heard referring to this unit as the Mode U transponder (U for its UHF uplink).

A group from Japan built a transponder for OSCAR 8 that reversed the frequencies of Mode B. Since it was rather awkward to refer to "the mode formerly used on OSCAR IV" and since attempts to officially name the unit the Mode B inverse or Mode B transpose transponder were totally ignored, it acquired the name Mode J (2 meter/ 70 cm), which reflected its origin, by default.

When a Russian group arranged to have Iskra 2 and 3 dropped out of the *Mir* space station they introduced the first transponder using HF links up and down. It was called Mode K (15 meter/10 meter) for reasons of which I am totally unaware.

Meanwhile a new frequency combination was being prepared for flight on OSCAR 10. In an attempt to reintroduce rationality into the transponder naming process the group resurrected the band designators adopted half a century ago when radar was being developed. The new transponder was called Mode L (23 cm/70 cm) with the L referring to the 23-cm uplink. Historians looking back at this period now know that the radar developers botched the name game too—major reference texts listing names for different bands are in conflict.

Wait, the story gets more interesting. FO-12 was launched with two transponders, one digital and one analog. Both used the Mode J frequency combination. When it was necessary to distinguish between the two transponders they were referred to as Mode JA (for J Analog) and Mode JD (for J Digital).

Next, the Russians, with the launch of RS-10/11, introduced transponders using multiple frequency bands on links. This gave us Mode KT (15 meter/10 meter and 2 meter), and Mode KA (15 meter and 2 meter/10 meter). Another new mode, Mode T (15 meter/2 meter) also appeared.

While the Russians were exploiting HF links the AMSAT Phase 3 team was pushing the envelope in the other direction. They introduced Mode S (another old radar band designation that this time, for some unknown reason, refers to the downlink frequency). Mode S was initially defined as (23 cm/13 cm) but the Mode S flight unit on OSCAR 13 used 70 cm/13 cm.

Those who have worked with radio amateur satellites over the last quarter of a century understand the logic leading to the current confused situation and have had plenty of time to become familiar with the transponder names currently in use. However, it's easy to understand why newcomers view the name situation as chaotic. With the launch of OSCAR 40 an attempt is being made to switch to a consistent naming procedure but only time will tell whether or not users actually adopt the new names. In any event, there's likely to be a long transition period with both old and new names in use. The old naming process is summarized in Table 4.1. The new naming process is summarized in Table 4.2.

DOPPLER COMPENSATION

Radio amateurs have been aware of Doppler shift ever since they listened to the Sputnik I 20 MHz beacon drifting down in frequency. Early on in the Radio Amateur Space Program there was some concern that Doppler shift might make SSB communications via satellite difficult but these worries proved groundless. Experiences with OSCARs III and IV made it clear that amateurs could easily accommodate to Doppler at frequencies as high as 435 MHz on rapidly moving LEO satellites. Doppler shift magnitude is proportional to frequency and relative spacecraft/ground station velocity—see Chapter 8 for details.

When OSCAR 6 was launched users realized that the frequency changes that they made to accommodate to Dop-

Table 4.1
Old Transponder Mode Designations

Mode	Uplink	Downlink	Satellites
A	145 MHz	29 MHz	AO-6, AO-7, AO-8, RS-1, RS-2, RS-5, RS-6, RS-7, RS-8, RS-10/11, RS-12/13, RS-15
B	435 MHz	145 MHz	P3A, AO-10, AO-13, RS-14/AO-21, AO-24
J	145 MHz	435 MHz	OSCAR 4, FO-12, FO-20, FO-29, AO-27
JA [1]	145 MHz	435 MHz	See Mode J
JD [2]	145 MHz	435 MHz	FO-12, FO-20, FO-29, UO-14, UO-22, KO-23, K25, AO-16, LO-19, IO-26
JL	1.2 GHz	435 & 145 MHz	AO-13
K	21 MHz	29 MHz	Iskra-2, Iskra-3, RS-10/11, RS-12/13
KA	21 MHz	29 & 145 MHz	RS-10/11, RS-12/13
KT	21 MHz	29 & 145 MHz	RS-10/11, RS-12/13
L	1.2 GHz	435 MHz	AO-10, AO-13
S [3]	435 MHz	2.4 GHz	AO-13, AO-24
T	21 MHz	145 MHz	RS-10/11, RS-12/13
U			([4] see Mode B)

[1] JA is short for J (A)nalog. Same as Mode J.
[2] JD is short for J (D)igital. Same input/output frequency bands as Mode J.
[3] Mode S was initially defined as 1.2 GHz / 2.4 GHz but this frequency combination has never been flown.
[4] This is an alternate name sometimes used for Mode B. U is for UHF.

Table 4.2
New Transponder Mode Designations

When naming a transponder the input (uplink) is always specified first. A slash "/" is used to separate input and output.

Input (Uplink) frequency, wavelength, or designator / Output (Downlink) frequency, wavelength or designator.

Link Designators

(Frequency)	(Wavelength)	(Designator)
21 MHz	15 m	H
29 MHz	10 m	T
145 MHz	2 m	V
435 MHz	70 cm	U
1.2 GHz [1]	24 cm	L
2.4 GHz	13 cm	S
5.7 GHz	6 cm	C
10.5 GHz	3 cm	X
24.0 GHz	1.2 cm	K

Transponder Names

Old name	New name
Mode A	V/T
Mode B	U/V
Mode J	V/U
K	H/T
KA	H,V/T
KT	H/T,V
L [1]	L/U
S	U/S
T	H/V

[1]International regulations stipulate that this band be used only as an uplink.

---

pler while a QSO was in progress caused their signals to creep across the transponder passband. This wasn't a problem for a single QSO but it appeared to be a potential problem if multiple QSOs were taking place. If individuals used different procedures to correct for Doppler they would creep at different rates, perhaps even in different directions and the probability of QRM due to collisions would be high. It appeared that if users would agree to use similar procedures to correct for Doppler all would tend to creep in the same direction and QRM would be minimized.

A number of technically inclined amateurs looked into the problem. Describing the Doppler situation for a beacon is relatively simple, there are two frequencies involved—the downlink frequency as measured by an imaginary observer on the satellite and the observed signal received at a ground station. The transponder problem is much more complex. With just two ground stations involved one has to keep track of 10 frequencies! Consider, each ground station is concerned with an uplink and two downlink frequencies and, at the satellite, there are two uplinks and two downlinks. If three amateurs are involved in a QSO the number of link frequencies involved jumps to 18.

The technical workers concluded that there was no simple procedure that would completely prevent collisions.

However, QRM could be minimized if users tended to creep in the same direction at similar rates and there was a relatively easy way to accomplish this. A guideline was issued that stated—*to minimize QRM amateurs using a transponder should make adjustments to the higher frequency link and attempt to keep the lower frequency link constant.*

The guideline was issued in about 1975. Since all transponders in orbit at this time (Mode A and Mode B on OSCARs 6 and 7) used the lower frequency for the downlink many (including this author) fell into the trap of saying keep the receive frequency fixed since this appeared to be easier to remember.

Everything went along fine for several years. Very few users pointed out that the guideline, when given careful thought, was really awkward and somewhat ambiguous. If both stations in a QSO kept their own downlinks constant, a QSO that began with both stations appearing on the same frequency ended up with a significant frequency spread. And, no mention was made as to when one should reset the transmitter frequency. The reasons things went so well are probably only marginally related to the technical merits of the guideline. QRM was minimal because the transponders weren't very crowded and duplex operation generally enabled users to find empty chunks of spectrum. Amateurs unaware of the guideline unconsciously tended to adhere to it, since adjusting the transmitter frequency at the beginning of each transmission so that the received signal would sound correct appeared to be the natural thing to do.

OSCAR 8 carried a Mode J transponder into orbit. Because the frequencies used were the same as on Mode B, Doppler shift wasn't expected to be a problem. However, as the user base for this transponder grew it became apparent that a problem did exist. Mode J operators fell into three groups. One group was using the proper procedure for Doppler compensation. By keeping the low link frequency constant their creep was minimal. The second group, misinterpreting the guideline, was attempting to keep the received frequency constant—the procedure that produced good results on Modes A and B. They tended to creep across large portions of the passband. A third group, totally unaware of any guideline, took the natural approach of adjusting the transmitter at the start of each pass. With Mode J this was the wrong choice. The situation was never totally resolved. However, QSOs (and complaints) continued.

Despite its ambiguities and shortcomings the recommended procedure for Doppler shift compensation when using a transponder that has been in effect for the past quarter century is a good one—*Keep the lower frequency fixed.*

However, times and guidelines change. When this guideline was introduced in the mid 1970s, personal computers like the Apple I were just making their appearance. Today's world is very different. Now, most amateurs involved in satellite communication have computers in the shack, powerful tracking software capable of calculating Doppler shifts is available and the frequency of modern amateur transmitters and receivers can be remotely controlled by computer.

This makes it possible to use full Doppler compensation

Table 4.3

Suggested Guidelines for Handling Doppler on all Transponders
(FDC = Full Doppler Compensation)

1. CASE I:
All stations in QSO have FDC.
Guideline: Use it!

2. CASE II:
One or more stations in QSO have FDC.
Guideline: All stations having FDC should use Doppler Compensation on *transmit* frequency. All others should adjust up *and* downlinks to accommodate to FDC station(s).

3. CASE III:
No station in QSO has FDC. (See Notes 1 and 2)
Guideline 1: Each station in QSO should make adjustments that keep his/her lower link frequency as constant as possible.
Guideline 2: (optional): Applies to LEO spacecraft only. This guideline produces slightly less creep than Guideline 1. In a QSO involving two or more stations select a reference station according to following principal: reference station should remain furthest from the SSP during the entire pass. The reference station should follow Guideline 1. All other stations should adjust up and downlinks to accommodate to reference station.

Note 1: (Re: CASE III) When implementing guideline, frequency adjustments should be made as follows:
While other station is transmitting only adjust RIT. At end of other station's transmission turn off RIT. Begin transmitting. Adjust higher frequency link for clear reception. Transmitting station should not make any further transmit frequency adjustments.
Note 2: (Re: CASE III) If you don't follow procedures precisely, or if you make an error, don't worry. A small shift in QSO location in satellite passband is of little concern.

(FDC) when using a linear transponder. With FDC the ground station adjusts transmitter *and* receiver frequencies so that uplink and downlink frequencies seen at the satellite are constant. This keeps each user at a fixed location in the transponder passband and places all stations involved in a QSO at the same fixed frequency in the passband. In 1996 a number of stations, using various pieces of equipment and software, verified the effectiveness of this procedure. Horizon to horizon SSB QSOs via LEO spacecraft were accomplished without touching transmitter or receiver dial. FDC, which was not even conceived as being possible in the mid 1970s, is clearly the direction of the future.

Our job now is to lay out interim plans that will provide a smooth transition period. The plans should minimize QRM, be easy to adhere to and make it possible for stations using FDC and those without it to coexist comfortably. Suggested guidelines are presented in Table 4.3.

Stepping back for a moment, it's interesting to note that the successful demonstrations of FDC may have a profound effect on amateur satellite activities going far beyond just simplifying procedures for Doppler compensation. In the past, LEO spacecraft have been restricted to using relatively low frequencies because it was felt that SSB operation would become difficult above the 435 MHz band. The frequencies available are extremely congested and, in many parts of the world, unusable. FDC will make it possible to employ higher frequency links on LEO spacecraft. This will simplify spacecraft antennas and provide users with more reliable links having wide bandwidths. It will also make it possible to employ the same link frequency combinations on high altitude *and* LEO satellites. As a result, in the future, a ground station selecting one pair of popular frequencies may have access to excellent transponders on both types of spacecraft.

USING A ROBOT

Several RS satellites have carried simple autotransponders, known as ROBOTs, which enable radio amateurs to "contact" the satellite using CW. If you call the spacecraft using the correct protocol, an onboard computer will (1) acknowledge your call, (2) assign you a serial contact number and (3) store your call letters and contact number for later downlinking to a command station. QSLs for these contacts are available from Box 88, Moscow.

The ROBOT receive window is only 2 or 3 kHz wide centered on the announced frequency (See *Satellite Profiles* Appendix). Be sure to take Doppler shift into account by transmitting a few kHz low when the spacecraft is approaching you and a few kHz high when it's receding. Many tracking programs will compute the correct offset frequency for you. The reference frequency you plug into your computer is the ROBOT receive frequency. This may have to be changed, even if you're using a transponder on the same band, since the Doppler reference frequency for the transponder is the sum of the difference of the two link frequencies. Any adjustments needed to the downlink frequency are most easily handled by tuning the receiver.

When the ROBOT is active (when it calls CQ) send a

few dits on the uplink frequency (*only* a few!). If you hear your dits regenerated on the downlink you're in the capture window. Call the satellite (clean CW at 10 to 30 wpm) as follows:

RS10 DE KA1GD *AR*

If you're successful Radio 10 will respond

KA1GD DE RS10 QSO NR 123 OP ROBOT TU FR QSO 73 *SK*

The 3-digit QSO number is incremented after each contact.

When it's switched on, the ROBOT will call CQ about once per minute. Please do *not* hold your key down on the ROBOT input frequency as this will simply cause the downlink to generate a continuous tone. If only a partial message is received by the ROBOT you may hear a response of QRZ, QRM, or RPT. In this case just try again. If the ROBOT wants you to send faster or slower it will respond QRQ or QRS. Clean, high-speed CW usually works best, probably because interference is less likely to be a problem. A memory dump of RS7 recorded the first 10 autotransponder QSOs for posterity:

00 UK3ACM	05 G3IOR
01 UV3FL	06 G4HUV
02 RS3A	07 G3IOR
03 UA3XBU	08 UK1BI
04 UI8BF	09 KA1GD

USING A PARROT

A PARROT transponder consists of an FM receiver, an FM transmitter and a digital recorder. It records all activity on a given frequency for a specified period of time, say 60 seconds and then plays back the recording in the next 60 second interval. This cycle is then repeated. The transponder may periodically interrupt to identify and provide directions. At present, the only PARROT existing is on SUNSAT-OSCAR 35, launched February 23, 1999.

To have your signal played back on a PARROT you have to transmit on the correct frequency at the correct time and hope that your signal isn't being buried under that of others trying to do the same thing. It should be easy to observe the timing cycle and synchronize your clock. Choosing the transmit frequency involves a bit more effort since Doppler shift is important. In general, you will not set your transmit frequency to the exact received frequency. You have to know the PARROT frequency as measured at the satellite. Although you should be able to obtain this from published information it's best just to observe a pass and make a note of the PARROT frequency when the satellite is at closest approach. Once you know this frequency

you check the downlink frequency and compute the offset frequency at the time of the measurement. For example, let's assume that the satellite is approaching you, the PARROT frequency is 145.830 MHz and the observed frequency is 145.835 MHz. The offset is 5 kHz. Set your transmitter to 145.825 MHz (5 kHz below the PARROT frequency). The satellite, which is approaching you will see your signal Doppler-shifted up to 145.830 MHz and record it. When it's played back on 145.830 MHz you'll see it Doppler-shifted up to 145.835 MHz.

Anyone with a background in academic psychology will realize that a PARROT makes a beautiful experiment in competition vs. cooperation. With many users competing to put a signal into the PARROT (and no simultaneous downlink to let you hear what's happening) the question of what strategy to use becomes very important. If all users make very short transmissions at randomly selected times the maximum number will succeed. If one particular station decides to "cheat" and give several calls that station's probability of success may go up. However, if several stations decide to "cheat" the total number of successes will decrease.

USING AN FM REPEATER

Using a satellite borne FM repeater is basically similar to using one on a local tower. However, one does have to take into account several unique characteristics related to the space platform. Non-geostationary repeaters will only be in range for limited periods of time and the links will exhibit Doppler shifts. This means that tracking is necessary and that measures must be taken to accommodate to Doppler. And, even for a very low platform like UO-14, the coverage area is much larger than for terrestrial repeaters. At present, there are two FM repeaters in space, the crossband (2 m/70 cm) units aboard UO-14 and AO-27. Frequencies for both are given in the *Spacecraft Profiles* Appendix. Doppler is a factor with both.

Some users accommodate Doppler by simply setting the scan function of their receiver to begin high and scan down during a pass. Use 1 kHz steps if possible, 5 kHz is marginally acceptable. Start 10 kHz high on 435 MHz, 5 kHz high on 146 MHz. Transmitter settings are just the opposite. Set the transmitter low at the start of the pass and creep upward during the pass. Specific transmitting frequency offsets can usually be obtained from most tracking programs. It's also possible to compute values using the information provided in Chapter 8. Another alternative is to note receiver offsets during a few passes and use these values (reversing direction) on the uplink during future passes.

Since the number of potential users on these repeaters is very high, it's very important that all transmissions be kept extremely short.

Chapter 5

Satellite Digital Communications

BACKGROUND

THE PACSAT CONCEPT

TODAY'S OPTIONS

GROUND STATIONS FOR LEO

Ground Station Software
TNC and Modem
RF Frequencies
9600 baud FSK system

RUDAK-U

FIGURES

TABLE

5 Satellite Digital Communications

BACKGROUND

Amateur satellite digital store-and-forward communication began in 1972 with the operation of the Codestore unit on OSCAR 6. Using Codestore, command stations uploaded brief messages on the command channel, which were then broadcast on the beacon. Since the messages were in Morse CW, a modem wasn't required for reception. Codestore did have some major limitations including data rate (about $1/2$ baud) and memory capacity (about 256 characters). Although Codestore was viewed as an experiment it actually proved very useful. Those monitoring the beacon frequently heard command stations in Canada and Australia using it to exchange messages. And a great many amateurs around the world found that Codestore was their most reliable source for information when the launch of OSCAR 7 was imminent.

In the late 1970s and early 1980s, as terrestrial packet radio developed, several amateurs experimented with satellite digital communications. The early tests involved transmitting digital signals through existing satellite linear transponders. Tests were run at 300 and 1200 baud using terrestrial HF and VHF modulation techniques. Although communication links were successfully established, the experiments showed that it was clearly desirable to use digital transponders and adopt modulation schemes more appropriate to the characteristics of the space links—ones that made more efficient use of power and bandwidth and that would provide better performance on a noisy link with Doppler shift and low signal/noise ratios.

A major milestone occurred in 1983 when two key papers were presented at the ARRL Amateur Radio Computer Networking Convention in San Francisco—*Modulation Techniques for PACSAT* by P. Karn, KA9Q and *The PACSAT Project* by D. Connors, KD2S. These papers provided a preview of what was going to occur over the next decade.

The following year, 1984, saw the launch of UoSAT-OSCAR 11 with its limited access DCE (Digital Communications Experiment), a digital transponder operating at 1200 baud.

A digital transponder differs from a linear transponder in that it receives, detects and reconstructs a clean signal that is transmitted on the downlink. As a result, any distortion acquired on the uplink, or during passage through a linear transponder is eliminated. The digital transponder also makes it possible to store messages on the satellite for transmission at a later time.

The group designing UO-11 wanted to use it as a test bed for system software development and to validate the operational feasibility of the store-and-forward concept. Producing a satellite, ground station hardware and the software that would make it work together in a short time frame was an immense task. Although the UoSAT team was aware of the advantages of using PSK for the links, doing so would require additional work. So they decided to use existing modem technology. The first option considered, FM-AFSK using terrestrial Amateur Radio equipment, just wouldn't hack it. The next choice, FM-AFSK using the Bell 202 standard, which employed modems commonly used for communication in the mainframe computer world, appeared suitable. Radio amateurs interested in receiving signals from UO-11 would need a 2-meter FM receiver, a Bell 202 type modem attached to the receiver's audio output terminals and a PC with communications software. It's very difficult to accurately estimate the hours needed to produce software to accomplish a particular task, and this project was no exception. The software flying on the spacecraft and the software on the ground were in effect all subprograms of a master system program. During the first several years of the mission new software was continually being uploaded to the spacecraft and tested.

The DCE system worked well,[1] but, the 1200 baud FM-AFSK signal required about 15 kHz and it was very susceptible to impulse noise. By using more efficient modulation schemes amateurs knew they could cut the bandwidth to 3 kHz for the same speed, or increase speed by a factor of eight using the same bandwidth, while simultaneously improving noise immunity and low signal performance. Both of these approaches were later implemented with the introduction of the 1200 baud MicroSats and the 9600 baud UoSAT series of spacecraft.

With UO-11, the number of authorized uplink stations had to be limited to a small number of gateways. The first open access PACSAT available to radio amateurs was Fuji-OSCAR 12, launched in 1986. It also operated at 1200 baud, but, it employed a Manchester-encoded FSK uplink and a PSK downlink. For brevity the satellite modem is generally referred to as a 1200 baud PSK unit to distinguish it from terrestrial 1200 baud FSK modems. Neither the 1200 baud modems designed for amateur terrestrial communications, nor the Bell 202 units used with UO-11, would work with this link. Modems and spacecraft were designed in parallel. The most widely used modem was a unit designed by G3RUH. Built entirely from written specifications for the satellite system, the modem performed exactly as planned and proved to be a key element in the success of FO-12.[2] Another widely used modem based on a design provided by the group who built FO-12[3] was made available by TAPR in kit form (TAPR/JAMSAT PSK modem).[4]

To set up a ground station for FO-12 one needed a 2-meter FM transmitter, a 70-cm SSB receiver, a TNC (terminal node controller) designed for terrestrial 1200 baud AFSK communications with the internal modem replaced by a G3RUH (or similar) PSK modem and a PC with appropriate software. FO-12 software was designed so that the satellite would operate like a computer bulletin board. This enabled ground stations to use communication software packages and communication techniques that had been developed for terrestrial bulletin boards. Modems were not available off-the-shelf. If you wanted to work with this satellite, you had to build one, from scratch or from a kit. To compound the difficulties encountered by prospective users, FO-12 suffered from being underpowered. As a result it was often shut down with all messages lost. As with any new system, software crashes were frequent. Despite all these difficulties, the Japanese team responsible for operating this spacecraft reported that more than 300 radio amateurs around the world successfully posted messages on FO-12. The members of this exclusive club were truly pioneers.

1990 was a very big year for satellite packet operation. It began with an ESA launch that placed six OSCARs in orbit including the first four MicroSats and two new UoSATs. Weeks later, Fuji-OSCAR 20 was launched to replace the aging FO-12. Four of the satellites had open access digital transponders. Three, AO-16, LO-19 and FO-20 supported the 1200 baud PSK mode used on FO-12. UO-14 carried the first amateur 9600 baud FSK transponder. 1990 also saw the introduction of the first off-the-shelf commercial modem for PACSAT communications by PacComm (PSK-1).

The most important development of 1990 may have been the publishing of the UoSAT/MicroSat File Transfer Protocol Suite at the 9th ARRL Computer Networking Conference.[5,6,7,8,9] This software reflected a major shift in strategy. In the past, satellite software was designed to make the satellite operate like a terrestrial bulletin board. This greatly simplified the software development process and made it relatively simple for ground stations to utilize the spacecraft. It, however, used satellite resources very inefficiently. In the future all software would be designed from scratch to maximally exploit spacecraft resources. At about this time UoSAT released two programs for ground station use, PG and PB, which were needed to transmit to and receive from, the digital transponders on amateur spacecraft. Companion software was installed on UoSAT and

MicroSat spacecraft. PG and PB would work with existing 1200 baud and 9600 baud spacecraft and any new modes introduced in the future. For a good summary of PB, PG and the PACSAT Protocol Suite see the reference at the end of this chapter.[10]

Also about this time, software development passed a critical juncture that went almost unnoticed. Changes made to spacecraft software were introduced in such a way that ground stations, using old software, could download new versions that would enable them to access the new spacecraft features. This enabled software development to take place at a frenetic rate. Key players in the software development process were Jeff Ward, G0/K8KA and Harold Price, NK6K. During the next few years several additional satellites using both 1200 baud PSK and 9600 baud FSK were launched. Off-the-shelf modems became available from a number of sources and software finally began to stabilize. By 1992 satellite digital communications was beginning to make the transition from experimental stage to operational stage. The next major development took place in 1994 when a software package called WiSP was introduced. Written by Chris Jackson, ZL2TPO, this program takes care of many of the details that PB and PG required the user to handle. If you want to downlink a file you essentially instruct WiSP to downlink the file. WiSP will check the directories on all spacecraft that it has been set to monitor, request the file when it has been located, make sure that all relevant packets have been received, reassemble the message, strip off any extraneous information added for the communications process, decompress it if necessary and notify you when it's available. Prior to WiSP amateurs had to use separate programs (PG, PB and various utilities) to perform each of these tasks individually. Much of the earlier software was written, often under severe time pressure, by and for people familiar with programming, UNIX, DOS and communications protocols. As a result, it was not what one would label "user friendly." WiSP changed everything; its appearance will likely be regarded as a major milestone marking the point where satellite digital communications was made accessible to a much larger segment of the amateur community. If this view is correct then the number of radio amateurs using this mode should double or even quadruple over the next five years.

The amateur community has witnessed remarkable progress in satellite digital communications in a very short time period. All the key elements needed to make this mode accessible and popular are now in place—satellites, ground station software, powerful computers and off-the-shelf hardware. This fact was dramatically illustrated in early 1997 when a DXpedition to Heard Island (VK0IR), one of the remotest locations on the Earth, used UO-22, KO-23 and KO-25 to send daily log data back to Belgium where it was entered on the Internet. The procedure enabled more than 20,000 amateurs to confirm their QSOs before the DXpedition even left the island.

Despite all these advances, using the digital modes available on satellites is still a challenge. Before attempting to set up a station, one should have some experience in most of the following areas: VHF and UHF communications systems (transmitters, receivers, antennas), satellite communications systems (tracking, Doppler shift, path losses) and digital communications techniques (using personal computers, packet radio, dial in bulletin boards, Internet FTP).

In many ways, satellite digital communications in 2001 has reached the position that satellite analog communications attained in 1972 when OSCAR 6 was launched. A new age is beginning. In the following sections we'll discuss the specifics of setting up a digital ground station.

THE PACSAT CONCEPT

We begin by looking at the basic idea behind the PACSAT concept. LEO spacecraft have small footprints (coverage areas). The probability that two stations wishing to communicate will be in a satellite's footprint at the same time is generally zero or small. The concept of store-and-forward communications therefore becomes very important. With store-and-forward communication a ground station uploads a message when the satellite is accessible. The message is stored on the satellite. A copy can then be downloaded by one or more recipients anyplace on the Earth when the satellite is accessible to them.

In order to store messages on the satellite, PACSATs use digital transponders instead of linear transponders. The digital transponder processes (detects and stores) all upcoming signals. Depending on the software in control of the satellite, the stored message can be retransmitted from milliseconds to days later to provide real-time or *store-and-forward* communications. LEO satellites emphasize the store-and-forward option. All transmissions involve reconstructed signals so that any distortion acquired on the uplink trip through the ionosphere or passage through the transponder is effectively eliminated.

PACSATs periodically broadcast directory packets that contain a list of the files that are currently being stored. The stored files vary greatly in size. They can be brief text messages (a few thousand bytes), long binary computer programs, or pictures encoded in various formats (hundreds of thousands of bytes). A ground station can send a new file up to the satellite or ask the satellite (the file server) to downlink a specific file. On an overhead pass of a relatively high PACSAT, like KO-23 that communicates at 9600 baud, a first-class ground station can downlink 800,000 bytes. On a typical pass of one of the other 9600 baud PACSATs 400,000 bytes would be more common. At 1200 baud a good pass would provide about 50,000 bytes.

To implement store-and-forward communications and use space-borne resources efficiently, the spacecraft needs lots of brain power and it must be in control of all links. If a ground station wants to upload a file, or have a specific file downloaded, the ground station must first register with the satellite by sending up a brief message. If this request is received, the satellite acknowledges and assigns the ground station to a queue where it awaits its turn to either

downlink or uplink. The satellite then works its way through the queues one station at a time, allotting each station a small time slot to accomplish its communication goals. If a station doesn't complete its task in the assigned time it goes to the bottom of the queue to await its next turn, during which it can attempt to complete the task.

The messages themselves are broken up into small packets that are assigned identification labels. If the satellite or ground station misses part of a message, a fill can be requested. Note that the ground station operator never directly activates the transmitter. Directions are given to the computer, which can request that a specific file be downloaded. From this point on the ground station is under the control of ground station software that is responding to on site conditions and satellite software. The ground station software decides when to transmit the request to enter the downlink queue, so as best to avoid colliding with other requests. The ground station software recognizes if the initial request is unsuccessful, it then decides when to try again. The ground station software captures the packets containing the message. This process may take several rotations through the queue and additional messages may have to be uplinked to the satellite to request fills for holes (packets that have been missed). Finally, the computer strips off all the packaging material (headers, packet identification labels, etc) and reconstructs the packets in the correct order to produce the desired file. During all these transmission and reception periods, which may only require a minute or two, the operator at the ground station is just an observer watching these steps take place on the computer screen.

For many years ground stations used two separate software packages to perform these functions—*PB* to download broadcast files and directories and *PG* to upload files. The actual file names are PB.EXE and PG.EXE. The extension EXE denotes an executable machine language file. The user just types *PB* or *PG* when calling these files from DOS. Today, most users have replaced *PB*, *PG* and a number of utilities that work in conjunction with them, with *WiSP*, which is far more convenient to use.

It should be clear from this brief overview that the software on the satellite is complex and that ground station software and satellite software are intimately connected. The software in use on the spacecraft was developed over several years of intensive effort. *WiSP*, used at the ground, involves more than 28,000 lines of code written in the C language; a complete listing would be longer than this book.

OSCAR 40 is a high altitude satellite that is in view of a large part of the Earth at most times and accessible to users many hours per day. As a result, the communications strategy used by the RUDAK system (digital transponder) on OSCAR 40 differs somewhat from that used by the LEO PACSATs. The probability that two stations who wish to communicate will be in the footprint at the same time is considerably increased. This permits real-time communications that eliminates a lot of the computational overhead involved in storing messages on the spacecraft. With a low altitude spacecraft, competition between potential users during brief passes is a big concern. With a high altitude satellite, the number of potential users in the footprint is higher but this is overshadowed by the long access periods that allow users to spread out in time. As a result, competition is likely to be less of a problem. Rather than increasing the amount of onboard memory at a rapid rate it may be more effective to set up a number of special data bank ground stations for mass storage. If someone needs a particular file that's not in spacecraft memory, the spacecraft can automatically connect the requestor to one of the data bank stations.

TODAY'S OPTIONS

A couple of years ago a well known amateur in QSO on OSCAR 13 was heard to say—"I'd like to set up to operate on the satellite digital modes but I've got two problems—hardware and software." Thanks to recent developments, most of the problems have disappeared or at least been drastically reduced in size. No matter what mode you opt for, the software program *WiSP* makes satellite operating much easier today than it was a few years ago. Commercial multimode Terminal Node Controllers with built-in modems (often DSP units) are currently available at reasonable cost. Today's VHF and UHF transceivers are being built with user needs in mind. In this section we'll look at each of the satellite digital systems available today and discuss the hardware and software required to use them.

A 1996 survey by Ray Soifer, W2RS,[11] showed that about 25% of those using satellites were equipped for the digital modes. Of these, about 18% were on 9600 baud FSK and 7% on 1200 baud PSK. If, on average, those operating 1200 baud and those operating 9600 baud devoted the same amount of time to communicating, the throughput on 9600 baud would have been about 20 times that of 1200 baud. The conclusion is based on a factor of 8 due to speed

and 2.6 due to number of operators. Several low altitude satellites are currently in orbit supporting each of these modes. The RUDAK payload on OSCAR 40 contains hardwired modems for 9600 baud FSK and DSP modems that can be configured to handle other modulation schemes at very high speeds. OSCAR 40 RUDAK scheduling reflects the fact that many more amateurs are currently set up to operate 9600 baud.

GROUND STATIONS FOR LEO

Ground stations for 9600 baud FSK and 1200 baud PSK are shown in Figure 5.1 and Figure 5.2. The computer and the software form the heart of both systems. The operator talks to the computer. The computer operates the station. One instruction to the computer—for example, download a file—may result in a series of interchanges between satellite and ground station. The operator can ignore the steps involved or follow them on the computer screen as they are accomplished.

Ground Station Software

As this is written, the software of choice for almost all situations is *WiSP*, running under Windows. To run this software you need an IBM compatible PC. A 40 MHz 486 should be considered a minimal system. Experienced users may elect to use alternate software such as *PB* and *PG* in certain special situations. It's a good idea to provide as much computing power as possible. A 166 MHz Pentium or faster would be a good choice. One good reason for acquiring extra horsepower is that, in the future, it's likely that the TNC and the modem may be replaced by software and an inexpensive digital/analog converter board (Sound Blaster compatible card) that plugs into the PC. Such a board would enable one to emulate most any type of communication or telemetry modem in software.

WiSP comes with a short text file discussing installation

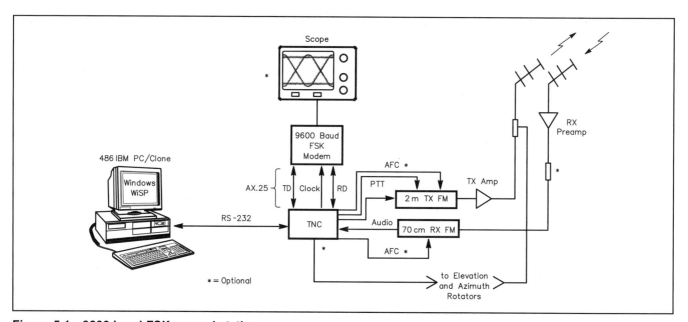

Figure 5.1—9600 baud FSK ground station.

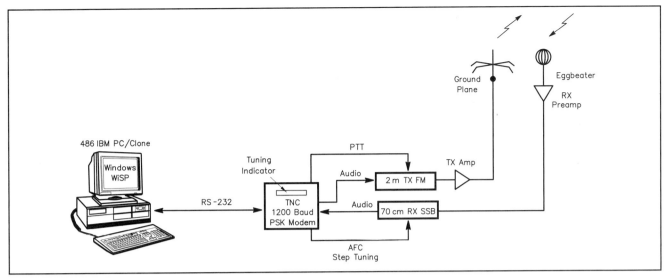

Figure 5.2—1200 baud PSK ground station.

and system set up. Once it's installed you'll have access to HELP files that are both context sensitive and arranged in a hypertext style. *WiSP* includes utilities designed to interface with a number of automated antenna tracking systems including the KCTracker and the JAMSAT/TAPR trakbox. *WiSP*, by itself, provides a great deal of information on digital communications. For example, checking the list of supported modems will tell you what is known to work. For additional information on *WiSP* see the references at the end of this chapter.[12,13]

TNC and Modem

The TNC and modem can be separate packages as shown in Figure 5.1, or integrated in a single box as shown in Figure 5.2. In fact, in the future, they may be replaced by a plug-in board residing in the PC that contains multiple digital-to-analog and analog-to-digital converters (Sound Blaster type card). The single box design may contain a hardwired modem for the mode of interest or it may use a DSP (digital signal processor) that can be programmed by software to emulate several types of modems. The user just picks the desired modem from a menu. If you're about to acquire a DSP modem make sure it can emulate *satellite* 1200 baud PSK and *satellite* 9600 baud FSK modems. If someone says the code will be available real soon now it's time to look somewhere else. The manual that comes with the modem is a critically important source of information. In many cases it's the best primer you'll have on digital communications.

The TNC and modem are connected to the computer through an RS-232 serial link and to the transmitter, receiver and possibly rotators through two signal lines and several control lines. Optional connections are marked with a "*." The signal lines consist of an audio signal from modem to transmitter called TD (transmit data) and an audio signal from receiver to modem called RD (receive data). The control lines include transmitter PTT (push-to-talk), receiver AFC (automatic frequency control), transmitter

AFC (*), antenna rotator azimuth and elevation (*).

RF Frequencies

Current LEO PACSATs all use 2-meter/70-cm Mode J links. The transmit and receive frequencies are independent of all other parameters. While RUDAK-U and future LEO satellites are likely to employ other link frequencies, the following information will remain valid. TechSat-A carried a 23-cm/70-cm digital repeater; unfortunately the launch vehicle failed to reach orbit.

9600 Baud SK System

SATELLITES

As this is written there are three spacecraft devoted exclusively to 9600 baud amateur operation in orbit. They are UoSAT-OSCAR 22, KITSAT-OSCAR 23 and KITSAT-OSCAR 25. In addition, OSCAR 40 carries four hardwired 9600 modems. Two additional spacecraft, UoSAT-OSCAR 14 and PoSAT-OSCAR 28, capable of providing 9600 baud amateur service are in space and operational. However, they are not operating in the Amateur Satellite Service at this time.

TNC AND MODEM

One can use an older TNC with the internal 1200 baud AFSK modem disconnected and a dedicated 9600 baud FSK modem connected in its place. Most of the dedicated modems are based on a design by G3RUH.[14] If the G3RUH call seems familiar, it should be. James also developed the most widely used modem for 1200 baud PSK satellite work and the 400 baud modem used for Phase 3 telemetry. Multimode DSP units are also available.

TX AND RX

For this mode the transmitter (2 meter) and receiver (70 cm) are both FM units. One can use separate units or a dual band transceiver. In most cases the transmitter and receiver have to be modified. The changes are necessary because the transmit data and receive data audio signals flowing between the TNC and the transmitter and receiver have components extending from about 100 Hz up to 7500 Hz; systems optimized for voice communications usually have a narrower passband. Since amplitude or phase distortion in these signals can have a drastic effect on system performance, one cannot just feed a signal into the microphone input jack or pick it off at the speaker output.

For transmitting, the data signal must be introduced directly to the modulator, generally at a varactor. For receiving, the data signal must be picked up directly at the discriminator. On some rigs the modifications are very easy. However, because of dense packaging and tiny components, they can be rather delicate. Some relatively recent radios have input and output jacks labeled as being for digital data but these are likely to have been designed to handle 1200 baud terrestrial systems. If this is the case, the jacks will probably *not* work with 9600 baud FSK—these units may still have to be modified.

Another common modification is to widen the receiver's passband by replacing the main IF filter by a somewhat wider unit. Replacing an 8 or 10 kHz wide IF filter (6 dB width) with a 15 or 20 kHz unit can significantly improve performance.

Deviation should be set to ±3 kHz. While using a higher deviation might improve throughput on a point-to-point terrestrial link, it will result in degraded performance on a Doppler-shifted satellite link.

How do you figure out whether a particular rig needs to be modified and if so, what the required modifications are? Information is available from various sources but you often have to dig for it. Several manufacturers have information detailing the necessary modifications. Write or e-mail them and request a 9600 baud FSK "applications note" or "service bulletin." Better yet, check to see if they have an Internet site. Sites, like the one provided by PacComm (**http://www.paccomm.com**), contain a great deal of information. One of the best places to obtain data is the AMSAT Internet site where notes are generally filed by make and model number. You'll have to download the notes by FTP (File Transfer Protocol). Several recent articles on the subject are referenced in Table 5.1.

If you try to listen to a 9600 baud FSK downlink you'll find that it's impossible to distinguish between a signal and background noise. If you want to know when a signal appears you have to set your receiver squelch at threshold and wait for it to break. For tuning you use a discriminator meter. Squelch and discriminator meters aren't always present and they only provide limited information. The scope shown in Figure 5.1 is included to rectify these problems. It isn't absolutely necessary but it can serve a number of functions including those just mentioned (indicating if a signal is present and correctly tuned) and providing information on overall system performance. A simple inexpensive scope is fine. Setup, operation and interpretation of the aptly named "eye" pattern are generally discussed in the modem instructions. See Table 5.1.

POWER, ANTENNA AND PREAMP

User reports and experiments at UoSAT have shown that ground stations using omnidirectional antennas for receiving and transmitting with about 25 W uplink power, can provide reasonably good performance. To be more specific, during a UoSAT experiment such a station averaged a throughput of 96 kbytes per pass with a maximum throughput of 520 kbytes.[15]

To improve receive performance one needs a directional antenna. Conventional wisdom says that once one opts for a directional receive antenna it's cost effective to use one of similar gain for transmitting. However, the three to one size ratio of comparable gain antennas may cause you to evaluate the trade-offs. A small 6 element 70 cm beam can be placed almost anywhere. For solid transmitting results you'll want about 8 to 10 dB gain above the 25 W to an omni antenna. You might consider 160 W to an omni or maybe 50 W to a beam having 6-8 dB gain. If you use beams, keep in mind that low gain is an advantage because it minimizes pointing accuracy requirements. Although azimuth and elevation rotation and circular polarization of the proper polarity are optimal, many users report good results using a linearly polarized antenna set at a fixed elevation angle of about 25°. Theoretically, one needs about 6 dB more gain on up and downlinks using 9600 baud FSK compared to 1200 baud PSK. Practical experience suggests this is correct.

DOPPLER CORRECTION

Frequency control with current LEO (1997) spacecraft is not very critical. However, if your transmitter and receiver frequencies can be changed by external control signals it's convenient to use this feature. One approach is to use full Doppler compensation (FDC)—your tracking software computes theoretical Doppler corrections and the computer directs the receiver and transmitter to change uplink and downlink frequencies. Another approach is to use a signal from the receiver discriminator or from the modem to control receive frequency. Both methods will give excellent results.

Although neither link is critically sensitive to frequency the uplink is least sensitive, since Doppler is less by a factor of three at 2 meters and the satellite receiver will track the uplink signal to some degree. In fact, if you leave your transmitter fixed at the nominal uplink frequency (and deviation is properly set at 3 kHz) you'll have access to the uplink for most of the pass. To improve performance you can just transmit on the low side of the nominal uplink frequency at the start of a pass (about 2 kHz) and end up on the high side (about 2 kHz) at the end of the pass. The downlink can generally be manually tuned if necessary as long as the tuning steps are less than 3 kHz and the receiver IF bandwidth is reasonably wide. Start listening on the high side (about 5 to 7 kHz) of the nominal downlink frequency. At the end of the pass you'll be listening on the low side. Tests using an FT-736R showed that purposely tuning the receiver up to ±3 kHz off frequency had no discernible effect on throughput.

Table 5.1

Ground Station Equipment for PACSAT Operations—an Annotated Bibliography of Hardware Oriented Articles

9600 Baud FSK

J. Bloom, KE3Z, "'9600-Ready' Radios: Ready or Not?," *QST*, May 1995, pp 24-29. This article provides measured data on bit error rates using unmodified transmitters and receivers claiming 9600 baud capabilities. Units covered include: 2 meters—ICOM IC-281H, Kenwood TM-251A, Standard C1208DA, Yaesu FT-2500M; 70 cm—TEKK KS-900; 2 meters and 70 cm—ICOM IC-820H.

J. Branegan, GM4IHJ, "Low Budget UoSAT-OSCAR 14 9600 Baud Reception," *The AMSAT Journal*, Sep 1990, pp 8-11. John reports on experiments with very simple receiving systems including:

System 1	ICOM IC-451
System 2	70-cm/10-meter converter feeding Kenwood Trio R2000 set to 29.07 MHz in FM mode.
System 3	70-cm/10-meter converter feeding UK CB radio (CB radios in UK use FM)
System 4	ICOM R7000 UHF Rx

S. Ford, WB8IMY, "How Low Can You Go?" *QST*, Aug 1994, p 91. Steve discusses putting together a simple station— 70-cm Receiving System: preamp (Hamtronics), 70-cm/10-meter converter (Microwave Modules) feeding an ICOM IC-745 HF transceiver with FM module (signal tapped at discriminator on FM board). Transmitting system: a modified Kenwood TS-700S (signal injected at varactor).

E. Krome, KA9LNV, "An Alternative Approach to UO-14/UO-22 9600 Baud Reception," *The AMSAT Journal*, March/April 1992 (reprinted Nov/Dec 94, pp 10-12). Reports on successful results using a 70-cm/10-meter converter feeding a Ramsey Electronics FR-10 10-meter FM receiver available in kit form for about $30. Performance nearly equaled that of a modified Kenwood TS430S. An accompanying article details a number of improvements.

H. Natzger, HB9AQZ, "More on 'An Alternative Approach to 9600 Baud Satellites,'" *The AMSAT Journal*, Nov/Dec 94, pp 13-17.

J. Miller, "9600 Baud Packet Radio Modem Design," *Proceedings of the 7th ARRL Computer Networking Conference*, Oct 1988, pp 135-140. This is the standard 9600 baud modem against which the performance of all others are measured.

1200 Baud PSK

R. Forbes, WB6GFJ, "Using the G3RUH 1200 Baud PSK Modem with the AEA PK-232," *The AMSAT Journal*, May 1990, pp 7-8, 14. Receive system consisted of ICOM IC-475 and an AEA PK-232 TNC.

S. Ford, WB8IMY, "The Road Less Traveled," *QST*, Apr 1996, pp 58-61. Steve discusses construction of a simple station—a 70-cm receive system, Eggbeater omni antenna (M^2), preamp, 70-cm/2-meter converter (Hamtronics), 10-meter transceiver (Uniden HR-2510)—a 2-meter transmit system, FM transmitter (ICOM IC-2AT), 30 W PA, TNC with built-in PSK modem (PacComm PSK-1T) and a groundplane antenna.

S. Ford, WB8IMY, "PacComm PSK-1T Satellite Modem and TNC," *QST*, July 1993, pp 46-47. Review.

D. Goodman, WA3USG, "The PacComm PSK-1," *73 Amateur Radio Today*, Dec 1990, pp 32-33. Overview of capabilities.

L. Johnson, WA7GXD, "The TAPR PSK Modem," *QEX*, Sep 1987, pp 3-8. This modem is based on the design of the team that produced the FO-12 spacecraft. Made available in kit form by TAPR. Also called the TAPR/JAMSAT PSK modem.

J. Miller, G3RUH, "A packet radio PSK modem for JAS-1/FO-12," *HamRadio*, Feb 1987, pp 8-12, 14, 16-18, 20-22. This is the standard 1200 baud modem against which all others are measured. Article contains a great deal of information on modem operation and system setup.

J. Miller, G3RUH, "Progress On the G3RUH PSK FO-12 Modem," *Amateur Satellite Report*, 146, Apr 6, 1987, pp 3-4. Discusses connection of 1200 baud PSK modem to AEA PK-64, AEA PK-232 and PacComm TNC-220 TNCs.

J. Miller, "FO-20 PSK Modem Improvement for Microsat Use," *The AMSAT Journal*, May 1991, p 12. The signals transmitted by OSCARs 16, 18 and 19 were observed to generate random phase noise. Article presents simple modifications to the basic G3RUH modem that improve performance in the presence of phase noise having the observed characteristics. Also discusses use of oscilloscope "eye pattern" for system evaluation.

1200 Baud PSK and 9600 Baud FSK

H. Sodja, W6SHP, "Microsat Operation With the PK-232," *The AMSAT Journal*, Jan/Feb 1994, pp 14-17.

H. Sodja, W6SHP, "Transmitter and Receiver Modifications For the FT-736 and Other Rigs for Microsat Operation," *The AMSAT Journal*, Nov/Dec 1995, pp 8-12. Reprinted from *OSCAR News*, Aug 1995. Also covers AEA's DSP-2232 modem and mentions G3RUH FSK, TAPR PSK, TAPR DSP-93, PK-232 modems and Kenwood TS-440 transceiver.

PACSAT Beginners Guide, available from AMSAT-NA. Contains a great deal of practical hardware and software information related to PACSAT operation.

1981-1997 *ARRL Digital Conference Proceedings* available from TAPR, 8987-309 E Tanque Verde Rd #337, Tucson, AZ 85749.

AMSAT Internet site (FTP site) **http://www.amsat.org/amsat/ftpsoft.html**

1200 Baud PSK System

SATELLITES

As this is written there are five satellites providing 1200 baud PSK communications services to the amateur community: AMSAT-OSCAR 16, LUSAT-OSCAR 19, ITAMSAT-OSCAR 26, Fuji-OSCAR 20 and Fuji-OSCAR 29. In addition, there are several additional spacecraft downlinking telemetry in this format. The OSCAR 40 RUDAK can also support this mode using DSP modems. A typical ground station is shown in Figure 5.2.

TNC AND MODEM

One can use an older TNC with the internal 1200 baud AFSK modem disconnected and a dedicated 1200 baud PSK modem connected in its place. PacComm and MFJ TNCs are especially easy to modify. They're essentially commercial versions of the original TAPR TNC-2 kit that was designed to make it easy to replace the internal modem. Most of the dedicated modems are based on designs by G3RUH[2] and JAMSAT.[3] James (G3RUH) also developed the most widely used modem for 9600 baud FSK satellite work and the 400 baud modem used for Phase 3 telemetry. Multimode DSP units are also available. All 1200 baud PSK modems provide a digital automatic frequency control (AFC) signal that is compatible with the various control schemes used in ICOM, Kenwood and Yaesu receivers/transceivers capable of changing frequency in steps of ≤100 Hz.

TX AND RX

The transmitter (2 meter) is an FM unit. The receiver (70 cm) is an SSB model. The transmit data and receive data audio signals flowing between the TNC and the transmitter and receiver lie in the narrow audio range used for amateur voice communications channels. As a result the modifications discussed in the section on 9600 baud communications shouldn't be necessary. Experience has shown that bypassing audio pre or post emphasis circuitry can significantly improve performance in some cases. The changes can be as simple as connecting a transmit data audio line to the microphone gain potentiometer instead of the microphone input jack or data input jack.

It's also necessary, at times, to compensate for IF filters with poor shapes. Since the sideband setting of the receiver is theoretically immaterial, it's a good idea to try both settings to ascertain if one filter has better characteristics (flatter passband and phase delay characteristics) than the other. Keep this fact in mind: when switching sidebands the automatic up/down Doppler correction lines from the PSK modem must be reversed.

How do you figure out whether a particular rig needs to be modified, and if so, what the required modifications are? As with 9600 baud systems, information is available from various sources but you often have to dig for it. Several manufacturers have information detailing the modifications necessary. Write or e-mail them and request a satellite 1200 baud PSK "applications note" or "service

bulletin." Better yet, check to see if they have an Internet site. Sites, like the one provided by PacComm (**http://www.paccomm.com**), contain a great deal of information. One of the best places for information is the AMSAT Internet site where notes are generally filed by make and model number. You'll have to download the notes by FTP (File Transfer Protocol). Several recent articles on the subject are referenced in Table 5.1.

One attractive feature of the 1200 baud system is that you can actually listen to the downlink. It may seem a bit odd to describe listening to a raspy, chainsaw like sound as attractive but this is a feature that one doesn't appreciate until it's missing (like on the 9600 system). After a little practice, a couple of seconds of monitoring by ear will confirm that everything in the receive system involved in getting the signal to the modem (tracking data, satellite performance, antenna aiming, receiver, preamp, feed lines, etc) is working properly. An oscilloscope can be useful in setting up a 1200 baud station, but the aural characteristics just described make it less necessary for day-to-day operation.

POWER, ANTENNA AND PREAMP

Another nice feature of the 1200 baud system is that one can obtain good results using low power and omnidirectional antennas. This is due in part to link performance but also to the fact that a smaller user base means there's less competition for the uplinks. 25 W reaching an omni antenna placed in a clear position should provide good uplink performance. An omni for receiving, with a decent (noise figure < 2 dB) preamp mounted at the antenna should also work fine.

DOPPLER CORRECTION

Doppler compensation of the downlink frequency is critical since the width of the downlink signal is only a few hundred Hz less than the passband of the receiver SSB filter. Because it's important to keep the downlink signal centered in the receiver passband, the receiver has to track the incoming signal to within about 200 Hz. All modems currently available provide control signals for automatic frequency tracking that will operate with receivers having synthesized oscillators using steps less than or equal to 100 Hz. If you're using a converter into an older non-synthesized HF receiver you'll have to continuously tune the receiver by hand during the entire pass while watching the center frequency bargraph on the modem. This is a delicate operation and you may have problems on overhead passes but many have been successful, especially on passes below a 30° elevation.

Transmitter frequency control is not nearly as critical. At 2 meters Doppler only amounts to about ±3 kHz. If you're using the correct deviation (3 kHz) the relatively wide receiver on the spacecraft should be able to track you through an entire pass. Of course, if your software and transmitter support Doppler compensation, use it. It's also possible to set your transmitter about 2 kHz low at the start of the pass, to nominal uplink frequency at the middle and about 2 kHz high at the end of the pass.

Perhaps the best method of handling Doppler is to use Full Doppler Compensation based on computed frequency shifts from tracking software in combination with the fine receive frequency control provided by the modem signals.

RUDAK-U

The name of the digital communications package aboard OSCAR 40 is called RUDAK-U. RUDAK-U is designed to be compatible with existing packet satellite systems, provide services currently unavailable to digital satellite users and be extremely flexible to allow for future developments.

The RUDAK characteristic that makes this system different from all other existing digital systems is a design philosophy that stresses real-time communications. All current terrestrial and satellite digital systems were developed to provide store-and-forward service. The difference is a fundamental one. Sure, RUDAK has all the old store-and-forward features you're familiar with but it also provides additional features. For example, with RUDAK-U you can chat keyboard-to-keyboard with anyone in the footprint, which at most times includes nearly half the Earth (and it ain't always the same half!). You can do this with pretty much the same RF power levels used for LEO spacecraft and you're not restricted to a keyboard. RUDAK supports multimedia, digital voice and so forth—all in real time. Some of the new features require very high data rates.

The RUDAK system was designed to be extremely flexible. Almost everything is under software control. RUDAK will support as many as 10 real-time communications channels. The actual number is, of course, under software

control and will be adjusted to accommodate user needs, which will themselves change over the years. Initial operation will most likely focus on 2-meter/70-cm 9600 baud FSK as with the UoSAT LEO spacecraft. Frequency bands can easily be modified at the spacecraft if other links provide significantly superior service. For example, a ground station using 2-meter and 70-cm FM transceivers for 9600 baud LEO satellite operations can easily switch to 70 cm/ 13 cm. The 70-cm FM transmitter is sitting idly by. All that's needed is a 13-cm/2-meter converter and a 13-cm antenna. Switching modulation schemes and/or data rates can also easily be done at the spacecraft. At the ground these changes may be more difficult today. In a few years it may be common to replace a TNC and modem with a plug-in D/A A/D board in the computer. When this happens the ground station will only have to load new software.

Frequencies for the digital transponders on OSCAR 40 are given in the *Spacecraft Profiles* Appendix. Note that the frequencies specified are actually band limits. Channels can be placed at different points inside the band. Channel width and placement will be appropriate to the modulation scheme and data rate being used.

A block diagram of the RUDAK system is shown in Figure 5.3. RUDAK-U consists of two CPUs (essentially independent computers). Each computer connects to the 10.7 MHz transponder IF through two hardwired modems configured for 9600 baud FSK. In addition, each CPU is connected to the IF through four extremely flexible DSP modems capable of supporting data rates up to 56 kbaud and various modulations schemes. A separate 153.6 kbaud modem can be switched between the two CPUs. Each CPU

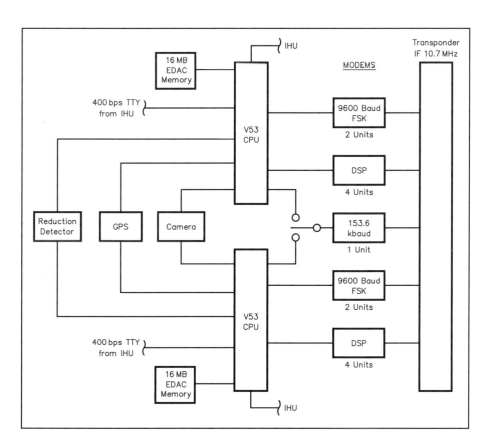

Figure 5.3—RUDAK-U block diagram.

has access to 16 Mbytes of error correcting memory. For comparison, AO-16 has about 256 kbytes of error correcting memory and just over 8 Mbytes of file memory.[16,17]

RUDAK-U provides the primary communications channel for all experiments on the spacecraft. This enhances spacecraft reliability and experimental flexibility. The experiments referred to include cameras, the GPS (Global Positioning System) satellite receivers and radiation detectors.

As with most projects of this type, the development team devoted most of the time leading up to launch perfecting the hardware. RUDAK began operation using the same software used for LEO communication. The software will evolve during the first few years OSCAR 40 is in orbit. It should be an exciting time because users will have an opportunity to observe and play an important role in this development. Users can expect to be able to download software updates, giving them access to each new feature as it's added.

The project manager for RUDAK-U is Lyle Johnson, WA7GXD. The development team included Peter Guelzow, DB2OS; Chuck Green, N0ADI; Harold Price, NK6K; and Jeff Ward, G0SUL/K8KA.

Notes

[1]R. Diersing and J. Ward, "Packet Radio in the Amateur Satellite Service," *IEEE Journal on Selected Areas In Communications*, Vol. 7, No. 2, Feb 1989, pp 226-234.
[2]J. Miller, G3RUH, "A packet radio PSK modem for JAS-1/FO-12," *Ham Radio*, Feb 1987, pp 8-12, 14, 16-18, 20-22.
[3]F. Yamashita, JS1UKR, "A PSK Demodulator for the JAS-1 Satellite," *QEX*, Aug 1986, pp 3-7.
[4]L. Johnson, WA7GXD, "The TAPR PSK Modem," *QEX*, Sep 1987, pp 3-8.
[5]H. Price and J. Ward, "PACSAT Protocol Suite—An Overview," *Proc. 9th Computer Networking Conference*, London, Ontario, Canada, 1990, pp 203-206.
[6]H. Price and J. Ward, "PACSAT Broadcast Protocol," *Proc. 9th Computer Networking Conference*, London, Ontario, Canada, 1990, pp 232-244.
[7]H. Price and J. Ward, "PACSAT Data Specification Standards," *Proc. 9th Computer Networking Conference*, London, Ontario, Canada, 1990, pp 207-208.
[8]J. Ward and H. Price, "PACSAT Protocol: File Transfer Level 0," *Proc. 9th Computer Networking Conference*, London, Ontario, Canada, 1990, pp 209-231.
[9]J. Ward and H. Price, "PACSAT File Header Definition," *Proc. 9th Computer Networking Conference*, London, Ontario, Canada, 1990, pp 245-252.
[10]*The ARRL Handbook for Radio Amateurs*, 1996, pp 23.19-23.25.
[11]R. Soifer, W2RS, "The Amateur-Satellite Service in 1996," *The AMSAT Journal*, Sep/Oct 1996, pp 5-8.
[12]S. Ford, WB8IMY, "Will O'The *WiSP*," *QST*, Feb 1995, p 90.
[13]B. Gorsky, WH6I, "*WiSP*," *The AMSAT Journal*, July/Aug 1994, pp 6-9.
[14]J. Miller, "9600 baud Packet Radio Modem Design," *Proceedings of the 7th ARRL Computer Networking Conference*, Oct 1988, pp 135-140.
[15]M. Allery, H. Price, J. Ward and R. Da Silva Curiel, "Low Earth Orbit Microsatellites for Data Communications Using Small Terminals," presented at the ICDSC-10, Brighton, UK 1995. You can obtain a copy of the paper on the Internet at **http://www.ee.surrey.ac.uk/CSER/UOSAT/papers/icdsc10/icdsc10.html**
[16]L. Johnson, WA7GXD, "RUDAK-U Digital Communications System to Fly on P3D," *The AMSAT Journal*, Sep/Oct 1994, pp 1, 4.
[17]H. Price, NK6K, Digital Communications Column, *QEX*, Feb 1995, pp 24-27. Reprinted in *The AMSAT Journal*, Mar/Apr 1995, pp 29-31.

Operating Notes

6 Operating Notes

ON-THE-SATELLITE ACTIVITIES

AMSAT Contest Policy

Radio amateurs have always enjoyed competing in contests and working toward awards—activities that encourage one to improve operating skills and station performance. In the Amateur Satellite Service, however, it's important to consider whether specific contests and awards are appropriate. Satellites are a shared resource and they're most effective when everyone cooperates, especially in using minimum necessary power levels.

When communicating via the ionosphere on HF, the operator of a low-power station can use skill and patience to compete successfully against those with higher power; no one can overload the ionosphere and make it useless for others. Satellites, however, can be overloaded by a few inconsiderate stations. When this occurs, no amount of skill or patience can overcome the problem. Contest formats that tempt participants to use spacecraft resources unfairly must be evaluated carefully.

Does this mean that satellites should not be used for contests or awards? Certainly not! AMSAT encourages a number of contests and activities that contribute to the advancement of the Amateur Satellite Service and the general enjoyment of those involved in satellite communication, especially when these contests stimulate users to improve ground station performance and hone operating skills. Several examples follow. In any event, remember that AMSAT's control is limited; anyone can sponsor a contest or award. Therefore, in a very real sense, the user community is ultimately responsible for what happens. Your interests, support and tolerance will determine the future of satellite contests and awards.

Techno-Sport

Many years ago, while president of AMSAT, Rip Riportella, WA2LQQ, coined the term *techno-sport* to describe contest-like activities that encourage the development of operational skills, the perfection of station performance and the enhancement of the operator's knowledge of satellite communications systems. AMSAT will actively support any group that wishes to sponsor a techno-sport activity provided, of course, that the proposed event does not undermine the cooperative nature of satellite communication.

ZRO Tests

One techno-sport activity that has proved immensely popular is the ZRO receiving tests, named in memory of Kaz Deskur, K2ZRO, a long-time AMSAT member. Kaz was best known for the major contributions he made to the development of the graphical tracking devices we all used BC (before computers). The ZRO tests are designed to provide users with a quantitative measure of their receive system performance. This gives operators a chance to compare the performance of their receiving systems to those of others and to evaluate changes over long time periods or when modifying systems.

The ZRO tests were held with Phase 3 satellites when their position and orientation with respect to the Earth were optimal. During the event the transmitting station running the test carefully adjusts uplink power to provide a downlink signal equal in strength to the beacon. A series of 3 dB attenuators are then inserted in the transmitter line. After each attenuator is inserted, CW code groups are sent at 10 WPM. The object is to receive the code groups correctly at the lowest possible level. Participants with super receive systems have been able to copy transmissions sent at 24 dB below the beacon level (the satellite transmitting power is below 10 mW at this point).

In order to achieve uniformity from test to test, dates and times must be carefully selected. The following criteria are taken into account, the spacecraft must be near apogee, the subsatellite point must be close to the region of the Earth where participants are concentrated, the satellite orientation must produce low values of squint angle to prospective participants. In addition, it's desirable to choose times that don't conflict with normal working hours. Although these criteria are restrictive, with OSCARs 10 and 13 it was usually possible to identify several appropriate times each year.

Field Day

Field Day is one of the most popular operating activities on the satellite contest calendar. This is an officially sanctioned AMSAT contest that runs at the same time as the ARRL event. While one can simultaneously take part in both contests it's important to note that there are slight differences in the rules. With respect to the Amateur Satellite Service, Field Day has two objectives: to provide operators with the practice necessary to set up a ground station and effectively operate via the satellites in an emergency situation and to expose radio amateurs and others not involved in satellite communications to amateur satellite operations.

DX Activities

Activities involving contacting or operating from remote locations have always had a great appeal to radio amateurs and satellite users are no exception. In the early days of the satellite program AMSAT directors were hesitant about endorsing DX activities. Anyone who has tried casual operating on 20 meters during a contest weekend knows why. Prodded by the membership, in the mid 1970s the directors took some tentative steps toward encouraging operation leading to WAS, WAC and DXCC. The results were very positive and now DX activities are an integral part of satellite work. To date, most DXers have exhibited a real commitment to the shared resource value system. The satellite DX world remains a place where cooperation and assistance earn one more prestige than having the highest number on the DXCC honor roll.

This doesn't mean that satellite DXers don't collect QSL cards or count countries. Far from it. It's just that operators still take pride in their skills. Maintaining this desirable situation will require ongoing efforts.

With the encouragement of AMSAT, the ARRL DXCC honor roll introduced a Satellite Endorsement. In early 1997 a number of amateurs are approaching the 240 country level.

The "misnamed" North American Satellite DX (NASDX) Fund (misnamed because many of the contributors are from outside NA) has been in existence for many years. Its primary goal is to encourage satellite activities on large DXpeditions and to encourage special DXpeditions that focus on satellite operations. The group used to hold informal meetings on OSCAR 13. By the time you read this the meetings should have resumed on OSCAR 40.

For many years, Craig Mellinger, N2MNA, wrote a column in *OSCAR Satellite Report* presenting ongoing information on DX activities. During this time he built up an information grapevine that made the column a prime source for DXers.

Straight Key Night

Another "contest" that's very popular on the analog spacecraft is AMSAT's Straight Key Night (SKN). SKN takes place the last night of the year—be there. As a contest, SKN is especially notable in that it has no rules except that you must use a straight key. There's no scoring and there are no logs to send in. In fact, entrants find that they frequently get sidetracked and end up "wasting" gobs of time talking to old friends they haven't heard from in years. Those who wish to do so are encouraged to send in nominations for "best fist" in the AMSAT SKN to Ray Soifer, **w2rs@amsat.org**, who has managed the contest for years.

AMSAT Awards Program

In the early days of the satellite program AMSAT introduced a number of achievement awards based on QSLs for cumulative distinct station QSO totals. Many of these awards are still available. When these awards were first announced, they often represented a significant accomplishment. Today most applicants tend to apply because of the appealing artwork or historical significance. For a complete list of what's available, check the AMSAT Web site, or see A. MacAllister, WA5ZIB, "The AMSAT Awards Program," *The AMSAT Journal*, Mar/Apr 1993, pp 10-12. Or, send an SASE with 2 units of postage to Andy MacAllister, AMSAT VP User Services, 14714 Knightsway Dr., Houston, TX 77083. Request a current AMSAT Awards Listing.

Experiments

At one time on the satellites, Mondays were reserved for QRP operation and Wednesdays were scheduled for special experiments. In recent years it was decided that these restrictions were no longer necessary. QRP operation and serious experimentation are still encouraged. Many experiments do not require any special satellite scheduling or impede other operations in any way. Amateurs interested in undertaking such experiments are encouraged to do so. Providing a written report to AMSAT or submitting a report for publication in an Amateur Radio or professional journal, newsletter or conference proceedings is very beneficial to the Amateur Satellite Program. These written reports help justify launches and frequency allocations.

If you wish to engage in experimentation that requires special scheduling or that may interfere with other ongoing activities, you should contact AMSAT in advance and be willing to describe your objectives in writing. AMSAT will consider all requests with a sympathetic ear but submitters must realize that the satellites are an international resource and that AMSAT must balance requests against the possibility that important unpublicized activities planned months in advance, like DXpeditions to remote areas, or Scout On The Air Jamborees, might be dependent on consistent scheduling.

INFORMATION RESOURCES

Information on the Amateur Satellite Program is available from a number of sources. These include the hard copy world of magazines, newsletters, conference proceedings and technical journals; traditional radio activities such as HF and satellite nets, and computer communications including 2-meter terrestrial packet, satellite packet and the Internet. Each of these sources has particular strengths and weaknesses. Nets, electronic mail and the Internet are excellent for rapid exchange of time critical information relating to orbital elements, operating schedules, new satellites, emergencies, etc. The Internet is extremely valuable for archive data. However, ink and paper remain a cost effective and convenient medium for disseminating detailed technical data. As a result, periodicals and books will continue to be a very important source for information on amateur satellites.

HF On The Air

WEEKLY HF NETS

For the last quarter century AMSAT has coordinated a worldwide series of HF nets that has provided up-to-date information on the satellite program. Initially, these nets were very important to those already working on the satellites. Nowadays, with the Internet available, and Phase 3D on the way, the HF Nets focus more on providing information to those just getting started and in exposing HFers to what's happening in the satellite world. See Table 6.1 for a list of frequencies and a schedule.

ALINS (LAUNCH) NETS

When major AMSAT coordinated spacecraft are launched special nets are often organized to broadcast the countdown and ensuing events around the world as they happen. These nets (called ALINS for Amateur Launch Information Net Service) often involve a complex information gathering and sharing operation with AMSAT personnel on the launch scene, present at major NASA or ESA facilities, and monitoring real-time satellite TV links used by the government agencies involved.

Some examples of events covered by ALINS nets follow. Shortly after FO-12 went up, an Amateur Radio operator in Argentina captured telemetry seconds after the spacecraft was released from the launch vehicle. Minutes later this telemetry was relayed back to Japan via an amateur station in the US. Amateurs listening to the nets heard the traffic being relayed. During the launches of OSCARs P3A, 10 and 13, the net control operator had access to the European Space Agency network, the NASA network, and strategically placed ground stations around the world. Those listening to the net during the launch of OSCAR P3A will probably never forget hearing the ESA control station in the background as it first reported "non nominal" conditions and shortly thereafter "splashdown." On a happier note, we also heard each of the stagings leading to OSCAR 13 being successfully deposited in its transfer orbit. Shortly after OSCAR 8 was launched, ALINS carried traffic from the command stations as they sent critically important signals to the spacecraft directing it to deploy its 10-meter antenna. Many amateurs in the eastern half of the US were able to monitor the ALINS net and the spacecraft telemetry simultaneously as the commands were being received and successfully implemented.

Launch net information is broadcast by AMSAT and the ARRL on their regular broadcasting frequencies. Several additional groups have helped disseminate information during recent launches. These include the radio clubs of the Johnson Space Center, Houston, TX (W5RRR); the Goddard Space Flight Center, Greenbelt, MD (WA3NAN); and the Jet Propulsion Laboratory, Pasadena, CA (W6JIO). For a list of HF frequencies normally employed, see Table 6.2.

Table 6.1

AMSAT Terrestrial HF Nets: Frequencies and Times

Service Area	Day	Time	Frequency
South Pacific	Saturday	2200 UTC	14.282 MHz
International	Sunday	1900 UTC	14.282 MHz
International	Sunday	1900 UTC	21.280 MHz [1]
International	Sunday	2300 UTC	18.155 MHz [1]
US East Coast	Tuesday	2100 EST [2]	3.840 MHz
US Central	Tuesday	2100 CST [2]	3.840 MHz
US West Coast	Tuesday	2100 PST [2]	3.840 MHz

[1]Generally inactive during low parts of the sunspot cycle.
[2]Net remains at 2100 when clocks are switched to Daylight Time.

Table 6.2

ALINS Frequencies

AMSAT Launch Information Network Service (ALINS) Participating Broadcast Stations (partial list)

AMSAT	3.840 MHz
	14.282 MHz
	21.280 MHz

Goddard Space Flight Center, Greenbelt, Maryland

WA3NAN	7.185 MHz
	14.295 MHz
	21.395 MHz

Jet Propulsion Laboratory, Pasadena, California

W6VIO	14.282 MHz
	21.280 MHz

American Radio Relay League, Newington, Connecticut

W1AW	See *QST* for bulletin frequencies (all modes)

Publications

PERIODICALS

Periodicals devoted to satellite activities have played an important role in providing information to satellite users over the years. Many of these have been produced as a membership service by the major amateur satellite organizations. Others were available by subscription. In addition, articles on satellite activities have appeared frequently in all major radio amateur publications.

Since AMSAT-NA was founded in 1969, it has provided members with a periodical published from 4 to 12 times per year. The name and format have changed a number of times. It was called *The AMSAT Newsletter* from 1969-1978, *Orbit* from 1980-1984, *Satellite Journal* from 1985-1986, *AMSAT Satellite Report* from 1987-1989 and *The AMSAT Journal* from 1989-present.

Another major English language periodical focusing on satellites is *OSCAR News*, the newsletter of AMSAT-UK. It has been published and distributed to members since 1972 and is a prime source for information on the UoSAT series of satellites. AMSAT-UK also publishes several booklets, manuals, and computer tracking and telemetry capture programs.

Those who read German will find the AMSAT-DL newsletter a source of information that's often available nowhere else, especially concerning Phase 3 spacecraft systems.

In addition to the periodicals focusing on radio amateur satellite activities there are numerous magazines devoted to Amateur Radio that include important information on the satellite program. Be sure to note the *Amateur Satellites* column in *QST*. Also see *QEX* (published by the ARRL), which contains numerous articles on VHF/UHF and microwave techniques, digital topics and satellite communications.

The most authoritative information on the Russian RS satellite program can be found in the Russian language journal *RADIO*. In the US, subscriptions are available from the Victor Kamkin Bookstore.

BOOKS AND CONFERENCE PROCEEDINGS

Books and conference proceedings are an excellent source for in-depth technical information on the Amateur Satellite Program. The main publishers of English language books focusing on this topic are AMSAT and the ARRL. An updated list of books available from the ARRL is published frequently in *QST*. Books available from AMSAT are usually listed in each issue of *The AMSAT Journal*. An up-to-date list is also at your fingertips if you have access to the World Wide Web; see the AMSAT and ARRL Home Pages. Technical books on non-amateur satellite systems are available from many publishers. These are referenced, when appropriate, in other sections of this book.

Conference proceedings are also an important source of information. The proceedings associated with the annual meetings of AMSAT-NA and AMSAT-UK have been especially valuable. Relevant articles can also be found in the *Proceedings of the Annual ARRL Digital Conferences* and a number of specialized VHF/UHF/microwave groups.

Table 6.3 contains a brief list of publications. Table 6.4 has key addresses.

As you can see, the number of publications available is large. If you need some specialized technical information there's a good chance it may be in print. If you do some innovative technical work that others may be interested in, there's an audience waiting to read about it.

AMSAT-NA Internet Site

AMSAT-NA maintains an Internet site that serves several functions. First, it provides AMSAT a home on the World Wide Web (WWW). Second, it's used to store a great deal of archived text and software. Anyone with access to the Internet can retrieve this material using a procedure known as File Transfer Protocol (FTP). Third, it supports a number of e-mail services including the operation of e-mail "mailing lists."

AMSAT ON THE WORLD WIDE WEB

The AMSAT Home Page on the WWW can be found at **http://www.amsat.org**. Entering the AMSAT WWW site by way of the AMSAT Home Page places you at the top of a pyramid of Web pages that include text material, images and sound bites. The upper level is like a glossy brochure describing AMSAT to the outside world. Those who know something about Amateur Radio, but who are new to the world of satellites, can click on special key words in the introduction to get access to the underlying layer of more detailed material. For example, you can find material that tells you how to get started on amateur satellites. Those already involved with the Amateur Satellite Program can click down to the next level to obtain detailed reference data or up-to-date information on special topics.

Much of this information has been compiled and prepared by specialists directly involved in AMSAT projects. For example, you'll find pages devoted to every active Amateur Radio spacecraft, current orbital element in both NASA 2-line and AMSAT formats and a collection of FAQs (frequently asked questions). You will also find links to WWW sites in England, Germany, France, Japan and Israel providing information on amateur satellite activities in these countries. Keep in mind that the WWW is a work in progress. It, and the AMSAT Web site, are growing at a rapid rate and any list of available information presented today is guaranteed to be outdated tomorrow. The best way to find out what's available is to jump in and look around.

AMSAT FTP

Some information, such as computer software, archived telemetry data and old magazine articles, may not be suited to translation into the WWW format, or the time required for the translation effort may not be justified. Whenever possible, AMSAT tries to make this information accessible to interested individuals via the Internet FTP process.

You can think of FTP as a procedure for searching for a file on the hard disk of a computer hundreds or thousands of miles away, and then copying it to your local machine. In the past, one had to use a series of operating system like commands to do this. Two factors have greatly simplified the procedure. First, there's an AMSAT Web page describing all the software offerings. You can access it by selecting "Downloadable Software" from the main page. Second, recent intelligent Web browsers like *Netscape* and *Internet Explorer* take care of many of the details for you. Check the manual or HELP files associated with your Web browser for specific directions. A few technical details may be of help. FTP access is available from **FTP.AMSAT. ORG** (host name) or use **ftp://ftp.amsat.org/amsat/** in your browser. If you're asked to provide a user name, the response *anonymous* is usually appropriate.

AMSAT MAILING LISTS

The AMSAT Internet site also supports a number of public mailing lists. In case you're not familiar with the operation of mailing lists (also known as e-mail reflectors), the following description of one particular list, the AMSAT-BB (AMSAT Bulletin Board), should help explain the function they serve.

Whenever an e-mail message is sent to the AMSAT-BB

Table 6.3

Periodicals, Books and Conference Proceedings

ARRL Books On Satellite Communications
The Satellite Handbook by Dr. Martin Davidoff, K2UBC. The successor to the popular *Satellite Experimenter's Handbook*.
   You're reading it! (Also available from AMSAT.)
Satellite Anthology, 4th Ed, 1996. A collection of recent articles from *QST*, information from the *ARRL Handbook*, Web
   Pages, and original contributions.
The Weather Satellite Handbook by Dr. Ralph Taggart, WD8DQT, 5th Ed, 1996. Simply the best practical guide to the
   subject at the introductory, intermediate and advanced level.
Proceedings of the AMSAT-NA Space Symposium. Some back issues available. Contact AMSAT.

ARRL Books On Closely Related Topics
ARRL Digital Conference Proceedings. Most back issues available. Contact TAPR
The ARRL Handbook
The ARRL Antenna Book, 18th Ed, 1997
The ARRL UHF/Microwave Experimenter's Manual
The ARRL UHF/Microwave Projects Manual
Packet: Speed, More Speed and Applications

AMSAT-NA Books
The AMSAT-NA Digital Satellite Guide. A complete step-by-step instruction guide to operating through the PACSATs.
Decoding Telemetry from the Amateur Satellites. A general reference source for amateur satellite telemetry.
The RS Satellites Operating Guide. A guide to aid amateur operators in working the RS satellites.
How to Use the Amateur Radio Satellites. This book is a single reference document for the casual listener or beginning
   user.
Mode S: The Book. A comprehensive guide to setting up and operating a Mode S satellite ground station. Contains
   articles by Ed Krome, KA9LNV, James Miller, G3RUH, and others. Includes new material and reprints of key articles
   from *The AMSAT Journal, OSCAR News, QST* and elsewhere.

Table 6.4

Addresses for Amateur Satellite Publications

ARRL (American Radio Relay League)
225 Main St.
Newington, CT 06111
voice: 860-594-0200
FAX: 860-594-0259
e-mail: pubsales@arrl.org
WWW: **http://www.arrl.org/**

AMSAT (Radio Amateur Satellite Corporation)
850 Sligo Ave., Suite 600
Silver Spring, MD 20910
voice: 301-589-6062
e-mail: **martha@amsat.org**
WWW: **http://www.amsat.org/**

AMSAT-DL
Holderstrauch 10
D-35041 Marburg
Germany
e-mail: **amsat-dl@amsat.org**
WWW: **http://www.amsat.org/amsat-dl/**

AMSAT-UK
R. J. C. Broadbent
94 Herongate Road
Wanstead Park
London E12 5EQ
England
FAX: (44) 181-989-3430

RADIO (RS Satellites)
Victor Kamkin Bookstore, Inc.
12224 Parklawn Drive
Rockville, MD 20852, USA

Tucson Amateur Packet Radio
TAPR (*ARRL Digital Conference Proceedings*)
8987-309 E Tanque Verde Rd #337
Tucson, AZ 85749
817-383-0000
e-mail: **tapr@amsat.org**
WWW: **http://www.tapr.org/**

it is automatically resent to everyone who has signed on to the list. The number of subscribers is currently more than 1100. There is no "subscription fee." As you can imagine, a list like this can be a great place for obtaining up-to-the-minute information, and for ferreting out hard to find data, especially if key members of AMSAT are reading what's posted and making contributions.

A mailing list is like a satellite in that it's a shared resource, and its utility depends on the self discipline of the users. There are no rules or regulations regarding what may be posted to the AMSAT-BB. There is, however, an implied request—please respect the focus, use common sense, be considerate, and act courteously. Some understanding of Bulletin Board operation and common pitfalls can help you achieve these goals.

Most of us are accustomed to the social norms of operating in small groups—an on the air three-way QSO, a half dozen people talking over coffee during a break at a radio club meeting, or even 25 individuals in a classroom. A subscriber to the AMSAT-BB is operating in a group containing more than 1100 members. To most people this is a new situation. Consider, for example, what happens if each subscriber posts just one note per week. Everyone on the list would receive more than 150 messages each morning. This quantity would probably drive many subscribers to sign off the list. The point is—think about consequences. Before posting a message consider whether the AMSAT-BB is the appropriate place, also take note of the following. Be careful about using the "respond to" key on your e-mail software—make sure you're not posting a message to the entire list when you really mean to respond to an individual. Learn the correct procedures for signing on and off the list—a note to everyone on the list doesn't accomplish this goal. If you do post a note make good use of subject titles. Finally, be patient. The number of subscribers to the AMSAT-BB is growing rapidly and the growth is likely to continue. This means that there will continue to be lots of newcomers around and it takes everyone a while to get up to speed.

AMSAT currently maintains five public mailing lists and several private mailing lists. The private lists are for small groups within AMSAT working together on specific projects. The public mailing lists are designed to serve the needs of those specifically interested in the radio amateur satellite program. They are: ANS (AMSAT News Service Bulletins), KEPS (Keplerian orbital elements), AMSAT-BB (an open discussion forum or Bulletin Board), SAREX (Messages about manned space activities involving the space shuttle, *Mir*, and Space Station) and AMSAT-DC (a Bulletin Board for those interested in amateur satellite activities in the DC/MD/VA area). The names pretty well describe the intended user community.

Signing on to a mailing list can produce a deluge of incoming messages so it's important to be selective. Don't sign on to any list unless you know the procedure for signing off! Finally, check the features provided by the e-mail program that you're using. Many contain a very convenient "filter" that permits you to separate your incoming "mailing list" e-mail from your personal e-mail.

For an up-to-date list of AMSAT mailing list services, including a list of current public lists, information on signing on/off, and directions for posting messages, send an e-mail note to **listserv@amsat.org** containing just one word—**help**. Note that mail to listserv just goes to one person (or one computer), the person (or computer) managing the mailing lists. At present, requests are handled by a person. In the near future, however, a computer may do the processing.

The Internet services provided by AMSAT, and the number of people using them, have grown rapidly in the past couple of years and this growth is likely to continue. By providing satellite users with a new means for sharing information and experiences, these services have contributed greatly to the amateur satellite community. AMSAT members are indebted to Paul Williamson, KB5MU, and the numerous others whose names you'll see at the end of each Web page, for making them available.

MISCELLANEOUS

Organizations

There are a number of organizations around the world whose primary purpose is to support amateur satellite construction and operation. They may differ in primary language, size and focus, but, all are joined together in the goal of placing spacecraft in orbit for the use of radio amateurs worldwide. One of the early such groups was AMSAT, The Radio Amateur Satellite Corporation. When other like-minded groups around the world began to organize, many adopted the AMSAT name and the original AMSAT became known as AMSAT North America, AMSAT-NA.

Most of these groups focus on one or more of the following activities: satellite construction, information dissemination to users, fund raising, and supporting on-the-air activities. Also included are the monitoring and defending the legal and regulatory position of the Amateur Satellite Service. This occurs with respect to issues such as frequency allocations, antenna restrictions, bio-hazard concerns, and publicizing the benefits of the Amateur Satellite Service and educational Amateur Radio activities to the nations concerned. Everyone who's active on the satellites should actively support at least one of these organizations. Because the organizations focus on different aspects of the amateur satellite program, it's common for satellite users to belong to several. Since most of these activities are covered elsewhere in this book our focus here will be on conferences.

Conferences

A number of famous Amateur Radio conferences are held around the world each year. Amateurs in North America are probably most familiar with the one in Dayton, Ohio, which occurs one weekend each spring. AMSAT has a big presence at Dayton and coordinates several events there, including talks, dinners and maintaining a booth. Dayton is a great event. If you're planning to attend, make sure you obtain a program of AMSAT events ahead of time (reservations for the AMSAT banquet are required in advance) and volunteer to spend a few hours working at the AMSAT booth—it's a great way to meet other active members.

AMSAT-NA also sponsors its own Annual Conference over a weekend each fall. For many years this meeting was held at Goddard Space Flight Center in Greenbelt, Maryland. In the early 1980s a decision was made to vary the location from year to year to make it possible for more members to have a chance to attend. The most recent meetings have been in Toronto, Tucson, Orlando, Washington, Fort Worth, Los Angeles and Atlanta. The AMSAT meeting is very different from Dayton. It focuses on technical presentations and attendance is generally in the range of 150 to 250 with many of those attending from outside the US.

Locations for the AMSAT annual meeting are selected for convenience. In most cases there's a major airport nearby and a rental car is not required. The lectures are usually at the central hotel, or at a local educational institution or government facility. In that case bus and van transportation are arranged for. Most everyone who has attended one of these meetings has been very pleased by the experience and expressed a desire to return to another one.

Another major conference specifically for satellite users occurs each year in conjunction with the AMSAT-UK annual meeting in England. It's held for three or four days in late July and/or early August. The location, Guildford, is 30 km southwest of London and the home of the University of Surrey, which houses the UoSAT spacecraft laboratories. This conference also attracts an international group of amateur satellite builders and users. Attendees who stay in university dormitories (basic single rooms without bath) have access to the lecture halls, pubs, dining areas, and laundry facilities within a 5 minute walk from their room. Attendees who prefer more classy accommodations can find them only minutes away in the beautiful town of Guildford on the river Wye. Since Guildford is very easy to reach from London's Heathrow and Gatwick Airports, and many special air fares involve these airports, those living in the US often find that it's cheaper and more convenient to travel to Guildford than many destinations in the States.

Local Area Coordinators

AMSAT consists of 99.9% volunteers. Very few of these people are actually building satellites. To make an organization like AMSAT work, people are needed for a great variety of tasks. These include giving talks at radio clubs, representing AMSAT at local and regional hamfests and helping newcomers get started. From the earliest days of AMSAT, it was realized that people doing this type of work could benefit by coordinating efforts, sharing resources, experiences, and so on. As a result, AMSAT decided to ask someone (a volunteer naturally) to prepare a plan for a Field Operations program. This led to the creation of the position of Local Area Coordinator and the appointment of a Vice President for Field Operations, whose job it was to organize and support the activities of the Local Area Coordinators.

AMSAT is always in need of volunteers interested in serving as Local Area Coordinators. The qualifications are simple, you must be a current AMSAT member and have a serious interest in representing the organization as your time permits. You must also have access to e-mail since this is the primary means by which Field Operations activities are coordinated. If you're interested in learning more about the position, contact the current VP for Field Operations by checking *The AMSAT Journal* for his/her call sign and sending an e-mail message to **callsign@amsat.org**.

ARRL Educational Programs

Amateur Radio and the Amateur Satellite Service can't exist without access to radio spectrum that has a very high monetary value. To maintain our spectrum allocations we must constantly struggle against well financed groups that are trying to acquire them. Therefore, we have to continually justify the existence of Amateur Radio to national governments by demonstrating how it contributes to a country's economic prosperity and political stability. One of the key ways Amateur Radio makes this contribution is through its support of science education.

Over the years the ARRL has carefully considered how to allocate its limited resources so as to best stimulate science education. In doing this, they realized that the Radio Amateur Satellite Program, especially activities involving manned space activities like SAREX (Shuttle Amateur Radio EXperiment—later renamed Space Amateur Radio Experiment), can play a key role. Since AMSAT itself was a relatively small organization, mainly run by volunteers working at odd (often very odd) hours, it is not in a position to run a formal educational program.

As a consequence, AMSAT and the ARRL decided to work together, and they approached NASA concerning the possibility of arranging for direct contacts between shuttle astronauts and school classrooms via Amateur Radio. Note that the agreed-upon primary SAREX mission goal was to arrange contacts between astronauts in space and school children in the hope of stimulating their interest in a scientific career. One of the first "extra" items to be added to the International Space Station was an Amateur Radio station. The Amateur Radio on the International Space Station (ARISS) program continues to link children with ham astronauts onboard the ISS by Amateur Radio. ARRL Field & Educational Services, under the direction of the ARISS working group at NASA handles the public and educational program coordination.

On most ARISS missions a handful of schools are selected from around the world to make scheduled contacts with the International Space Station. Schools wanting to arrange a contact with the astronauts are required to submit proposals and an ARISS school application to the ARRL. For further information on this program contact the Field & Educational Services at ARRL or see the ARRL Web site **http://www.arrl.org/**.

Satellite Operating Schedules

Most satellites operate according to a pre-announced schedule that indicates which transponders will be on and what frequencies will be used at specific times. Several factors go into determining the schedule. These include satellite health, other technical factors, mission goals and user preferences. An example from each category follows; spacecraft temperature or battery condition might dictate that transponders be turned off several hours per day. Satellite orientation may make it impossible to use certain directional antennas and the associated transponder during certain parts of the orbit. A transponder like the one on AO-27, that can only be used for short periods of time, due to power budget constraints might be activated during normal school hours to facilitate educational programs. And finally, an attempt is made to balance the desires of various groups interested in using different transponders or frequencies.

Scheduling is a somewhat thankless task—no matter what you do, someone is bound to feel cheated. In the past, thought was given to the idea of separating the functions of building and operating satellites. The builders would be responsible for construction and checkout in orbit. The spacecraft would then be turned over to the operations group. This was actually done with OSCAR 8, which was essentially built by AMSAT under contract to the ARRL. After it was placed in orbit operations and scheduling were handled by the League.

This procedure is going to be followed in a more formal way with OSCAR 40. Scheduling responsibility has been turned over to a consortium consisting of representatives from the ARRL, AMSAT-NA, AMSAT-DL, AMSAT-UK and other groups who have made major contributions, in cash or in hardware, to the project. Participating organizations will be responsible for communicating with their members and then getting together to arrange an operating schedule. The technical crew will be consulted on all matters that concern spacecraft health.

US 435 MHz Transmitting Restrictions

For many years the FCC has restricted amateurs who use the 420-450 MHz band to 50-W input power in certain parts of the US. In response to growing satellite activity and a concurrent increase in requests for Special Temporary Authorizations (often referred to as STAs) to use higher power, the FCC has acted to "ease" the restrictions.

As a result of FCC actions, beginning in April 1981 (1) additional restricted areas were introduced and (2) the power limitations were divided into two categories, one for terrestrial operations and another for satellite communications. In August 1982, the restricted regions were increased in number and size.

The restricted areas now include:

1) Those portions of Texas and New Mexico bounded by latitudes 33°24' N and 31°53' N, and longitudes 105°40' W and 106°40' W.

2) The entire state of Florida, including the Key West area and the areas enclosed within circles of 320-kilometer (200-mile) radius of Patrick Air Force Base (28°21' N, 80°43' W) and Eglin Air Force Base (30°30' N, 86°30' W).

3) The entire state of Arizona.

4) Those portions of California and Nevada south of latitude 37°10' N, and the area within a 320-km (200-mile) radius of the US Naval Missile Center (34°09' N, 119°11' W).

5) In the state of Massachusetts within a 160-kilometer (100-mile) radius of Otis Air Force Base (41°45' N, 70°32' W).

6) In the state of California within a 240-kilometer (150-mile) radius of Beale Air Force Base (39°08' N, 121°26' W).

7) In the state of Alaska within a 160-kilometer (100-mile) radius of Elmendorf Air Force Base (64°17' N, 149°10' W).

8) In the state of North Dakota within a 160-kilometer (100-mile) radius of Grand Forks Air Force Base (48°43' N, 97°54' W).

The 50-W input-power limit continues to apply to stations that are engaged in terrestrial communication in the restricted areas. Amateurs engaged in satellite communication on frequencies between 435 and 438 MHz in those areas, however, will be permitted to use 1000 W EIRP provided their antenna elevation is adjusted so that the half-power points of the radiated pattern remain at least 10° above the horizon. See Sections 97.61, 97.421 and 97.422 of the Amateur Rules and Regulations.

Chapter 7

Tracking Basics

7 Tracking Basics

This chapter covers satellite tracking. The focus is on practical questions, and we'll look at examples involving three types of orbits of special interest to radio amateurs: low altitude circular orbits used by most Phase 2 satellites, elliptical orbits used by Phase 3 spacecraft and geostationary orbits. Today most radio amateurs use a computer and one of the many low cost computer tracking programs to obtain information. The graphical displays that these programs provide would have made NASA engineers envious a few years ago. While the programmers who wrote these tracking programs had to know a great deal about the mathematics and physics underlying satellite motion, users need not concern themselves with these details. If you are interested in the basic science underlying tracking, you'll find the material covered in other chapters.

Note that both the computer based tracking methods and the low-tech graphical tracking methods (presented later in this chapter) work for almost all man-made satellites orbiting the Earth. Also covered are a number of interesting orbits that haven't been used by radio amateur spacecraft.

Before we become involved in the details of tracking, note that there are situations where tracking can be ignored. For example, if you spend considerable time in the shack and tune a receiver to 145.900 MHz with an omni antenna connected, sooner or later you'll hear weak SSB signals from OSCAR 10 or P3D. You can then switch to a beam (if available) and adjust azimuth and elevation to peak the incoming signals. It's a bit like checking 15 meters near a sunspot minimum—patience helps. Although you can conceivably operate this way, listening to white noise on a receiver gets very boring. The ability to track greatly reduces frustration and it adds to operating enjoyment by enabling you to arrange schedules with stations in specific locations, plan nets and demonstrations, and schedule operating time efficiently. We now turn to the details of tracking.

TRACKING: INTRODUCTION

To a scientist, tracking means being able to specify a satellite's position in space and its velocity at any time. Radio amateurs are more concerned with practical questions. Since satellites are generally moving targets, the most fundamental question is: "When will a particular satellite be in range (accessible to my station)?" The answer can vary from never to always. For example, a ground sta-

tion more than 45° from the equator and a US Shuttle in a low altitude-low inclination orbit will never be seen. When a ground station is inside the coverage circle of geostationary spacecraft, it will always be seen.

If you're using a directional antenna the next question you face is "where should I point it?" In the early days of the radio amateur satellite program experimenters were content with finding the answers to these two questions. Once they began using computers to obtain the answers, it quickly became apparent that the computers could easily be programmed to provide a great deal of additional information.

Today we tend to ask a great deal more of our tracking programs. Assume you're interested in a particular satellite. You might like your tracking program to report on:

- The spacecraft's operating schedule, including which transponders and beacons are on.
- Predicted frequency offset (Doppler shift) on the link frequencies.
- The orientation of the spacecraft's antennas with respect to your ground station and the distance between your ground station and the satellite. This data is needed to predict communications performance.
- Which regions of the Earth have access to the spacecraft; that is, who's in QSO range?
- Whether the satellite is in sunlight or being eclipsed by the Earth. Some spacecraft only operate when in sunlight.
- When the next opportunity to cover a selected terrestrial path (mutual window) will occur. You will probably want changing data updated at least once per minute.

Many stations want a tracking program that also automatically aims the antenna, compensates for frequency offsets and decodes telemetry. Some software can even be configured to turn a station on/off at the correct time and automatically collect data (for example, as one of the PACSATs flies by while the chief operator is away from his shack). Remember, we've just been talking about one satellite here.

Adding additional spacecraft to the scenario suggests more questions: which satellites are currently in range, how long will each one be accessible, will any new spacecraft be coming into range in the near future? and so on. Obviously there is a great deal of information of potential interest. Programmers developing tracking software often find that the real challenge is not solving the underlying physics problems, but deciding what information to include and how to present it in a useful format. This is especially true since users have different interests and needs. Some prefer to see the information in a graphical format, such as a map showing real-time positions for all satellites of interest. Others may prefer tabular data such as a listing of the times a particular spacecraft will be in range over the next several days.

TRACKING: BACKGROUND

As soon as the launch of Sputnik I was announced, radio amateurs began to develop low-tech methods to track satellites using maps and transparent overlays. Devices like the OSCARLOCATOR and Satellabe, designed for circular orbits, were simple to use, low cost and very effective. Later, when amateurs became interested in elliptical orbits, they designed new low-tech tracking devices able to handle the more complex situation. Before the tracking devices for elliptical orbits came into widespread use, radio amateurs began to get their hands on the new microcomputers just becoming available and their attention shifted to computer tracking. At the end of this chapter we'll briefly look at some of the low-tech methods that radio amateurs played so prominent a role in developing.

In the late 1970s Dr. Tom Clark, W3IWI, managed to compress the kernel of a large mainframe tracking program, used by scientists involved in space research, into a BASIC program that could be run on the "primitive" microcomputers being used by AMSAT development teams and control stations. The IWI program was published in *Orbit* in 1981.[1] Over the next few years, dozens of amateurs translated it into other BASIC dialects and several other languages, modified it to make it more user friendly and added numerous useful extensions. In 1982 AMSAT-UK published a booklet of tracking programs in BASIC by John Branegan, GM4IHJ,[2] and in 1985 *OSCAR News* published the first of many articles on computer tracking programs by James Miller, G3RUH.[3] The RUH programs and the accompanying commentary remain the best introduction to the physics and mathematics underlying tracking available to radio amateurs.

By the time OSCAR 10 was launched in 1983, small computers were becoming widely available, and a great many amateurs were using them in conjunction with versions of the "IWI" and similar tracking programs. Many were being informally distributed. By today's standards the microcomputers available then were painfully slow, limited in memory and had primitive graphics capabilities. As a result, early software was at times awkward to use and generally confined to producing a tabular listing for a single spacecraft.

A key feature of almost all tracking programs currently being circulated is that they handle both elliptical orbits and circular orbits. Since no orbit is ever perfectly circular they do this by treating all orbits as being elliptical.

While the initial group of tracking programs were written for those familiar with programming, the situation was about to change. In the mid 1980s, modifications by Roy Welch, WØSL, and others made the programs easier to install and use. Options were added for graphical displays and provisions for handling multiple satellites. By the late 1980s the majority of radio amateurs, including those who had no idea how to write a line of code in BASIC or any other language, were using computers and plug-and-play software for tracking. Today, radio amateurs can choose between several low cost or free tracking programs. Although most are for IBM PC compatible computers, versions for the Apple and numerous other platforms are also available. Many are really much more than tracking programs—"satellite ground station management software" is a more appropriate descriptor. Since most do an excellent job of tracking, user preferences are usually related to subjective criteria involving the design of the user interface, the number of keystrokes it takes to switch between operating modes of primary interest and the availability of support features.

COMPUTER TRACKING

Let's assume that like most radio amateurs you're going to use a PC and packaged computer software for tracking. There are three steps involved: selecting and obtaining the software, installing, customizing it, and learning to operate it. We'll look at each of these steps shortly. It's interesting to note that a new computer-based alternative is just beginning to appear. There are several Internet sites where you can do your tracking on line. This eliminates all the hassles associated with acquiring and installing software. The currently available online tracking sites are not as powerful or flexible as the software you can install on your PC, however. One interesting site of this type is **http://acsprod1.acs.ncsu.edu/scripts/HamRadio/sattrack**.

Selecting and Obtaining Tracking Software

A software package *must* match the computer and operating system it is used with. A package designed to run on a Mac, or one written to run on an IBM under Windows, will be useless on an IBM type PC operating under DOS. The match goes even further. Software frequently has minimum or type requirements related to the amount of RAM, processor speed, video display, presence of math coprocessor and Operating System version. For example, a program written to run under Windows 95 may not run under Windows 3.1. Most of the latest software requires at minimum of a 386 type machine with a hard disk operating at a speed of at least 40 MHz. Keep in mind that many of the older programs are very serviceable and will operate on much simpler platforms.

Most software is distributed on floppy disk(s). A number of tracking programs can be downloaded from the Internet or local Bulletin Boards; in that case, you'll probably place the files in a subdirectory on your hard disk. The software package will generally consist of a collection of program and data files including several of the following: the actual tracking program, a short program to handle the installation process, a simple database management program for storing and updating orbital elements, several files containing the data needed to draw maps, a text file containing the instruction manual and so on. When you order a program from AMSAT or other retail sources, you should receive a complete package. Make sure your order is specific. For example, if you opt for *NOVA* be sure to order *NOVA DOS or NOVA Windows*. When obtaining software through other channels check that you have all relevant files.

To give radio amateurs an opportunity to select tracking software that best meets their needs, most programs have been made available in either shareware, demo, or limited trial formats. Shareware software is usually a fully functioning program that is distributed under an honor system. Shareware is often available from friends or at hamfests for slightly more than the price of the disks. If after testing the program the user adopts it, he/she should submit the requested registration fee. The fee supports and encourages future development efforts and in many cases, directly finances the Amateur Satellite Program. The registration screen will usually indicate if proceeds are being donated to AMSAT. A demo program is usually a simulation designed to provide the user an opportunity to become acquainted with the software look, feel and capabilities. It generally does not enable one to track real satellites. A limited trial copy is usually a nearly complete program that is limited either by omitting some key data, such as antenna azimuth and elevation pointing angles, or by restricting the number of times it can be used.

Table 7.1 lists some popular tracking software packages designed for radio amateur use. Most are very competently engineered programs, but you won't see the glitzy packaging and multicolored manuals associated with mass market commercial packages. You should be aware that these packages are not designed to teach you how to use your computer—they're aimed at those already familiar with fundamental computer operations such as disk copying, loading an applications program, setting up subdirectories and so on. Table 7.2 lists sources for further information.

Installing and Customizing Software

The following discussion assumes that the reader has some previous experience with applications software. IBM compatible systems are used as a model, but the focus is on issues common to all programs and computers. The object is to provide a basic understanding of the steps involved in installing and customizing tracking software, why they're needed and pitfalls to avoid. In other words, we'll be providing generic directions for IBM architecture machines. Note that you do *not* have to know how to program in BASIC or any other language to use any of the packages listed in Table 7.1.

Software must be installed on your computer before it

can be used. If you've purchased the latest version of the program from AMSAT, it probably arrived with written instructions describing how to get started. Follow these instructions!

If the software you've obtained is distributed without written documentation, the instructions you need are probably in one of many files on the distribution disk(s). Each of these files contains a separate program. For example, a database program for handling orbital elements, a batch tracking program, a real-time tracking program without graphics, a real time tracking program with graphics or an instruction manual, may be included.

Your first job is to obtain a list of the files on the disk(s) so you can locate the instruction manual or the installation instructions. To find the pertinent file print out a list of all files in your package. One way to do this is to use the DOS *DIR* (directory) command. Be sure to search through all subdirectories. Look for files with names like "read.me" or "readme.txt" or "readme.1st" or "text.doc" or "install.txt." The file you're looking for is a simple text file that can be viewed and printed from any word processor or from DOS. It's a good idea to make a hard copy of this file so that you can refer to it as you go through the installation process. I generally use my word processor to make the hard copy. Printing at 80 characters per line with a relatively small constant pitch type should produce a neat copy. If you use DOS the relevant commands are TYPE and PRINT.

Once you obtain the installation directions follow them! In the old days (last year?) installation generally involved setting up a subdirectory and copying all files from the distribution disk(s) to the subdirectory. Today the installation process may be more complex because recent software packages contain a large number of compressed files organized using a multilevel subdirectory structure.

Some software packages must be installed manually. The directions (the ones you printed out or the written ones that came with the program) will generally walk you through the process step-by-step. As a result, you don't have to know the operating system commands needed to set up subdirectories, transfer groups of files to the appropriate location, or decompress (unzip) them. These are some of the things you'll be doing and familiarity with operating system operations demystifies the process.

Other software packages will contain an install program that automatically handles setting up the subdirectories, unzipping compressed files and prompting you to provide the information needed to customize the software. Customization involves providing information such as the communications port for your printer, your call letters, the latitude, longitude, height above sea level of your ground station, initial screen preferences, and so on. The name of the installation file generally includes the word "install" but it must be somewhat distinctive to prevent it from duplicating the name of an installation file used by some other applications software package.

Whether you're installing manually or using an install program, there are some common problems you may encounter. The best strategy is to adopt an approach that enables you to complete the installation process as quickly as possible and then pay attention to customization. For example, you may be prompted for information that is not immediately available. It's often possible to accept default values by just pressing **Enter** (for DOS) or clicking your mouse (for Windows) on the OK symbol. If you use this approach be aware of the consequences. For example, if you were being asked to give your latitude and longitude and you accepted default values, you might have just claimed to be situated at the center of the US, at the author's location or at the intersection of the Greenwich Meridian and the equator. You'll be able to run the tracking program, but the information provided will not apply to your true location. Once the program is up and running, making location changes and changing other data is generally quite easy. Here is another example involving the use of default values. Suppose the program asked for ground station height above sea level and you did not know the correct value. Instead of going shopping for topographic maps or phoning the local airport, just enter zero. Even if you live in Denver (over 5000 ft) entering zero, or accepting zero as a default by just pressing **Enter** would hardly make any

Table 7-1
Satellite Tracking Programs

When purchases are made through AMSAT-NA, a portion of the price is usually contributed to support the Amateur Satellite program and AMSAT members generally receive a discount.

Program Name	Platform	Operating System	Comments
FodTrak 2.5	IBM	DOS	by XQ2FOD
GrafTrak 4.01 Silicon Ephemeris	IBM	DOS	by W5SXD. See http://www.rcallen.com. Complete original commercial package. No charge but donation to AMSAT requested.
InstantTrack	IBM	DOS	by N6NKF. Y2K update released 3/2000
MacDoppler	Mac	Varies	See Dog Park Software Ltd website **http://www.dogpark.software.com**
MacDopplerPRO			See above
Nova for Windows	IBM	Windows 95, NT	by W9IP. See Northern Lights website **http://www.nlsa.com/**
OrbiTrack 2.1.5	Mac	4.1 or later	by WD4IXI
Plan13	—	—	Source code in BASIC and tutorial on tracking calculations by G3RUH. See AMSAT FTP site.
PREDICT	IBM	DOS, Linux	by KD2BD
Satellite TrackingGPS	IBM	Windows	See **http://www.fortunecity.com/skyscraper/ techie/233/**
SatTrack 3.1.5	IBM	Linux (X11R5), UNIX	by W6/DL5KR. Includes source code in C. See **http://www.bester.com/sattrack.html**
SatTrak	Mac	—	Shareware (not related to SatTrack)
The Station Program	IBM	Windows 3.1, 95, NT	by VP9MU. Features full ground station automation, optimized for analog communications
STSOrbit Plus Ver.0005	IBM	DOS	by D. Ransom. Graphics designed to simulate NASA's Shuttle Mission Control Center. See **http://www.dransom.com/**
TRAKSAT 4.00	IBM	DOS	by P. Traufler. See WinTrak. Click on Satellite Tracking GPS.
WinOrbit 3.6	IBM	Windows 3.1, 95, 98, NT 4	by K8CG, freeware from AMSAT FTP site.
WinTrak	IBM	Windows 3.1	See **http://www.hsv.tis.net/~wintrak/index.html**
WinTrak Pro	IBM	Windows 95, 98, NT	See above.
WiSP	IBM	Windows 95/98, NT-40	by G7UPN/ZL2TPO. Features full ground station automation, optimized for digital communications

Notes
[1]All software in this table is reported to be Y2K compatible.

[2]For an updated list of tracking software see the AMSAT web site at **http://www.amsat.org** and click on AMSAT Catalog: Software & Downloadable Software from **FTP.AMSAT.ORG**. A printed list can be obtained by sending a request with a self-addressed-stamped envelope to AMSAT, 850 Sligo Ave, Silver Spring, MD 20910, USA.

[3]Many programs listed are shareware (available at no charge but with a small registration fee requested if you find the program useful). Others are for purchase at modest cost. See comment in caption about purchasing through AMSAT.

[4]Some interesting tracking programs prepared by space buffs and visual astronomers can be found at
    http://skyshow.com
    http://www.fourmilab.ch/earthview/satellite.html
    http://www.madmansdream.com/Personal_Pages/adamo/Adamo.DFL

Table 7.2
Radio Amateur Tracking Software Overviews/ Reviews

FodTrack, M. Mornhinweg, "The FodTrack Realtime Tracking System"
The AMSAT Journal, May/June 1996, pp 8-11.

InstantTrack, G. Jones, GØ/WD5IVD "Instant Track: An Overview"
The AMSAT Journal, May/June 1992, pp 22-24.

ORBITS III, R. Welch, "ORBITS II and ORBITS III"
The AMSAT Journal, Sep 1991, pp 14-16.

QuikTrak, K. Pugh, W5IU "N4HY Quiktrak v4.0a Review"
The AMSAT Journal, March/April 1992, pp 24-26.

STSOrbit_Plus, K. Emandes, N2WWD and D. Ransom "Doppler Shift Compensation in STSORBIT PLUS"
The AMSAT Journal, Sep/Oct 1994, pp 18-22.

WinSat, M. Mraz, N6MZ "WinSat Version 1.0: New Windows-Based Satellite Tracking Software"
The AMSAT Journal, May/June 1994, pp 28-29.

WiSP, B. Gorsky, WH6I "WiSP"
The AMSAT Journal, July/August 1994, pp 6-9.

"Will O' The WISP," Steve Ford
QST, Feb 1995, p 90.

Misc, G. Smith, WA4SXM "Which AMSAT Tracking Program Should I Get?" Covers InstantTrack, QuickTrak, Orbits II, Orbits III
The AMSAT Journal, Jan/Feb 1992, pp 20-23.

---

difference in the tracking information the program provides. The point here is to be flexible. Using default values is a perfectly reasonable way to get the program up and running. Just make sure that values that significantly affect results are corrected before you try to use the program for actual tracking.

Another common problem encountered in the installation process involves an error message stating that a file can't be found. First of all, the fact that a file can't be found doesn't mean it's missing. It's often present but not in the directory being checked. The solution involves locating the file and either moving it or making sure the search is covering the proper places. If the missing file has a name like unzip.exe (the file to decompress all the other files in the package), it's possible that, for copyright reasons, it may not be included with your package even though it's widely available for free. If this is the case the printed documentation should mention the fact and suggest sources such as a local computer store, hobby group, computer bulletin board or the Internet.

The process of customizing your software includes providing both required data, such as your ground station location, description of the orbit and optional information, such as screen colors, latitude for centering screen maps and map display preferences. The satellite-specific infor-

mation consists of a set of numbers called *orbital elements* that fully describe a satellite's orbit. The meaning of each of these "numbers" will be discussed in the course of this chapter. When you first receive the program it may already have orbital element data included for a number of satellites but the information is likely to be out of date. If your tracking program comes with orbital elements use these values, even if they are out of date, to familiarize yourself with the program's operation. Be aware that a satellite probably won't be where the program says it is until you've updated the values.

For most satellites, orbital element data should be updated every few months. For spacecraft at very low altitudes, like the Shuttle and *Mir*, the orbital elements may have to be updated daily, and of course, after every orbital maneuver. Later in this chapter we'll go into this in more detail and discuss sources for obtaining up-to-date data.

Operating A Tracking Program

After the program has been installed you're ready to run it. While the instruction manual that you printed out will probably tell you exactly what to do, anyone with a bit of computer experience will probably prefer to "wing it" from this point on and just refer to the manual for very specific questions. Trial and error is often the quickest way to learn how to use a program.

STARTING

If you're using Windows, starting the program generally involves clicking your mouse on the "Tracking Icon." If you're using a DOS-based system, starting the program generally involves switching to the appropriate subdirectory and typing the name of the main program. To find the correct name check the directions or look at your list of files for a shortened version of the program name followed by the extension ".exe." For example, using *QuickTrak* the main program name is *qt.exe*. To start it just type **qt** and press the **Enter** key. Users familiar with DOS might prefer to write a short *batch* program to perform the directory switch and start the program in one step. A typical name for this program would be *qt.bat* and it would reside in the main directory.

Computers can be very frustrating even when you have considerable experience in their use. The following hints are meant for novices but others may find them helpful. When you're asked a question that requires a yes or no answer, most DOS programs will accept a one letter response, but some may require a lower or upper case y or n; others may require that you press the **Enter** key after you respond. Trial and error is the quickest way to determine the correct approach.

When entering latitude, longitude (and other angles) make sure you know whether the computer expects degree-minute or decimal degree notation. Following the notation used by the question usually works. Also make sure you understand the units and sign conventions being used. For example, are longitudes specified in degrees East or West of Greenwich, are southern latitudes specified by a negative sign? Fractional parts of a degree will have very little effect on tracking data so in most cases you can just round off your ground station location to the nearest degree.

Dates can also cause considerable trouble. Does the day or month appear first? Can November be abbreviated Nov. or must you enter 11? The number is almost always required. Must you write 1990 or will 90 suffice? Should the parts be separated by colons, dashes or slashes? The list goes on and on. Once again, the prompt is your most important clue. For example, if the prompt reads "Enter date (DD:MM:YY)" and you want to enter Feb. 9, 1998 follow the format of the prompt as precisely as possible and write 09:02:98.

When entering numbers, commas should never be used. For example, if a semi-major axis of 20,243.51 km must be entered, type 20243.51 with the comma and units omitted. It takes a little time to get used to the quirks of each software package, but you'll soon find yourself responding automatically.

MAIN MENU

When the main program begins the first screen shown will probably be the main menu that offers you a number of choices. The generic main menu that follows provides 11 choices.

Main Menu
1) One Satellite: Batch (tabular)
2) One Satellite: Real time (tabular)
3) One Satellite: Real time (graphical)
4) Multiple Satellites: Real time (tabular)
5) Multiple Satellites: Real time (graphical)
5) Mutual Windows
6) Update/Add/Delete Orbital Elements
7) Ground station characteristics
8) Modify/Update/Customize PC screens/resources
Q Exit Program
? Help
ESC Return to previous step or Main Menu

When you make a selection from the main menu you'll likely be asked a series of questions. For example, if you respond "1" to obtain batch tracking data, the computer needs to know which satellite you're interested in, the date

---

Table 7.3
Sample of Tracking Program Batch Output

AMSAT-OSCAR 13

Ground Station: Lat. = 39°N, Long. = 77°W, height = 200 miles
Minimum Elevation = 0°
Day #287   Sunday, October 13,1996

UTC HHMM	Az (deg)	El (deg)	Doppler (Hz)	Range (km)	Height (km)	Lat (deg)	Long (deg)	Phase (<256>)
				ORBIT #6395				
0000	194	8	—	38958	33990	32.3	92.4	84
0015	196	6	597	40064	34888	−33.9	94.5	90
0030	197	4	−522	41029	35648	−35.4	96.7	96
0045	198	3	−449	41859	36276	−36.9	98.9	102
0100	200	1	−377	42556	36773	−38.3	101.0	108
				ORBIT #6397				
1845	346	70	—	2808	2684	44.6	78.1	6
1900	131	48	−2525	7481	6570	22.4	57.8	12
1915	138	35	−2536	12173	10304	9.2	52.1	17
1930	142	29	−2175	16199	13682	0.5	50.2	23
1945	146	25	−1888	19693	16715	−5.8	49.9	29
2000	149	22	−1661	22767	19442	−10.7	50.4	35
2015	152	19	−1476	25497	21897	−14.7	51.5	40
2030	155	18	−1320	27939	24112	−18.0	52.9	46
2045	157	16	−1185	30131	26108	−20.9	54.5	52
2100	160	15	−1065	32102	27906	−23.4	56.3	58
2115	163	13	−958	33875	29520	−25.7	58.2	64
2130	165	12	−860	35466	30963	−27.7	60.2	69
2145	167	11	−770	36891	32245	−29.6	62.3	75
2200	170	10	−685	38159	33375	−31.4	64.4	81
2215	172	9	−606	39280	34358	−33.0	66.6	87
2230	174	7	−530	40260	35202	−34.6	68.7	92
2245	176	6	−457	41106	35910	−36.1	70.9	98
2300	178	5	−386	41821	36486	−37.5	73.0	104
2315	179	4	−318	42408	36933	−38.8	75.1	110
2330	181	2	−250	42871	37253	−40.2	77.2	116
2345	182	1	−183	43210	37448	−41.4	79.3	121

and time to start the calculations, the duration and timestep desired and so on. Exploring and familiarizing yourself with the capabilities of today's powerful and flexible software takes some time.

BATCH TRACKING

Batch output (#1 on the main menu) for a single satellite is especially helpful for planning future operations. If you aim your antennas manually, it also allows the computer to be used for other purposes during passes. Table 7.3 shows the batch output provided by a typical program.

The heading identifies the satellite as OSCAR 13, the ground station location given as latitude, longitude and height, and the starting date. The computer was instructed to print out data whenever the elevation angle of the satellite was greater than 0° for the 24-hour period beginning 00:00 UTC October 13, 1996 using 15-minute timesteps. Although most users find it convenient to assume the satellite will be "in range" when the elevation angle is greater than zero, there are situations where a different value for the "minimum elevation" might be more appropriate.

The first three columns in the body of Table 7.3 present time and data for antenna pointing. The antenna pointing information is presented in the form azimuth and elevation. Azimuth is the angle in local horizontal plane measure clockwise from north and the elevation angle measured above the local horizontal plane. Two separate passes occur this day. The first, during orbit 6399, is already in progress as the day begins. From the decreasing antenna elevation values (Column 3) we see that we're just catching the tail end of the pass and that OSCAR 13 drops below the horizon between 01:00 and 01:15. Another pass, Orbit 6397, begins about 18 hours later. It comes into range sometime between 1830 and 1845 UTC and remains in view until sometime between 23:45 and 24:00 UTC. If we had wanted to ascertain the acquisition time more accurately we could have rerun the batch tracking program from 1830 to 1845 hours using one minute timesteps.

Column 4 provides data on Doppler shift. The values listed refer to a frequency specified during the customization process. The OSCAR beacon frequency of 145.812 MHz was used. When these numbers are negative it means the satellite is receding from the ground station. The fact that all the numbers in this column are negative is unusual. If we check Column 5, which lists the distance between satellite and ground station, we see that the satellite is indeed always receding during both of these passes. From the table we see that at 20:45 UTC the beacon signal will appear 1,185 Hz below its published frequency of 145.812 MHz. Because the algorithm used to compute Doppler shift requires range values at the start and end of the timestep, no value is computed for the first time listed for each pass, 00:00 UTC and 18:45 UTC. You can easily estimate values for these times by looking at the trends in Column 4. If we wanted the computer to provide Doppler data for the transponder instead of the beacon we would have had to insert different information during the customization procedure. For an inverting transponder we

would have inserted the difference between the uplink and downlink frequencies (for example, for Mode B 289 MHz = 435 MHz − 146 MHz). For a noninverting transponder the sum of the uplink and downlink frequencies would have been used.

As mentioned, Column 5 gives the distance between your ground station and the satellite. When the satellite is close, signals are generally stronger though this trend may be negated by the direction of the satellite antennas. Column 6 provides the height of the satellite above the Earth (actually above mean sea level.) Once again, trends provide a great deal of information. During both orbits the satellite disappears from view as it approaches its high point (called the apogee). Such passes are excellent for DX.

Columns 7 and 8 provide the latitude and longitude of the subsatellite point. Longitudes are in degrees west and northern latitudes are positive. Keeping a globe handy one can see that during Orbit 6395 the satellite disappears from view about 1000 miles southeast of Easter Island. During Orbit 6397 it disappears near Concepcion, Chile.

Column 9, the Phase, is an important parameter to anyone working with satellites such as OSCAR 13 that switched modes following a published operating schedule. Schedules are generally modified every few months when satellite orientation is adjusted to compensate for changes in the sun angle on the spacecraft. A typical schedule used for OSCAR 13 looked like this:

Off: from MA 0 until MA 49
Mode B: on from MA 50 until MA 128
Mode S: on from MA 129 until MA 159
Mode B: on from MA 160 until MA 255

The MA units in the schedule refer to entries in the Phase column of Table 7.3. Checking Column 9 we see that the Mode B transponder is on during the entire time we have access during Orbit 6395 and after 2040 during Orbit 6397. The abbreviation MA stands for the term mean anomaly. The expression "anomaly" is just fancy term for angle. Astronomers have traditionally divided orbits into 360 mean anomaly units, each containing an equal time segment. Because of the architecture of common microprocessors, it was much more efficient to design the computers controlling Phase 3 spacecraft to divide each orbit into 256 segments of equal time duration. Radio amateurs refer to these as mean anomaly or phase units. The duration of each segment is the satellites period divided by 256. For example, a mean anomaly unit for OSCAR 13 was roughly 2.68 minutes. At MA 0 (beginning of orbit) and MA 256 (end of orbit) the satellite is at perigee (its lowest point). At MA 128 (halfway through the orbit) the satellite is at apogee or high point.

Because radio amateurs and astronomers use the term mean anomaly in a slightly different way, there's sometimes a question as to which system is being used. Any confusion is minor and usually easily resolved. Most OSCAR telemetry with real-time MA values and schedules use the 256 system. The term phase and the fact that no numbers larger than 256 ever appear are significant hints. Computer tracking programs designed for non-radio amateur audiences generally use the traditional astronomical notation. It's easy to determine when this is the case because the mean anomaly column will contain entries between 257 and 360.

Orbits are numbered consecutively from launch with switch over taking place at perigee. From a practical viewpoint the main use of orbit numbers is for reference in discussions like the preceding one.

There are several additional output parameters (not illustrated in Table 7.3) that some tracking programs provide. A column labeled Echo or Delay provides the time delay introduced by the up and downlinks. At OSCAR 13's apogee, this amounted to slightly more than a quarter second. A column labeled Squint Angle describes how the directive antennas on a satellite (such as Phase 3 satellites) are pointed with respect to your ground station. Squint angle can vary between 0° and 180°. A squint angle of 0° means the satellite antennas are pointed directly at you that generally indicates that good link performance can be expected. When the squint angle is above 20° signal level begins to drop and a disruptive amplitude flutter called *spin modulation* on up- and downlinks may become apparent. The causes of spin modulation are discussed in the Antenna Basics chapter. The squint angle at which spin modulation becomes a problem depends on the specific spacecraft and links in use. In some cases problems may begin at 10°, in other cases at 30°, etc. Programs that include algorithms to calculate squint angle require information about the orientation or attitude of the satellite. This information is generally available from sources that provide the basic orbital elements and on telemetry sent directly from the satellite of interest. The parameters needed are labeled Bahn latitude and Bahn longitude. They are also known as BLAT and BLON or ALAT and ALON where the prefix "A" stands for attitude.

Programs that provide squint angle may also contain a column labeled Predicted Signal Level. Values are usually computed using a simple prediction model that takes into account satellite antenna pattern, squint angle and spacecraft range. The model is discussed in detail in the Satellite Systems chapter. For Phase 3 satellites the model assumes a 0 dB reference point with the satellite overhead, at apogee and pointing directly at you. At any point on the orbit the predicted level may be several dB above (+) or below (–) this reference level.

TABULAR REAL-TIME TRACKING

Another option on the main menu provides real-time tabular output with positions of one or more satellites updated every few seconds. An illustration focusing on the seven orbiting amateur spacecraft (plus *Mir*) having linear transponders in 1996 is shown in Table 7.4.

Ten additional amateur spacecraft, with digital transponders operating at the time, have not been included. Many programs will permit you to assign a name to a list of spacecraft, so the output of Table 7.4 could have been obtained by requesting the name that you chose for amateur spacecraft having linear transponders.

The column headings in Table 7.4 should be clear from our previous discussion of batch output. A quick check of the elevation column in Table 7.4 shows that two satellites, OSCAR 13 and RS-15, were in range at the time of the printout, 21:00:47 UTC. Most computer programs highlight spacecraft currently in range and even color code those coming into range in the next few minutes or beep when a new spacecraft becomes accessible. Real-time output does not mean current time output. You can generally specify whatever starting time you wish and check what the status will be at some future time with the display being updated in real time. This is generally accomplished by temporarily changing the current time stored in the computer's clock.

GRAPHICAL REAL-TIME TRACKING

Real-time graphical output takes the subsatellite location data from the longitude and latitude columns of Table 7.4 and plots this information on a map on the computer screen. A Cartesian map is usually used but some programs will give you the option of using other map projections. The graphical display will probably also list key data for at

---

Table 7.4
Example of Real-Time Output in Tabular Form

Baltimore
REAL-TIME SATELLITE TRACKING
Coordinates on 10-13-1996 at 21:00:47 UTC

Name	Az	El	Rng km	Hgt km	Lat	Long	Orbit	Phase
AO13	*160*	*15*	*32197*	*27993*	*−23.5*	*56.4*	*6397*	*58*
AO10	119	−22	21949	14054	−26.0	1.2	4221	229
RS10	159	−69	12971	992	−70.9	298.2	46645	66
RS12	324	−74	13260	983	−13.0	238.2	28534	61
RS15	*316*	*19*	*3856*	*2077*	*54.0*	*106.3*	*7416*	*175*
Mir	210	−25	6106	378	−11.4	101.0	60855	44
FO20	163	−57	11971	1161	−72.6	17.2	31311	45
FO29	196	−66	13012	1300	−76.7	201.3	782	109

least one satellite and perhaps include a coverage circle around the spacecraft showing which terrestrial stations have access to the satellite at the moment being pictured. The material on low-tech graphical tracking techniques that follows this section will provide a great deal of additional information helpful in interpreting graphics screens. Whenever I'm sitting in my radio room reading I usually leave the computer on with the graphical mode running. Every now and then I'll glance at the screen so that if a satellite I'm interested in happens to be nearby I can quickly switch on the receiver.

ORBITAL ELEMENTS

Orbital elements are a set of six numbers that completely describe the orbit of a satellite at a specific time. Although scientists may occasionally use different groups of six quantities, radio amateurs nearly always use the six known as Keplerian Orbital Elements. Called *keps*, they are described below. Orbital elements are frequently distributed with additional numerical data, which may or may not be used by a software tracking program.

Option 4 on the tracking software main menu places you in a database program where information on specific satellites is entered and updated. When you select this option you'll probably be queried as to whether you want to add orbital elements for a new satellite, change the elements of an old satellite or delete a satellite's elements. Suppose you choose to add a new satellite. The program will respond by asking you to enter a series of questions requiring numeri-

cal responses. To respond, you need current information on the orbital elements of the satellite of interest. This data is available from sources listed later in this chapter. Two formats are commonly seen. One is the AMSAT format shown in Table 7.5. The other is the NASA Two Line format discussed later in this chapter. Since the published orbital data must work with a large variety of programs the table may include several entries that your program does not require. It helps to have some understanding of the meaning of each entry and to know if it's optional.

The first two entries identify the spacecraft. The first line is an informal satellite name. Since you'll be using this name when you run the program, select a label that's clear and easy to type—you do not have to enter the name exactly as listed. The second entry, Catalog Number, is a formal ID assigned by NASA. This item is optional.

The next entry, Epoch Time, specifies the time the orbital elements were computed. The number consists of two parts, the part to the left of the decimal point that describes the year and day, and the part to the right of the decimal point that describes the time of day. For example, 96325.465598 refers to 1996, day *325*, time of day *.465598*. See Sample Problem 7.1 at the end of this chapter for an explanation of the time of day. Some programs ask you to enter the year and date separately; others ask for both parts to be entered as shown.

The next entry, Element Set, is a reference used to identify the source of the information. For example, 199 indicates element set number 199 issued by AMSAT. This information is optional. If your program asks for it you can either repeat the information provided or leave the entry blank.

The next six entries are the six key orbital elements. All programs require them. A brief informal description of what each one refers to follows. A more detailed description is given in the Satellite Orbits chapter.

Inclination describes the orientation of the satellite's orbital plane with respect to the equatorial plane of the Earth.

RAAN, Right Ascension of Ascending Node, specifies the orientation of the satellite's orbital plane with respect to fixed stars.

Eccentricity refers to the shape of the orbital ellipse.

Argument of Perigee describes where the perigee of the satellite is located in the satellite orbital plane. When the argument of perigee is between 180 and 360° the perigee will be over the Southern Hemisphere. Apogee will therefore occur above the Northern Hemisphere.

Mean Anomaly locates the satellite in the orbital plane at the epoch. All programs use the astronomical convention for mean anomaly units. The mean anomaly is 0 at perigee and 180 at apogee. Values between 0 and 180 indicate that the satellite is headed up toward apogee. Values between 180 and 360 indicate that the satellite is headed down toward perigee.

Mean Motion specifies the number of revolutions the satellite makes each day. This element indirectly provides information about the size of the elliptical orbit. Some old

Table 7.5

Example of Orbital Elements Provided for Computer Tracking Programs

Parameter name	Value	Units
Satellite:[1]	RS-15	
Catalog number:	23439	
Epoch Time:	96325.46559868	days
Element Set:	0199	
Inclination:	64.8126	deg
RAAN:[2]	130.3567	deg
Eccentricity:	0.0156329	
Arg. of Perigee:[3]	171.1813	deg
Mean Anomaly:	189.1913	deg
Mean Motion:	11.27529249	rev/day
Decay Rate:[4]	−3.9e−07	rev/day/day
Epoch Rev:[5]	7840	
Checksum:	339	
Bahn Latitude:[6]	—	deg
Bahn Longitude[7]	—	deg

Alternate parameter names:
[1]Object
[2]Right Ascension of Ascending Node; RA of Node
[3]Argument of Perigee
[4]Drag factor: Rate of change of mean motion, first derivative of mean motion
[5]Revolution number, orbit number
[6]ALAT, BLAT
[7]ALON, BLON

Table 7.6
Summary of Tracking Terms

access range—acquisition distance

acquisition circle—"Circle" drawn about a ground station and keyed to a specific satellite. When the SSP is inside the circle the satellite is in range.

acquisition distance—Maximum distance between subsatellite point and ground station at which access to spacecraft is possible.

AOS—Acquisition Of Signal/Satellite.

apogee—Point on orbit where satellite height is maximum.

argument of perigee—An angle that describes the location of a satellite's perigee. When the argument of perigee is between 0° and 180° perigee is over the Northern Hemisphere. When the argument of perigee is between 180° and 360° the perigee is over the Southern Hemisphere.

ascending node (EQX)—Point where ground track crosses equator with satellite headed north.

azimuth—Angle in the horizontal plane measured clockwise with respect to North (North = 0°)

Bahn latitude and Bahn longitude (ALAT, ALON; BLAT, BLON)—Angles that describe the orientation of a satellite in its orbital plane. When Bahn latitude is 0° and Bahn longitude is 180° the directional antennas on the satellite will be pointing directly at the SSP when the spacecraft is at apogee. For P3D, BLAT and BLON change as the spacecraft moves in its orbit.

coverage circle—With respect to a particular ground station, the region of Earth that is eventually accessible for communication via a specific satellite. With respect to a particular satellite, the region around the instantaneous SSP that is in view of the satellite.

decay rate—Short name for rate of change of mean motion. A parameter specifying how atmospheric drag affects a satellite's motion.

descending node—Point where ground track crosses equator with satellite headed south.

elevation—Angle above the horizontal plane.

elevation circle—The set of all subsatellite locations about a ground station where the elevation angle to a specified satellite is a fixed value.

epoch (epoch time)—A reference time when orbital elements are specified.

geostationary satellite—A satellite that appears to hang motionless over a fixed point on the equator.

ground track/subsatellite path—Path on surface of Earth traced out by SSP as satellite moves through space.

inclination—An angle that specifies the orientation of a satellite's orbital plane with respect to the Earth's equatorial plane.

Increment—Longitudinal increment

longitudinal/increment—Change in longitude of ascending node between two successive passes of specified satellite. Measured in degrees West per orbit (°W/orbit).

LOS—Loss of Signal or Loss of Satellite

mean motion—Number of revolutions (perigee to perigee) completed by satellite in a solar day (1440 minutes.)

mean anomaly (MA)—Values in [ ] are used in software designed for visual astronomers and other scientists. A number between 0 and 256 [360] that increases uniformly with time. Used to locate satellite position on orbital elllpse. When MA is 0 or 256 [360] satellite is at perigee. When MA is 128 [180] satellite is at apogee. When MA is between 0 and 128 [180] satellite is headed up toward apogee. When MA is between 128 [180] and 256 [360] satellite is headed down toward perigee.

node—Point where satellite ground track crosses the equator.

orbital elements—Set of six numbers specified at particular time (epoch) that completely describe size, shape and orientation of satellite orbit.

OSCARLOCATOR—A tracking device designed for satellites in circular orbits.

pass—satellite pass.

perigee—Point on orbit where satellite height is minimum.

period—The amount of time it takes a satellite to complete one revolution, perigee to perigee, about the Earth.

Phase—See *mean anomaly*.

P3 Tracker—A tracking device related to the OSCARLOCATOR that is designed to be used with a satellite in an elliptical orbit.

RAAN/Right Ascension of Ascending Node—An angle that specifies the orientation of a satellite's orbital plane with respect to the fixed stars.

range circle—Circle on surface of Earth of specific radius centered about ground station.

reference orbit—Orbit following reference node.

satellite pass—Segment of orbit when a satellite passes in range of particular ground station.

spiderweb—Set of azimuth curves radiating outward from a particular terrestrial location or a set of concentric elevation (equal range) circles about, a particular terrestrial location.

Squint angle—Angle between aiming direction of satellite antenna and line between satellite and your ground station. Squint angle is zero when satellite antenna is pointed directly at your ground station.

SSP—subsatellite point

stationary satellite—geostationary satellite

subsatellite path—ground track

subsatellite point/SSP—Point on surface of Earth directly below satellite.

window—For a specific satellite, the overlap region between acquisition circles of two ground stations. Communication between the two stations via the specified satellite is possible when SSP passes through window.

Notes
True circles on the globe are often distorted when transferred to a map. Some minor differences will be found between the informal definitions in this table and those in the Glossary, where emphasis has been placed on technical precision.

programs require semi-major axis or period instead of mean motion.

Table 7.6 summarizes the informal definitions of the orbital elements provided here and other important tracking terms introduced in this chapter. More formal definitions are given in later sections of this book and the Glossary. We'll return to orbital elements later in this chapter and consider where and how to obtain them, and how frequently they should be updated. We'll also look at the different formats used to present them.

Decay Rate is a parameter used in sophisticated tracking models to take into account how the frictional drag produced by the Earth's atmosphere affects a satellite's orbit. It may also be referred to as rate of change of mean motion, first derivative of mean motion, or drag factor. Although decay rate is an important parameter in scientific studies of the Earth's atmosphere and when observing satellites that are about to reenter, it has very little effect on day-to-day tracking of most Amateur Radio satellites. If your program asks for drag factor, enter the number provided. If the element set does not contain this information enter zero—you shouldn't discern any difference in predictions. You usually have a choice of entering this number using either decimal form or scientific notation. For example, the number –0.00000039 (decimal form) can be entered as –3.9e–7 (scientific notation). The e–7 stands for 10 to the minus seventh power (or 10 exponent –7). In practical terms e–7 just means move the decimal in the preceding number 7 places to the left. If this is totally confusing, just remember that in most situations entering zero will work fine.

Epoch revolution is just another term for the expression Orbit Number that we discussed earlier. The number provided here does not affect tracking data, so don't worry if different element sets provide different numbers for the same day and time. In fact, in most cases it's simplest to just enter a zero here and ignore information on epoch revolution provided by the program.

The Checksum entry in Table 7.5 is a number constructed by the data transmitting station and used by the receiving station to check for certain types of transmission errors in data files. It does not bear any relation to a satellite's orbit.[4]

MODIFYING—UPDATING—CUSTOMIZING

This section of the program will generally be used to handle all changes and customizing that does not involve orbital elements. A little time spent familiarizing yourself with these options can make any program more user friendly. For example, setting it to boot to the section of the main menu you generally use, redrawing maps so that they're centered at your longitude, turning off annoying beeps, and so on. The flexibility provided can also be used in unanticipated ways. For example, if you have a slow computer you might want to select a low resolution graphics mode to speed up tracking calculations.

OTHER MAIN MENU ITEMS

The main menu may contain several additional items. For example, selecting Mutual Windows provides tabular output showing when a selected path involving two or more ground stations can be covered using a particular satellite. The "?" provides access to on screen help files. Some software authors provide extensive written instructions while others devote their energy to producing help files. Finally, it's important to exit the program properly. Typing "Q" from the main menu will avoid the possible corruption of data files.

LOW-TECH TRACKING

The low-tech approaches to tracking presented in this section, many of which were developed 40 years ago by radio amateurs, still work fine. They're being presented here for two reasons. First, because situations where they're useful, such as in classrooms in underdeveloped countries, still exist and second, because they give important insights into how the information provided by computer real-time graphical displays can be understood. The latter because both methods rely on the interpretation of maps of the Earth showing positions of spacecraft and groundstations. Several new tracking terms will be introduced. As before, explanations will be informal and practical. See the summary in Table 7.6. The point on the surface of the Earth directly below a satellite is called the *subsatellite point, SSP*. The position of the SSP is specified by giving its latitude and longitude. For all but geostationary satellites, the location of the SSP constantly changes as the spacecraft moves across the sky. If we were to watch the SSP as a satellite travels along its orbit, the SSP would trace a curve on the surface of the Earth called the satellite's ground track or subsatellite path.

The basis of all tracking techniques can be summed up in a simple statement: A satellite will be in range when the SSP is close to your ground station location and out of range when the SSP is far away from your location.

Of course, we have to define how close "close" is. Computer approaches and the low-tech approaches use different approaches to figure the actual satellite to ground station distance—the computer goes through a series of mathematical calculations, while the low-tech approach uses visual observations of various curves drawn on a map. We begin with the simplest case, a satellite in a circular orbit.

A satellite in a circular orbit has a critical acquisition distance associated with it. When the distance between your ground station and the SSP is less than the acquisition distance, the satellite is in range of your station. This distance depends on the satellite's height above the Earth—the higher the satellite the larger the acquisition distance. Since a satellite in a circular orbit has a fixed height, the acquisition distance is constant. The height of a satellite in an elliptical orbit is constantly changing and so is its acquisition distance. This is what makes tracking satellites in elliptical orbits more challenging. See Table 7.7 for data on acquisition distances.

We can use the acquisition distance to draw an acquisition circle about a ground station. Figure 7.1 shows an acquisition circle drawn about Baltimore, MD, for RS-15

Table 7.7
Maximum Acquisition Distance

When the satellite is at an elevation angle above 0° it is considered to be in range. Maximum acquisition distance is at 0°. Distances between SSP and ground station (elevation circle radii) corresponding to selected elevation angles are given in km, miles and arc length along a great circle.

Satellite Name	Satellite Height	Elevation circle radius		
		0°	30°	60°
OSCARs 14-19	830 km	3089 km	1110 km	416 km
	516 mi	1920 mi	690 mi	259 mi
		27.8°	10.0°	3.7°
UoSAT-OSCAR 11	690 km	2840 km	958 km	354 km
	429 mi	1765 mi	595 mi	220 mi
		25.5°	8.6°	3.2°
RS-15	2030 km	4523 km	2107 km	858 km
	1262 mi	2811 mi	1309 mi	533 mi
		40.7°	18.9°	7.7°
RS-10/11	1003 km	3362 km	1286 km	490 km
	623 mi	2089 mi	799 mi	305 mi
		30.2°	11.6°	4.4°
AMSAT-OSCAR 40				
apogee	47,000 km	9245 km	6012 km	2955 km
	29,211 mi	5745 mi	3736 mi	1836 mi
		83.1°	54.1°	26.6°
perigee	4000 km	5793 km	3098 km	1347 km
	2486 mi	3600 mi	1925 mi	837 mi
		52.1°	27.9°	12.1°

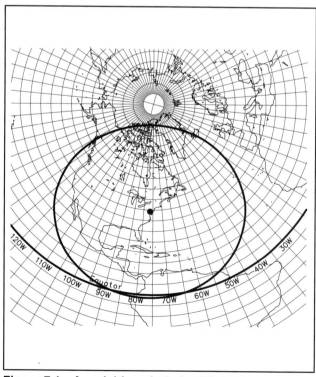

Figure 7.1—Acquisition circle for RS-15 about Baltimore, MD.

having an altitude of 2030 km. Note that a circle on the surface of the Earth (a sphere) does not look like a circle when it's drawn on most flat maps—its shape depends on the type of map being used. Figure 7.1 uses a polar map but other types of maps would be fine for this discussion.

Assume that your station is located in Baltimore. If the ground track for a specific orbit of the satellite passes inside the acquisition circle, the satellite will be in range during that segment of the orbit during which the SSP is inside the access circle. Figure 7.2 shows a ground track for part of an orbit added to Figure 7.1. The tick marks on the ground track show how far the satellite moves in two minutes.

Acquisition of Satellite (AOS) occurs when the SSP enters the acquisition circle. As this occurs, the satellite's elevation angle passes through zero headed in a positive direction. *Loss of Satellite* (LOS) occurs when the SSP leaves the acquisition circle As this occurs the satellite's elevation angle passes through zero headed in a negative direction. The satellite is in range between AOS and LOS. Referring to Figure 7.2, AOS occurs at point A, LOS occurs about 30 minutes later at point B. Computer programs give actual clock times instead of providing relative information. Ten minutes after AOS the satellite will be at point C.

Although Figure 7.2 contains the information needed to answer the basic question of when a spacecraft will be in range, we still need azimuth and elevation antenna aiming data. Figure 7.2 already contains some information on elevation—we know that the antenna elevation is 0° at AOS and LOS. The acquisition circle we discussed earlier actually shows all points where the satellite elevation would be 0°. If we wanted to be formal we could call it an "iso-elevation contour" but "constant elevation circle" or "acquisition circle" sounds simpler. We can draw additional constant elevation circles about the ground track using selected values for the elevation angle. This is frequently done for 30° and 60°.

Figure 7.2 can provide azimuth pointing data if we add another set of lines on the map—a set radiating outward from the ground station at selected fixed azimuths, say every 30°. Taken together, the concentric circles (constant elevation circles) and radial lines (constant azimuth lines) are called a spiderweb. See Figure 7.3.

Figure 7.3 is interpreted as follows. If, at some point in time, we know the position of the SSP we can estimate azimuth and elevation directly from the figure. For example, at AOS the SSP is on the 0° elevation circle and between the radial lines labeled 210° and 240°. Using "eyeball" interpolation we estimate azimuth as 230°. We have therefore determined elevation and azimuth at AOS. To obtain antenna pointing data at point C, we note that the SSP is between the 30° and 60° elevation circles and between the 240° and 270° radial lines. Again, using eyeball interpolation, we can state that 10 minutes after AOS the elevation is approximately 40° and the azimuth is about 255°. If we knew the actual clock time at AOS, we would have all the information we need to track RS-15 during this pass.

Placing a complete spiderweb on a computer screen produces a cluttered display so most software programs just show the map and SSP and perhaps the acquisition circle and provide azimuth, elevation, SSP latitude and SSP longitude in a numerical format. Since all this data is changing, the display is updated several times a minute.

Circular Orbits—The OSCARLOCATOR

Several low-tech graphical tracking devices designed to handle satellites in low altitude circular (or nearly circular) orbits were widely used from the '60s to the '80s. These include the *Satellabe*, designed by K2ZRO, the *W2GFF Plotter* and the *OSCARLOCATOR*. The OSCAR-LOCATOR will be used to illustrate how these devices operate by focusing on a ground station in Baltimore, MD, that tracks RS-15. The operation of the OSCARLOCATOR is based on two facts. First, all ground tracks drawn on a polar map have the same shape, which makes it possible to draw a single ground track overlay that can be repositioned for future orbits. And second, the time and distance (along the equator) from the start of one orbit to the next are constant. This provides the information needed to reposition the ground track overlay from orbit to orbit.

The OSCARLOCATOR consists of two parts:

1) *Map Board*. A map centered on the North Pole like the one shown in Figure 7.1. A blank full-size map is presented in Appendix G.

2) *Ground-Track Overlay*. An overlay, usually drawn on transparent material, like the one shown in Figure 7.4. The overlay is pinned to the map board at the North Pole so it can be rotated.

Before you use an OSCARLOCATOR you have to prepare the Map Board for a specific satellite by drawing a spiderweb around your location using appropriate distances for the elevation circles. If you're using an omnidirectional antenna an acquisition circle will suffice. Drawing a spiderweb is a tedious job but it only has to be done once. One way is to transfer points, one by one, from a globe to the map. An easier method is to use the program *SWEB*

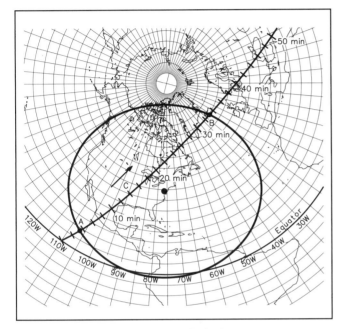

Figure 7.2—RS-15 ground track during pass near Baltimore, MD.

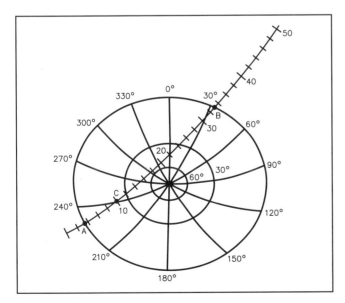

Figure 7.3—RS-15 ground track during pass near Baltimore, MD, showing full spiderweb about Baltimore.

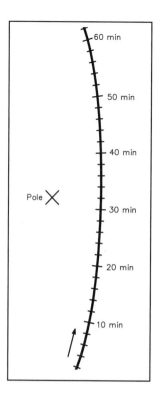

Figure 7.4—RS-15 Ground Track Overlay for OSCARLOCATOR.

to provide data points. For those interested, the calculations involved are discussed in the Tracking Topics chapter.

You must also prepare the Ground Track Overlay. The program *GTCIRC* provides the data needed. For those interested, the calculations involved are discussed in the Satellite Orbits chapter. Some shortcuts are discussed later in this section.

To use the OSCARLOCATOR we need to know how to position the overlay and the time at AOS. We've already seen how the results are interpreted; see the discussion accompanying Figure 7.3.

Information on positioning the overlay is usually given by providing the time and location of the SSP as it passes over the equator headed into the Northern Hemisphere. The point on the equator where this occurs is called the ascending node. This orbit starting at this node is called the reference orbit.

For example, suppose we know that an ascending node for RS-15 (Orbit #10706) occurs at 15:56 UTC at 110.2° W longitude. We rotate the Ground Track Overlay until the marker is set to 110.2° W on the Map Board. Figure 7.3 shows the situation. When we combine the time at the ascending node, which we now know with the time intervals to reach AOS, LOS and point C that we already knew we can provide clock times for these key points. AOS occurs at 16:00 UTC, the SSP is at point C at 16:10 UTC and LOS occurs at 16:30 UTC.

To make predictions about future orbits we need two additional pieces of information about RS-15's orbit. We need its period, the amount of time it takes for the satellite to make one complete revolution around the Earth, and its longitude increment, the distance along the equator between any two successive ascending nodes. The relevant

numbers are 127.713 minutes (period) and 31.928° W per orbit (increment).

To preview the next orbit we add the period and increment to the reference orbit ascending node. The orbit following the reference orbit begins at 18:05.713 UTC (15:58 + 127.713 minutes) with the ascending node occurring at 142.128° W (110.2° + 31.928°.) We now set the Ground Track Overlay to this point and proceed as before. To preview the next orbit we just add another 127.713 minutes and 31.928° to the ascending node time and longitude, and so on.

How long can we keep doing this before errors accumulate and make the results useless? In the mid '70s, at the beginning of each year, AMSAT published an *Orbit Calendar*. It contained a list of all ascending nodes for all amateur satellites in orbit for a year. The results were generally good to within a minute or two by December. The satellites being tracked at the time were in circular low Earth orbits but well above the atmosphere. At heights between 600 and 800 km predictions would only be reliable for a couple of months. To minimize error accumulations in long term predictions one must use very accurate values for the period and orbit increment; in fact, they must be more accurate than those used in the example.

Building and using an OSCARLOCATOR or similar device obviously requires some initial information. Where does this information come from? Most of it can be calculated with little more than a scientific calculator following procedures discussed later in this book once you have a basic description of the satellite orbit. For example, an announcement saying a satellite was just launched into a 1500 km high circular orbit with an inclination of 98.2° contains all the information needed to draw an accurate ground track, calculate period, longitude increment and draw an appropriate spiderweb. Data describing one reference orbit is still needed but this can be determined from observations of radio signals from the satellite over the course of several days.

Simple extensions of the information just presented make it possible for us to use an OSCARLOCATOR to determine those regions of the Earth eventually accessible to us via a specific satellite and those orbits suitable for communicating with specific distant stations. Again RS-15 will be used as an example. Since the maximum acquisition distance for this satellite is 2811 miles (Table 7.7), two stations separated by twice this distance (5622 miles) can communicate with one another if the SSP passes over the midpoint of the great circle path joining them.

To select suitable orbits for communicating from New York to Moscow, one could draw acquisition circles for both stations on the OSCARLOCATOR Map Board as shown in Figure 7.5. Whenever the RS-15 SSP is in the overlapping region, called the window, communications between the two stations is possible. Note that RS-15 never enters the part of the window north of 64.8°, which is the orbital inclination of RS-15.

SIMPLIFIED OSCARLOCATOR

There are some tricks that old-timers used to quickly

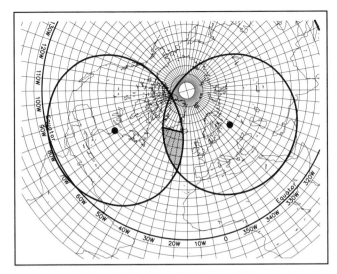

Figure 7.5—Mutual Window Baltimore-Moscow for RS-15.

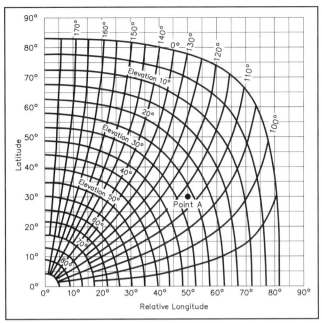

Figure 7.6—Antenna aiming chart for geostationary satellite. Example shown for ground station in New Orleans (30°N, 90°W) and satellite at 40°W. For blank chart see Appendix G

prepare crude but useful OSCARLOCATORs whenever a new spacecraft was launched. The procedure begins with a sketch of the Ground Track Overlay on a copy of the Map Board using just three reference points—two nodes and the northernmost SSP. Mark an ascending node at the Greenwich Meridian. Mark a descending node (SSP headed south across the equator) at 180° plus one half the increment further west. The spacecraft will be at its northernmost point halfway between these two nodes. At the northernmost point, the SSP latitude is equal to the satellite's inclination, or 180° minus the inclination, if the inclination is greater than 90°. If the inclination is less than 90° choose the smaller distance (longitude change) when marking the midpoint of the longitude. If the inclination is greater than 90° choose the larger distance when marking the midpoint of the longitude. Sketch a smooth curve using the two nodes and the midpoint. This is the master for your ground track overlay. The time between ascending and descending nodes is one half the period. Using this value, divide the ground track into equal increments to show time.

On the Map Board, locate the longitude line going through your ground station. Obtain the degree value for the acquisition circle radius given in Table 7.7. Using this distance place a mark above and below your ground station latitude on the Map Board, ignoring map distortion, sketch in a crude acquisition circle around your location. That's it—you're finished.

Additional information about low-tech tracking devices for satellites in circular orbits is presented in a collection of references.[5] These references document early amateur contributions and ensure that the techniques they developed will remain accessible to those who may need them in the future.

Geostationary Orbits

Tracking a satellite that remains over a fixed longitude on the Earth's equator (stationary satellite) involves determining whether the spacecraft is in range of your ground station and obtaining antenna azimuth and elevation angles.

Since the satellite position appears stationary this has to be done only once. If you know your latitude and longitude and the longitude of the satellite, this is easily accomplished using a computer, programmable calculator or chart like the one shown in Figure 7.6. The following approach works for all geostationary spacecraft including weather satellites and TV broadcasting satellites.

An example illustrates how Figure 7.6 is used. Assume that a ground station in New Orleans located at latitude 30° N and longitude 90°W, is interested in accessing a stationary satellite located at 40°W longitude.

Step 1. Compute a relative longitude by subtracting the ground station's longitude (90° W) from the satellite's longitude (40° W): 40° W – 90° W =–50° W. Plot the point consisting of the absolute values of (a) the relative longitude just computed and (b) the latitude of the ground station. See point A (50°, 30°) on Figure 7.6.

Step 2. If the point is inside the 0° elevation curve the satellite is in range of the ground station. The location of point A indicates that the satellite is in range of New Orleans.

Step 3. Noting intersections of elevation curves and radial (azimuth) curves near point A, use "eyeball interpolation" to estimate the antenna elevation and radial values. In our example the elevation value is 27° and the radial value is 113°. Azimuth is determined from the radial value. For Northern Hemisphere stations the azimuth is equal to either: (a) the radial value or (b) 360°– (radial value), depending on whether the satellite is east or west of the ground station. For Southern Hemisphere stations the azimuth is equal to either: (a) 180°– (radial value) or (b) 180° + (radial value), depending on whether the satellite is east or west of the ground station.

Step 4. The antenna should be aimed as calculated in Step 3 and then the direction varied slightly to peak received signals. If the satellite is being kept accurately on station the resulting antenna azimuth and elevation will remain fixed.

A full-size chart of the type used for Figure 7.6 is contained in Appendix G. Computational methods for obtaining antenna pointing data for geostationary satellites are covered in the Satellite Orbits chapter.

Elliptical Orbits—The P3 Tracker

As mentioned earlier, the basic OSCARLOCATOR can not be used to track satellites in highly elliptical orbits. The key problem is that the size of the acquisition circle changes as the satellite height changes. One device devised to handle this problem was called the P3 Tracker.[6] Like the OSCARLOCATOR it consists of two parts, a Map Board using a polar map and a Ground Track Overlay that can be rotated around the pole. The P3 Tracker is most useful for elliptical orbits where the satellite's high point in the orbit (apogee), occurs over a fixed latitude. When this occurs the Ground Track Overlay does not change. The P3 Tracker is also useful when the apogee occurs at a latitude that changes no more than a few degrees per month. In these cases the Ground Track Overlay will change, but one can use an overlay for a few months before updating it.

The P3 Tracker works by dividing the Ground Track Overlay into segments related to minimum possible communication distance. For example, during one segment the minimum possible communications distance is 7000 km, during the next segment the minimum possible communications distance is 6000 km and so on. The circles on the spiderweb are then drawn to represent fixed distances using the same values employed to label the Ground Track Overlay. Instead of elevation circles, the spiderweb now consists of a set of acquisition circles, one for each segment of the orbit. To use the P3 TRACKER set the Ground Track Overlay, as with the OSCARLOCATOR, and look for segments of the orbit where the minimum communications distance is inside the corresponding acquisition circles. For example, if the 6000 km section of the orbit is inside the 6000 km acquisition circle the satellite will be in range the entire time.

This approach provides us with information on when the spacecraft will be in range. Azimuth data can be read directly from the SSP location, but it appears that elevation data is missing. This is not the case. One can set up a table relating acquisition circle distance and ground track minimum communications distance to provide approximate satellite elevation values.

Since the target orbits for Phase 3 radio amateur satellites all involve cases where the latitude at apogee was constant or slowly changing, a P3 Tracker would have provided radio amateurs with basic tracking information. As mentioned earlier, however, the first spacecraft in the P3 series was lost due to a launch failure. By the time the second P3 series spacecraft (OSCAR 10) was launched in 1983, radio amateurs had already sensed the role small computers would play in tracking and devoted their energies toward software.

ORBITAL ELEMENTS

Earlier in this chapter we discussed what orbital elements were and why computer tracking programs require them. In this section we'll look at how frequently they have to be updated and where and how to obtain them.

Frequency of Updating

The question: "How frequently must orbital elements be updated?" is faced by everyone. The answer depends on several factors including the satellite orbit, the location of the ground station, the directional patterns of the ground station antennas, whether one is interested in short DX windows at AOS/LOS, if Doppler compensation is being used on PACSATs and so on. With all these factors affecting the situation, there can't be a single simple answer, but looking at some relevant information and considering a number of typical situations can provide some helpful guidelines. Note that the age of a set of elements is measured from the epoch time, not from when they're received.

The mathematical algorithms used by government agencies who distribute orbital elements are designed to provide very good predictions for periods less than 10 days. One result is that the long term effects of small periodic and sporadic perturbations due to atmospheric drag, magnetic storms and other factors can either be over- or understated. In the early days of the OSCAR program (mid 1970s) amateurs produced their own smoothed orbital elements for LEO spacecraft that averaged-out these small perturbations. In many cases, the amateur produced elements gave better long term results than today's high precision values. For example, with OSCARs 6, 7 and 8 and early RS spacecraft, orbital elements produced in the amateur community were used to generate Orbit Calendars that were accurate to within a couple of minutes over a 12 month period. With Phase 3 satellites the situation is similar. When OSCAR 13 was still operating, G3RUH would periodically produce a set of smoothed orbital elements for the command team. These elements provided excellent predictions for up to a year.

Since the elements currently distributed by AMSAT and other groups are generally from government sources (optimized for short term predictions) our discussion will focus on them. A ground station using either a low gain beam or an omni antenna working a linear transponder on a satellite in a low altitude circular orbit, will generally find that an accurate set of orbital elements will provide good results for three to six months if the satellite height is above 1000 km. For heights in the range 600 to 800 km, updating every second month should be sufficient. For heights below 600 km, like those for the International Space Station, daily updating is often required. They are also required after every orbital maneuver. Of course, you may find it desirable to update more frequently if you're using a very high gain narrow beamwidth antenna, if you're especially interested in mutual DX windows lasting fractions of a minute or if you use computer software to compensate for Doppler frequency shifts.

Table 7.8
Example of NASA's Two-Line Orbital Element Set (OSCAR 10)

```
          1         2         3         4         5         6
123456789012345678901234567890123456789012345678901234567890123456789

1 14129U 83058B   96299.11613815 -.00000305  00000-0 10000-3 0   4631

2 14129  25.8792 182.5891 6052907  60.2572 346.3435 2.05882271  72548
```

Explanation
Column numbers (1-69) have been added here so that they can be referenced below. Note that leading zeros are not printed. However, they may be counted when assigning column positions. Blanks must always be in positions indicated.

Line 1
column:

01	line number = 1
02	blank
03	NASA catalog number = 14129 (OSCAR 10)
08	U = Unclassified
09	blank
10	launch year = 83, launch no. of year = 058, launch piece = B
18	blank
19*	epoch = 96299.11613815 (1996, day 299 = Oct 25 at 02:47:14.3 UTC)
33	blank
34	first derivative (rate of change) of mean motion = 0.00000305
53	blank
54	drag = .001
64	blank
65	element set number = 463
69	checksum = 1 (number is modulo 10)

Line 2
column:

01	line number = 2
02	blank
03	NASA catalog number = 14129
08	blank
09*	inclination (degrees) = 25.8792
17	blank
18*	RAAN (degrees) = 182.5891
26	blank
27*	cccentricity (note: leading decimal point is missing) = 6052907
34	blank
35*	argument of perigee (degrees) = 60.2572
43	blank
44*	mean anomaly (degrees) = 346.3435; Multiply by 256/360 for phase units.
52	blank
53*	mean motion (rev./day) = 2.05882271
64	revolution at epoch = 7254
69	checksum = 8 (number is modulo 10)

Notes
*Fundamental orbital element required by all tracking programs.

For information on entries not covered request *Format Explanation of the Two-Line Orbital Elements*, from: Project Operations Branch, Code 513; Goddard Space Flight Center; Greenbelt, MD 20771.

For Phase 3 type orbits, orbital elements should be updated at least two or three times a year. If operation around perigee is important, however, updating every month or two may be necessary. Of course, all these values are just suggestions and the details of your particular situation may warrant different values.

Remember that these suggestions are for maximum times you can go without updating before tracking errors become a problem. Where does this advice come from? Basically from this author's three plus decades of experience working with amateur satellites, discussions with other long time operators and with computer experiments. You are encouraged to duplicate the following experiments if tracking data is critical to your application.

Take several consecutive orbital element sets for a particular satellite of interest and enter them into your computer using different names so each set is treated as a separate satellite—AO16a, AO16b, AO16c, for example.

Prepare a batch output for a day about six months after the epoch date for the earliest element set and examine the differences. If the differences are small (the definition of small is determined by your operating requirements) updating elements for this satellite more frequently than two or three times per year is not necessary. It's also very enlightening to rerun the element sets with the drag coefficient set to zero. For satellites above 800 km the difference in the projected values should be very small. In fact, if the difference is large the element set used is probably not a very good one.

The following statement may be surprising—not all element sets are as good as others, even though they come from the same government tracking agency. Performing a computer experiment like the one just described often turns up "bogus" element sets, ones that do not contain known misprints but whose predictions diverge rapidly over time from sets that come slightly earlier or later.

It's very easy for misprints to creep in when Tables of Orbital Elements are prepared or transmitted. Therefore, when updating a specific satellite, it's prudent to treat the operation as adding a "new Satellite" instead of a change or update. If the existing satellite is named RS15, call the new satellite RS15a. Your program will treat RS15 and RS15a as two separate satellites. Follow both spacecraft for several weeks. If the differences in position are small, the new element set is probably okay and the old set can be discarded.

Aside from orbital maneuvers, which pertain to the International Space Station, the main cause for change in the orbital elements of low altitude satellites is atmospheric drag. When the sun is inactive the average status of the atmosphere can be well predicted and drag can be taken into account. However, when the sun is active, atmospheric composition changes radically over a short period of time, making it impossible to take drag into account. As a result, we're placed in a rather poor position. Drag effects can be accurately incorporated in a tracking model only when they're small and relatively unimportant. When they're large, we have no reliable way of modeling them. When using the suggested time intervals for updating orbital elements, keep in mind that you might want to shorten the intervals near sunspot maxima and lengthen them near sunspot minima.

Some early tracking programs used a prediction algorithm that required that the prediction year and the orbital element epoch match except during January when elements from the previous year were accepted. If you're using one of these programs you'll get an error message if you don't update all orbital elements during January.

Where and How to Obtain Orbital Elements

The primary source for orbital element information used by radio amateurs is the North American Air Defense Command (NORAD). NORAD provides this data to NASA for dissemination to scientists and the public. NASA publishes this data in the NASA Two Line format shown in Table 7.9. This information is often translated into the AMSAT format before it is distributed through radio amateur channels.

AMSAT can provide its own orbital elements when necessary and has done so on many occasions. However, with nearly 20 operating spacecraft using amateur frequencies, the amount of work would be significant and since NORAD data is available, the rational thing to do is use it.

Orbital elements from secondary sources are often used. Some of the major ones include e-mail, the Internet, AMSAT Nets, satellite telemetry, packet radio Bulletin Board, newsletters, journals and government mailing lists. Some specific sources follow.

Today, a great many amateurs obtain orbital elements from electronic sources such as e-mail reflectors, local computer Bulletin Boards, the Internet and so forth. If you have access to the Internet the best source for amateur and nonamateur satellites is **http://www.grove.net/~tkelso/**. For additional sources check **http://www.amsat.org/amsat/keps/menu.html**. For rapidly updated information during US Shuttle missions check **http://www.amsat.org/amsat/sarex/orbit.html**.

If you'd like to have elements for all radio amateur satellites sent automatically to your e-mail address, you can subscribe (no charge) to the AMSAT Keps mailing list. E-mail a request to **listserv@amsat.org**. The words "subscribe keps" followed by your e-mail address should appear in the body of the e-mail. Be prepared to be deluged with lots of e-mail. See Chapter 6, or better yet, the AMSAT Internet site for full details since procedures for signing on/off the AMSAT mail list may change.

If you prefer to obtain your orbital elements by mail, you'll find them in the bimonthly *AMSAT Journal,* which is sent to all AMSAT members. AMSAT's address is AMSAT, 850 Sligo Ave, Silver Spring, MD 20910. Since elements obtained via post will always be a bit dated, this approach is not suitable for the Shuttle, or other situations requiring rapid updating.

If you obtain orbital elements by landline electronics or via radio, it's often possible to insert them in your tracking program without manual typing. Many tracking software packages have utilities that will accept specific types of data files and use them to update orbital elements. Some of these utilities are part of the software packages they work with, but many have been written by users and posted on the AMSAT Internet site. Note that the checksum provided on each line of the NASA Two line elements is not the same as the single checksum on the AMSAT elements. For details on how the checksum can be used to determine if the data has been corrupted see the reference at the end of this chapter.[4]

CONVERSIONS

For those who use tracking devices, it is often necessary to convert units between various systems and formats. The following examples illustrate techniques for performing several different common types of conversions.

Time Zone Conversions

Ground stations in the United States who want to convert to UTC from local time, or to local time from UTC, will find

Table 7.9
Time Zone Conversion Chart for USA

Standard Time

Time Zone	EST	CST	MST	PST	AK/HI
Time difference	5	6	7	8	10

Daylight Time

Time Zone	EDT	CDT	MDT	PDT	AK/HI
Time difference	4	5	6	7	9

To convert from UTC to (time zone) *subtract* (time difference) hours.

To convert from (time zone) to UTC *add* (time difference) hours.

Table 7.10
Chart for Converting Between Day/Month and Day of Year Notation

Day of year = day of month + number listed

Month	Normal Year	Leap Year
January	0	0
February	31	31
March	59	60
April	90	91
May	120	121
June	151	152
July	181	182
August	212	213
September	243	244
October	273	274
November	304	305
December	334	335

Sample Problem 7.1
Convert day 97089.37166448 to Standard Date/Time Notation

Standard date/time notation:

YY:MM:DD = Year:Month:Day

HH:MM:SS = Hour:Minute:Second

Epoch time: 97089.37166448

97089.37166448 = 1997, day of year 089, +.37166448 day

day of year

089 = 59 + 30 = March 30 (See Table 7.10)

time of day

.37166448 day = (.37166448) × (24) hours = 8.9199475 hours
.9199475 hours = (.9199475) × (60) minutes = 55.1968512 minutes
.1968512 min = (.1968512) × (60) seconds = 11.81 seconds

Day 97089.37166448 = 1997, March 30 at 08:55:11.81 UTC

Sample Problem 7.2
Convert from (YY:MM:DD/HH:MM:SS) Date/Time Notation to Epoch Time

date/time = 1997, March 30 at 8 hours, 55 minutes, 11.81 seconds

= 97:03:30/08:55:11.81(YY:MM:DD/HH:MM:SS)

Month 3 + day 30 = 59 + 30 = 89 day of year
(see Table 7.10)

55 minutes = (55) × (60) seconds = 3300 seconds

08 hours = (08) × (60) × (60) seconds = 28,800 seconds

08:55:11.81 = (28,800 + 3,300 + 11.81) seconds = 32,111.81 seconds

1 day = 86,400 seconds

32,111.81 seconds = (32,111.81 / 86,400) days = .37166447 days

Epoch date/time: 97:03:30/08:55:11.81 = 97089.37166447

Sample Problem 7.3
Conversions Involving Latitude and Longitude

To convert from degrees West of Greenwich to degrees East of Greenwich subtract from 360.

Example (Washington, DC): 77°W = (360–77)°E = 283°E

To convert from degrees East of Greenwich to degrees West of Greenwich subtract from 360.

Example (Moscow): 36°E = (360–36)°W = 324°W

To convert from degree-minute to decimal degree notation

Example: 38 deg 41 min 16 sec (or 38° 41' 16")
38 + 41/60 + 16/3600 = 38 + .6833 + .0044 = 38.6877 deg.
38 deg 41 min 16 sec = 38.6877 deg.

To convert from decimal degree to degree-minute notation

Example: 38.6877 degrees
.6877 deg = (.6877)(60) = 41.262 minutes
.262 minutes = (.262)(60) = 16 seconds
38.6877 deg = 38 deg 41 min 16 sec

Sample Problem 7.4
Find the AMSAT Day Number Corresponding to 10 September 1998

Let the date of interest be specified by:
year = YY
day of year = DOY (See Table 7.10)

The AMSAT day number (ADN) is given by

ADN = (YY–1978) × 365 + (DOY–1) + INT[(YY–1977) / 4]

where the last term adjusts for leap years by taking the *integer* part of the quotient.

From Table 7.10 we note that 10 September is the 253rd day of 1998

ADN = (1998–1978) × 365 + (253–1) + INT[(1998–1977) / 4]

= 7300 + 252 + 5 = 7557

Table 7.9 and the accompanying instructions useful. The switch between daylight and standard time can introduce a lot of confusion when planning future events. The Uniform Time Act of 1966 (as modified in 1987) specifies that Daylight Saving Time will be observed for approximately six months each year, beginning the first Sunday in April and ending the last Sunday in October. However, Arizona, Hawaii, Michigan, parts of Indiana and possibly other regions, do not conform.

Epoch Time and Standard Time Notation

When using tracking devices you will normally not be required to convert between month/day and day of year notation or between epoch time and standard date/time notation. However, these problems occasionally arise, so we have presented Table 7.10 and two Sample Problems (7.1 and 7.2) to illustrate how these conversions are accomplished.

Angle Units

When working with angles such as latitude and longitude, you may have occasion to switch between decimal degree and degree-minute notation. Sometimes it is necessary to convert longitudes from degrees west of Greenwich to degrees east of Greenwich. Sample Problem 7.3 illustrates how these conversions are accomplished.

AMSAT Day Number

Shortly before the launch of the Phase 3A spacecraft, amateurs developing software for the project found it convenient to select a specific day to use as a reference for orbit calculations. The day selected, January 1, 1978, is referred to as day zero. AMSAT day numbers appear on Phase 3 satellite telemetry. Sample Problem 7.4 shows how

to compute the AMSAT day number when the calendar date is known.

Notes

[1]T. Clark, W3IWI, "BASIC Orbits," *Orbit*, Mar/Apr 1981, pp 6-11, 19-20, 29.

[2]J. Branegan, GM4IHJ, *Satellite Tracking Software for the Radio Amateur*, AMSAT-UK, Sep 1982.

[3]Series of tracking programs by J. Miller, G3RUH. First appeared as OSCAR 10.BAS, *OSCAR News*, no. 45, Dec. 1983 (insert). Enhancements and modifications issued as a series of articles in *OSCAR News* beginning in Dec 1984 under the name PLAN10. Most recent version published in Oct 1990 as PLAN13. Available from AMSAT Internet site. See Table 7.1.

[4]D. Campbell, N3FKV, "Keplerian Element Checksum Program," *The AMSAT Journal*, Nov/Dec 1992, pp 26-27.

[5]The following collection of references discuss low-tech tracking devices for satellites in circular orbits.

(i) W. Danielson and S. Glick, "Australis-OSCAR 5, Where It's At," *QST*, Oct 1969, pp 54-56.

(ii) L. Edler, "An Aid for Plotting Satellite Orbits," *QST*, March, 1970, pp 50, 65.

(iii) K. Nose, "Making Your Own Satellite Tracking Nomogram," *QST*, March 1974, pp 40-41, 78.

(iv) W. Widger, "A Plotting Device for Predicting the Orbit of an Earth Satellite," *Scientific American*, Vol 230, May, 1974,, pp 126-131.

(v) K. Deskur, "Shoot OSCAR with a Satellabe," *73*, July 1975, pp 33-36, 38-44.

(vi) P. D. Thompson, "A General Technique for Satellite Tracking," *QST*, Nov 1975, pp 29-34.

(vii) M. Davidoff, *Satellite Experimenter's Handbook*, 1st Ed (1984) and 2nd Ed (1990), ARRL, summarizes the contents of i-vi.

[6]The following collection of references discuss low-tech tracking devices for satellites in elliptical orbits.

(i) M. Davidoff, K2UBC, "P3 Tracker," Event #2560, American Society for Engineering Education, Knoxville, TN June 1976.

(ii) M. Davidoff, *Using Satellites in the Classroom: A Guide for Science Educators*, 1978, Catonsville Community College Press. Available on microfiche from ERIC (Educational Resources Information Center) Document #162 635 or via OCLC (national interlibrary loan service.)

(iii) M. Davidoff, "Phase 3 on the Horizon," *QST*, May 1980, pp 46-48.

(iv) M. Davidoff, *Satellite Experimenter's Handbook*, 1st Ed (1984) and 2nd Ed (1990), ARRL, summarizes the contents of i-iii.

Chapter 8

Satellite Radio Links

8 Satellite Radio Links

This chapter focuses on the radio signals linking satellites and ground stations. The topics we'll cover include basic physical phenomena such as Doppler shift and Faraday rotation, unusual forms of propagation that may be encountered and a discussion of the process of selecting transponder frequencies.

The Doppler Effect

Have you ever noticed how the pitch of a horn on a passing car or truck appears to decrease? A passenger in the vehicle, listening to the same horn at the same time, wouldn't notice a change in frequency. Whose perceptions are correct? Both. The frequency of the sound you hear depends on the relative motion between the source (the horn) and you (the observer). Since the vehicle passenger moves along with the source, while the distance between you and the source is continually changing, each of you observes a different audio frequency. This phenomenon is known as the Doppler effect (after Johann Doppler, 1803-1853).

Though radio waves are very different from the sound waves we've just been discussing, they do exhibit a similar effect: An observer that is at rest with respect to a transmitter will measure a frequency f_o, while an observer who is moving with respect to the transmitter will measure a different frequency, f^*. The relation is given by

$$f^* = f_o - \frac{v_r}{c} f_o \qquad \text{[Eq 8.1]}$$

where

   f_o = frequency as measured by an observer at rest with respect to the source (source frequency)

   f^* = frequency as measured by an observer who is moving with respect to the source (apparent frequency)

   v_r = relative velocity of observer with respect to source

   c = speed of light = 3.00×10^8 m/s

Eq 8.1 is often written

$$\text{Doppler shift: } \Delta f = f^* - f_o = -\frac{v_r}{c} f_o \qquad \text{[Eq 8.2]}$$

Note that v_r is negative when a spacecraft is approaching. The apparent frequency will therefore be higher than the source frequency. When a spacecraft is receding, v_r is positive and the apparent frequency is lower than the source frequency. We'll settle for an intuitive understanding of Eq 8.1 and leave the details of the derivation to a physics text. The situation is easier to grasp when expressed in terms of period; since period = 1/frequency, we don't lose anything by doing so. Note that the period we use here is *not* the orbital period of the satellite, but the time for one complete cycle of the transmitted radio wave to pass.

Refer to the moving satellite and fixed observer located at G in Figure 8.1. For convenience, consider that the source, aboard the satellite, is transmitting a linearly polarized wave and that the period is the time interval between two successive crests (occurring at A and B) in the transmitted electric field (E-field). From the diagram, it's clear that the slant range $\overline{AG}$ is longer than the slant range $\overline{BG}$. Therefore, it takes less time for a signal that is sent from B to reach G than it does for a signal that is sent from A. Our observer at G, recording the time interval between the two successive E-field crests, will therefore record the time as being shorter that that measured by someone who remains equidistant from the satellite or who is sitting on it. So, for an approaching satellite, our observer records a shorter period than that measured at the spacecraft. Consequently, the observed frequency is higher.

Two primary questions related to Doppler shift are of interest to satellite users: (1) What will the actual Doppler shift be on a given link at a given time? and (2) What is the maximum Doppler shift that can be expected on a given link? We'll look at each of these questions in turn.

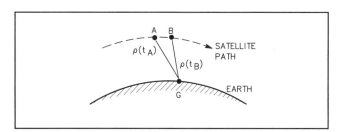

Figure 8.1—Doppler shift is observed when the distance between the satellite and ground station is changing.

DOPPLER SHIFT

To calculate the instantaneous Doppler shift (the shift at any instant), we apply Eq 8.1 to Figure 8.1. If we assume that the source frequency is known, then the only unknown quantity in Eq 8.1 is v_r, the relative velocity. Relative velocity during a short time interval can be approximated by dividing the change in slant range by the change in time, in other words:

$$\bar{v}_r = \frac{\rho(t_B) - \rho(t_A)}{t_B - t_A} \qquad \text{[Eq 8.3]}$$

where

$\bar{v}_r$ = approximate relative velocity

t_B = time satellite passes point B

t_A = time satellite passes point A

$\rho(t_A)$ = slant range at time t_A

$\rho(t_B)$ = slant range at time t_B

To calculate the slant range at two times, we can apply Eq 13.6, which gives us slant range as a function of satellite height and the ground-station-to-SSP distance. In sum, if you have a computer or calculator program that is written to predict basic tracking information (latitude and longitude of SSP and satellite height), adding Eq 13.6 for slant range and Eqs 8.2 and 8.3 for Doppler shift is a simple matter.

DOPPLER SHIFT AT CLOSEST APPROACH

A graph of apparent frequency against time for a specific satellite pass and ground station is called a Doppler curve. A typical Doppler curve, plotted from observations made during an AMSAT-OSCAR 7 pass, is shown in Figure 8.2. For circular orbits, the steepest part of the graph occurs at the point of closest approach (position where slant range is a minimum), and the observed frequency at this point is equal to the actual source frequency. Referring to Figure 8.2, we can determine that closest approach occurred at time 10:31:20 and the source frequency is 145.9727 MHz ± the accuracy of our frequency measurement. From the steepness (slope) of the curve at closest approach, we can compute the minimum slant range using the formula.

$$\rho_o = -\frac{f_o v^2}{c m^*} \qquad \text{[Eq 8.4]}$$

where

ρ_o = slant range at closest approach (minimum slant range)

f_o = transmitter frequency

v = magnitude of satellite velocity (note: this is *not* the relative velocity discussed above)

c = speed of light = 3.00×10^8 m/s

m^* = slope of tangent line at TCA

To obtain m^* from an experimental graph like the one in Figure 8.2, align a transparent ruler over the central part of the curve until you get the steepest match and draw that line. Using any two convenient times, complete the right triangle as shown. Slope m^* is given by the ratio of the vertical side to the horizontal side of the triangle.

While situations occur in which one may want to predict the actual Doppler shift, radio amateurs using a satellite transponder are often satisfied to monitor the downlink and just twiddle their transmitter frequency control while sending a few dits until the downlink is at the desired spot. One particularly useful piece of information for operators, however, is the value of the maximum Doppler shift that any ground station might see on a given link.

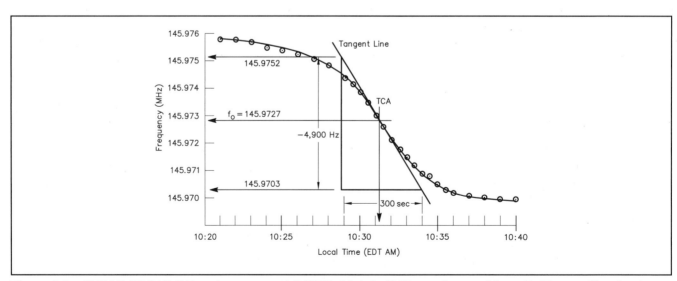

Figure 8.2—AMSAT-OSCAR 7 Doppler curve, orbit 7603, 14 July 1976, as observed from Baltimore, Maryland. Using the triangle shown, we evaluate the slope at TCA: $m^* = (-4900 \text{ Hz})(300 \text{ sec}) = -16.3$ Hz/s. The satellite velocity was determined in Sample Problem 11.4, $v = 7.13$ km/s, Applying Eq 8.4, we obtain the slant range at closest approach, $\rho_o = 1520$ km.

DOPPLER SHIFT LIMITS

At any given time, there's a maximum and minimum Doppler shift that can be seen by any ground station. Most stations will observe a shift somewhere between these two extremes. For a circular orbit, the two limits remain constant; for an elliptical path, the limits vary over the course of the orbit.

We'll consider both cases, but first let's look at the two factors that contribute to the relative velocity term in Eq 8.1: (1) satellite motion in the orbital plane and (2) rotation of the Earth about its N-S axis. In any given situation, these two factors can be combined (velocities add as vectors) to produce a relative velocity having a magnitude that can range from the arithmetic difference to the arithmetic sum of the two components. Since our objective is to determine the worst-case limits for a practical situation, we need only calculate each contribution separately and then form the sum and difference. First we look at the angular rotational velocity of the Earth.

Rotation of Earth: The Earth rotates about its N-S axis at an angular velocity of approximately

$$\dot{w}_E \sim 360°/\text{day} = 15°/\text{hour} = 0.25°/\text{min}$$

$$= 0.000073 \text{ radian/sec}$$

The tangential velocity of a point on the surface of the earth at latitude ϕ is

$$v_E = \dot{w}_E R \cos\phi$$

where

R = radius of Earth
ϕ = latitude
$\dot{w}_E$ = angular velocity of Earth (expressed in radians)

The maximum value of v_E will occur at the equator, $v_E(\text{max}) = 465$ m/s. To get a handle on the size of the Doppler shift that arises exclusively from the rotation of the Earth, assume a link frequency of 146 MHz and a ground station on the equator that sees a satellite due east on the horizon. (In this position, the tangential velocity of the Earth and the relative ground-station-to-satellite velocity are equal.) Using Eq 8.2,

$$\Delta f = \frac{465}{3.00 \times 10^8} \times 146 \times 10^6 = 226 \text{ Hz}$$

So, at 2 meters, the worst-case contribution to Doppler shift produced by the rotation of the Earth is less than a quarter kilohertz. As shown in Figure 8.2, observed Doppler shifts are often much larger. The contribution of the satellite orbital motion to Doppler shift must therefore be very important. Let's look at this contribution, first for a circular orbit, then for the case of elliptical motion.

Satellite Motion: Circular Orbits. Figure 8.3 shows the geometry of this problem in the orbital plane. The ground station that sees the largest relative velocity lies in the orbital plane and sees the spacecraft at 0° elevation. The velocity (v in meters per second) of a satellite in a circular orbit is given by

$$v^2 = \frac{GM}{r} = 3.986 \times 10^{14}(1/r) \qquad \text{[Eq 12.8]}$$

From Figure 8.3, the relative velocity seen by the ground station is

$$v_r = v\cos\theta = v\cos(180° - \beta) = -v\cos\beta = v\frac{R}{r}$$

If the direction of the satellite in Figure 8.3 were reversed, the satellite would be receding from the ground station. The Doppler shift would be equal in magnitude, but would represent a decrease in frequency. A short example shows how this information can be applied. See Sample Problem 8.1.

Combining the results of Sample Problem 8.1 (3.22 kHz) and the earlier calculation of the maximum shift contributed by the rotation of the Earth (226 Hz), we see that the Doppler shift on the OSCAR 16 (Pacsat) 146-MHz link will never exceed 3.45 kHz. For our needs, it's more appropriate to express the maximum as less than ±3.5 kHz. Note

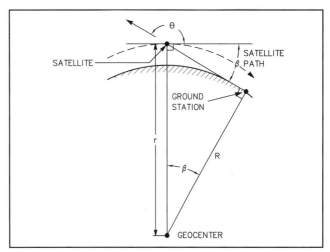

Figure 8.3—Geometry for computing contribution to worst-case Doppler shift from satellite motion only (circular orbit).

Sample Problem 8.1

Consider OSCAR 16 (Pacsat). Find the contribution to the maximum Doppler shift from orbital motion on the 146-MHz uplink.

Solution:
h = 800 km
R = 6371 km
r = R + h = 7171 km

$$V^2 = 3.986 \times 10^{14}\left(\frac{1}{7.171 \times 10^6}\right)$$

$$= 0.5558 \times 10^8 \text{ (m/s)}^2$$

v = 7456 m/s

v_r = −v(R/r) = −7456(6371/7171) = −6624 m/s

Δf = −(v_r/c)f_0 = (6624 × 146 × 10^6)/(3.00 × 10^8)

= 3.22 kHz

---

that this is the maximum shift from the actual transmitted frequency. An "imaginary observer" aboard OSCAR 16 listening to an uplink as the spacecraft approached a ground station would record a frequency between the transmitted frequency and a value 3.5 kHz higher. As the satellite recedes, the observer would measure the frequency as being between the transmitted frequency and a value 3.5 kHz lower. The range of observed frequencies would be less than 7.0 kHz on this 146-MHz satellite link. A similar analysis applies when a ground station is monitoring a downlink.

Satellite Motion: Elliptical Orbits. We now consider the contribution to Doppler shift provided by satellite motion when the orbit is an ellipse. The geometry, shown in Figure 8.4, is somewhat more involved. The ground station observing the largest velocity (station A) lies in the orbital plane and sees the spacecraft at 0° elevation. The ground station observing the smallest relative velocity (station B) also lies in the orbital plane and sees the spacecraft at 0° elevation. The following series of steps enables one to compute the Doppler for stations located at the special points A and B. Note that the locations of A and B change; we're not considering two fixed stations. We assume that the semimajor axis (a) and eccentricity (e) are known.

Step 1. Use Eqs 12.10 and 12.11 to solve for θ.

Step 2. Use Eq 12.12 to solve for r.

Step 3. Solve for the angle ψ shown in Figure 8.4.

$$\psi = \arctan\ [(e^2 - 1)(r \cos \theta + ae)/(r \sin \theta)]$$

(Note: This equation was derived using the techniques of elementary calculus to solve for the slope of a line that is tangent to an ellipse.)

Step 4. Solve for β^* using $\sin \beta^* = \dfrac{R}{r}$

Step 5. Solve for $\gamma = 180° - \theta$

Step 6. Solve Eq 12.8 for the satellite velocity, v.

Step 7. Solve for the relative velocity seen by ground station at A: $v_{rA} = v \cos(\psi + \gamma - \beta^*)$ and ground station at B: $v_{rB} = v \cos(\psi + \gamma + \beta^*)$

Step 8. Solve for the Doppler shift using Eq 8.2.

In preparation for the AMSAT Phase 3A launch, this procedure was applied to the transfer orbit, since Doppler shift limits were needed to design the command-station network. The resulting graph that includes the effects of satellite motion and rotation of the Earth is shown in Figure 8.5. Keep in mind that this is *not* the Doppler shift seen by a particular ground station. The graph represents the maximum possible shifts that could be seen from somewhere on the Earth at any instant during the orbit. Note that for elliptical orbits, Doppler shift limits are generally inversely related to satellite height: Greatest near perigee, least near apogee.

DOPPLER SHIFT AND TRANSPONDERS

So far, all our Doppler shift calculations have focused on a single link. When communicating via a transponder, there are two links involved—the uplink and the downlink. Let f_d represent the downlink frequency corresponding to an uplink frequency of f_u when the relative velocity between satellite and ground is zero.

We begin by looking at the situation where you are monitoring your own downlink. If the spacecraft is approaching, both links will be shifted up in frequency. To calculate the total shift for a noninverting transponder, just add f_u and f_d and plug the result in Eq 8.2 for f_o. In most situations, just plugging in the sum of the center frequen-

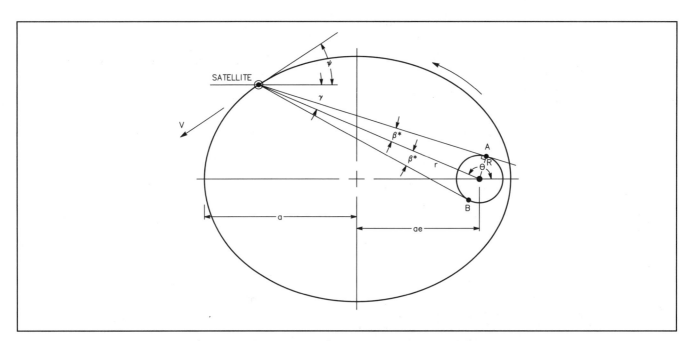

Figure 8.4—Geometry for computing contribution to worst-case Doppler shift produced by satellite motion only (elliptical orbit). Ground station A sees maximum shift. Ground station B sees minimum shift.

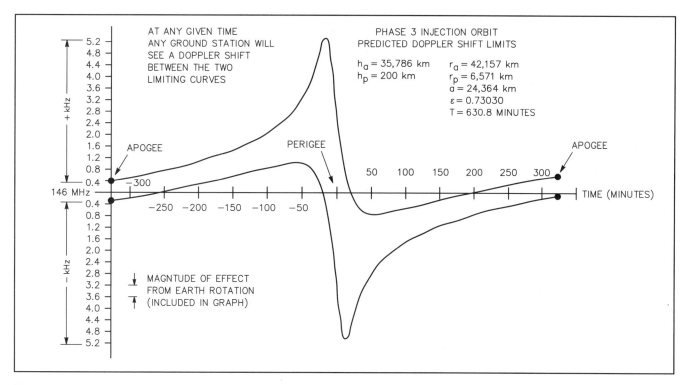

Figure 8.5—Doppler shift limits for Phase-3 injection orbit as seen by ground station anywhere on Earth.

cies of the uplink and downlink passbands is sufficiently accurate. For example, to calculate the total shift on Mode A, use 175 MHz (146 + 29) for f_o. The resulting shift is simply the sum of the two shifts calculated separately.

Now consider the case where you're monitoring your own downlink through an inverting transponder. We'll use Mode B (435 MHz up, 146 MHz down) aboard a low-altitude satellite as an example. Assume the spacecraft is approaching you on a nearby pass. The spacecraft will see your uplink frequency shifted up about 6 kHz (f_u + 6); after inversion in the transponder, the frequency is f_d – 6. On the downlink, the signal is again shifted up, this time about 2 kHz, so the signal you receive will appear at f_d – 4. In other words, your downlink signal is about 4 kHz lower than it would be if Doppler were neglected. This might be somewhat surprising, since we've gotten used to thinking that an approaching spacecraft means the frequency is shifted up. If we reworked this example using a Mode J transponder, we would find that the downlink signal was 4 kHz higher than predicted if Doppler were neglected. The direction of the resulting shift clearly depends on how the spacecraft link frequencies are assigned. For an inverting transponder, we get the expected result—signal shifted up in frequency when the spacecraft is approaching—only when the downlink is the higher frequency.

An easy way to remember the expected shift direction is to note that the higher link frequency always dominates. If the higher frequency is on the downlink (after transponder frequency inversion), we see the normal shift direction (up shift as spacecraft approaches). If the higher frequency is on the uplink (before transponder frequency inversion), the normal shift direction is reversed.

No matter how the link frequencies are assigned, replacing f_o by ± (f_d – f_u) in Eq 8.2 provides the shift. Many tracking programs provide a readout of Doppler shift for the spacecraft beacon. If you replace the spacecraft beacon frequency by ± (f_d – f_u) (passband center frequencies work fine), you can use this utility to compute the Doppler shift on your own signal. Select the sign that produces results consistent with the shift direction specified in the previous paragraph.

As we noted in Chapter 4, when two or more stations are in contact, Doppler shift and frequency retuning cause downlink signals to creep across the band. Since different geometries lead to different shifts, QRM often results as QSOs collide. Based on the information presented in this chapter, an operating protocol that minimizes creep was suggested in Chapter 4. Briefly, when using a low-altitude satellite, the station farthest from the SSP at closest approach should keep his/her highest link frequency constant (that is, on Mode J keep the 435-MHz receive frequency constant; on Mode B, keep the 435-MHz transmit frequency constant). For reference, the maximum expected Doppler shifts for several beacons and transponders of interest are presented in Table 8.1.

ANOMALOUS DOPPLER

In 1972, an experimenter who was collecting Doppler data from the 435-MHz beacon aboard AMSAT-OSCAR 6 noticed a strange effect on a northbound pass. For the first few minutes after AOS, the frequency of the observed signal increased, instead of decreasing as would normally be expected. Departures of up to 700 Hertz from predicted values were observed. After thoroughly checking a number of factors that could have accounted for the observa-

Table 8.1

Maximum Doppler Shifts on Various Satellite Radio Links

	Maximum Doppler Shift (kHz)					
	Satellite/Height					
Beacon freq[1]	*OSCAR 11*	*Pacsat*	*RS-12/13*	*OSCAR 12*	*OSCAR 13 (perigee)*	*OSCAR 13 (apogee)*
	690 km	*800 km*	*1003 km*	*1495 km*	*2545 km*	*36265 km*
29.5 MHz (0.045)	0.72	0.70	0.67	0.62	0.52	0.09
146 MHz (0.226)	3.53	3.45	3.32	3.04	2.56	0.45
435 MHz (0.674)	10.5	10.3	9.88	9.03	7.60	1.33
1.27 GHz (1.967)	30.7	30.1	28.9	26.4	22.2	3.9
2.40 GHz (3.722)	57.9	56.7	54.5	49.8	41.9	7.4
10.5 GHz (15.500)	252.8	247.4	237.8	217.3	182.8	31.5
Transponder						
Mode A[2] (0.271)	4.23	4.13	3.97	3.63	3.06	0.54
Mode B/J (0.448)	6.98	6.83	6.57	6.00	5.05	0.89
Mode L (1.293)	20.1	19.7	19.0	17.3	14.6	2.56
Mode S (1.755)	27.4	26.8	25.8	23.6	19.8	3.48
Mode S[†2,3] (3.047)	68.5	66.9	64.4	58.9	49.6	8.72

[1]Numbers in ( ) are maximum Doppler shift, in kHz, due to rotation of Earth. Doppler shift values in table include contributions from satellite motion in the orbital plane and rotation of the Earth.
[2]Noninverting transponders. All other modes are for inverting transponders.
[3]Mode S[†] refers to AO-13 only (435 MHz/2.4 GHz).
Not all links shown are in existence—values quoted are for comparison purposes.

tions (for example, drift in ground-station frequency-measuring equipment, change in satellite temperature that would affect the beacon oscillator frequency, and so on), it was concluded that an interesting physical anomaly was being seen. The effect was later observed on navigational satellites that were operating near 400 MHz.

An exhaustive experimental investigation was undertaken to delineate the spatial and temporal (time of day, season of year, and so on) extent of the anomaly and to determine the frequency range over which it occurred. It was hoped that this data would make it possible to correlate the effect with physical changes in the ionosphere that were suspected of being related. Although a great deal of data was collected, no firm conclusions have ever been reached as to the cause of anomalous Doppler. For additional information, see W. Smith, "Doppler Anomaly on OSCAR 6 435-MHz Beacon," *QST*, May 1973, pp 105-106; J. Fox and R. Dunbar, "Inverted Doppler Effect," *Proceedings of the ARRL Technical Symposium on Space Communications*, Reston, VA, Sep 1973, Newington, CT: ARRL, pp 1-30.

DOPPLER: ORBIT DETERMINATION AND NAVIGATION

We saw earlier how a Doppler curve enables us to determine time of closest approach (TCA), slant range at closest approach and the actual transmission frequency. A single Doppler curve actually provides us a unique signature for a satellite's orbit. Applying a sophisticated model, one can use Doppler data collected over one or more orbits to determine the six parameters needed to characterize an elliptical orbit, or the four parameters needed to characterize a circular orbit. A flowchart illustrating how this is done is shown in Figure 8.6. The task of determining the orbital parameters (elements) for a satellite is usually simplified if a combination of Doppler and ranging measurements are used.

A closely related problem is that of using Doppler data from a satellite whose orbital elements are known very accurately to determine the latitude and longitude of a ground station. This technique is used with navigation satellites such as the Transit series, and by search-and-rescue satellites in the cooperative SARSAT (US, Canada, France) and

COSPAS (USSR) series. Radio amateurs are justified in being proud that the satellite-aided search-and-rescue concept was first tested using the Mode-A transponders aboard AMSAT-OSCARs 6 and 7. For additional information, see R. Bate, D. Mueller and J. White, *Fundamentals of Astrodynamics*, New York: Dover, 1971; P. Escobal, *Methods of Orbit Determination*, New York: Krieger, 1975; P. Karn, KA9Q, B. McGwier, N4HY, "Spread Spectrum Ranging for Phase IV and Nonlinear Filtering for Orbit Determination in Phase III-C and Phase 4," *Proceedings of the AMSAT-NA Fifth Space Symposium*, Southfield, MI, Nov 1987, ARRL, Newington, CT; S. Eckart, DL2MDL, "Determination of Orbital Parameters Through Distance Measurements," *AMSAT-DL Journal*, No. 6/16, Dec '88/Feb '89, English translation in *Oscar News*, Apr 1989, pp 22-25.

Faraday Rotation

When a linearly polarized radio wave travels through the ionosphere, its plane of polarization rotates about the line of travel. The effect, known as Faraday rotation, depends on the frequency of the radio wave, the strength and orientation of the Earth's magnetic field over the path, and the number of electrons encountered. As a satellite moves along its orbit, the downlink path changes. As a result, the amount of rotation of the polarization plane changes also. This can lead to severe signal fading when the antennas at both ends of a satellite downlink are linearly polarized.

Other factors being equal, the number of revolutions of the plane of polarization for an uplink or downlink signal is roughly proportional to λ^m (λ = wavelength), with the exponent m having a value between 2 and 3. The predictions of a simple model of Faraday rotation are summarized in Table 8.2. The absolute number of revolutions that the plane of polarization undergoes is not of much practical interest. The change in this number is, however, because we expect to experience two deep fades in signal strength for each unit change in the total number of revolutions. While the model is very simple, comparing the predictions with observations is interesting.

Let's consider the 29-MHz beacon on AMSAT-OSCAR 8. The model (Table 8.2) predicts 60 deep fades in the 9 minutes it takes A-O-8 to go from horizon to overhead. This amounts to one deep fade every 5 seconds on average. The model actually predicts a shorter time interval between fades when the elevation angle is near 90° and a longer interval at low elevation angles. Observations of the beacon generally showed a time interval between fades of 20 to 100 seconds. This is not necessarily in contradiction to the model, since the maximum spacecraft elevation angle on most passes was relatively low and the results do depend, to a significant extent, on the actual satellite path and the location of the ground station.

From an operational viewpoint, Faraday rotation is important at 29 MHz, of minor concern at 146 MHz, and of little effect at higher frequencies. Variations in downlink signal strength may be caused by many factors, including those listed in Table 8.3. From a communications standpoint, we're interested mainly in minimizing fading. Using

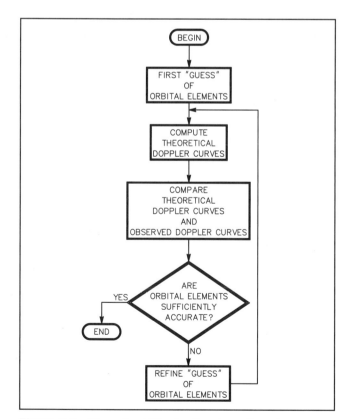

Figure 8.6—Flowchart illustrating how Doppler observations are used to compute the orbital elements of a satellite.

Table 8.2
Faraday Effect: Revolutions of Plane of Signal Polarization*

Let N = Total number of revolutions of plane of polarization as signal passes through ionosphere at specified elevation angle.

ΔN = Change in N as satellite moves from horizon to overhead

Frequency	N at 0° elevation	N at 90° elevation	ΔN
29 MHz	89	28	61
146 MHz	4.4	1.4	3
435 MHz	0.8	0.25	0.5

*As predicted by the simple model outlined in G. N. Krassner and J. V. Michaels, *Introduction to Space Communications Systems*, New York: McGraw-Hill, 1964.

Table 8.3
Variables Affecting Strength of the Downlink Received Signal

1) Satellite (antenna) orientation with respect to ground station.
2) Satellite spin producing a time-dependent antenna pattern.
3) Changing slant range (inverse power law).
4) Signal absorption in the ionosphere.
5) Ground-station antenna pattern.
6) Faraday rotation.

circular polarization at the ground station or the spacecraft does reduce fading from several of the factors listed.

Experimenters who are interested in observing Faraday rotation directly will look at Table 8.3 in a different light. How can the effects of Faraday rotation be separated from the other factors? One strategy would be to concentrate on those links where Faraday rotation is very prominent. A 29-MHz beacon on a low-altitude satellite that uses a linearly polarized antenna is clearly the link of choice. If the ground station uses two linearly polarized antennas that are mounted at right angles to one another and perpendicular to the incoming wave, it's possible to switch back and forth between them to monitor the signal strength alternately at each polarization. With this information, we can separate out most of the factors listed in Table 8.3. Faraday rotation will appear as fading on the two antennas, one reaching a peak as the other reaches a minimum, with the period changing slowly in a regular manner. Studies of the Faraday effect are often used to deduce electron concentrations in specific regions of the ionosphere. For additional information on the Faraday effect, see G. N. Krassner and J. V. Michaels, *Introduction to Space Communication Systems*, New York: McGraw-Hill, 1964 (this text discusses the model upon which Table 8.2 is based); J. D. Kraus, *Radio Astronomy*, New York: McGraw-Hill, 1964, Chapter 5, section 5; and W. A. S. Murray and J. K. Hargreaves, "Lunar Radio Echoes and the Faraday Effect in the Ionosphere," *Nature*, Vol 173, no. 4411, May 15, 1954, pp 944-945.

Spin Modulation

Satellites are often stabilized by being spun about a particular axis. When the spacecraft spin axis is not pointing directly at your ground station (non-zero squint angle), you're likely to see amplitude, and possibly polarization, changes resulting from the spacecraft rotation. These changes, which affect the up- and downlinks, occur at an integer multiple of the satellite spin frequency. The magnitude of the effect will generally become greater as the squint angle increases.

Polarization changes which result from a linear component of polarization at the spacecraft can, to a large extent, be handled at the ground station by using a circularly polarized antenna. Gain variations are considerably more difficult to compensate for. Using a very sensitive receiving system and a very short AGC time constant will always reduce the problem, but not necessarily to a manageable level.

With Phase 2 satellites having magnetic-bar stabilization systems, spin rates were on the order of 0.01 Hz. This resulted in relatively short duration deep fades every few minutes. Early Phase 3 satellites were spin stabilized at approximately 20 r/min. Due to their antenna configuration, spin-modulation variations tended to cycle at a 1.0 Hz rate. The effect was most noticeable when squint angles were greater than 20°. OSCAR 40 was designed to be three-axis stabilized with its directional antennas pointed at the center of the Earth. When this is achieved, spin modulation should not be observed on its links.

Unusual Propagation

While ionospheric effects on 29-MHz satellite links were both expected and observed, most discussions of VHF and UHF links treat the ionosphere as if it ceases to have any impact, other than Faraday rotation, above 40 MHz. Contrary to traditional thought, amateur measurements show that satellite links are clearly affected by the ionosphere at both 146 and 435 MHz. Significant signal attenuations of 12 dB or greater that were attributable to the state of the ionosphere were frequently observed on the downlinks of Phase II spacecraft. S. Eckart, in his orbit-determination article (previously mentioned), noted that refraction at 146 MHz often resulted in ranging errors amounting to 100 km.

When the F2 layer is efficiently reflecting terrestrial 10-meter signals back to the Earth, it's also reflecting 10-meter signals arriving from space back to whence they came. As a result, an open 10-meter band often coincides with an absence of observable 29-MHz Mode-A downlink signals.

Turning to higher frequencies, John Branegan, GM8OXQ/GM4IHJ, collected detailed quantitative information on 70-cm downlink signal strength over a large number of orbits involving OSCARs 7 and 8 and other spacecraft. Statistical procedures were then used to separate the temporal and spatial extent of the attenuation region(s) from antenna orientation and other effects. For details, see J. Branegan, "Reception of 70-cm Signals from Satellites, Summary of Results March to Oct 1978," *AMSAT Newsletter*, Vol X, no. 4, Dec 1978, pp 10-14.

Sporadic E. In a later study, Branegan reported that high attenuation levels on VHF/UHF satellite downlinks were correlated positively with enhanced terrestrial propagation attributable to sporadic E. Sporadic E refers to relatively dense clouds or patches of ionized particles that often form at heights approximately the same as the E layer. To monitor terrestrial sporadic E, he selected VHF TV and FM stations located so that the same general region of the ionosphere was shared by both satellite and terrestrial links. For additional information, see J. Branegan, "Sporadic-E Impact on Satellite Signals," *Orbit*, Vol 1, no. 4, Nov/Dec 1980, pp 8-10.

FAI. OSCAR operation was directly responsible for the discovery of a new mode of VHF propagation, called FAI (magnetic-field-aligned irregularities), after the mechanism thought to be responsible. The first observations of signals via this medium were reported by stations in equatorial zones who listened for direct signals from amateurs uplinking to OSCAR spacecraft at 146 MHz. The positive results led to direct terrestrial experiments at 2 meters and 70 cm, which helped determine the properties of the FAI mechanism. For details, see J. Reisert and G. Pfeffer, "A Newly Discovered Mode of VHF Propagation," *QST*, Oct 1978, pp 11-14; and T. F. Kneisel, "Ionospheric Scatter by Field-Aligned Irregularities at 144 MHz," *QST*, Jan 1982, pp 30-32.

Antipodal Reception. Soon after Sputnik I was launched, observers noticed that the 20-MHz signal from the satellite was often heard for a short period of time when the satellite was located nearly antipodal to the observer. (If you were to dig a hole right through the center of the Earth, the spot where you'd emerge is called the antipodal point.) The phenomenon was quickly dubbed the "antipodal effect," and a number of articles appeared in IEEE journals during the late 1950s discussing its causes. Antipodal effects were later observed on the 29.5-MHz beacon of OSCAR 5. See R. Soifer, "Australis-OSCAR 5 Ionospheric Propagation Results," *QST*, Oct 1970, pp 54-57.

The likelihood of antipodal reception is correlated positively with solar activity. During sunspot maxima, it is relatively common on 29.5-MHz satellite beacon signals. Although most occurrences are thought to result from normal multihop propagation under the influence of a favorable maximum usable frequency, signal strength is at times exceptionally high. This suggests that a ducting mechanism may sometimes be responsible.

Auroral Effects. Radio signals that pass through zones of aurora activity acquire a characteristic distorted sound, described as raspy, rough, hissy, fluttery, growling and so on. Low-altitude satellites in near-polar orbits are excellent tools for studying auroral effects. One can, for example, use beacons on high inclination LEO OSCARs to map the extent of and note changes in the auroral zone experimentally at various frequencies. The changes at particular frequencies or locations may turn out to be excellent predictors of HF or VHF openings that are caused by various modes. See K. Doyle, "10 Meter Anomalous Propagation with Australis OSCAR [AMSAT-OSCAR 5]," *CQ*, May 1970, pp 60-64, 89.

General. A great deal is still to be learned about ionospheric propagation of VHF and UHF signals, and amateurs are in a unique position to collect important data. UoSAT, with its array of beacons ranging from HF to microwave frequencies, is especially well suited to propagation studies. Beginning in about 1985, two UoSAT spacecraft began collecting and downlinking whole-orbit telemetry data on a regular basis from many of the onboard experiments. As a result, amateurs interested in studying propagation now have access to measurements made outside their normal radio horizon. See R. J. Diersing, N5AHD, "Processing UoSAT Whole-Orbit Telemetry Data," *Proceedings of the 4th Annual AMSAT Space Symposium*, Dallas, TX, Nov 1986, ARRL, Newington, CT.

This discussion of unusual propagation has touched upon only a few of the curious phenomena that occur. Other topics of possible interest include RF noise (atmospheric, manmade, cosmic, terrestrial, oxygen and water vapor, solar), attenuation (electron, condensed water vapor, oxygen and water vapor), refraction (ionospheric, tropospheric) and scintillation. For a general overview of all

---

Table 8.4

International Telecommunication Union Amateur Satellite Service Frequency Allocations

1971 WARC	*1979 WARC*
7.000-7.100 MHz	7.000-7.100 MHz
14.000-14.250 MHz	14.000-14.250 MHz
	18.068-18.168 MHz
21.000-21.450 MHz	21.000-21.450 MHz
	24.890-24.990 MHz
28.000-29.700 MHz	28.000-29.700 MHz
144.000-146.000 MHz	144.000-146.000 MHz
435.000-438.000 MHz*	435.000-438.000 MHz* (3644/320A)
	1.26-1.27 GHz* [uplink only] (3644/320A)
	2.40-2.45 GHz* (3644/320A)
	3.40-3.41 GHz [* in Region 2 and 3 only] (3644/320A)
	5.65-5.67 GHz* [uplink only] (3644/320A)
	5.83-5.85 GHz [downlink only] (3761C)
	10.45-10.50 (3780A)
24.00-24.05 GHz	24.00-24.05 GHz
	47.0-47.2 GHz [Amateur Exclusive]
	75.5-76.0 GHz [Amateur Exclusive]
	76-81 GHz
	142-144 GHz [Amateur Exclusive]
	144-149 GHz
	241-248 GHz
	248-250 GHz [Amateur Exclusive]

*The Amateur Satellite Service may use these frequencies subject to not causing harmful interference to other services operating in accordance with provisions of Allocation Table. This applies to space stations and ground stations.
For additional information, see "Extracts From the International Radio Regulations for the Amateur and Amateur-Satellite Services," *QST*, Feb 1980, pp 62-71 and Appendix F of this book. Paragraph numbers ( ) refer to relevant sections of the Regulations.

these propagation effects, see G. N. Krassner and J. V. Michaels, *Introduction to Space Communications Systems*, New York: McGraw-Hill, 1964.

Frequency Selection

The selection of frequencies for an Amateur Radio spacecraft transponder is a complicated process. Consideration must be given to

1) legal constraints (national and international laws governing the use of the RF spectrum);

2) technical factors (including propagation, type of orbit, ability of amateur community to produce required flight hardware, and so on);

3) user-community needs and preferences;

4) frequency management (cooperative agreements concerning frequency use among the worldwide amateur community).

We'll look at how each of these factors affects the selection process.

LEGAL CONSTRAINTS

The Amateur Satellite Service was formally recognized by the ITU (International Telecommunication Union) at the 1971 WARC (World Administrative Radio Conference) for Space Telecommunications. The US Amateur Satellite Service was established by the FCC in 1973. Prior to this date, amateur satellites were licensed under the rules and regulations governing the Amateur Radio Service.

At the 1971 WARC, the ITU allocated frequencies for the Amateur Satellite Service. These allocations are shown in column 1 of Table 8.4. The tremendous gap between 438 MHz and 24.0 GHz placed serious limitations on the future development of amateur space communications.

At WARC-79, the frequencies allocated to the Amateur Satellite Service were opened for discussion. A concerted effort by IARU, ARRL, AMSAT and other interested amateur groups succeeded in securing several additional frequency bands. (See Chapter 2 for a review of the 1971 and 1979 WARCs.) The complete list of allocations adopted at this meeting is given in column 2 of Table 8.4.

US amateur access to WARC allocations is, of course, not immediate. New allocations have to be ratified by the Senate and then implemented by the FCC. For specific details, see Appendix F: FCC Rules and Regulations Governing the Amateur-Satellite Service. Since 1990, the frequencies listed in column 2 of Table 8.4 have been available for US Amateur Radio space projects.

TECHNICAL FACTORS

A great many technical factors are involved in the selection of frequencies for satellite links. We'll look at several of these factors, beginning with some general considerations and then moving on to specifics.

Many of the desirable features of a satellite communication link depend on operating the transponder and ground station in a duplex mode (simultaneous transmission and reception). A crossband transponder is needed to allow duplex operation without inordinately complex equipment

at each ground station. Therefore, our objective here will be to pick (from the list in Table 8.4) the two optimal bands, based purely on technical considerations. We'll also consider how other bands compare to our optimal choices in case we encounter obstacles that prevent their use.

From a system viewpoint, the downlink is the "weak link" in the communication chain. If necessary, ground-station transmitter power levels can exceed the power allocated to a single user at the spacecraft by considerably more than 20 dB. And, even with a sophisticated attitude-stabilization system, satellite antenna gain must be limited in order to provide a sufficiently broad pattern (footprint) for full Earth coverage during most of the orbit. Consequently, the "best" band should be used for the downlink unless there are compelling reasons to do otherwise. Frequencies will therefore be evaluated as downlinks. If a band provides good downlink performance, it almost certainly will be excellent as an uplink.

We now focus our attention on high-altitude spin-stabilized spacecraft such as OSCARs 10 and 13 and compare downlink performance at several frequencies. For the comparison, we'll also assume that transponder power and bandwidth are constant and that ground stations provide good, but not necessarily state-of-the-art, performance. Most of the following observations apply equally well to P3D and Phase 4 spacecraft.

Free-space path loss increases with frequency. Column 2 of Table 8.5 presents information on relative path loss at the frequencies under consideration. Since we're interested in relative performance, we choose a convenient reference level—2 meters in this case. Though beam antennas can be used on spin-stabilized high-altitude satellites, for reasonable Earth coverage satellite antenna gain must be limited to approximately 12 dBi. (We will discuss the possibility of higher-gain antennas later.) This gain can be achieved at UHF and higher frequencies, but at 146 MHz, antenna size becomes a problem. At 29 MHz, a gain antenna presents monstrous mechanical problems that so far have made it impossible to place such a device on an AMSAT satellite. Reasonable estimates for achievable antenna gain on a spin-stabilized Phase 3 satellite have been included in column 3 of Table 8.5.

The ground-station antenna-gain entries in Table 8.5 are based on a constant boom length of 8 feet at 10 meters, 2 meters and 70 cm. At 23 cm, a 4-ft-diameter dish produces about the same gain as an 8-ft-boom loop Yagi; therefore we've selected a 4-ft dish as a comparable ground station antenna at 23 cm and 13 cm. Finally, the last column in Table 8.5 summarizes relative link performance taking into account the factors listed in columns 2-4: path loss, satellite antenna gain and ground-station antenna gain.

Based on the information presented so far, 2 meters would be our choice for a downlink and 10 meters for an uplink. Recall, however, the information on sky noise arriving at an antenna, which was presented in Table 11.1. As a result of the steep increase in noise below 1 GHz, a good receiver is capable of recovering much weaker signals at 2 meters than it is at 10 meters. The relative advantage of

2 meters over 10 meters can reach 15 dB. Also, atmospheric absorption at 10 meters may amount to as much as 20 dB, especially during peaks of the sunspot cycle. Taking these facts into account, we'd conclude that 146 and 435 MHz are the best link frequencies available. Based entirely on Table 8.5, we'd once again choose 2 meters as a downlink. Taking sky noise into account, the selection of a downlink, 2 meters or 70 cm, is really a toss-up.

Our analysis so far has considered only relative performance. The conclusion that 2 meters and 70 cm will provide similar performance does not mean that either will provide an acceptable downlink signal, so we have to make contact with the absolute levels of the real world.

Absolute signal levels can be predicted if factors such as receiver noise figure and bandwidth, and cosmic noise are taken into account. We will show how to do this in the example that concludes this section. Although calculations of absolute link performance are very useful, there's no substitute for experience. Amateurs have always attempted to collect data on beacon performance before a frequency was used on a transponder. Data of this type is an extremely valuable aid in predicting transponder performance. When calculations of relative performance are coupled with measurements made on beacons, excellent projections of transponder performance are possible.

As a result of calculations of this type, it was possible to predict in the mid-1970s that a Phase 3 200-kHz-wide transponder with a 50-W PEP downlink on 146-MHz would provide users a signal-to-noise ratio of 18-23 dB. Such a link would provide excellent performance. Experience with OSCARs 10 and 13 has confirmed these figures. Other possible downlink frequencies will be compared to this link.

As stated earlier, a transponder using 2 meters and 70 cm is therefore a prime choice, with the selection of downlink a toss-up. Three important reasons led to the selection of 2 meters as the downlink (Mode B) back in the mid-1970s. First, the number of amateurs having receiving equipment for 2 meters was considerably greater than that for 70 cm; second, low-noise preamps that could take advantage of the sky noise advantage at 70 cm were not widely available; third, receiver desensing was a serious obstacle to Mode-J ground stations.

The reason why Mode B was employed on OSCAR 7 and on the Phase 3A spacecraft should be clear. Over a two-decade time span, the factors entering into frequency selection are apt to change. Today, we have to take into account the fact that equipment for 70 cm is as easily and widely available as that for 2 meters, and that low-noise preamps for 70 cm are relatively inexpensive. Also, in some portions of the world 145.8-146.0 MHz is so congested that a 2-meter downlink is unusable.

Finally, Mode J is a more efficient stepping stone to Mode L than Mode B. In sum, there are excellent arguments for switching to Mode J. However, there is also a new important factor favoring Mode B—the need to provide continuity of service to those who have supported the amateur satellite program over the years. It would have been very unfair to ask amateurs who set up for Mode B on OSCAR 10 to switch to Mode J for OSCAR 13. For these reasons, we're likely to see both modes supported in coming years.

There are other advantages and disadvantages of various modes. One key factor is total available bandwidth. Whether we opt for Mode B or Mode J, we're restricted to 200 kHz total spectrum, and this is already clearly inadequate for supporting CW and SSB communications. Using a 70-cm and 23-cm combination for a transponder provides 3 MHz of bandwidth. There's no downlink choice here, since the allocation table states that 23 cm can only be used as an uplink. Mode L is clearly a preferred mode for direct amateur-to-amateur CW, SSB and digital communications over the coming decades.

If amateurs were to restrict themselves to communicating via CW, SSB and today's digital modes, Mode L would suffice for a long time into the future. However, if we wish to use satellites for real-time video, digital backbone systems and terrestrial repeater linking, the bandwidth provided by Mode L is not sufficient. (These are just a few of the ideas being pursued for future spacecraft.) Mode S (23 cm up, 13 cm down) can provide 10 MHz per spacecraft, and several spacecraft can operate on a non-interfering basis. Even if this is not a high immediate priority, Mode S must be utilized as a satellite link if we wish to retain it for the future. OSCAR 13 carried a transponder with a 13-cm downlink that was scheduled on a regular basis. This transponder provided excellent service.

As we go to higher frequencies, the link performance figures from Table 8.5 look a little disturbing. However, we can use spot beam antennas and/or shaped beam anten-

Table 8.5
High-Altitude Satellite Link Performance at Several Frequencies†

Band	Relative free-space path loss	Spacecraft antenna gain	Ground station antenna gain	Relative performance
29 MHz	14 dB	0 dB	+5 dB	+19 dB
146 MHz	0 dB	+7 dB	+12 dB	+19 dB
435 MHz	10 dB	+10 dB	+16 dB	+16 dB
1.26 GHz	19 dB	+12 dB	+21 dB	+14 dB
2.4 GHz	24 dB	+12 dB	+26 dB	+14 dB

Notes

†These figures take into account path loss, practical spacecraft antennas and ground-station antennas of similar physical size.
‡50 MHz and 222 MHz are not included because these frequencies are not authorized for Amateur Satellite Service use.

nas to improve the situation. With spot beam antennas on the spacecraft, operation at even higher frequencies is possible and will be looked into.

The considerations leading to frequency selection for low-altitude satellites are considerably different. First, there are actually at least two distinct classes of low-altitude spacecraft. One type carries linear transponders with at least one HF link. This class continues to have widespread appeal and it serves an important function by attracting new blood to the amateur satellite service, so it deserves continuing support. The second class is the Pacsat, which requires the reliable link performance provided by VHF and UHF links. Frequency selection for this service is not clear. The Mode-J combination is the current choice, but increased bandwidths associated with rising data rates and a proliferation of spacecraft may result in a need to switch to Mode L.

PREDICTING SIGNAL LEVELS: AN EXAMPLE

The performance of a 435-MHz satellite downlink from geostationary altitude (Phase 3 or 4) may be calculated in the following manner.

Spacecraft Characteristics
Transponder
Total power = 35 watts average
Bandwidth = 300+ kHz

Antenna
Gain = 10 dBi
Apogee height = 35,800 km

Ground Station Characteristics
Antenna
Gain = 13 dBi
Sky temperature as seen by antenna (T_s) = 150 K
(often much better—see Fig 11.1)
Receiver
Total noise figure (F_T) = 2.2 dB
Bandwidth (B) = 3 kHz (for SSB)

Ground station-Satellite distance
(slant range) = 42,000 km (ground station at edge of coverage cone at apogee)

Our objective is to calculate the expected signal-to-noise ratio (SNR) of a typical downlink SSB signal.

$$SNR = \frac{Received\ Signal\ Power}{Received\ Noise\ Power} = \frac{W_s}{W_n}$$

$$SNR\ [in\ dB] = 10\log W_s - 10\log W_n = P_s - P_n$$

Our approach will be to (1) compute P_s, (2) compute P_n and (3) evaluate SNR.

Step 1: Computation of Received Signal Power

Assume that the transponder is handling 70 equal-power SSB contacts. The average power allocated to each user is therefore 0.5 watt. For unprocessed SSB, this represents about 3 watts PEP (34.8 dBm). (Note: dBm = dB above 1 milliwatt). Free-space path-loss may be calculated from

$$L = 10\log\left(\frac{4\pi\rho}{\lambda}\right)^2$$

where
L = free-space path-loss in decibels
ρ = slant range in meters
λ = wavelength in meters

For calculation it's easier to use the equivalent formula

$$L = 32.4 + 20\log f + 20\log \rho \qquad [Eq\ 8.5]$$

where
f = frequency in MHz
ρ = slant range in km

When applying Eq 8.5, be sure to express the variables in the units indicated. In our example

$$L = 32.4 + 20\log (435) + 20\log (42,000) = 177.6\ dB.$$

We now evaluate P_s

P_s = transmitted signal power [in dBm]
+ satellite transmit antenna gain [in dBi]
+ ground station receive antenna gain [in dB]
– free-space path-loss [in dB].

$$P_s = 34.8\ dBm + 10\ dBi + 13\ dBi - 177.6\ dB$$

$$= -119.8\ dBm.$$

Step 2: Computation of Received Noise Power
Received noise power is given by

$$W_n\ [in\ milliwatts] = k\ T_e B$$

where
k = Boltzmann's constant = 1.38×10^{-20} [in (milliwatts)/(hertz)(kelvin)]
T_e = effective system temperature (discussed below)
B = receiver bandwidth [in hertz]

Note: All temperatures are in kelvins. Temperatures in the Kelvin scale are referenced to absolute zero and are given by the Celsius temperature + 273°. Room temperature is defined as 17° C = 290 K. "290 K" is read as "290 kelvins"—there's no degree sign and the expression "degrees kelvin" is *not* used.

The effective system temperature (T_e) takes into account (1) noise picked up by the receive antenna (cosmic noise plus radiation from the Earth at ~290 K that enters the main or side lobes) and (2) noise generated in the receiver. The temperature of the receive system (T_R) can be computed when the system noise figure (F_T in dB) is known. (See Fig 11.3 for a discussion of F_T.)

$$T_R\ [in\ K] = 290\ (10^{F_T/10} - 1) \qquad [Eq\ 8.6]$$

When using Eq 8.6, any feed-line losses between the antenna and first active receiver stage must be included in the receiver noise-figure computation, as illustrated in Fig 11.3. Applying Eq 8.6 to our example, we obtain

$$T_R = 290(10^{0.22} - 1) = 191 \text{ K}$$

The sky temperature was given as $T_s = 150$ K, so we now have everything needed to evaluate T_e

$$T_e = 191 + 150 = 341 \text{ K}$$

The total received noise power can now be calculated

$$P_n \text{ [in dBm]} = 10 \log W_n \text{ [in milliwatts]} = 10 \log (k T_e B)$$

$$= 10 \log k + 10 \log T_e + 10 \log B$$

$$= 10 \log (10^{-20}) + 10 \log (1.38) + 10 \log (341)$$

$$+ 10 \log (3000)$$

$$= -200 + 1.4 + 25.3 + 34.8 = -138.5 \text{ dBm}$$

Step 3: Calculation of SNR

$$\text{SNR [in dB]} = P_s \text{ [in dBm]} - P_n \text{ [in dBm]}$$
$$= -119.8 - (-138.5)$$
$$= 18.7 \text{ dB}$$

An 18.7-dB SNR indicates a very good quality signal. Note that the calculations were based on a good (but in no way exotic) 70-cm receive setup situated as far as possible from the spacecraft. For paths where the slant range is shorter, the sky noise temperature behind the satellite is lower or the preamp in use is better, the link SNR will exceed the value calculated. For situations where a user doesn't have sufficient uplink EIRP to drive the transponder to the indicated output power, or where the number of stations simultaneously using the transponder is greater than the 70 assumed, the link SNR will be less than the calculated value.

For additional information on calculating link performance, see the following references:

1998 ARRL Handbook (Newington: ARRL, 1997), Chapter 23: Repeaters, Satellites, EME and Direction Finding, p 23.56.

B. Atkins, "Estimating Microwave System Performance," *QST*, Dec 1980, p 74. Contains a brief but very clear example of calculating link performance at 10 GHz.

J. D. Kraus, *Radio Astronomy*, New York: McGraw-Hill, 1966. Chapters 3 and 7 (by M. E. Tiuri) contain advanced-level information on calculating ultimate receiver sensitivity.

Also see references in Table 11.3.

FREQUENCY MANAGEMENT

Now that the legal constraints and the technical trade-offs have been considered, we get down to the difficult problem: All frequencies allocated to the Amateur Satellite Service are shared with the Amateur Radio Service. Therefore, it's extremely important for satellite users and the general amateur community to establish guidelines for frequency use. Satellite buffs can pursue two paths: (1) Use bands that are sparsely populated, or (2) educate the general amateur population as to the goals and constraints of the Amateur Satellite Service so that, even if not personally interested in space communications, they'll understand how space activities help justify the existence of the Amateur Service.

The significance and difficulty of the educational task should not be underestimated. When a local radio club has pioneered in the development of fast-scan ATV repeaters over many years, it will take considerable tact to convince them to invest time and cash in switching to a different segment of the 70-cm band. Likewise, when a country has 100 times as many amateurs equipped for 2-meter FM as for satellite operation, a dedicated effort will certainly be needed to explain why certain segments of the crowded 2-meter band should be considered off-limits.

The Amateur Satellite Service is taking a balanced approach. For several years, worldwide support for establishing exclusive satellite segments at 29.300-29.500 MHz, 145.800-146.000 MHz, 435.000-438.000 MHz, 1.26-1.27 GHz and 2.40-2.45 GHz has been growing. Three decades ago, when the 10-meter and 2-meter proposals were made, the band segments were almost empty. Today, nearby crowding often leads amateurs who are unaware of the "gentlemen's agreements" on frequency management to move into the "open space," not realizing that they're disrupting satellite links. A continuing, tactful educational program is a necessity.

Returning to our primary concern, choosing transponder frequencies, it's clear that the 2-meter segment utilized by Modes B, J and A has already become severely overcrowded. Links using 1.2 GHz, 2.4 GHz and higher frequencies will become more important over the next decade.

SUMMARY

An understanding of the frequency selection process should make it clear that AMSAT designers have not rushed up the frequency ladder with callous disregard for users' needs. The complex constraints and trade-offs involved in transponder frequency selection have always been considered carefully, and some difficult decisions have had to be made.

For detailed information on the frequency selection process, see the papers by R. Soifer "Frequency Planning for AMSAT Satellites" (pp 101-127) and K. Meinzer, "Spacecraft Considerations for Future OSCAR Satellites" (pp 137-143) in the *Proceedings of the ARRL Technical Symposium on Space Communications*, Reston, VA, Sep 1973, Newington, CT: ARRL. Despite advances in low-noise microwave transistors, the new emphasis on high-altitude Phase 3 and geostationary satellites, the availability of new bands, and the introduction of Pacsats, the conclusions of both of these studies are still basically valid.

Chapter 9

Antennas for Space Communications: Basics

GAIN AND EIRP

GAIN PATTERNS

TRANSMITTING vs RECEIVING

EFFICIENCY

POLARIZATION

Technical Description
Circular Polarization Sense
Link Comparisons
Producing Circular Polarization
  Method I
  Method II
  Method III
  Comparing Methods I and II

SPIN MODULATION

FARADAY ROTATION

CONCLUSIONS

FIGURES

TABLES

9 Antennas for Space Communications: Basics

Ground station performance is affected by many factors, but one stands out as being critically important: the antenna system. Although there are no intrinsic differences between antennas for satellite use and those for terrestrial applications, some designs are clearly better suited to satellite work than others. Properties that make a certain type of antenna desirable for HF operation may make it a poor performer on a satellite link, and vice versa. In this chapter we'll consider the relation between basic antenna characteristics and satellite radio links. In the next chapter we'll look at several types of practical antennas useful for satellite communications.

Simply stated, an antenna for monitoring downlink signals should be chosen to provide an adequate signal-to-noise (S/N) ratio at the receiver output; an antenna for transmitting on the uplink should be chosen to provide the desired signal level at the satellite. While pursuing these goals we also try to keep costs down and minimize the complexity associated with large mechanical structures and high aiming accuracy.

The antenna system characteristics we'll focus on include:
1) Directional properties (gain and pattern)
2) Transmitting vs receiving properties
3) Efficiency
4) Polarization
5) Link effects (spin modulation, Faraday rotation)

One basic concept we'll refer to time after time is the *isotropic antenna*: an array that radiates power equally in all directions. No one has ever been able to build a practical isotropic antenna but the concept is still very useful as a "measuring stick" against which other antennas can be compared. Closely related is the *omnidirectional antenna*, one that radiates equally well in all directions in a specific plane. Practical omnidirectional antennas are common; the ground plane is one example. Any antenna that tends to radiate best in a specific direction (or directions) may be called a *beam antenna*. Several beams (the Yagi, quad, loop Yagi and helix) are shown in Figure 9.1. Even the common dipole can be regarded as a beam since it has favored directions. The "first law" of antennas is: You don't get something for nothing. A beam can only increase the power radiated in one direction by borrowing that power from

someplace else. In other words, a beam acts by concentrating its radiated energy in a specific direction. To quantify how well it accomplishes this task, we compare it to the isotropic antenna, our measuring stick.

GAIN AND EIRP

An imaginary radio link with two stations, A and B, as shown in Figure 9.2, will help illustrate how the properties of a beam are specified. We'll discuss the transmit characteristics first since they're easier to grasp. Later we'll see how transmitting and receiving properties are related. As the type of antenna at Station B (the receiving station) isn't important for the comparison, a dipole is assumed. Station A (the transmitting station) has a choice of two antennas, a beam whose properties we wish to determine and an isotropic radiator. Our "thought experiment" begins with A using the beam antenna and some convenient power (P). A adjusts his antenna's orientation until B records the strongest signal, and notes the level. A then switches to the isotropic antenna and adjusts the power (P_i) until B reports the same signal level as noted earlier. The gain (G) of the beam is given by the formula

$$G = \frac{P_i}{P} \qquad \text{[Eq 9.1]}$$

For example, if 25 watts to the beam produced the same signal level at B as 500 watts to the isotropic, the gain of the beam would be

$$G = \frac{500}{25} = 20$$

This is roughly what would be expected from a well designed Yagi with a boom length of 2 wavelengths.

Now suppose that B is the satellite and A is your uplink system. Aha! The satellite sees exactly the same signal whether you run 500 watts to an isotropic radiator or 25 watts to the beam. In either case we'd say the ground station *EIRP* (effective isotropic radiated power) is 500 watts. EIRP and the quantity P_i in our "thought experiment" are identical. We can rewrite Eq 9.1 as $P_i = GP$ (EIRP is equal to the product of "gain" and "power being fed into the antenna"). An EIRP of 500 watts can also be produced by a beam with a gain of 4 that is fed 125 watts, a beam with a gain of 10 that is fed 50 watts, and so on. The definition

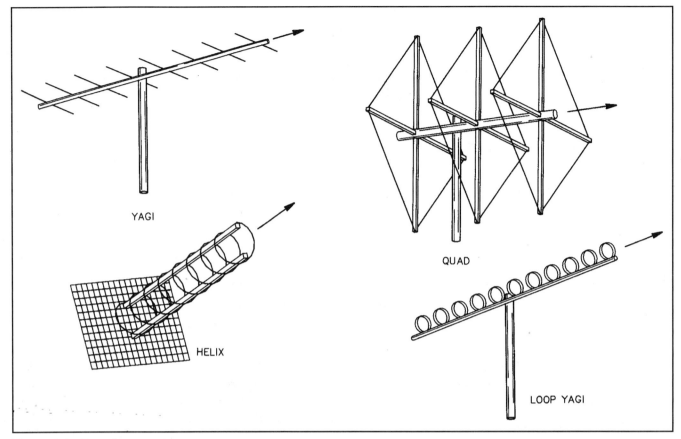

Figure 9.1—Four beam antennas.

of EIRP we've been using just depends on gain and power fed to the antenna. Later we'll see how this can be generalized to include transmitter output power, feed-line losses and even the effects of a misaimed antenna.

To simplify certain calculations, gain is often expressed in decibels (dB).

$$G\left[\text{in dB}\right] = 10 \log \frac{P_i}{P} \text{ or,} \qquad \text{[Eq 9.2A]}$$

$$G\left[\text{in dB}\right] = 10 \log G \text{ or,} \qquad \text{[Eq 9.2B]}$$

$$G = 10^{G/10} \qquad \text{[Eq 9.2C]}$$

Since we refer to G and G as "gain," it's important to note the units. If gain is simply a number (a ratio), we're talking about G (Eq 9.1); if gain is given in decibels we're referring to G.

Eq 9.1 and Eq 9.2 clearly depend on what antenna is used for comparison (the reference antenna); it's the isotropic. At times, a half-wave dipole is used for this purpose. The half-wave dipole has a gain of 1.64 (2.14 dB) over an isotropic radiator. As a result, the gain of a specific beam looks better when the reference antenna is an isotropic than when it's a dipole. Eqs 9.3A and 9.3B describe how the figures can be translated.

$$G\text{ [isotropic reference]} = (1.64)(G\text{ [dipole reference]})$$
$$\text{[Eq 9.3A]}$$

$$G\text{ [isotropic reference]} = G\text{ [dipole reference]} + 2.14 \text{ dB}$$
$$\text{[Eq 9.3B]}$$

Obviously, it's very important to specify the nature of

the reference. This is sometimes done by expressing gain in either dBi or dBd, where the last letter describes the reference antenna as *i*sotropic or *d*ipole. Note that so far we've looked only at the one direction in which the maximum signal is radiated.

GAIN PATTERNS

We've seen how one very important antenna characteristic, gain, is specified. Gain tells us nothing, however, about the three-dimensional radiation pattern of an antenna. A beam with a given gain might have one broad lobe as

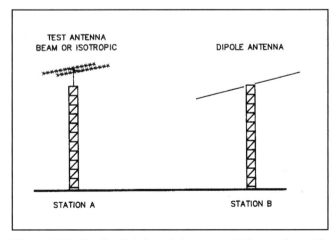

Figure 9.2—Radio link involving two stations, A and B.

shown in Figure 9.3A, or several sharp lobes as shown in Figure 9.3B. A single broad lobe is generally more desirable because it makes the antenna easier to aim and is usually less susceptible to interfering signals. Because drawing quantitative three-dimensional pictures, like those in Figure 9.3, is difficult, the directional properties of an antenna are more often pictured using one or two two-dimensional cross-sections drawn to include the direction of maximum radiation. In Figure 9.4 we show two common cross-sections (gain patterns) used to describe a Yagi. When beams are installed for terrestrial communications the cross-sections may conveniently be referred to as horizontal plane (azimuth plane) and vertical plane (elevation plane) patterns. When working with antennas that can be aimed upward or those using circular polarization, it's important to clearly specify the relation between any two-dimensional pattern pictured and physical orientation of the antenna. Before we continue, note that the gain pattern of an isotropic antenna is a circle in any cross-sectional plane, and the gain pattern of the omnidirectional antenna is a circle in one specific plane.

Gain patterns can be specified in terms of either power or field strength (field intensity). As power is directly proportional to the square of field intensity, translating back and forth between the two descriptions is relatively simple. For example, when field intensity drops to 0.707 of its maximum value, power will have dropped to 0.5 of its maximum since $(0.707)^2 = 0.5$.

One important characteristic of the gain pattern of an antenna is the beamwidth: the angle between the two straight lines that start at the origin of the pattern and that go through the points where the radiated power drops to one half its maximum value. See Figure 9.4. Since high antenna gains are obtained by concentrating the radiated power in a specific direction, it's clear that beamwidth and gain must be related. High gains can only be obtained by sacrificing beamwidth. It's possible, and sometimes desirable, to design an antenna so that two gain cross-sections taken at right angles are shaped significantly differently. For many familiar beam antennas, however, the two patterns are very similar. In cases where an efficiently designed antenna produces a symmetrical pattern (one that's independent of cross-section orientation), the maximum beamwidth, θ, for a given gain is given approximately by Eq 9.4.

$$\theta \left[\text{in degrees} \right] = 10 \sqrt{\frac{400}{G}} \qquad \text{[Eq 9.4]}$$

For example, an antenna with a gain of 20 would have a beamwidth of roughly 45°. Tracking a slowly moving target like an elliptical-orbit Phase 3 satellite near apogee with such an antenna would pose no problem. Tracking a speedy, low-altitude satellite, however, might be difficult.

Most discussions of antennas begin with a *free space* model that represents an antenna as if it were in outer space with no nearby objects to affect its performance. In the real world, RF reflections can have a large impact on an antenna's behavior. This is especially true for vertical plane patterns. At low elevation angles, for example, a receiving antenna will see two signals: a direct signal and a ground-reflected signal. Depending on the phase difference, these signals might add, giving up to 6 dB of ground reflection gain, or destructively interfere to produce a null. The real-world vertical pattern will therefore often consist of a series of peaks and nulls.

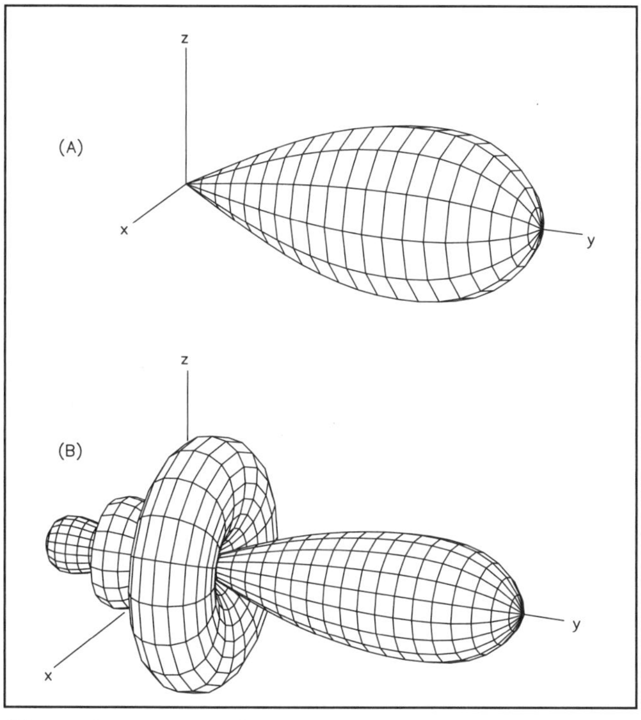

Figure 9.3—Three-dimensional illustrations of beam patterns. (A) single lobe and (B) multi-lobe.

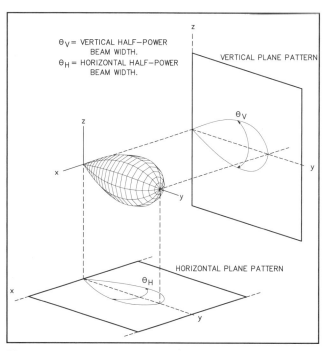

Figure 9.4—Relation between three dimensional gain pattern and horizontal and vertical cross-sections.

Ground reflection also has an impact on phase. A vertically polarized wave is reflected without any phase change, while a horizontally polarized wave undergoes a 180° phase change when reflected.

So far, we've been looking at the properties of antennas from a transmitting point of view. How do these properties relate to reception?

TRANSMITTING VS RECEIVING

A basic law of antenna theory, known as the *reciprocity principle*, states that the gain pattern of an antenna is the same for reception as for transmission. Let's see how this can be applied to the link shown in Figure 9.2. This time consider the situation where Station A is at the receiving end of the link and assume that the incoming natural background noise at A is independent of direction. If Station A measures the noise power arriving at the receiver with both a beam antenna and an isotropic antenna of the same efficiency, he'll obtain the same result. The beam actually picks up more noise than the isotropic from the primary direction and less noise than the isotropic from other directions, but the overall result is that both antennas capture the same total noise power. Now let's see what happens when Station B transmits a reference signal at any convenient fixed power. The total amount of signal power reaching Station A is fixed but the power is arriving from a particular direction. A beam antenna pointed toward Station B will provide Station A with more signal power than would an isotropic antenna. As a result, when signal and noise are present, the beam produces a better S/N power ratio at the input to A's receiver. For well-designed antennas, the improvement in the S/N power ratio over a communications link will be the same whether the antenna switch—beam for isotropic—is made at the transmitting end or the receiving end.

The reciprocity principle does *not* state that a particularly desirable receiving antenna is consequently also desirable as a transmitting antenna, or vice versa (though this is often the case). In transmitting, the objective is to produce the largest possible signal level at the receive point. High efficiency and gain are therefore very important. When receiving, the objective is to obtain the best possible S/N ratio. Though high efficiency and gain contribute to this goal, the shape of the gain pattern and the location of nulls may have a significant impact on S/N ratio by reducing noise and interfering signals. One reason for this is that, in the real world, background noise depends on direction. In sum,

> A good antenna for transmitting to a satellite is not necessarily a desirable antenna for receiving signals from a satellite.

Since separate antennas are required for the uplink and downlink at a satellite ground station, we can select each antenna independently.

EFFICIENCY

A transmitting antenna that is 100% efficient radiates all the power reaching its input terminals. Reduced efficiency causes an antenna to radiate less power in every direction; it has no effect on antenna pattern. A transmitting antenna that is 50% efficient only radiates half the power appearing at its input terminals. Since building high-efficiency VHF and UHF antennas is relatively easy, and producing transmit power at 146 MHz and higher frequencies is difficult, inefficient transmitting antennas should never be used at a satellite ground station.

The trade-offs are somewhat different for receive systems. A receiving antenna that's 50% efficient passes along only half the signal *and* half the noise power it intercepts. If the receive chain's S/N ratio is limited by atmospheric or cosmic noise arriving at the antenna, poor antenna efficiency may not affect the observed S/N ratio. In practice, the only situation where relatively inefficient receive antennas may be considered is on the 29-MHz Mode A downlink where a compact half-size Yagi (or crossed-Yagi array) may provide the same performance as a full-size model.

Low antenna efficiencies are usually caused by (1) physically small (relative to design wavelength) elements that require inductive loading, (2) lossy power-distribution and matching systems, especially in multi-antenna arrays, or (3) poor ground systems (when the ground is an integral part of the antenna). Remember, efficiency does not affect the pattern of either transmit or receive antennas.

POLARIZATION

Our treatment of polarization begins with a technical description of the term polarization as it's applied to radio waves and antennas and goes on to examine how polarization affects satellite radio link performance.

TECHNICAL DESCRIPTION

Radio waves consist of electric and magnetic fields, both of which are always present and inseparable. Since most amateur antennas are designed to respond primarily to the electric field, it is possible to limit our discussion to it. When a radio wave passes a point in space, the electric field *at that point* varies cyclically at the frequency of the wave. When we discuss the *polarization of a radio wave* we're focusing on how the electric field varies.

The electric field can vary in *magnitude*, in *direction* or in both. If, at a particular point in space, the magnitude of the electric field remains constant while the direction changes, we have *circular polarization* (CP). [Note: All changes referred to here are cyclic ones at the frequency of the passing wave, and the direction of the electric field is confined to a plane perpendicular to the direction of propagation.] If, on the other hand, the direction of the field remains constant, while the magnitude changes, we have *linear polarization* (LP). If both magnitude and direction are varying we have *elliptical polarization*.

Imagine that we have a special camera set up at a fixed point in space, which allows us to obtain a series of time lapse photographs of the electric field of a passing radio wave during one complete cycle. We begin our "thought experiment" by taking a set of pictures for each of three linearly polarized waves. See rows A, B and C of Figure 9.5. The three waves

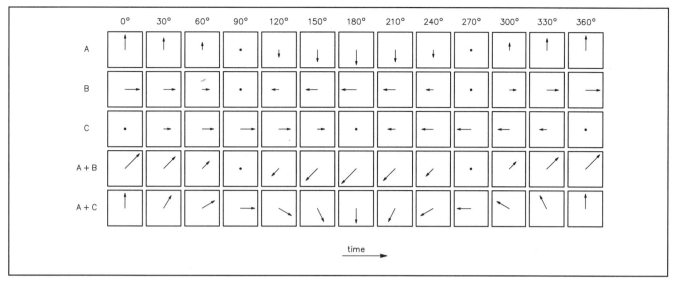

Figure 9.5—Simulated time lapse photographs of radio waves having various polarizations arriving at distant location. Camera pointed at transmitter.

have the same frequency and same maximum amplitude. The electric fields of waves B and C (rows B and C) are physically perpendicular to the field of wave A (row A). Wave B is in phase with wave A (both electric fields are a maximum at the same time), while wave C is 90° out of phase with wave A (the electric field of one is a maximum when the other is a minimum).

If we combine (vectorially) linearly polarized waves A and B we obtain the linearly polarized wave shown in the fourth row. Note its orientation and maximum amplitude (about 1.4 times the magnitude of the components). Observing its amplitude we see that it undergoes one complete cycle in the same time period as each component.

If we now combine (vectorially) linearly polarized waves A and C we obtain the circularly polarized wave shown in the last row. Note that its magnitude remains constant while its direction undergoes one complete cycle in the same time period as each component cycles in amplitude.

In sum, two linearly polarized waves having the same frequency and amplitude can be combined to produce either a linearly polarized wave or a circularly polarized wave—*it all depends on the phasing.*

As a result of this imaginary experiment we can think of a circularly polarized wave, like the one shown in the bottom row of Figure 9.5, as consisting of two linearly polarized components having the same frequency and maximum amplitude but oriented at right angles and having a phase difference of 90°.

Let's consider the most general type of polarization—elliptical polarization. Of the various ways in which elliptical polarization can be described, two are of practical interest to radio amateurs. The first pictures an elliptically polarized radio wave as consisting of a linearly polarized component and circularly polarized component. If the magnitude of the electric field varies only slightly in the course of each cycle, the circular component dominates. If the magnitude of the electric field decreases to nearly zero

during each cycle, the linear component dominates.

The second approach to describing polarization also treats the elliptically polarized wave as having two components; but this time each component is linearly polarized with the two components at right angles physically and 90° out of phase electrically. The maximum amplitude of the electric field of each component is independent of the other. If the maximum values of both components are equal we have circular polarization. If one electrical field component is always zero we have linear polarization.

Both of the viewpoints mentioned treat circular polarization and linear polarization as special cases of elliptical polarization. And, both are helpful in understanding antennas and radio link performance.

The polarization characteristics of a radio wave depend on the transmitting antenna; the transmitter itself has absolutely nothing to do with polarization. Like radio waves, antennas can be assigned a polarization label: the polarization of the wave that *they transmit in direction of maximum gain.* The common terms "linearly polarized antenna" and "circularly polarized antenna" can be confusing if you aren't aware that "in the direction of maximum gain" is meant, even though it's not stated explicitly.

The following example illustrates this potential source of confusion. Consider the transmitting antenna and the three observing locations shown in Figure 9.6. The antenna pictured, known as a turnstile, consists of two crossed dipoles fed 90° (a quarter cycle) out of phase. An observer at A will see a circularly polarized wave; an observer at C will see a linearly polarized wave; and an observer at B will see an elliptically polarized wave. Since an observer at A, located in the direction of maximum gain, sees a CP wave, the turnstile is called a circularly polarized antenna even though observers off the z axis, at B and C, see something different.

Most of the circularly polarized antennas that we'll be looking at, such as the helix and properly phased crossed

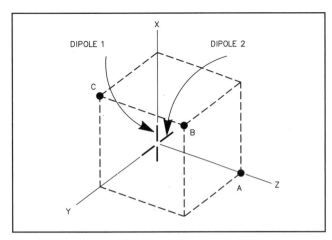

Figure 9.6—Turnstile transmitting antennas (two dipoles fed 90° out of phase). Observers measuring the polarization of the radiated signal are positioned at points A, B and C.

Yagis, are similar to the turnstile in that only observers in the direction of maximum gain actually see circular polarization. When using such an antenna at a ground station it's important to keep the array pointed at the spacecraft to reap the benefits of circular polarization. If an antenna of this type is being used on a spacecraft, the only time you'll be receiving a CP wave is when the satellite antenna is pointed in your direction. Some antennas produce circularly polarized radiation over most of the beam. We'll look at two such antennas, the quadrifilar helix and Lindenblad, in the next chapter.

CIRCULAR POLARIZATION SENSE

Our description of a circularly polarized radio wave emphasized that at a particular point in space, the constant magnitude electric field rotated at the frequency of the source. It's important to be able to specify whether the sense of rotation is clockwise or counterclockwise. For historical reasons, physicists and electrical engineers specify polarization sense in opposite ways, a fact that can cause confusion. The IEEE (Institute of Electrical and Electronic Engineers) standard is the one used in most recent radio amateur literature. To specify the sense of a circularly polarized wave using the IEEE standard, imagine yourself behind the transmitting antenna looking in the direction of maximum radiation. Pick a specific point on the main axis (any point will do) and note the position of the electric field at a particular instant and follow it through a cycle. If you observe the electric field rotating clockwise, the wave is right-hand circularly polarized (RHCP). If the electric field appears to be rotating counterclockwise, the wave is left-hand circularly polarized (LHCP). As we obviously cannot "see" the transmitted electric field, we'll discuss shortly how you can determine the sense of a helix or crossed-Yagi array by inspecting the antenna.

Although polarization-sense labels attached to an antenna depend entirely on its transmit properties, the same labels are applied when the antenna is used for reception. A circularly polarized receiving antenna responds best to circularly polarized radio waves of matching sense.

When a circularly polarized wave is reflected off an object (a metal screen, the ground or a house, for example), the sense of its polarization is changed. A RHCP signal aimed at the moon returns as an LHCP signal; a feedhorn irradiating a parabolic reflector with LHCP produces a main beam that's RHCP.

LINK COMPARISONS

We now look at how polarization affects a communications link involving two stations: T (the transmitting station) and R (the receiving station). Each station can choose from antennas that provide RHCP, LHCP or LP. All antennas are assumed to have the same gain and each is aimed at the other station. When we refer to the orientation of a linearly polarized antenna we're referring to the direction of the electric field it produces. For a Yagi this field is parallel to the elements. The orientation of an LP antenna on our test link can be varied by rotating the antenna about the line joining T and R.

Various possible link combinations can be characterized by the polarization at T, the polarization at R, and the relative orientation (one or both antennas linearly polarized) or sense (both antennas circularly polarized) of the antennas used. For example, (LP, CP, random) in Table 9.1 can mean either T has an LP antenna and R a CP antenna, or vice versa, and that the orientation of the LP antenna is random. The ambiguity is intentional; since the reciprocity relation previously mentioned states that system performance will be the same in both cases, there is no need to distinguish between them. When one antenna is circularly polarized, random orientation means the LP antenna can be vertical, horizontal or anywhere in between. When both antennas are linearly polarized, random orientation means the angle between the two antennas can be any value between 0 and 90°. Only five distinct combinations need be considered. (See Table 9.1.) Arbitrarily choosing the Type 1 link as a reference, we compare the performance of the other four combinations.

Type 1 link (LP, LP matched). The received signal level is constant. This link is our reference.

Type 2 link (LP, LP random). The received signal strength varies monotonically from a maximum equal to the reference level when the two antennas are parallel down to zero (theoretically) when the two antennas are perpendicular. In practice, the attenuation is rarely more than 30 dB for the perpendicular situation.

Type 3 link (LP, CP, random). The received signal strength on this link is constant at 3 dB down from the reference level and is independent of the orientation of the LP antenna and the sense of the CP antenna.

Type 4 link (CP, CP, same sense). The received signal strength on this link is constant and equal to the reference level.

Type 5 link (CP, CP, opposite sense). A simple theoretical model predicts infinite attenuation compared to the reference signal link, but in practice attenuations greater than 30 dB are rare.

Table 9.1

Communications Links Categorized by Antenna Polarization

Type 1 link (LP, LP, matched)
Type 2 link (LP, LP, random)
Type 3 link (LP, CP, random)
Type 4 link (CP, CP, same sense)
Type 5 link (CP, CP, opposite sense)

Table 9.2

Methods for Producing Circular Polarization Using Linearly Polarized Antennas

1) Pair of similar antennas fed 90° out of phase
2) Pair of similar antennas fed in phase
3) Dual-mode horn
4) Combination of electric and magnetic antennas
5) Transmission-type polarizers
6) Reflection-type polarizers

For information on methods not covered in this text see:
    H. Jasik, *Antenna Engineering Handbook* (New York: McGraw Hill, 1961), Chapter 17.

Having looked at the five basic links, we now compare the performance of various ground station antennas when operated in conjunction with a specific satellite antenna. If the satellite antenna is linearly polarized, our choice of ground station antenna is equivalent to choosing a Type 1, 2 or 3 link. Of the three, the Type 1 may appear best since it provides the strongest signals. From a practical viewpoint, however, in most cases it is nearly impossible to implement since the orientation of the incoming wave is continually changing. In reality our choice is limited to a Type 2 or Type 3 link. Although the Type 2 link will sometimes provide up to 3 dB stronger signals (matched orientation), the Type 3 link will equally likely provide up to 30 dB stronger signals than the Type 2 (perpendicular orientation). Of the two, the Type 3 link is clearly preferable.

We can perform a similar analysis for a satellite antenna that is circularly polarized. The choice of ground station antenna here is equivalent to choosing a Type 3, 4 or 5 link. A Type 4 link is clearly preferable. But, it should be noted that the Type 3 link results in signals that are only 3 dB weaker with none of the severe fading problems of Type 2 links. As a result, on links where the spacecraft is transmitting a CP wave and the S/N ratio is generally good, someone designing a ground station might elect to trade a little performance for the mechanical simplicity of LP antennas.

Signals arriving from most satellites are elliptically polarized. As we've noted, an elliptically polarized wave can be thought of as having linear and circular components. Since a CP ground station antenna produces the best performance whether the signal from a spacecraft is circularly polarized or linearly polarized, a CP receiving antenna at a ground station will provide the best results in the case where the downlink signal is elliptically polarized. A CP transmitting antenna at the ground station will also provide optimal results on the uplink.

PRODUCING CIRCULAR POLARIZATION

Numerous techniques for constructing circularly polarized antennas exist. One approach is to build an antenna like the helix (see Chapter 10) which, by its fundamental design, produces a CP wave. Another approach is to combine LP antennas in the proper manner. Several methods for producing a CP wave from LP antennas are listed in Table 9.2. The first two methods have been used widely by radio amateurs. Several EME operators have had success using the third method at frequencies above 1 GHz as a feed for parabolic antennas. The remaining approaches do not appear suitable for amateur applications at satellite ground stations, so they will not be covered here.

We'll look at Methods I and II in detail. Each requires a pair of matched LP antennas. Two identical two-element Yagis, carefully adjusted to provide a 50 ohm resistive input impedance, will be used to illustrate each method. Two dipoles, two multielement Yagis, two Quagis, and so on, could also serve. (With adjustments in the phasing/matching harness, other impedance antennas would also work.)

METHOD I

In this method the two antennas are mounted as shown in either Figure 9.7A (known as a single-boom or concentric boom array) or Figure 9.7B (known as a dual-boom or cross-boom array). The feed system is critical to the operation of these arrays. A phasing/matching harness that produces the correct power division, matching and delay parameters is shown in Figure 9.8. Only when the two antennas are fed 90° *out of phase* with *equal power* will the array produce a circularly polarized wave. The effects of various errors in power division and phase difference are described in Table 9.3. For the feed system to perform its function, each antenna must be carefully adjusted to provide an unbalanced, 50-ohm, purely resistive input impedance before it's incorporated into the array. Small adjustment errors in each antenna, even though they may be identical, can have a large effect on power division and phasing and thereby produce an elliptical wave with a large linear component. This may occur even though the SWR in the main feed line remains acceptable.

Although each array in Figure 9.7 shows one Yagi mounted vertically and the other horizontally, this particular configuration needn't be employed as long as the Yagis are mounted at right angles to one another. The tilted arrangement shown in Figure 9.9 is commonly used so that interaction with the cross boom or rotators is balanced.

There's little difference in performance between the horizontal-vertical and skewed arrangements when a ground station antenna is aimed above about 20°. At low elevation angles, however, where ground reflections have a pronounced effect due to the different phase changes imparted to the horizontal and vertical components of the signal, the skewed design may be preferable.

How do we determine the polarization sense of the antenna in Figure 9.7A when it's fed with the harness in Figure 9.8A? We could measure the polarization by testing the antenna on a link with CP antennas of known polarization

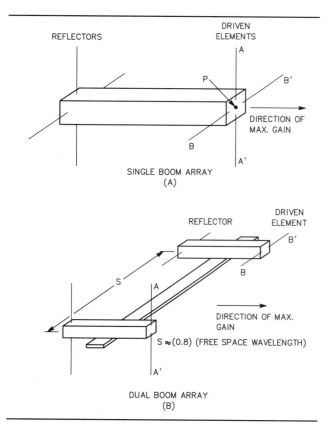

REFLECTORS

DRIVEN ELEMENTS

DIRECTION OF MAX. GAIN

SINGLE BOOM ARRAY
(A)

REFLECTOR

DRIVEN ELEMENT

DIRECTION OF MAX. GAIN

S ≈ (0.8) (FREE SPACE WAVELENGTH)

DUAL BOOM ARRAY
(B)

Figure 9.7—Yagi placement for Method I (antennas fed 90° out of phase) production of circular polarization.

at the other end or we could figure out the sense analytically as follows. Imagine yourself standing behind the single-boom array of Fig 9.7A looking in the direction of maximum gain.

Focus your attention on the electric field at the point P located at the center of the driven elements. The field at P results from the sum of two linear components: one component that is parallel to AA' (contributed by element AA'), and a second component that is parallel to BB' (contributed by the BB' element). Because of the 90° phasing, one component will be a maximum when the other one is zero. We wait until the field at P points toward 12 o'clock (parallel to AA', pointing in the direction of the element connected to the center conductor of the feed line, as shown in Figure 9.8A). Exactly one quarter cycle (90°) later, the RF cur-

rents at the end of the delay line will produce an electric field parallel to BB', pointing toward 3 o'clock since element B is connected to the center conductor of the delay line. From your observation position in back of the antenna, you see the electric field at P rotate from 12 o'clock to 3 o'clock (90° clockwise) during this quarter cycle. This configuration therefore produces right-hand circular polarization (RHCP).

How can we change the sense of polarization? We can switch from RHCP to LHCP by interchanging *either* (1) the connections at B and B' *or* (2) the connections at A and A'. Switching both sets of connections will not change the polarization sense. Switching to LHCP can also be accomplished by modifying the matching section of Figure 9.8 so that the two extensions differ by an odd number of electrical half wavelengths. Any of the techniques just mentioned can, of course, also be used to switch from LHCP to RHCP.

The polarization sense of the dual-boom array of Figure 9.7B can be predicted by imagining the two antennas slipped together (sideways motion only) until the booms overlap and form an array like the one in Figure 9.7A. As both arrays will have the same sense of circular polarization, and as we already know how to determine whether a single-boom array is RHCP or LHCP, the problem is solved.

As stated earlier, the 90° phase difference and the equal power division are critical to achieving circular polarization. The phasing/matching harness of Figure 9.8A was designed to work with antennas having an unbalanced, 50 ohm input impedance that's purely resistive. Using the functional block diagram of Figure 9.8B as a guide, we'll step through its operation starting at the antenna end and ending at the feed point. Temporarily ignore the feed-line extensions. Since the array's operation depends on a 90° phase difference between the two sets of elements, the first thing we incorporate is a delay line. A piece of coax that's electrically ¼-wavelength long does the job. (One wavelength is 360°, one-quarter wavelength is 90°.) The coax delay line would also act as an impedance transformer if the characteristic impedance of the line didn't match the antenna. To obtain the proper power division we don't want any impedance transformation here. Therefore, we use 50-ohm cable. Next, we could connect the two branches in parallel at a coaxial T connector and have both equal power division and correct delay, but the feed-point impedance would be 25 ohms, a value that's awkward to match. In-

Table 9.3

The Effects of Feed Phase and/or Power Division Errors of the Performance of the Yagi Arrays shown in Figure 9.7A and Figure 9.7B

Phase Difference (θ)	Power Division	Resulting Wave Along Major Axis
90°	equal	circular polarization
90°	unequal	elliptical polarization
0°	equal	linear polarization in plane midway between planes of two Yagis
0°	unequal	linear polarization; plane depends on power division
0°<θ<90°	equal	elliptical polarization
0°<θ<90°	unequal	elliptical polarization

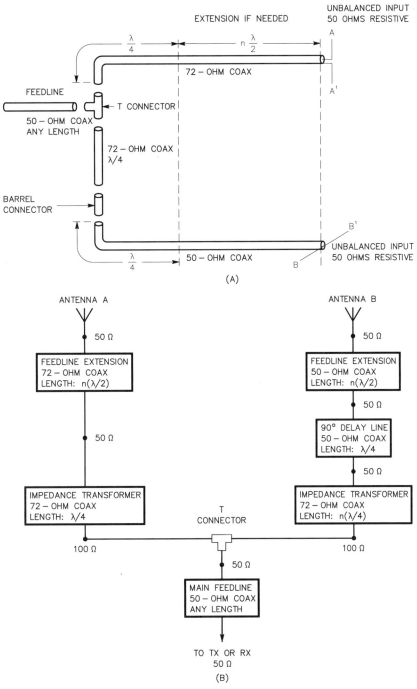

Notes:
1) n may be either 0, 1, 2, and so on, depending on how many half—wavelength extensions are needed (see text).
2) All cable dimensions refer to electrical length λ = (velocity factor of cable) (free—space wavelength). Values for the velocity factor of 0.66 (polyethylene—dielectric) and 0.81 (foam—filled cable) are often used. However, large variations are common. Because small errors in the matching harness can significantly degrade performance, one should either, (1) measure the electrical length of each cable or (2) measure the actual velocity factor of the cables being used. Methods for doing this are discussed in Chapter 10.
3) Since the antenna impedance repeats every half wavelength along the feed line, regardless of the feed—line impedance, we can use 72—ohm coax to feed antenna A and eliminate one splice in the matching harness.

Figure 9.8—Feed system for antennas in Figure 9.7.

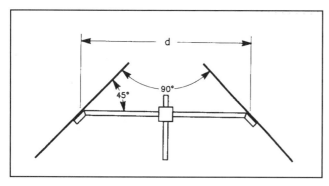

Figure 9.9—Yagis mounted in skewed orientation. d≈λ (free-space wavelength).

stead, we install two identical impedance transformers consisting of ¹/₄ wavelength sections of 72-ohm coax to step up the impedance of each branch to 100 ohms. When the two 100-ohm lines are connected in parallel at a coaxial T connector, we obtain a good match to 50-ohm feed line. The two impedance transformers do, of course, also act as delay lines. But, since we've used a pair of equal lengths, the phase *difference* between the two Yagis isn't affected.

The harness is now complete except for one mundane consideration: The two branches may not be long enough to reach the antennas. Two identical pieces of 50-ohm coax (any length) would work as extensions; we can eliminate a coax connector and its consequent losses, however, by using electrical-half wavelength sections cut from coax of

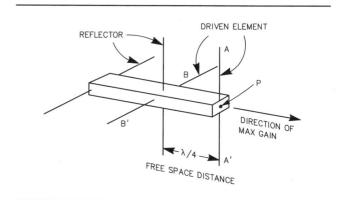

Figure 9.10—Yagi placement for Method II (antennas fed in phase) production of circular polarization.

Crossed Yagis mounted in skewed orientation.

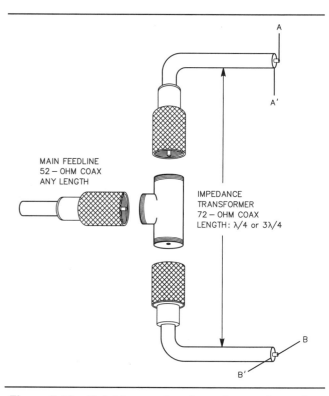

Figure 9.11—Matching system for antenna shown in Figure 9.10. Note: adding a half wavelength to either impedance transformer will change polarization sense.

different impedances as shown. (The input impedance of an electrical half-wavelength section is independent of the coax impedance—it depends only on the load.) Note that adding an extra half wavelength to one of the feed-line extensions will reverse the sense of polarization.

This completes our discussion of Method I. We now turn to the second technique for obtaining circular polarization.

METHOD II

To illustrate Method II we again use two 2-element Yagis. They can be mounted on a single boom as in Figure 9.10 or on two separate booms as in Figure 9.7B. A 90° phase difference is again the key to the antenna's operation. This time it's obtained by physically offsetting one Yagi a quarter of a wavelength in the direction of propagation and feeding the two Yagis in phase. With this approach, no delay line is needed in the feed harness. The feed system need only take into account impedance matching and power splitting. An appropriate matching harness is shown in Figure 9.11. Starting at the antenna end, it operates as follows. The 1/4 wavelength sections of 72-ohm coax step up the impedance of each Yagi to 100 ohms. When the two 100-ohm impedances are connected in parallel at the T connector, a good match to 50-ohm feed line results.

To analytically determine the polarization sense of the array shown in Figure 9.10, imagine yourself standing behind it looking in the direction of maximum gain. Focus your attention on the electric field at point P, the center of the front driven element. The field results from the sum of two contributions, one from element AA' in the vertical direction, and the second from element BB' in the horizontal direction. Note that, because of the time it takes to travel through space, the contribution from element BB' at point P was actually produced by BB' a quarter cycle earlier.

We're going to compute the direction of the electric field at P by combining the fields produced at the center of each element at three different times. Table 9.4 will help us keep track of all the needed information.

We start our observations at *Time 1* when the RF current in the feed line is producing a maximum field at each element. *Time 2* occurs after a quarter cycle has elapsed. Time 3 occurs after an additional quarter cycle has passed. In the second column of Table 9.4 we describe the field at the center of element BB', from this element only, at each of the three times. In the third column we describe the field at the center of element AA', from this element only, at each of the three times. Finally, we fill in the last column of Table 9.4 for each time by vectorially adding together the field at the center of AA' and the field that was produced at the center of BB' a quarter of a cycle earlier which is just reaching P.

The last column opposite *Time 1* has been left blank since we didn't compute the contribution of BB' a quarter cycle earlier. From our observation position in back of the antenna we see the electric field at point P rotate from 9 o'clock to 6 o'clock as a quarter cycle elapses. The wave is therefore counterclockwise (LHCP).

Table 9.4
Data Used to Compute Polarization Sense of Antenna and Feed Shown in Figures 9.10 and 9.11

	Field at Center of BB'(from element BB' only)	Field at Center of AA'(from element AA' only)	Total Field at P
Time 1	9 o'clock	12 o'clock	
Time 2	zero magnitude	zero magnitude	9 o'clock
Time 3	3 o'clock	6 o'clock	6 o'clock

Yagis using a balanced driven element such as a folded dipole are particularly well suited to Method II. An efficient matching harness using open wire balanced line of an appropriate impedance and a 1:1 or 4:1 balun as needed can be designed and constructed easily.

METHOD III

As amateur satellites begin to use links at 1.2 GHz and 2.4 GHz, antenna arrays consisting of a parabolic dish and feed may become more popular. At these frequencies, the horn antenna makes a convenient and effective feed. Since parabolic dishes are passive reflectors, a linearly polarized feed-horn will result in a linearly polarized array and a circularly polarized feed will produce a circularly polarized array. Amateurs have learned from experience that a surprisingly efficient horn can be built from a tin can containing a quarter wave monopole soldered to a coax chassis connector mounted on the inside curved surface. The dimensions of the can and placement of the probe depend on the operating frequency and the shape of the dish. Circular polarization can be obtained by using a dual mode horn consisting of a single monopole and several strategically placed tuning screws. Information on parabolic dish antennas and feeds is contained in the next chapter.

COMPARING METHODS I AND II

The analytic procedures described for determining the polarization sense of a crossed Yagi or similar array may leave your brain feeling numb. Don't worry; you're in good company—the telecommunications engineers responsible for the first satellite transatlantic TV broadcast via TELSTAR set up a link with RHCP at one end and LHCP at the other! You can sidestep the calculation approach to determining antenna polarization sense by testing an unknown antenna on a link with a CP antenna of known sense at the other end. A small helix makes a good test antenna since its polarization is easily determined (see next chapter). If you have an array whose polarization sense can be switched from the operating position, you can even ignore the sense—just select the switch position that produces the strongest signals.

Using either method, two identical antennas having a gain of, for example, 10 dBi, can be combined to form an antenna array having a gain of 10 dBic. The "c" is sometimes used to indicate a CP antenna when there's a possibility of confusion. Note that combining the same two an-

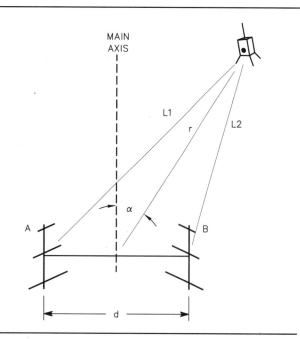

MAIN
AXIS

L1

r

L2

α

A

B

d

Figure 9.12—Polarization interferometer effects.

tennas with a phasing harness designed to produce linear polarization results in an array having a gain of 13 dBi.

One significant advantage of Method II over Method I is that the adjustment of each Yagi is not nearly as critical. As long as both Yagis are identical, small errors in the input impedance, or the presence of a reactive component, will not disturb the equal power split or phasing; the errors will only affect SWR. As long as the SWR is acceptable, the antenna will produce the desired circularly polarized pattern.

With either method one can mount the two antennas concentrically as in Figure 9.7A or Figure 9.10 or using the dual-boom arrangement illustrated in Figure 9.9. Both configurations produce the same results when aimed directly at the target.

To compare off-axis performance of the two approaches (antenna not aimed directly at target), we model the dual-boom array (using either Method I or II) in Figure 9.12. (Our analysis is very similar to the description of the operation of an interferometer using LP antennas.) Assume the figure represents a ground station transmitting an RHCP signal to the spacecraft. When the spacecraft is on-axis L1 = L2 corresponding to α = 0°, and the satellite sees an RHCP signal. Now consider the situation where α, the squint angle, is such that L1 – L2 = ¹/₄ wavelength. The spacecraft now sees the electric fields produced by the two antennas as differing by 180° (90° due to the feed harness plus 90° due to the squint angle). The resulting field will be linearly polarized. If the squint angle is such that L2 – L1 = ¹/₂ wavelength, the satellite will again see a circularly polarized signal but it will now be LHCP! When r is very much greater than d, as it is in all practical amateur installations, we obtain the following relation

$$L2 - L1 = \pm\, d \sin \alpha \qquad \text{[Eq 9.5]}$$

How large must the squint angle, α, be before these

effects become noticeable? Consider a typical amateur antenna with d = one wavelength and select L2 – L1 = ¹/₄ wavelength. Solving Eq 9.5 for the squint angle, we obtain the value 14.5°. This means that when the antenna is off pointed by 14.5° (in the direction shown), the satellite will see an LP signal. And, when the antenna is off pointed by 29°, the satellite will see a CP signal of the wrong sense! The conclusion is clear—the concentric boom arrangement is superior. However, the concentric boom method cannot be used in all cases. When combining antennas like the quad, Quagi and loop Yagi, interaction between elements of the two component antennas seriously compromises performance. Therefore one should use the dual-boom configuration with these antennas and make allowances for the fact that accurate antenna pointing will be a more critical concern.

Note that the interferometer-like effects we've been discussing also affect spacecraft antennas. Since the 2-meter and 70-cm antennas on OSCARs 10 and 13 are essentially arrays of linearly polarized antennas, they can be analyzed in a similar manner. This explains why, when the spacecraft squint angle was greater than about 10°, the links appeared to have a significant linear component. When the squint angle was large enough, the circularly polarized component of the downlink even appeared to have the "wrong" sense.

SPIN MODULATION

Since a satellite antenna and its gain pattern are firmly anchored to the spacecraft, a ground station's position relative to the pattern will change moment by moment. As we've noted, both the polarization and gain of an antenna vary with the observer's location. A ground station will therefore see gain and polarization changes on a downlink signal resulting from satellite rotation. These changes are called *spin modulation*. The spin modulation frequency depends on the spacecraft's rotation which, in turn, depends on the attitude stabilization technique employed. After a few weeks in orbit, OSCARs 5, 6, 7 and 8 rotated at frequencies on the order of 0.01 Hz (about one revolution every four minutes). Spin modulation at 0.01 Hz sounds much like a slow fade. Its effect on intelligibility is minor unless the signal drops below the noise level.

The attitude stabilization scheme used for OSCARs 10 and 13 differed considerably. The spacecraft were spun at roughly 20 revolutions per minute (RPM) about an axis ideally parallel to the line joining the apogee and the center of the Earth. Because of the tri-star shape of these Phase 3 satellites, gain and polarization variations on the links occur at three times the spin rate (60 RPM, or 1 Hz). When a ground station is located on the fringes of the satellite's antenna pattern, it may observe gain variations that exceed 10 dB. To a user, spin modulation at a frequency of 1 Hz resembles rapid airplane flutter. It can be very annoying and have a severe impact on intelligibility.

How serious a problem is spin modulation? It is mainly of concern with spin-stabilized spacecraft of the type used with early Phase 3 elliptical orbits. Even with these spacecraft the effects become annoying only when the ground station was

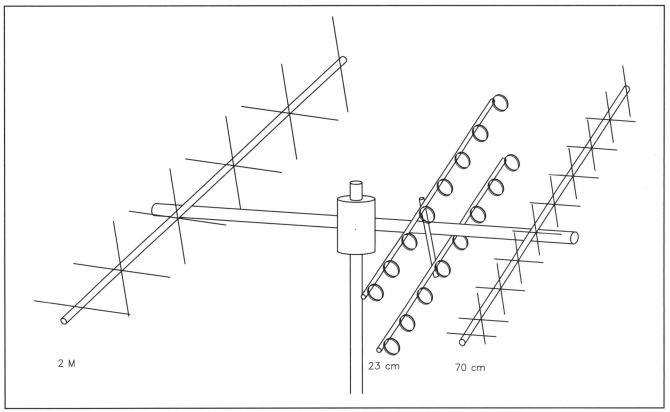

2 M

23 cm   70 cm

Figure 9.13—High performance antenna system for working with Phase 3 spacecraft Modes B and L. Array uses crossed Yagis for 2 meters and 70 cm and a pair of loop Yagis on 23 cm, for circular polarization on all bands.

looking at the spacecraft from off to its side (large squint angle). A ground station can't do much to alleviate true gain variations due to asymmetries in the satellite's antenna gain pattern, but variations caused by polarization mismatch can be minimized by using a circularly polarized antenna.

FARADAY ROTATION

As a linearly polarized radio wave passes through the ionosphere, the direction of the electric field rotates slowly about the direction of propagation. This rotation, known as the *Faraday effect* (see Chapter 8) is most noticeable at lower frequencies, such as 29 MHz and 146 MHz. Its effects can be observed by ground stations that use linearly polarized antennas; slow fades will occur as the angle between the linear component of the incoming wave and the ground station antenna changes during a pass. Faraday rotation is especially noticeable on the 29-MHz downlink since all amateur satellites have used linearly polarized antennas for Mode A. The use of a CP antenna at the ground station would eliminate these effects, but very few ground stations employ CP at 29 MHz. It's important to note that circular polarization won't cure all Mode A fading, since much of it arises from the constantly changing orientation of the gain pattern of the antennas aboard the spacecraft as it spins. Other factors, such as absorption in the ionosphere, can also contribute to fading.

CONCLUSIONS

1) A circularly polarized ground station antenna will outperform a linearly polarized antenna most of the time. If you opt for the additional complexity of a circularly polarized antenna, it's definitely worthwhile to include provision for switching polarization sense since the off-axis signal produced by the spacecraft may, at times, have a sense opposite to the on-axis signal at 2 meters and 70 cm.

2) If you elect to use a circularly polarized array consisting of two linearly polarized antennas, the best approach is to select Yagis so they can be mounted using the concentric boom method. To simplify matching and phasing, and to assure equal power splitting, use the physical offset method to produce the 90° phase shift.

3) If you're interested in communicating by Phase 3 satellites and you're willing to restrict yourself to operating times when squint angles are small, a linearly polarized ground station antenna will provide excellent results.

4) For optimal performance, you may elect to use different antennas for Phase 2 and Phase 3 spacecraft.

5) Read the sections in the next chapter concerning preamps and preamp switching circuits before designing an antenna system.

6) An example of a suggested high-performance antenna system for working with Phase 3 spacecraft is shown in Figure 9.13.

Chapter 10

Antennas for Space Communication: Practical

THE DIPOLE AND ITS VARIANTS

TWO LINEARLY POLARIZED BROAD BEAMWIDTH ANTENNAS

The Groundplane
The J-Pole
Matching Antenna to Application

BEAM ANTENNAS

Yagi, Quad and Related Beams
Circular Polarization from Linearly Polarized Antennas
The Helix

FOUR CIRCULARLY POLARIZED BROAD BEAMWIDTH ANTENNAS

Lindenblad
Quadrifilar helix
TR-Array
Eggbeater
Summary

REFLECTOR ANTENNAS

Parabolic Dish
Related Antennas

MISCELLANEOUS

Horn, Lens and Patch Antennas

ANTENNA SYSTEMS

Feed Lines and Connectors
Delay and Phasing Lines
Rotators (Azimuth and Elevation Control)
Radome Material
Calculating EIRP
Closing Hints

FIGURES

TABLES

10 Antennas for Space Communication: Practical

This chapter focuses on several practical antennas that may be used at a satellite ground station. You'll no doubt recognize many, as they're also popular for terrestrial HF and VHF communication. We'll point out the advantages and disadvantages of each for accessing low and high-altitude spacecraft, for construction difficulty, and for general utility as part of an overall antenna system. Construction details are provided for the more unusual models, and references to readily available sources of information are provided for the popular types.

THE DIPOLE AND ITS VARIANTS

The horizontal half-wave dipole (Figure 10.1A) is a familiar antenna that can be used at satellite ground stations. Two offshoots of the dipole, the inverted V (Figure 10.1B) and the somewhat less familiar V (Figure 10.1C), have also been used. Be sure not to confuse the V antennas discussed here with the V beam, which is radically different in construction and operation. Our discussion will focus on the inverted V since it has been investigated thoroughly. Nonetheless, it's safe to assume similar characteristics for the V.

The dipole and Vs are usually mounted fixed in the same configuration for both satellite and terrestrial applications (as in Figure 10.1). It therefore makes sense to label patterns as vertical and horizontal. Gain patterns in the horizontal plane for the dipole and inverted V are shown in Figure 10.2. Note how the horizontal dipole has higher gain broadside and deeper nulls off the ends. Their low gain renders the dipole and V suitable mainly for use with low-altitude satellites. Their broad beamwidth provides reasonably good coverage when the antennas are fixed mounted. Dipoles are most often used to receive the 29-MHz Mode A downlink. A few amateurs have tried them successfully on 146 MHz uplinks and downlinks in conjunction with low-

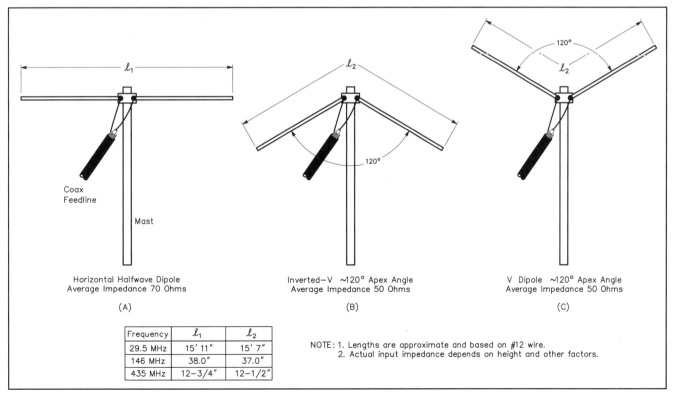

Frequency	ℓ_1	ℓ_2
29.5 MHz	15' 11"	15' 7"
146 MHz	38.0"	37.0"
435 MHz	12−3/4"	12−1/2"

NOTE: 1. Lengths are approximate and based on #12 wire.
2. Actual input impedance depends on height and other factors.

Horizontal Halfwave Dipole
Average Impedance 70 Ohms
(A)

Inverted−V ~120° Apex Angle
Average Impedance 50 Ohms
(B)

V Dipole ~120° Apex Angle
Average Impedance 50 Ohms
(C)

Coax Feedline

Mast

Figure 10.1—Three variations of the half-wave dipole.

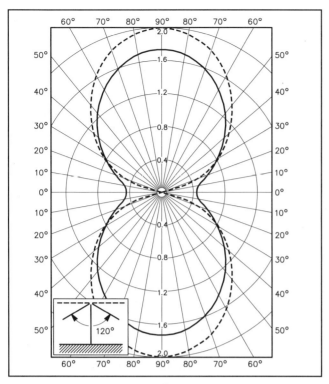

Figure 10.2—Horizontal-plane patterns showing relative field intensity for inverted V with 120° apex angle (solid line) and horizontal dipole (dashed line). For additional information on inverted Vs, see D. W. Covington, "Inverted-V Radiation Patterns," *QST*, May 1965, pp 81-84.

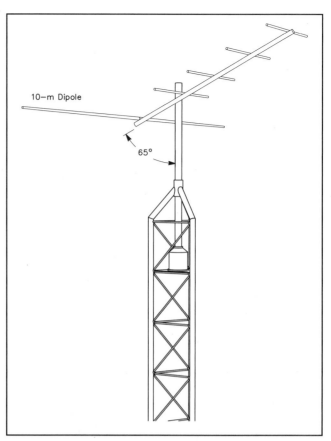

Figure 10.3—An effective linearly polarized antenna system for operating Mode A, consisting of a half-wave 10-m dipole mounted in back of a small 2-m beam. The main boom is inclined at approximately 25° above horizontal (65° from vertical) and only an azimuth rotator is used.

altitude spacecraft on Modes A, B and J, but this has mainly been for experimental, not for general, communication.

Let's look at some practical applications of dipoles and Vs at 29 MHz. Given the patterns in the horizontal plane, most amateurs who are constrained to using a single fixed antenna choose the V to reduce the effects of the deep nulls associated with the dipole. Slightly better overall performance can be obtained by using two totally independent dipoles mounted at right angles to one another. If feed lines for both are brought into the operating position, switching between them to find the dipole that produces the best received signal is a simple matter.

Another application, offering even better performance, consists of mounting a 10-m dipole behind a small 2-m beam, using a light-duty azimuth rotator to turn the whole array (Figure 10.3). Azimuth aiming requirements will be lax and, by inclining the 2-m beam at roughly 25° above the horizon, the elevation rotator can be eliminated. You'll note that for all three examples just presented, improved performance seems to go hand-in-hand with increased complexity.

The free-space gain pattern of the dipole in the vertical plane really isn't of much interest to us because ground reflections change it drastically. As it turns out, the gain pattern depends on the height of the dipole. Look at the patterns in Figure 10.4 for three specific heights: $1/4$, $3/8$ and $1^1/2$ wavelengths above an infinite, perfectly conducting ground. The pattern in Figure 10.4C is very poor for satel-

lite work since signals will fade sharply each time the satellite passes through one of the nulls. In reality, the nulls are not as severe as shown because the ground is not a perfect conductor and signals reflected off nearby objects often arrive at the ground station receiving antenna from several directions. The pattern in Figure 10.4B is most desirable since gain variations tend to balance out changes in signal level as the distance between spacecraft and ground station varies. In other words, the gain pattern of Figure 10.4B is high toward the horizon where signals are weak (large satellite to ground-station distances), and low in the overhead direction where signals are strong (small satellite to ground-station distances). The pattern in Figure 10.4A is acceptable, though not as good as the one in Figure 10.4B. Gain patterns for the V antennas are similar when height is measured from the feed point to the conducting surface.

As the effective *electrical* ground does not generally coincide with the *actual* ground surface, you can't simply measure height above ground to figure out which pattern applies to a given antenna. Many dipole users just orient the antenna with regard to the horizontal pattern and mount it as high and as clear of surrounding objects as possible. Although this does not always produce the best system performance, the results are usually adequate. Some users have tried to obtain the desired vertical patterns (Figures 10.4A or 10.4B) by simulating a ground with a grid of wires placed beneath the dipole as shown in Figure 10.5. Subjective reports suggest that even a single wire (the one labeled A) placed beneath a dipole or V may improve 29-MHz Mode A reception. At 146 MHz and higher frequencies, a reflecting screen can be used for the ground so that a vertical pattern similar to the one of Figure 10.4B can be achieved with the antenna mounted in a desirably high location. Because the ground screen is finite, gain at takeoff angles below about 15° is reduced.

The basic half-wave dipole can also be mounted vertically. In this orientation the horizontal plane pattern is omnidirectional while the actual vertical plane pattern,

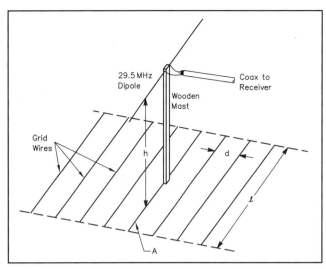

Figure 10.5—Dipole mounted above reflecting screen. Best results are obtained when h=³/₈ wavelength, d is less than 0.1 wavelength and ℓ=0.6 wavelength. Note that it is not necessary to physically connect the grid wires to the dipole or feed line.

which depends on mounting height, is likely to have one or more nulls at high radiation angles. Although the characteristics of this antenna appear suitable for work with low-altitude satellites, there is a hitch: the feed line must be routed at right angles to the antenna for at least a half wavelength if one hopes to obtain the patterns described. As a result, it's usually easier to use a groundplane antenna (see next section), which has similar characteristics. One novel configuration that has proved effective for working DX on Mode A consists of a vertical dipole for 29 MHz hung at the end of a tower-mounted 2-m beam. When the tower-to-dipole distance is set at roughly 6 feet, the tower will tend to act as a reflector and the resulting 29-MHz pattern will be similar to that obtained with a vertically mounted 2-element beam.

In truth, we've paid considerably more attention to the dipole and V than their actual use justifies. Nevertheless, they clearly illustrate many of the tradeoffs between effective gain patterns and system complexity that a ground station operator is faced with.

TWO LINEARLY POLARIZED BROAD BEAMWIDTH ANTENNAS

The Groundplane

The groundplane (GP) antenna, familiar to HF and VHF operators alike, is sometimes used at satellite ground stations. Physically, the GP consists of a ¹/₄ or ⁵/₈-wavelength vertical element and three or four horizontal or drooping spokes that are roughly 0.3 wavelength or longer. At VHF and UHF, sheet metal or metal screening is often used in place of the horizontal spokes. The GP is a low-gain, linearly polarized antenna. The gain pattern in the horizontal plane is omnidirectional. Because of its low gain the GP is not generally suitable for operating with high-altitude satellites, though it may be used in special cases. We'll focus

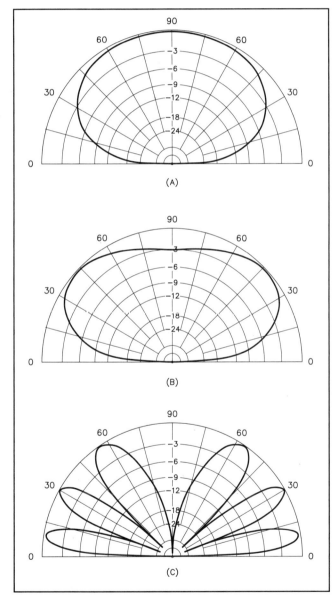

Figure 10.4—Vertical-plane gain patterns showing the relative field intensity for half-wave dipole above perfectly conducting ground. Pattern at right angles to dipole. (A) is for height of ¹/₄ wavelength, (B) is for height of ³/₈ wavelength, and (C) is for height of 1.5 wavelengths.

on its possibilities with respect to low-altitude spacecraft.

Gain patterns in the vertical plane for ¹/₄-wavelength GP antennas are shown in Figure 10.6 Although the vertical plane patterns suggest that performance will be poor when the satellite is overhead, stations using the GP report satisfactory results. The reasons are most easily explained in terms of reception. Downlink signals. usually arrive at the ground station antenna from several directions after being reflected off nearby objects. These reflected signals can either help (when the direct signal falls within a pattern null) or hinder (when interference between the main and reflected signals results in fading). In practice, the good effects appear to far outweigh the bad; the GP is a good all-around performer for working with all low-altitude OSCARs (heights under 1000 miles) and the MIR and US Space Shuttle.

A GP may be useful for receiving signals from high-altitude satellites in certain situations. For example, although the downlink S/N ratio using a GP generally will not be adequate for communication, it should be sufficient for spotting (determining if the spacecraft is in range). The omnidirectional horizontal plane) pattern of the GP makes it especially suitable for this purpose. Also, the GP may be

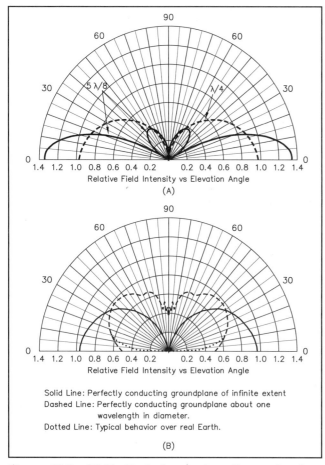

Figure 10.6—(A) Vertical-plane gain patterns showing relative field intensity for ¹/₄ wavelength and ⁵/₈ wavelength groundplane antennas over ideal Earth (perfectly conductivity and infinite extent). (B) The effects of a limited ground plane and/or resistive ground on the ¹/₄ wavelength groundplane antenna.

useful near perigee of elliptical-orbit missions if spin modulation is not excessive. Some broad-beamwidth, circularly polarized antennas better suited to working with Phase 3 satellites near perigee are discussed later in this chapter. We now turn to some practical GP antennas.

GP antennas designed for the 27-MHz CB market are inexpensive and widely available. For Mode A downlink operation the ¹/₄-wavelength GP usually outperforms the "bigger is better" ⁵/₈-wavelength model because its vertical plane radiation pattern (Figure 10.6) is better suited to satellite operation. To modify a ¹/₄-wavelength CB antenna for 29.4 MHz the vertical element should be shortened about 9%. If a matching network is used it might also require a slight adjustment.

GP antennas designed for the 146-MHz and 435-MHz amateur bands are available commercially at moderate cost. Once again, the ¹/₄-wavelength models produce good results. Some users, however, prefer to use a ⁵/₈ GP when the satellite is at low elevation angles, and a different type of antenna when the satellite is at higher elevation angles. A VHF or UHF ¹/₄-wavelength GP can be assembled at extremely low cost (see the illustration in Figure 10.7).

Tilting the vertical element of a ¹/₄-wavelength GP modifies the gain pattern in the vertical plane as shown in Figure 10.8B. Note how the overhead null has been eliminated. The horizontal pattern is slightly skewed, but remains essentially omnidirectional. Tilting also tends to reduce the already low input impedance of the GP. One way to compensate for this reduction is to use a folded element as shown in Figure 10.8A. As in the folded dipole, the folded ¹/₄-wave element in a tilted GP steps up the input impedance and gives a broader-bandwidth antenna. The dimensions shown should give a good match to 50-ohm coax.

The J-Pole

Another simple antenna with an omnidirectional pattern in the horizontal plane and a vertical plane pattern very similar to the ¹/₄ wavelength groundplane is the J-pole. The J pole antenna is fundamentally an end-fed ¹/₂ wavelength antenna that uses a ¹/₄ wavelength matching transformer. Dick Jansson, WD4FAB, an engineer who's been designing and building OSCAR satellites for two decades, brought this antenna to the attention of the amateur community soon after the MicroSats were launched. In an article in March 1990 in *The AMSAT Journal* he provided practical information on constructing a dual band (2 m and 70 cm) J-pole based on a design from the 1976 edition of *FM and Repeaters for the Radio Amateur* by the ARRL. Mechanically it's much more compact than two separate groundplanes and it provides somewhat better performance at the lowest elevation angles.

Detailed construction articles for single band models are readily available. See "An All-Copper 2-m J-Pole" in *The ARRL Handbook For Radio Amateurs*, 1998, pp 20.56-20.58 (based on an article by M. Hood, KD8JB); and "A Microsat J Pole Antenna [70 cm]," *The AMSAT Journal*, Sep/Oct 1996, pp 16-17 by D. Guimont, WB6LLO. Responding to questions about this antenna on the AMSAT-

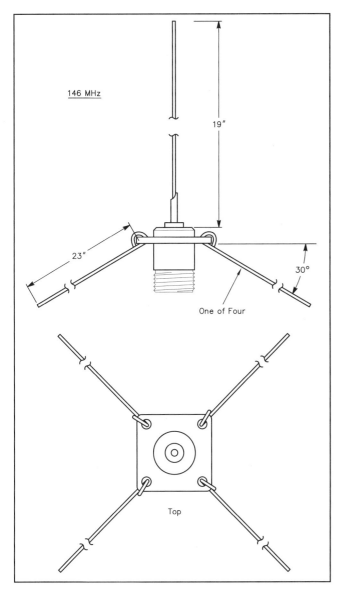

146 MHz

19"

23"

30°

One of Four

Top

Figure 10.7—A groundplane antenna for 146 MHz is easily constructed using a chassis-mount coax connector. A Type N connector is preferred, but a UHF type is acceptable at 146 MHz. Drooping the radials increases gain slightly at low elevation angles and raises input impedance to produce a better match to 50-ohm feed line.

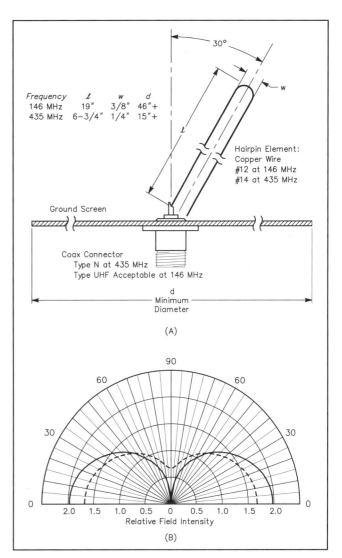

Frequency	ℓ	w	d
146 MHz	19"	3/8"	46"+
435 MHz	6-3/4"	1/4"	15"+

30°

w

Hairpin Element: Copper Wire #12 at 146 MHz #14 at 435 MHz

Ground Screen

Coax Connector Type N at 435 MHz Type UHF Acceptable at 146 MHz

d Minimum Diameter

(A)

90

60   60

30   30

0   0
2.0 1.5 1.0 0.5 0 0.5 1.0 1.5 2.0
Relative Field Intensity

(B)

Figure 10.8—(A) ¼-wavelength groundplane antenna with tilted vertical element. Groundplane may be square or circular, solid or mesh. (B) Vertical-plane relative field intensity for ¼ wavelength groundplane; solid line—element vertical; dashed line—element tilted 30° from vertical.

BB (Internet) Dave provided the following performance information. On recent passes, using the J-pole he was able to download: 386k on a 65° elevation pass of KO-23, 195k on a 28° elevation pass of KO-25 and 198k on a 32° elevation pass of UO-22.

Matching Antenna to Application

Low gain omnidirectional antennas like the GP and J-pole are especially useful with low altitude satellites. How does one choose which particular antenna is most suitable? One important consideration is the antenna's vertical plane radiation pattern. This pattern should be matched to the daily average time that the satellite will appear at specific elevation angles. To analyze the situation we'll divide elevation angles into three sectors: 0 to 30°, 30 to 60°, and 60 to 90°. We'll then compute the ratio of the access time in a given sector to the total access time and express the result as a percentage.

For a satellite in a circular orbit the desired information depends on the ground station latitude and on the satellite's orbital inclination. However, a reasonably accurate estimate for mid-latitude ground stations and satellites in near polar orbits can be obtained by assuming that average daily access time in a given sector is proportional to the terrestrial area between the corresponding elevation circles. For example, the average daily time that RS-10/11 will appear between 30 and 60° in elevation is proportional to the area between its 30 and 60° elevation circles, and the average time it will be in range is proportional to the area between its 0 and 90° elevation circles (area inside access circle). Details of the calculations may be found in Chapter 13. The results are shown in Figure 10.9. A more thorough analysis

10.9. A more thorough analysis shows that, even for space-craft like the US Space Shuttle where our assumptions are generally not valid, the results still hold.

From Figure 10.9 we see that a satellite at a height of 1200 miles will appear at elevation angles greater than 30° about 22% of the time it's available to us while a spacecraft at a height of 200 miles will appear at elevation angles greater than 30° less than 7% of the time it's available. Clearly, the lower the satellite height, the less important high elevation angle performance of a ground station antenna becomes. As a consequence, the ¹/₄-wavelength GP and the J-pole are good all around performers for working with low earth orbit spacecraft—the lower the orbit the better the performance.

BEAM ANTENNAS

Whether you work with low- or high-altitude satellites there are many situations in which a beam will be the preferred ground station antenna.

With low-altitude spacecraft, a beam could be used for (1) an uplink antenna when available ground station transmitter power is very low, (2) a downlink antenna when a very high downlink S/N ratio is required or (3) both link antennas when one is attempting to contact stations with the spacecraft near or below the normal radio horizon. Superior performance has its costs: the cash spent on rotator(s), and the inconvenience of having to "ride" the azimuth and elevation controls during a pass.

If several passes of a low-altitude satellite are previewed using a tracking program, you'll see that the satellite often just grazes the outskirts of your acquisition circle. During these horizon passes the satellite elevation angle will generally be between 0 and 15°, and azimuth changes, though larger, will usually be less than 90°. Readers who are already equipped for terrestrial VHF or UHF operation with a beam mounted on an azimuth rotator aimed at the horizon will find that their setup provides good satellite access on these horizon-grazing passes. Before the pass begins, the antenna can be set to an azimuth about 20° past AOS. One or two azimuth updates will usually suffice for the entire pass.

For general operation with high-altitude satellites, beams are necessary for obtaining an adequate downlink S/N ratio and cost effective for obtaining the desired uplink EIRP. The burden of keeping the antennas properly aimed during a pass is not as severe with high-altitude elliptical orbits of the Phase 3 type as it is with low-altitude satellites because spacecraft motion near apogee appears very slow. With stationary satellites the antenna is simply aimed during the initial setup and then clamped in position. Once you commit to using a beam and rotators for the downlink, it's generally cost effective to use a beam with similar gain on the uplink.

Free-space gain patterns for well-designed Yagis, quads, Quagis, loop Yagis and delta loops of equal boom length are very similar. The patterns are roughly symmetrical (all cross sections look nearly the same) with a shape somewhat like the beam pattern of Figure 9.4. The relation between half-power beamwidth and gain (Eq 9.4) has been used to prepare Table 10.1.

Ground reflections are of concern with all antennas, including beams. The vertical gain pattern of a beam mounted with its boom parallel to the surface of the Earth does *not* look like the clean, free-space pattern shown in Figure 10.4. Instead, it breaks up into several lobes interspaced with nulls, the number and position depending on the antenna height (in wavelengths). An example can be

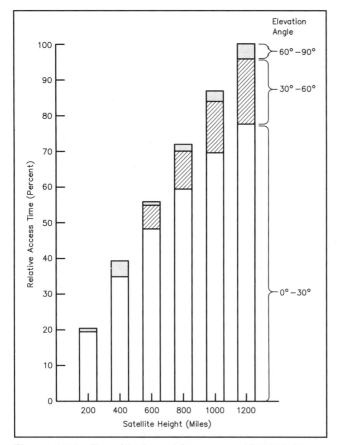

Figure 10.9—For circular orbits, as satellite height decreases a ground station's relative access time at high elevation angles also decreases. Relative values use 1200 mile height as a basis.

Table 10.1

Half-power Beamwidth as a Function of Gain for Well Designed, Symmetric Pattern, Beam Antennas

G (gain)	G (gain)	θ* (half-power beamwidth)
6 dBi	4.0	100°
8 dBi	6.3	80°
10 dBi	10.0	63°
12 dBi	16.0	50°
14 dBi	25.0	40°
16 dBi	40.0	32°
18 dBi	63.0	25°
20 dBi	100.0	20°
22 dBi	159.0	16°
24 dBi	251.0	13°

seen in Figure 10.4C. These lobes and nulls result from constructive and destructive interference between the direct and ground-reflected signals, as discussed earlier in this chapter. In contrast, when the same beam is pointed significantly above the horizon, the ground-reflected signal contains only a relatively low proportion of the total power; interference effects (both constructive and destructive) become very small. As a result, the tilted beam does produce a clean pattern resembling that in free space.

To illustrate the practical implications of ground effects on vertical patterns, consider a typical ground station antenna for working with Phase 3 satellites. It gives 13 dBi gain and 45° beamwidth. Let's focus on the downlink and look at the satellite near apogee. Assume that both the satellite and the antenna are initially at an elevation angle of 40°. Suppose that one hour later the elevation rotator has not been touched, though the satellite has climbed to an elevation angle of 62.5°, a change of one half our antenna beamwidth. With the antenna set at 40° elevation, very little ground-reflected power reaches the antenna and the pattern can be thought of as a clean pencil beam. When the satellite is at 62.5° elevation, it is at a point 3 dB down on the ground station antenna pattern; we'd expect the downlink signals to have decreased by 3 dB. Practical experience confirms these expectations.

Now consider a similar situation with the same satellite near apogee and same antenna, but this time let the initial elevations of both satellite and antenna be 5°. Assume that one hour later the satellite elevation increases to 15° while the antenna elevation remains at 5°. What happens to the link? A prediction based on free-space patterns would yield an almost trivial 1 or 2-dB decrease in signal level since the 10° change in elevation is far less than the 22.5° (half-beamwidth) change it takes to reduce signals by 3 dB. But predictions based on the free-space model are totally inadequate at low antenna elevations where ground reflections play a very pronounced role. In reality, it's nearly impossible to predict the outcome, but changes in the downlink amounting to a decrease of 30 dB, an increase of 3 dB, or anything in between wouldn't be surprising. Even though the outcome can't be predicted, understanding the situation is important: At low satellite elevation angles, aiming the antenna in elevation becomes more critical. With a broad-beamwidth antenna it's very easy to ignore a small, seemingly insignificant change in satellite elevation. While this oversight is safe at high elevation angles, it can severely degrade performance at low angles.

Our discussion has focused on the downlink. The uplink is analogous except for one fact. Even if uplink and downlink antennas have identical free-space patterns and are mounted at the same physical height, their actual vertical patterns will not be the same since their electrical heights (measured in wavelengths) will be different.

When working at low elevation angles you may find, a small percentage of the time, that an elevation setting that results in good uplink signals is associated with a poor downlink and vice versa. The only solution, short of mounting each array on its own set of rotators, is to pick a compromise position. For reliable operation when a satellite is close to the horizon it's critically important to monitor your downlink and adjust antenna elevation as often as necessary.

Yagi, Quad and Related Beams

We now turn to some of the practical concerns involved in choosing among the Yagi, quad, Quagi, loop Yagi and delta loop. Since the performance of these antennas is similar in terms of pattern and ground effects we'll focus on difficulty of construction, mounting ease, commercial availability and suitability for later use as part of a circularly polarized system. Each type of antenna will be evaluated in terms of these criteria.

The Yagi has a number of positive attributes including its simple structure, light weight, and low wind load for a given gain. As a result, most commercial manufacturers favor it over other types of beams at 2 m and 70 cm. Until recently, however, most published Yagi designs operated satisfactorily only over a very narrow bandwidth (often 1-2% of operating frequency). As a result, home-brewers had to be extremely careful to replicate all dimensions and materials exactly as described to duplicate the performance of the original. The narrow bandwidth also made the antenna very susceptible to detuning effects from the mounting, nearby antennas, and rain, ice and snow. Back in the 1970s, attempts to conquer the bandwidth limitation focused on the use of log-periodic feeds. This approach was successful but the extra elements added to weight and wind load.

Until recently many engineers believed that the narrow-band nature of the Yagi was an intrinsic characteristic. But Steve Powlishen (K1FO), using computer design tools that became available in the late 1980s, demonstrated that it's possible to design high performance arrays with bandwidths on the order of 8% having extremely clean patterns (very low power in sidelobes). Computer analysis is ushering in a golden age in Yagi design. Although most of the cutting edge work is being done on very large antennas for EME operation, the smallest of these antennas make excellent building blocks for producing circularly polarized antennas. CP antennas formed from these new Yagi designs will be leading performers on 2 m, 70 cm and 23 cm satellite links over the next decade.

Quad antennas are easy to match and their dimensions are relatively uncritical. However, large quads have not been very popular at VHF and UHF because they're structurally cumbersome. Similar comments apply to the delta loop. Construction details for an easily duplicated 146 MHz, 3-el quad are given in Figure 10.10. I've had good results using this simple antenna for uplinking on Mode A and as part of a system designed to illustrate the minimal requirements for monitoring the OSCAR 13 Mode B downlink (a 1.0-dB preamp was mounted on the antenna). In addition, a set of these antennas used to construct an interferometer for a student experiment in orbit determination provided excellent performance.

The Quagi is a cross between quad and Yagi. It uses a quad reflector and driven element for easy, efficient matching, and Yagi directors for good gain, low wind load and

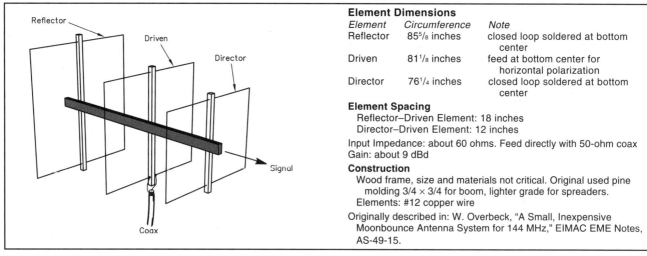

Element Dimensions

Element	Circumference	Note
Reflector	85⅝ inches	closed loop soldered at bottom center
Driven	81⅛ inches	feed at bottom center for horizontal polarization
Director	76¼ inches	closed loop soldered at bottom center

Element Spacing
  Reflector–Driven Element: 18 inches
  Director–Driven Element: 12 inches
Input Impedance: about 60 ohms. Feed directly with 50-ohm coax
Gain: about 9 dBd

Construction
  Wood frame, size and materials not critical. Original used pine molding 3/4 × 3/4 for boom, lighter grade for spreaders. Elements: #12 copper wire
Originally described in: W. Overbeck, "A Small, Inexpensive Moonbounce Antenna System for 144 MHz," EIMAC EME Notes, AS-49-15.

Figure 10.10—A 3-el quad for 146 MHz.

simple structure. After its introduction in 1977, the Quagi quickly became popular with new VHF and UHF operators who wanted a simply constructed homemade antenna that, when put on the air without any specialized test equipment, performs up to expectations.

The loop Yagi (Figure 9.1) and the delta loop are close relatives of the quad and Yagi. Both have been used for satellite communication. Recently, the loop Yagi has received considerable attention. Since its structure is mechanically awkward at VHF and lower frequencies, it hasn't seen much use in this part of the radio spectrum.

The loop Yagi is gaining in popularity at 1260 MHz and higher frequencies where a very straightforward mechanical design has evolved. Each loop is formed into a circle from a strip of flat, springy conductor. A single screw holds the loop in shape and secures it to an aluminum boom. Good loop Yagi designs appear at least to equal, and perhaps exceed, Yagis of the same boom length. As the bandwidth of a loop Yagi is several times that of currently existing Yagi designs, construction tolerances are considerably relaxed. Commercially made loop Yagis were one of the most popular uplink antennas for Mode L operation with OSCAR 13.

The quad, Quagi, loop Yagi and delta loop all suffer from the same shortcomings. If one wants to construct a circularly polarized array using two antennas they must be configured using the cross boom mounting to minimize interaction.

A list of relevant construction articles featuring the Yagi, quad, Quagi, loop Yagi and delta loop is contained in Table 10.2. It may take a little research to select the antenna that best meets your needs. Each year, at major VHF/UHF conferences around the US, test ranges are set up to compare antennas. The results are often presented in *QST*'s World Above 50 MHz column. Consistent top performers are quickly adopted by serious contesters and EME buffs, so you can also check recent contest results to see what antennas are being used. As a rule of thumb, if an array of eight brand-X Yagis is popular with EME operators, one brand-X Yagi will provide good performance to a Phase 3 satellite, and a pair, configured for

circular polarization, will provide excellent results.

Circular Polarization from Linearly Polarized Antennas

The basic engineering concepts describing how two linearly polarized antennas (the component antennas) could be combined to produce a circularly polarized array were presented in Chapter 9. We now look at some of the practical aspects of implementing these ideas. There are two key, and totally independent, choices that have to be made: (1) whether to use a concentric boom or a crossboom configuration; and (2) whether to use a delay line or to physically offset the antennas in the direction of propagation in order to achieve the required 90° phase difference.

The concentric boom configuration is preferable in that it eliminates off-axis circularity changes (the interferometer-like effects discussed in Chapter 9). However, of the beams discussed, it can only be used with the Yagi. With the Quagi, quad, loop Yagi or delta loop, the crossboom configuration must be used. When using the crossboom arrangement it's important to use the least separation possible to minimize off-axis circularity effects. A rule of thumb is to mount each component antenna at a 45° angle to the cross boom and to space the antennas so that there's a half wavelength between the tips of the closest elements. The cross boom should be nonconducting material (preferably fiberglass). If suitable material isn't available, a metal cross boom with nonconducting extensions fabricated from PVC plastic plumbing pipe can be used.

It's best to empirically check for interaction between the component antennas, and between each antenna and the cross boom. Set the array up at ground level and pointing at a high elevation angle. Disconnect any phasing/ matching harness. Connect an SWR meter to one of the component antennas with a short length of coax and note the SWR. RF energy can be dangerous so use a low power level and keep clear of the antenna when it's energized. Move the other component antenna about and note whether the SWR is affected. Then remove the nonenergized antenna from the cross boom. Rotate the energized antenna and again

Table 10.2

Sources for Construction Articles on Linearly Polarized Beam Antennas and Power Splitters Suitable for OSCAR Operation

YAGI

The ARRL Antenna Book , 18th Ed., 1997, Chapter 18.

J. Huang, "Planar Microstrip Yagi Antenna," *NASA Tech Brief*, Vol 14, No 9, Item #26. Available from Technology Utilization Office, Jet Propulsion Laboratory (JPL), Pasadena, CA. Contains information on model for 1.58 GHz.

S. Powlishen, "Improved High-Performance Yagis for 432 MHz," *Ham Radio*, May 1989, pp 9-10, 12, 17, 19-22, 25.

S. Powlishen, "An Optimum Design for 432-MHz Yagis, Part 1," *QST*, Dec 1987, pp 20-24; "Part II," Jan 1988, pp 24-30.

S. Powlishen, "High-Performance Yagis for 432 MHz," *Ham Radio*, July 1987, pp 8-9, 11-13, 15, 17-23, 25-27, 29-31. Correction, Oct 1987, p 97. Comment, Sep 1987, p 6.

J. Reisert, "Optimized 2- and 6-Meter Yagis," *Ham Radio*, May 1987, pp 92-93, 95-97, 99-101. Correction, Aug 1987, p 41. Correction, Jul 1987, p 49.

S. Jaffin, "Applied Yagi Antenna Design, Part I: A 2-meter Classic Revisited," *Ham Radio*, May 1984, pp 14-15, 17-20, 23-25, 27-28.

R. J. Gorski, "Efficient Short Radiators," *QST*, Apr 1977, pp 37-39. Describes a 2-el Yagi design tested at 100 MHz. Should be excellent for Mode A reception when scaled to 146 MHz.

QUAD

The ARRL Antenna Book , 18th Ed., 1997, Chapter 18. Description of 2 and 4-el quads for 144 MHz.

J. Reynante, "A Five-Element Quad Antenna for 2 Meters," *QST*, Jan 1995, p 67.

W. Overbeck, "A Small, Inexpensive Moonbounce Antenna System for 144 MHz," EIMAC EME Notes, AS-49-15. Describes an array of 16 3-el quads. The dimensions of the individual quads, scaled to 145.9 MHz, are given in Figure 10.10.

QUAGI

The ARRL Antenna Book, 18th Ed, 1997, Chapter 18.

W. Overbeck, "Reproducible Quagi Antennas for 1296 MHz," *QST*, Aug 1981, pp 11-15.

W. Overbeck, "The Long-Boom Quagi," *QST*, Feb 1978, pp 20-21. Includes design for 432 MHz. Also see "Technical Correspondence," *QST*, Apr, 1978, p 34, for comments concerning scaling Quagis to other frequencies.

W. Overbeck, "The VHF Quagi," *QST*, April, 1977, pp 11-14. Includes designs for 144.5, 147 and 432 MHz.

LOOP-YAGI

The ARRL Antenna Book , 18th Ed, 1997, Chapter 18.

E. Krome, "A Satellite Mode S Loop Yagi Antenna," *The AMSAT Journal*, May/Jun 1993, pp 4-7.

B. Atkins, "The New Frontier," *QST*, Oct 1980, p 66. Includes two designs for 1296 MHz by G3GVL, a 38-element array on a 10 ft boom with about the same gain as a 4-ft dish and a 27-element array on a 7.5-ft boom with about 1.5 dB less gain. Contains good construction diagrams.

R. Harrison, "Loop-Yagi Antennas," *Ham Radio*, May 1976, pp 30-32. Includes designs for 28.5, 146 and 435 MHz.

DELTA-LOOP

A. A. Simpson, "A Two-Band Delta-Loop Array for OSCAR," *QST*, Nov 1974, pp 11-13. Includes designs for 146 and 435 MHz.

POWER SPLITTERS

J. Reisert, "VHF/UHF World," *Ham Radio*, May 1988, pp 80, 82-83, 85-86, 88-89.

---

check for SWR changes. If the SWR is not affected by either operation the antenna configuration is acceptable.

Of the two methods described for obtaining the required 90° phase shift, our analysis in Chapter 9 showed that the physical offset method is clearly superior due to the simplicity and noncritical nature of the matching harness. It's not widely known that this is true even when a cross beam mounting is being used. Phasing/matching harnesses for the two methods are shown in Figures 9.8 and 9.11. These harnesses will only work with antennas having a 50-ohm resistive feed. The harness of Figure 9.8 provides a 90° phase shift. It will work for both the concentric boom and cross-boom arrays that require a shift. The harness of Figure 9.11 is designed for arrays using a physical offset to produce the needed 90° phase shift. It will work for both concentric boom and cross-boom arrays.

The phasing/matching harnesses just mentioned will also work with loop Yagis having a 50-ohm resistive input impedance. The loop Yagis must be mounted using the cross boom configuration with one feed at the bottom of the driven loop and the other fed at either 3 or 9 o'clock. The physical offset method of obtaining the required 90° phase shift is again preferred.

To obtain optimal performance from an antenna you should be able to switch polarization from the operating position. Choices might include circular or linear—sense if circular, orientation if linear. Using a pair of identical linearly polarized antennas mounted as in Figures 9.7 or 9.10, it's theoretically possible to obtain any polarization—linear (any orientation), circular (RH or LH) or elliptical (any combination of linear and circular)—by adjusting the power division between the two antennas and the relative phasing. In practice, systems providing a continuous range of choices are very complex and really unnecessary. When working with a satellite link where the polarization of the satellite signal is constantly changing, one only needs to select between RHCP and LHCP. Several simple switching systems requiring only a SPDT coax relay are illustrated in Figure 10.11. Although the illustrations in the figure employ a dual-boom configuration, all examples work fine with a concentric boom mounting.

Theoretically, the antenna switching shown in Figure

10.11C can actually be accomplished using a mechanical switch at the operating position if you run two feed lines down to the shack. Even though the total feed line length is now twice as long, there's no additional loss. Although this may contradict intuition it's easily confirmed. Consider two identical 200-watt ground stations using crossed Yagi antennas. Let station A use a single 100-ft feed line and a power splitter at the antenna. Let station B use two feed lines, each 100 ft, and a power splitter at the operating position so that switchable polarization can be employed. Assume that 100 ft of feed line has 3 dB loss at the frequency of interest.

STATION A

Transmitter output: 200 watts

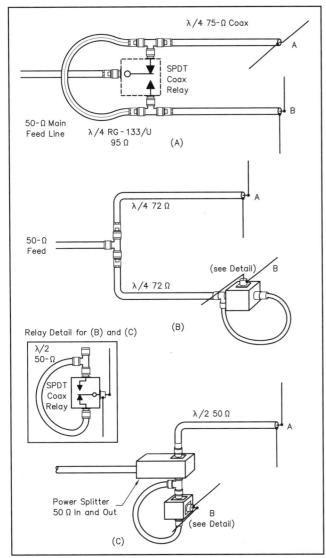

Power at antenna end of feed line: 100 watts (3 dB loss)
Power reaching each Yagi: 50 watts (after power splitter)

STATION B

Transmitter output: 200 watts
Power into each feed line: 100 watts (after power splitter)
Power reaching each Yagi: 50 watts (3 dB loss on each feed line)

Even though there's no additional loss with the two feed line system, it's definitely not recommended for several reasons. Fabricating cables of equal electrical length to the precision necessary is a difficult job and the cost of the extra coax usually eats up any savings on other components. In addition, the method does not lend itself to placing a preamp at the antenna.

The Helix

Imagine a beam antenna that (1) produces a circularly polarized wave without a complex feed harness, (2) operates over a wide bandwidth and (3) is very forgiving with respect to dimensions and construction techniques. Unlike the isotropic antenna, this one's for real. Called an axial-mode helix (helix for short), it's used by many satellite operators. It was also used on OSCAR 13 for the 1.2 and 2.4 GHz links. Before we get carried away describing the advantages of the helix, note that it does have several drawbacks which will be mentioned shortly.

A helix is characterized by three basic parameters:

C, the circumference of the imaginary cylinder on which the helical element is wound (usually expressed in terms of wavelength so that it's frequency independent)

α, the pitch angle, essentially a measure of how closely the turns of the helical element are spaced (also frequency independent)

n, the total number of turns

When these parameters lie in these ranges,

$0.8\ \lambda \geq C \geq 1.2\ \lambda$
$12° \leq \alpha \leq 14°$
$n \geq 3$

the helix will produce a beam pattern similar to the Yagi and quad. Dimensions are given in Figure 10.12. A 6-turn helix suitable for use with OSCAR 40 is shown, but the number of turns may be scaled up or down (see Table 10.3) to change the gain and beamwidth.

When a helix is built with the circumference equal to the wavelength it is designed for, it will work well at frequencies between 20% below and 30% above the design frequency. The wide bandwidth is advantageous: It allows you to be a little less precise than usual when measuring the proper antenna dimensions. It also makes it possible to use the 146-MHz helix described in Figure 10.12 for monitoring scientific satellites that transmit near 137 MHz, and the 435-MHz model for listening to navigation satellites near 400 MHz. The bandwidth of the helix can contribute to

Figure 10.11—Systems for switching between LHCP and RHCP. Component antennas must be 50 ohms resistive. Component antennas may use either the concentric boom or crossboom configuration. (A) System using 90° delay line (driven elements in same plane), (B) system using ¼ wavelength physical offset, and (C) system using ¼ wavelength physical offset and power splitter (50 ohms in and out).

receiver desensitization problems, however, if high-power commercial stations are located nearby. Unfortunately, megawatt EIRP TV and radar transmitters are common in the part of the spectrum that radio amateurs use for satellite links. A sharp band-pass filter at the receiver input may help if you encounter any trouble.

The input impedance of a helix that is fed at the center is usually close to 140 ohms. A matching transformer con-sisting of an electrical quarter wavelength of 75-ohm coax (RG-11) or 80-ohm coax (Belden no. 8221) will provide a decent SWR when 50-ohm feed line is used. The SWR improvement, however, exists only over a relatively small bandwidth.

In recent years a new matching approach with several advantages has become increasingly popular with profes-sional space communication engineers. When the helix is

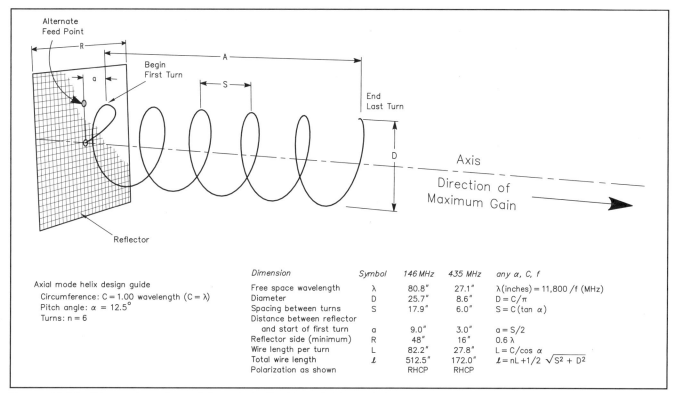

Figure 10.12—Dimensions for axial mode helix. For additional information, see: J. D. Kraus, *Antennas* (New York: McGraw-Hill, 1950), Chapter 7; H. E. King and J. L. Wong, "Characteristics of 1-8 Wavelength Uniform Helical Antennas," *IEEE Trans on Antennas and Propagation*, Vol AP-28., no. 2, Mar 1980, pp 291-296; *The ARRL Antenna Book*, 18th Ed., 1997, Chapter 19.

Table 10.3

Helix Characteristics[†]

No. of turns (n)[1]	Gain (G)[2]	Gain (G)	Half-power beamwidth[3]	Approx boom length[4] 146 MHz	435 MHz
3	10.0	10.0 dBi	64°	5.0 ft	2.0 ft
4	13.3	11.0 dBi	55°	6.5 ft	2.5 ft
5	16.6	12.2 dBi	49°	8.0 ft	3.0 ft
6	20.0	13.0 dBi	45°	9.5 ft	3.5 ft
7	23.3	13.7 dBi	42°	11.0 ft	4.0 ft
8	26.6	14.2 dBi	39°	12.5 ft	4.5 ft
9	30.0	14.8 dBi	37°	14.0 ft	5.0 ft
10	33.3	15.2 dBi	35°	15.5 ft	5.5 ft
11	36.6	15.6 dBi	33°	17.0 ft	6.0 ft
12	40.0	16.0 dBi	32°	18.5 ft	6.5 ft

[1] For n less than 3 the helix pattern changes radically.
[2] Theoretical values: Measurements suggest these values are 1 or 2 dB too high. Gain (G) ~ 15 n tan α[†]
[3] Half power beamwidth = $52° \sqrt{n \tan \alpha}$ [†]
[4] Boom length = λ (n + 0.5) tan α
[†]Based on 1-wavelength circumference (C = λ) and 12.5° pitch angle (α)

fed at the alternate feed point on the periphery, as shown in Figure 10.12, the first turn may be thought of as an impedance transformer. To use this feed point, dimension a should be doubled (that is, set a equal to S, the spacing between turns). Displacing the first quarter turn toward the reflector tends to produce a better match to 50-ohm feed line. To bring the SWR down even closer to 1:1, increase the effective wire diameter of the first quarter turn by soldering a strip of thin brass shim stock or copper flashing (width roughly 5 times the wire diameter) to it. This technique is described in detail by J. D. Kraus in "A 50-ohm Input Impedance for Helical Beam Antennas," *IEEE Transactions on Antennas and Propagation*, Vol AP-25, No. 6, Nov 1977, p 913, and J. Cadwallader, "Easy 50-ohm Feed for a Helix," *QST*, June 1981, pp 28-29. With this matching technique the SWR remains below 2:1 over a range of about 40% of the center frequency.

The helical element must be supported by a nonconductive structure. Two common approaches to building such a frame are illustrated in Figure 10.13. Lightweight woods with good weathering properties, such as cedar or redwood, are preferred for large 146-MHz lattice structures, while varnished pine or oak dowels may be used for the smaller 435-MHz model. The construction of the reflector is not critical as long as it meets the minimal size requirements. Square or round sections of hardware cloth for 435-MHz helices, or 2"×4" welded wire fencing for 146-MHz helices are suitable. A small aluminum hub with 18 or more evenly spaced spokes radiating outward can also be used. At 146 MHz the helical element may be wound from 1/4-inch flexible copper tubing or from a length of old coaxial cable (impedance is not important) with the inner conductor and outer braid shorted together. At 435 MHz and higher frequencies, no. 12 wire is acceptable.

The main problem with using a helix is its cumbersome physical structure. Comparing a well-designed crossed Yagi array and a helix with the same gain, you'll find that generally the Yagi array will be considerably shorter and have less than half the weight and windload (see Table 10.4). Several serious EME operators, experimenting with arrays of helices, have concluded that helices are not suitable for providing the very large gains required for EME communication.

A second problem with the helix is that there is no way to flip the polarization sense. Despite these problems you should consider the helix if you need an easily reproducible, moderate-gain, inexpensive antenna for satellite operation.

To determine the polarization sense of a helix, picture yourself standing in back of the reflector looking out in the direction of maximum gain. If you were to place your index finger on the feed point and slide it forward along the surface of the helical element, you would see it trace out either a clockwise pattern or a counterclockwise pattern. Clockwise corresponds to an RHCP helix; counterclockwise corresponds to an LHCP helix. As mentioned earlier, a 3-turn helix makes an excellent reference antenna for determining the polarization sense of a crossed Yagi or similar array.

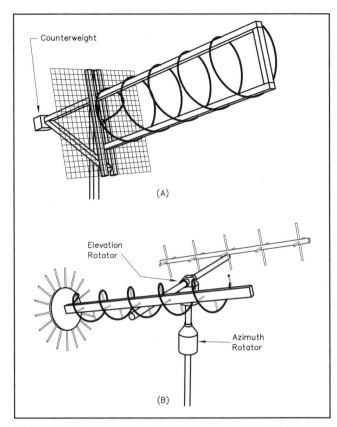

Figure 10.13—Frameworks that may be used for building helix antennas. A lattice structure, often used at 146 MHz, is shown at A; the structure in B is popular at 435 MHz. For practical information on helix structures, see D. Jansson, "Helical Antenna Construction for 146 and 435 MHz," *Orbit*, Vol 2, no. 3, May/Jun 1981, pp 12-14, and R. Life, "Improved Mechanical Design for the Helical Antenna," *QEX*, Jan 1993, pp 13-16.

Construction information for a 16 turn 2.4 GHz Helix can be found in two articles by J. Miller, G3RUH, in *The AMSAT Journal*: "Small iS beSteSt," July/Aug 1993, p 12, and "S-Band 16t Helix Update," Nov/Dec 1993, p 29. These articles should be available via the AMSAT Web site—check under downloadable software for articles by G3RUH.

FOUR CIRCULARLY POLARIZED BROAD-BEAMWIDTH ANTENNAS

Four additional circularly polarized antennas are of interest. All are low-gain, broad-beamwidth designs primarily suited for use with low-altitude spacecraft.

Lindenblad

The Lindenblad antenna, shown in Figure 10.14A, has been used for decades on VHF links at airport control towers where its omnidirectional pattern and circular polarization are a near perfect match for null free reception from the linearly polarized, randomly oriented signals arriving from incoming and departing aircraft.

The Lindenblad consists of four dipoles spaced equally around the perimeter of an imaginary horizontal circle

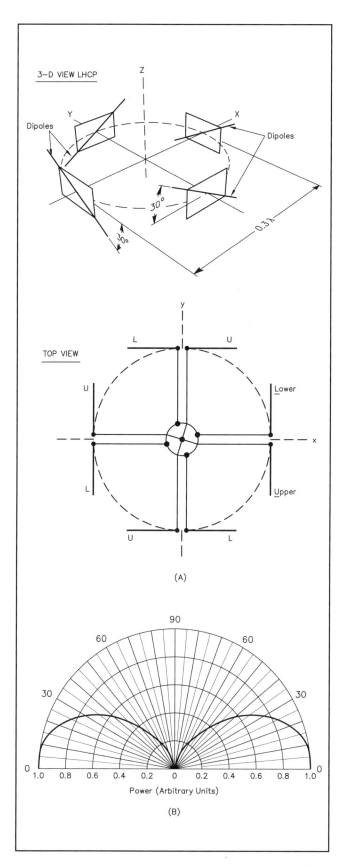

3-D VIEW LHCP

Z

Y

X

Dipoles

Dipoles

30°

30°

0.3 λ

TOP VIEW

L   U

U   Lower

U   Upper

L

U   L

y

x

(A)

90

60   60

30   30

0   0
1.0 0.8 0.6 0.4 0.2 0   0.2 0.4 0.6 0.8 1.0
Power (Arbitrary Units)

(B)

Figure 10.14—(A) The Lindenblad antenna consists of four λ/2 dipoles oriented as shown in the 3-D view and fed as illustrated in the top view. (B) Free-space vertical-plane power vs elevation angle for Lindenblad antenna. Ground reflections decrease gain at very low elevation angles and introduce nulls.

about 0.3 wavelength in diameter. Each dipole is tilted 30° out of the horizontal plane; rotation (tilt) is about the axis joining the mid point of the dipole to the center of the circle. All four dipoles are tilted in the same direction: either clockwise (for RHCP) or counterclockwise (for LHCP) from the perspective of an observer located at the center of the array.

Radiation from the Lindenblad is omnidirectional in the horizontal plane and favors low elevation angles in the vertical plane (see Figure 10.14B). When used with low-altitude, circular-orbit satellites, the increased power at low deviation angles compensates somewhat for increased satellite ground station distance; signal levels therefore remain fairly constant over a considerable range of elevations. The radiated signal is nearly circularly polarized in all directions, a very desirable characteristic. Construction details for 2-m and 70-cm versions are given in Figure 10.15. Since all dipoles are fed in phase, power division and phasing are simple and the array can easily be duplicated without test equipment. Furthermore, using folded dipole elements simplifies impedance matching.

A number of radio amateurs experimenting with the Lindenblad reported that although performance (pattern and circularity) was excellent, SWR was in many cases very high. Howard Sodja, W6SHP, analyzed the antenna using MININEC and identified the cause. (Reference in Table 10.5.) Interaction between the dipoles was affecting the feedpoint impedance of each. He found that he could improve the SWR by modifying the size, and thus the feedpoint impedance, of each dipole. The dimensions provided by Howard are given in Figure 10.15. It's interesting to note that because of the intrinsic symmetry of the antenna these changes do not effect the power division or phasing of the dipoles (pattern and circularity do not change)—they should, however, provide a better SWR.

As mentioned earlier, the polarization sense is determined by the direction in which the dipoles are rotated (tilted) out of the horizontal plane. Polarization can't be reversed by modifying the feed harness; if you want to change from RHCP to LHCP, or vice versa, you must change the antenna structure.

Quadrifilar Helix

The quadrifilar helix (Figure 10.16A) consists of four ¹/₂-turn helices (A, A', B, B') equally spaced around the circumference of a common cylinder. Opposite elements (A and A', B and B') form a bifilar pair; the two bifilars must be fed equal amounts of power but 90° out of phase. As with other antennas requiring a 90° phase difference and equal power division, problems arise in designing an adequate feed system.

The solution favored by professional antenna engineers is to make one bifilar slightly undersize so it resonates above the operating frequency (input impedance has a capacitive component) and the other bifilar slightly oversize so it resonates below the operating frequency (input impedance has an inductive component).

Each bifilar pair has its diameter adjusted to make the reactive and resistive components of its input impedance

Table 10.4

Comparison of Three Circularly Polarized Beam Antennas

	Crossed Yagis with Delay Line	Crossed Yagis Offset $1/4\,\lambda$ in Direction of Max Gain	Single Helix
Length for 12 dBi gain	$1.0\,\lambda$	$1.25\,\lambda$	$1.4\,\lambda$ (plus boom for counterweight if needed)
Bandwidth	~2% of center frequency	~ 2% of center frequency	From 20% below to 30% above center frequency
Matching/phasing system	Highly complex	Moderately complex	Relatively simple
Adjustment procedure	Complex	Complex	Simple
Are dimensions and construction materials critical?	Yes	Yes	No
Relative, size, weight, mounting complexity	Small, light, simple	Small, light, simple	Moderately large, heavy, complex
Can polarization sense be externally switched?	Yes	Yes	No

equal. As a result, the current in the small bifilar will lead the input by 45° and the current in the large bifilar will lag by 45°. This yields the desired 90° phase difference and a purely resistive input impedance of about 40 ohms when the two bifilars are fed in parallel. In effect, matching and phasing are built into the antenna itself. An "infinite balun"

is conveniently used in conjunction with the self-phased quadrifilar.

The radiation pattern of a quadrifilar helix is omnidirectional in the plane perpendicular to its main axis. In a plane containing the main axis (Figure 10.16B) the maximum gain is about 5 dBi, and the beamwidth 114°. Radiation is nearly circularly polarized over the entire hemisphere irradiated. In many situations an antenna with these characteristics is ideal for a ground station. For example, it could be used as part of an unattended automated command or data retrieval station. The quadrifilar helix also makes an excellent spacecraft antenna. One was used on AMSAT-OSCAR 7 for the 2.3-GHz beacon.

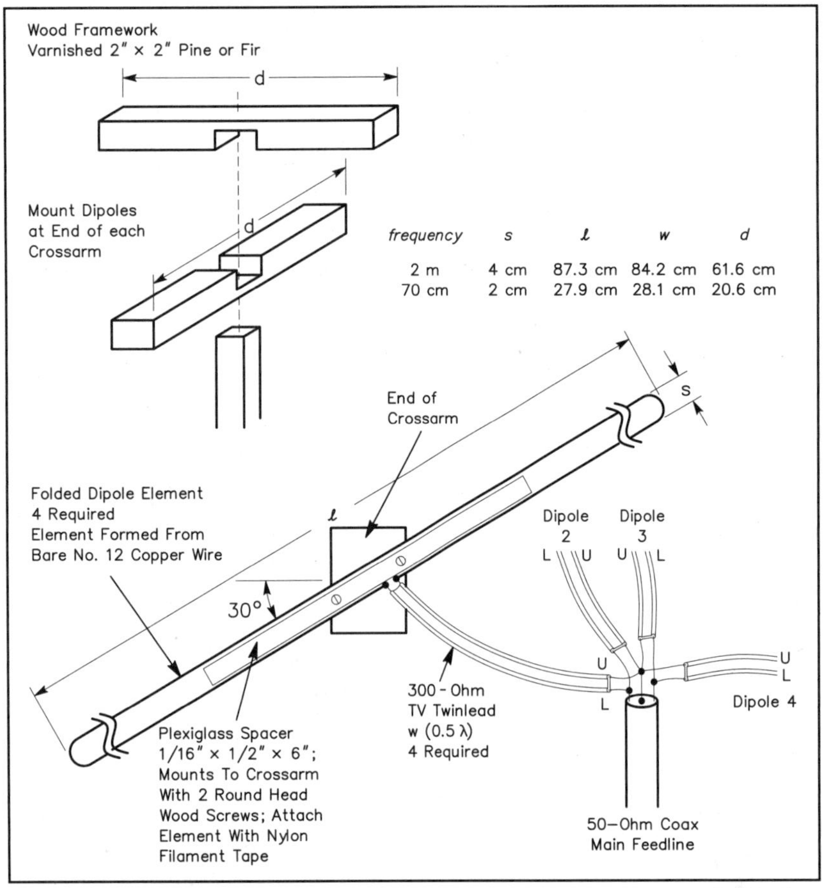

Because small changes in the dimensions and dielectric properties of the quadrifilar support structure, and the presence of nearby objects, can have a large effect on power division and phasing, the radio amateur without sophisticated test equipment may have difficulty duplicating the desired performance. Nevertheless, the intrepid experimenter will find construction details for 146-MHz and 435-MHz quadrifilars in Figure 10.17 and Table 10.6. Dimensions, scaled from a 2-GHz model, should only be regarded as a guide. Phasing and balun details are also included.

T-R Array

The T-R array (turnstile-reflector array) shown in Figure 10.18A consists of a pair of dipoles mounted above a reflecting screen and fed equal power, 90° out of phase. Performance is almost identical to the crossed 2-element Yagi array (Figure 9.7).

The T-R array produces a nearly omnidi-

frequency	s	ℓ	w	d
2 m	4 cm	87.3 cm	84.2 cm	61.6 cm
70 cm	2 cm	27.9 cm	28.1 cm	20.6 cm

Figure 10.15—Construction details for Lindenblad antenna. Folded dipoles have been used to simplify matching. If desired, a 75 to 50-ohm transformer and/or balun may be inserted between the antenna and main feed line.

Table 10.5
Design and Construction References for Four Low-gain, Circularly Polarized Antennas Compared in Table 10.7

REFERENCES

LINDENBLAD

G. H. Brown and O. M. Woodward, Jr, "Circularly Polarized Omni-directional Antenna," RC*A Review*, Vol 8, Jun 1947, pp 25-269.

R. Ott, "A Lindenblad Circularly Polarized Antenna for Amateur Satellite Communications," *The AMSAT Journal*, Vol 14, no. 6, Nov/Dec 1991, pp 10-12.

H. Sodja. "Lindenblad Serendipity and Enlightenment," *The AMSAT Journal*, Vol 14, no 6, Nov/Dec 1991, pp 15-18. Also see **http://www.amsat.org/amsat/articles/w6shp/lindy.html**

QUADRIFILAR HELIX

C. C. Kilgus, "Resonant Quadrifilar Helix," *Microwave Journal*, Dec 1970 pp 49-54

C. C. Kilgus, "Resonant Quadrifilar Helix," *IEEE Trans on Antennas and Propagation*, Vol 17, May 1969, pp 349-351.

R. W. Bricker, Jr and H. H. Rickert, "An S-Band Quadrifilar Antenna for Satellite Communications," Presented at 1974 International IEEE/P-S Symposium, Georgia Institute of Technology, Atlanta, GA. Authors from RCA AstroElectronics Div, Princeton, NJ 08540.

C. C. Kilgus, "Shaped-Conical Radiation Pattern Performance of the Backfire Quadrifilar Helix," *IEEE Trans on Antennas and Propagation*, Vol 23, May 1975, pp 392-397.

E. Ruperto, "The W3KH Quadrifilar Helix Antenna," *QST*, Aug 1996, pp 30-33.

D. Guimont, "Quadrifilar Antennas for Amateur and 137 MHz Satellites*," The AMSAT Journal*, Mar/Apr 1994, pp 11-13.

M. Maxwell, Re*flections: Transmission Lines and Antennas*, ARRL, 1990, Chapter 22: The Quadrifilar Helix Antenna. [Out of print.]

T-R ARRAY

M. Davidoff, "A Simple 146-MHz Antenna for OSCAR Ground Stations," *QST*, Sep 1974, pp 11-13.

M. F. Boister, "A New Type of Circular Polarizer Using Crossed Dipoles," *IRE Trans on Microwave Theory and Techniques*, Sep 1961, pp 385-388.

EGGBEATER

D. Thornburg and L. Kramer, "The Two-Meter Eggbeater," *QST*, Apr 1971, p 44-46.

S. Ford, "M² Enterprises EB-144 Eggbeater Antenna," *QST*, Sep 1993, pp 75-76. (Review)

S. Ford, " M² EB-432 Eggbeater Antenna, *QST*, Jan 1996, pp 74-75. (Review)

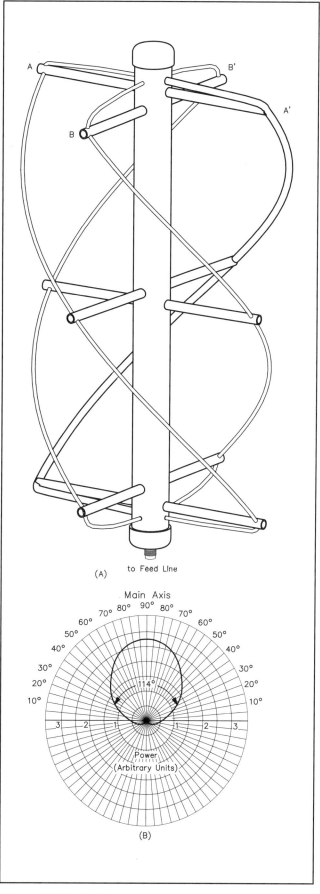

Figure 10.16—(A) The quadrifilar helix antenna; (B) power gain pattern of quadrifilar helix.

rectional horizontal-plane gain pattern. Vertical plane patterns, which depend on the dipole-to-reflector distance, are shown in Figure 10.18B for spacings of λ/4 and 3λ/8. The 3λ/8 spacing produces an especially desirable pattern for a fixed ground station antenna. At high elevation angles, where this antenna is most useful, the changing gain tends to compensate for variations in ground station to satellite distance, yielding a relatively constant signal level. The T-R array produces a circularly polarized signal along the main axis. Off-axis circularity is fairly good at high elevation angles, but the Lindenblad and quadriflar helix are superior in this regard.

The power division and phasing problems encountered with the crossed-Yagi array (Figure 9.7) are repeated with the T-R array. Figure 10.19A contains a matching/phasing harness for ³/₈-λ spacing. Note that the impedance of the dipoles varies with dipole-reflector distance, so the matching network shown will not work with other spacings. An adjustment procedure, which requires only an SWR meter, should produce a 146-MHz version that yields optimal performance. Set up two slightly long dipoles ³/₈λ above the reflector. Feed one as in Figure 10.19B; let the other one float. Prune the active dipole for minimum SWR at 146 MHz. Don't worry about the actual SWR as long as it's below 1.5:1. Cut the second dipole to the same length. Reconfigure the feed system as in Figure 10.19A. Then increase the dipole-to-reflector spacing slightly until you obtain minimum SWR.

It is possible to "self-phase" the T-R array as was done

with the quadrifilar helix by using one long dipole (resistive and inductive components of input impedance equal) and one short dipole (resistive and capacitive components of input impedance equal). Feeding these two dipoles in parallel will yield correct phasing, an approximately equal power split and a resistive input impedance. If you wish to experiment with the self-phasing approach, you may be able to determine dipole lengths by calculating values as explained in the article by M. F. Bolster (Table 10.5) or by using the new antenna modeling software.

Eggbeater

The Eggbeater antenna consists of two vertical circular full-wave loops. See Figure 10.20. The loops are perpendicular and fed 90° out of phase at the bottom. Each loop behaves similar to the driven element in an HF quad and has an input impedance of about 100 ohms.

The pattern produced by the Eggbeater is omnidirectional and linearly polarized in the horizontal plane and circularly polarized directly overhead. The overall behavior is much like the TR-array with some additional gain toward the horizon. The optional reflector kit provided in a commercial version produced by M² Antennas increases

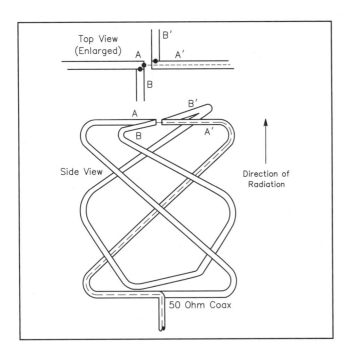

Figure 10.17—Quadrifilar helix employing self-phasing and infinite balun. Note: Coax may be used to form all four helices. On three, the inner conductor and outer braid are shorted at cut ends. The fourth helix is part of the feed as shown. RG-58 and RG-8 may be used at 435 MHz and 146 MHz, respectively, but slight adjustments in the lengths of the helices will be needed since the element diameters will be smaller than specified in Table 10.6.

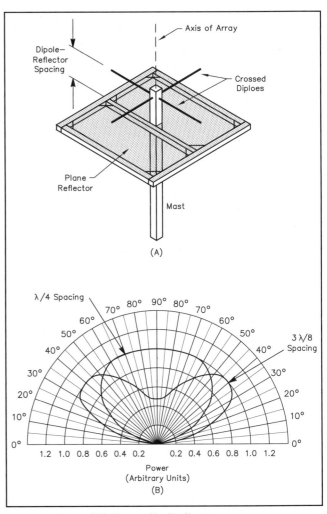

Figure 10.18—(A) Turnstile-Reflector array. (B) Vertical-plane power patterns for dipole-reflector spacings of λ/4 and 3λ/8.

Table 10.6

Design Data for Quadrifilar Helix

	Small Bifilar			Large Bifilar			
	D	L	Length A-A'	D	L	Length B-B'	Wire Diam
146 MHz	12.62 in.	19.25 in.	82.19 in.	13.99 in.	21.03 in.	90.60 in.	0.71 in.
435 MHz	4.23 in.	6.46 in.	27.57 in.	4.69 in.	7.05 in.	30.39 in.	0.24 in.
Any frequency (λ)	0.156	0.238	1.016	0.173	0.260	1.120	0.0088

Note: Dimensions should be regarded only as a guide. Special thanks to Walter Maxwell, W2DU, for providing this information.

the overhead gain at the expense of gain toward the horizon. Subjective reviews from those using the M² Antenna report good throughput using digital communications via the MicroSats.

The dimensions for a 2-m Eggbeater and suggested feed system shown in Figure 10.20 are from a 1971 *QST* article by Thornburg and Kramer (see Table 10.5).

Summary

The properties of the four low-gain, circularly polarized antennas suitable for working with low-altitude satellites are summarized in Table 10.7. Table 10.5 contains design and construction references for all four antennas.

If you've been using a GP antenna on a particular link and it has been yielding acceptable results, give the Lindenblad a try—it should result in a noticeable improvement. Amateurs interested in setting up an inexpensive Mode A station or an unattended station for Mode J packet radio should consider the T-R array. When making your decision keep in mind the fact that a given satellite will appear at elevation angles above 30° only a small percentage of the time it's in range (Figure 10.9).

REFLECTOR ANTENNAS

Reflector antennas consist of a feed antenna and a large (generally at least 6 wavelengths) passive focusing surface. The best known member of the family is the parabolic. The 8 to 10-foot dishes commonly seen in backyards and on rooftops are usually parabolics being used to re-

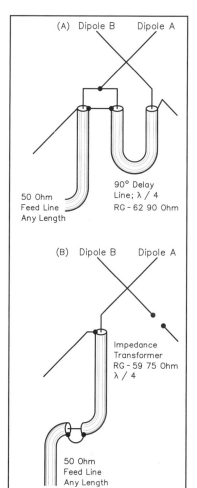

Figure 10.19—(A) Phasing/matching harness for T-R array. (B) Test harness for adjusting T-R array.

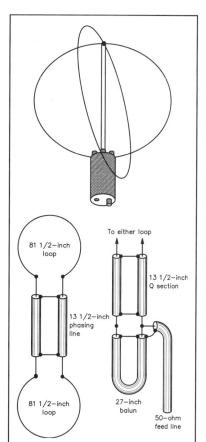

Figure 10.20—The two loops of the Eggbeater are fed 90° apart, through a quarter-wave balanced phasing section. The 50-ohm feed system includes a 4:1 balun and a quarter-wave Q section. Lengths shown are for 2-m antenna using RG-58/U for phasing line, Q section and balun. Variations in coax velocity factor may affect lengths.

ceive 4-GHz TV transmissions from geostationary satellites. Two other members of this family are the spherical dish and corner reflector.

Parabolic Dish

To understand how the parabolic dish antenna operates, we have to look at dish geometry and feed systems, and the relationship linking these two factors. The shape of the reflecting surface is formally known as a paraboloid, but following common usage we'll refer to both the reflector and the entire antenna as a dish or parabolic dish. The three-dimensional dish surface is formed by rotating a parabolic curve (see Figure 10.21) about its main axis. The operation of the dish is based on the fact that incoming signals which arrive parallel to the main axis are concentrated at a point (the *focal point*) after being reflected off the dish. Similarly, a signal source located at the focal point that illuminates the dish will produce a beam parallel to the dish's main axis, in much the same way a flashlight focuses the light emitted by its bulb.

The location of the focal point depends on dish geometry. It's usually specified in terms of *focal length* (f): the distance between the vertex (center) and the focal point. Note that modifying the diameter of a dish, by sawing off the outer rim or adding extensions, does not change the focal length. One key characteristic of a dish is its focal length to diameter ratio, f/d. The easiest dishes to feed properly are those having f/d ratios between 0.5 and 0.6.

The feed system is a critical element in the performance of a reflecting antenna. It's placed at the focal point and aimed at the center of the dish. A parabolic dish feed is usually designed so that its gain pattern is about 10 dB down at the edge of the dish (compared to the center). The pattern shape must therefore be selected to match the f/d ratio of the dish being used. The horn is very effective when the f/d ratio is in the range 0.5-0.6. The NBS standard-gain antenna is often used when f/d is about 0.5. For lower values of f/d, a dipole or loop over a reflector can be employed. Details may be found in the references listed in Table 10.8.

The polarization of a parabolic dish antenna depends entirely on the feed. A linearly polarized feed antenna will result in a linearly polarized signal, a circularly polarized feed will result in a circularly polarized signal. With circularly polarized signals the sense is reversed upon reflection. An LHCP feed will therefore produce an RHCP signal (and vice versa).

One of the most popular feeds is the cylindrical horn shown in Figure 10.22. Metal cans of various sizes make surprisingly efficient horns: 1-gallon motor oil cans (~7" diameter) work well at 1.2 GHz, and 1-pound coffee cans (4" diameter) are often used at 2.4 GHz. A horn feed at 435 MHz would be the size of a small garbage can. The diameter, not the original contents, is the important parameter. A quarter-wave monopole soldered to a coax connector typically is used to excite the horn. The arrangement shown in Figure 10.22 produces a linear wave, the dimensions are approximate. By varying the diameter and length of the feed horn (size of can), the spacing between the monopole and the closed end of the can, and the dimensions of the monopole element, we can shape the beamwidth and adjust matching. Brass screws protruding into the can and collars around the open end of the can are also frequently employed to improve performance. Optimizing performance often involves a trial-and-error approach. Working with a dish on a receiving station for a 2.1-GHz terrestrial TV link, I modified a horn similar to the one shown in Figure 10.22 by adding three 8-40 brass bolts parallel to the monopole and spaced at 1/4 wavelength intervals toward the open end. Nuts were soldered to the outside of the can so the bolts could be easily inserted to any length. The bolts were then adjusted while watching a received picture. A considerable improvement was noted. When setting up a parabolic dish on amateur frequencies the usual approach is to use the antenna on the receiving end of a link and adjust all parameters for maximum received signal level.

A circularly polarized horn-type feed can be produced in several ways. One method is to employ two monopoles at right angles fed 90° out of phase using an external delay

---

Table 10.7

Four Low-Gain, Circularly Polarized Antennas

	Lindenblad	Quadrifilar Helix	T-R Array	Eggbeater
Horizontal plane gain pattern	Omnidirectional	Omnidirectional	Omnidirectional	Omnidirectional
Vertical plane gain pattern	Favors low elevation angles	Favors main axis	Favors high elevation angles	Favors low elevation angles
Half-power beamwidth	N/A	114°	140° (3/8 λ spacing)	N/A
Circularity	Excellent in all directions	Excellent in all directions	Falls off away from main axis, good over most of pattern	Poor except when overhead beam utilized
Construction	Easy to build	Moderately difficult to build	Easy to build	Easy to build
Adjustment	Simple	Special test equipment required	Simple	Simple
Bandwidth	±8%	±2%	±4%	±8%

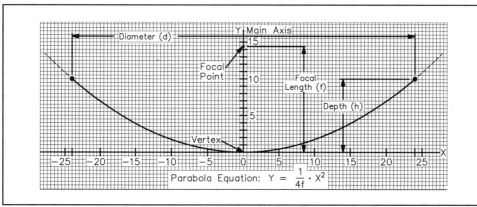

Figure 10.21—Parabola geometry and definitions. When a 2-D parabola is rotated about is main axis, a paraboloidal surface is formed. The parabola shown has an f/d ratio of 0.3.

desirable because it has a lower wind resistance. This is really a fallacy. At low wind speeds a mesh dish does present a much lower cross section than a comparably sized solid dish, but at high wind speeds, where problems are most likely to occur, any mesh smaller than 1" chicken wire will produce nearly the same cross section as a solid dish. The real advantage of mesh is construction ease.

The gain and beamwidth of an efficiently fed parabolic dish are given by

$$G = 7.5 + 20 \log d + 20 \log F \qquad \text{[Eq 10.1]}$$
$$\text{(assumes 55\% feed efficiency)}$$

and

$$\theta = \frac{70}{(d)(F)} \qquad \text{[Eq 10.2]}$$

where

G = gain in dBi
d = dish diameter in feet
F = frequency in GHz
θ = 3-dB beamwidth in degrees.

The gain (Eq 10.1) is plotted in Figure 10.23. Observed

line. A second method is to use the same monopole geometry in conjunction with a series of tuning screws to produce the phase shift (one plane retarded, the other advanced). The third method is to use a single monopole and a more complex arrangement of tuning screws to construct a device known as a dual-mode horn (references are in Table 10.8). Circular polarization can also be obtained by using a T-R array employing the self-phasing method (described in conjunction with the quadrifilar helix) or a 3-turn helix as the feed antenna.

A dish's reflecting surface can be either solid or mesh. If mesh, the openings should be less than 1/10 wavelength in the largest dimension. Many people believe that mesh is

---

Table 10.8
Sources of Information on Parabolic and Related Antennas and on Feed Design

PARABOLIC ANTENNAS

Stressed Rib Design

R. T. Knadle, Jr, "A Twelve-Foot Stressed Parabolic Dish," *QST*, Aug 1972, pp 16-22. Reprinted in *The ARRL Antenna Book*, 15th Ed., 1988, Chapter 19.

A. Katz, "Simple Parabolic Antenna Design," *CQ*, Aug 1966, p 10.

Feed Design

B. Larkin, "Dipole-Reflector Parabolic Dish Feeds for f/D of 0.24 to 0.4," *QEX*, Feb 1996, pp 3-11.

P. Wade, "Practical Microwave Antennas, Part 2—Parabolic Dish Antennas," *QEX*, Oct 1994, pp 13-22.

E. Krome, "Dish Feeds For Mode S Reception," *The AMSAT Journal*, Sep/Oct 1994, pp 7-11.

J. Miller, "A 60 cm S-Band Dish Antenna," OSCAR News, April 1993; Reprinted in *The AMSAT Journal*, March/April 1993, pp 79.

T. Hill, "A Triband Microwave Dish Feed," *QST*, Aug 1990, pp 23-27.

N. J. Foot, Cylindrical Feed Horn for Parabolic Reflectors," *Ham Radio*, May 1976, pp 16-20.

N. J. Foot, Second Generation Cylindrical Feedhorns," *Ham Radio*, May 1982, pp 31-35.

N. J. Foot, Cylindrical Feedhorns Revisited," *Ham Radio*, Feb 1986, pp 20-22.

J. DuBois, "Mode L Feed Hom With Circular Polarization," *Orbit*, Mar/Apr 1983. (Reprinted in the 1989 *ARRL Handbook*, Chapter 23, pp 23, 24.)

2.3 GHz dual-mode horn, The ARRL Antenna Book, 13th Ed, 1974, pp 259-260.

Offset Fed Parabolic Dishes

P. Wade, "More on Parabolic Dish Antennas," *QEX*, Dec 1995, pp 14-22.

P. Wade, "Noise Measurement and Generation," *QEX*, Nov 1996, pp 3-12.

For additional information on offset-fed dishes see **http://www.tiac.net/users/wade** and **http://www.nitehawk.com/rasmit/offset.html**

Spherical Reflector

General

A. W. Love, "Spherical Reflecting Antennas with Corrected Line Sources," *IRE Trans on Antennas and Propagation,* Vol AP-10, pp 529-539, Sep 1962.

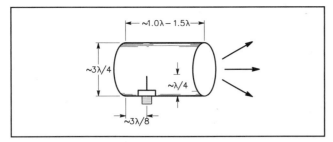

Figure 10.22—Feed horn suitable for illuminating a parabolic dish with an f/d ratio of 0.5 to 0.6. Horn has about 10 dBi gain.

gains tend to be about 2 dB lower than the predicted values.

No dish is perfect. The surface will always depart slightly from a true paraboloid. If a mesh surface is used some signal will always leak through. The feed horn pattern will depart from the ideal, the horn and its mounting will block the beam path and the horn might not be positioned precisely at the focal point. How do these imperfections affect dish operation? Gain is surprisingly tolerant of sloppy construction and other imperfections. A home brew dish with a mesh surface having holes up to $1/10$ wavelength in diameter and random surface inaccuracies on the order of $1/8$ wavelength will probably exhibit a gain within 1 to 2 dB of a far more precise unit. However, the imperfections will degrade the pattern shape, often producing high-level sidelobes. As a result, the parabolic makes an effective transmitting antenna at frequencies above 1.2 GHz, where a 6-foot-diameter dish has a gain on the order of 25 dB. However, the same antenna that works well on transmission may be a poor performer on reception because noise leaking in via sidelobes, spillover and feedthrough may severely reduce the ultimate S/N ratio that can be obtained. An antenna with lower gain and a cleaner pattern could provide better reception.

In the past, amateurs have experimented with surplus dishes acquired from various commercial sources, modified parabolic TV antennas designed for terrestrial UHF TV reception, and dishes they've built from scratch. One construction method that has remained popular over the years involves the stressed rib design shown in Figure 10.24 and described by R. Knadle (K2RIW) and A. Katz (K2UYH) (see Table 10.8). It employs flexible ribs of wood or aluminum radiating out from a stiff central hub. Each rib is formed into a shape that's approximately parabolic by a string connecting the tip of the rib and the feed support. The ribs are covered by a flexible mesh reflecting surface. Antennas of this type, with diameters up to 16 feet, have been used for EME at 432 MHz and 1.2 GHz and for receiving 2.3-GHz transmissions from the Apollo Command module as it traveled to the moon. Lightweight dishes produced using this method tend to lack rigidity. As a result, they don't stand up very well under severe weather and the pattern is generally not very clean. However, when the weather cooperates, they are suitable for temporary installations.

Early direct satellite to home TV at 4 and 12 GHz has changed the dish availability situation radically. Second-hand dishes in the 2 to 12-foot-diameter range are now widely available. You don't even have to wait for a hamfest. Just check the classified ads in the Sunday papers under "Moving." Since these dishes were designed to operated at at least 4 GHz, even those marginally adequate at this frequency should provide good performance at 1.2 and 2.4 GHz.

It's important to check the focal length of a dish before it's purchased in order to determine whether feeding it will be a problem and to determine its real value. The focal length can be computed from two dimensions that can be readily measured, the dish diameter (d) and the depth (h) (see Figure 10.21).

$$f = d^2/16h \qquad \text{[Eq 10.3]}$$

For example, suppose you locate an 8-foot diameter dish (d = 96")with a depth of 16" (h = 16"). Substituting in Eq 10.3 we find that f = 36". Since the value of f/d is 0.375 (36"/96"), a feed horn does not appear appropriate. However, the dish could be used with a feed horn if one is willing to accept reduced performance. To estimate the effectiveness of the dish you have to determine how much of the dish a horn would illuminate. Let d' be the effective diameter of the dish. Assume a horn f/d ratio of 0.5 and solve the equation f/d' = 36"/d' = 0.5. The resulting effective diameter is 6 feet. If the 8-foot dish is cheaper than 6-foot models, it might be a good buy.

If the thought of purchasing a small dish and enlarging it by adding extensions has occurred to you, note that any extension will reduce the f/d ratio. Since efficiently feeding parabolics with low f/d ratios is difficult, this approach is generally not feasible.

One advantage of the dish antenna is that a single reflection surface can be used on both the uplink and downlink. The two feed horns are mounted side by side. Though both may be offset slightly from the focal point and mutually block a small part of the main beam, the effect on gain is negligible (a fraction of a decibel). Once again, the main im-

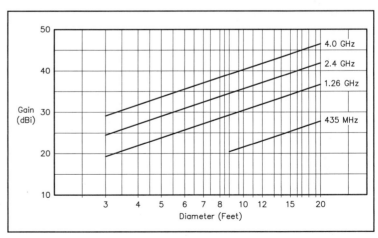

Figure 10.23—Parabolic dish theoretical maximum gain vs diameter for several frequencies of interest. Actual gain tends to be about 2 dB less.

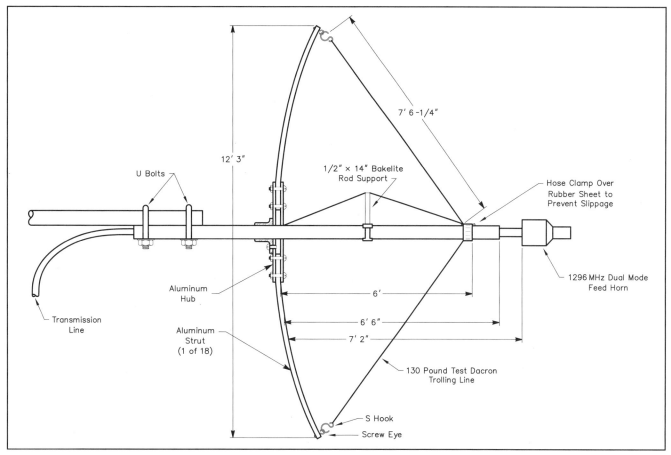

Figure 10.24—Side view of the stressed parabolic dish. See *The ARRL Antenna Book*, **18th Ed. (1997), Chapter 19, for details.**

pact is on pattern sidelobes. When positioning the feeds for a satellite link it's best to either place the receive feed at the focal point and offset the transmit feed (best receive performance), or place the two feeds so they're offset by equal amounts in terms of wavelength, not in actual distance.

The situations where one is most likely to consider a dish antenna are in conjunction with 1.2-GHz and higher frequency links to Phase 3 and Phase 4 satellites. Since regulations restrict 1.2 GHz to use as an uplink, the sidelobe problem mentioned earlier is not of concern. Dishes were used by several OSCAR 13 Mode L stations, but commercially available loop Yagis seem to be preferred. The complexity of the azimuth elevation rotation system associated with each approach is clearly an important factor in this preference. The parabolic dish was widely used for reception of OSCAR 13's 2.4-GHz Mode S transponder.

The 1.2-GHz antenna on OSCAR 13 was a single helix. A single helix was also used at 2.4 GHz. As a result, these links did not exhibit the off-axis interferometer-like circularity changes discussed earlier. Since this effect is one of the primary factors that makes circular polarization (especially with switchable sense) desirable, ground stations found that using a linearly polarized feed only introduced a small performance penalty.

Related Antennas

Several other reflector-type antennas are potentially useful at radio amateur satellite ground stations. We'll briefly look at three: modified parabolas, the spherical reflector and the toroidal reflector.

Professional antenna designers have investigated a number of variations of the simple parabolic we've been discussing. One can, for example, introduce a subreflector so the feed horn can be placed at the vertex of the parabola or even below the dish. These variations can lead to increased gain, superior pattern shape, or a more convenient feed location (making it easier to switch feeds). Construction and performance testing of such antennas is a major undertaking—see the index to *IEEE Trans on Antennas and Propagation* for specific information.

THE OFFSET FED PARABOLA

The offset fed parabolic antenna, shown in Figure 10.25, is of special interest. The reflecting surface is a section of a normal parabolic reflector that generally does not include the center of the dish. As a result, the focal point lies outside the radiated beam and there is no feed blockage. Since feed blockage is a significant cause of losses in small dishes a well designed offset fed dish is more efficient than a regular dish of similar dimensions.

The offset fed dish has several additional advantages over a regular dish. When used for satellite reception spillover reaching the feed is generally from a cold part of the sky instead of the 290K Earth. And, since the feed point is outside the beam, it's easier to mount a preamp directly at the feed and eliminate any runs of coaxial cable.

Paul Wade, N1BWT, computed the expected performance of a 30 inch conventional dish and an 18-inch offset fed dish set up to operate under real world conditions at 10 GHz. He concluded that the smaller dish would produce a 3 dB better noise figure! (see Table 10.8, Nov 1996). His analysis makes it clear why the small 12 GHz direct satellite TV dishes sprouting everywhere use an offset feed design.

THE SPHERICAL REFLECTOR

Spherical reflectors are nothing more than sections of a sphere. A spherical reflector does not focus incoming signals at a point, so it makes little sense to talk about focal length. Instead, spherical reflectors are characterized by the radius (r) of the sphere they're cut from, rim-to-rim diameter (d) and r/d ratio. The gain of a spherical reflector is about 2 dB less than that of a parabolic reflector of the same diameter, but the spherical reflector does offer other advantages beyond its simpler geometric shape. Notably, moving the feed antenna up to about 45° off axis is possible before gain begins to decrease substantially. As a result, it's possible to use a fixed reflector in conjunction with either a single feed on a movable mount for tracking a satellite over a considerable region of the sky, and/or multiple feeds to access several spacecraft simultaneously.

Although a feed designed specially for this application should be used, especially if the feed will be placed off axis, under the following conditions one can experiment by using a horn like the ones previously described. Select the diameter of the reflector so that (r/2)/d is in the range 0.5 to 0.6. Place the horn on axis pointing toward the center of the reflector at a distance of r/2 from it. Adjust the horn to reflector spacing for maximum gain. Adjust horn tuning screws and collar for maximum gain.

As a side note, the famous 1000-foot-diameter radio telescope at Arecibo, Puerto Rico, uses a spherical reflector covering 20 acres and having an accuracy of 1/8 inch! [A slide-tape presentation on the Arecibo "monster" is available for loan from the ARRL.] See D. DeMaw, "The Story of El Radar," QST, Sep 1965, pp 24-27.

THE TOROIDAL REFLECTOR

Another reflector geometry of possible interest is the

torus. This configuration has been examined carefully by COMSAT Laboratories because its properties make it especially well suited for simultaneously receiving signals from several stationary satellites that are spaced along the geosynchronous arc above the equator (Figure 10.26). Commercial toroidal reflectors and matched feeds for 4-GHz satellite TV downlinks were first marketed in 1980, and a large number are now used at cable TV Earth stations.

MISCELLANEOUS

Horn, Lens and Patch Antennas

As the UHF and microwave bands begin to take a more central role in the amateur satellite service, horn, lens and patch antennas will begin to receive more attention.

The pyramidal horn looks like a pyramid with its apex attached to a wave guide feed. The conical horn looks like a funnel with the narrow end consisting of a coffee can type feed. These antennas provide moderate gain in small package and they're easily duplicated without special test equipment. Horn antennas can be used by themselves, or as a feed for a reflector type antenna or in conjunction with a lens (described below). Recent articles in amateur publications have described small linearly polarized pyramidal horn antennas for the 5.6 GHz and 10 GHz amateur bands and a 2.3 GHz conical horn. Depending on the feed method, the conical horn can produce either a linearly polarized or a circularly polarized signal. Both of these antennas provide gains in the 17 dBi range. For a thorough introduction to horn antennas and practical construction information see: P. Wade, "Practical Microwave Antennas, Part 1—Antenna fundamentals and horn antennas," QEX, Sept 1994, pp 3-11.

The lens antenna functions much like an optical lens. When it's placed in front of a beam that has already been collimated it acts to focus or concentrate the beam in a fixed direction. There are several types of lens antennas. The one of major interest is the metal plate lens which may be placed in front of a horn or coffee can feed. Note that the lens itself, like the reflecting surface in reflector antennas, is just a passive device so it must be used in conjunction with a driven antenna.

In one common configuration the lens looks somewhat like a venetian blind in the open position—the metal slats often do not have the same width or spacing. In some cases the slats are formed into concentric circles. The operation of the lens antenna is based on the fact that the spaces between the slats function like wave guides. Since the speed of a radio wave in free space differs from that in a wave guide the wave front leaving the lens differs from that entering. This fact is exploited to produce a focusing effect. For specific information see P. Wade, "Practical Microwave Antennas, Part 3—Lens antennas and microwave antenna measurements," QEX, Nov 1994, pp 16-24. Also see the section in **http://www.arrl.org/qexfiles** where the program *HDL_ANT* resides.

The patch antenna consists of a conducting sheet (driven element) that may be a circle, ellipse or rectangle having a maximum dimension on the order of 1/2 wavelength which is mounted a small fraction of wavelength above a ground

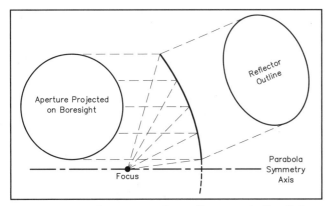

Figure 10.25—Geometry of an offset parabolic dish antenna.

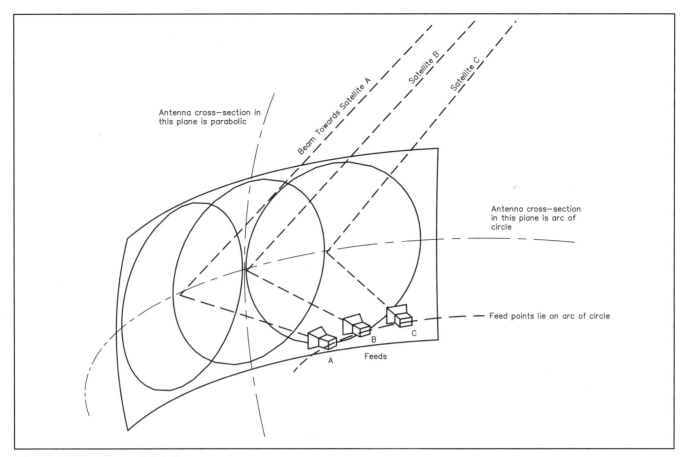

Figure 10.26—The multiple-beam torus antenna.

plane. Depending on the design, the space between the driven element and the ground plane can be air, vacuum, or a specially selected dielectric. The method by which the driven element is fed determines the polarization of the radiated signal. The patch antenna has low gain in the direction perpendicular to the plane of the driven element.

The patch antenna is most attractive to users when a ground plane is already available and the low profile is an advantage. Two familiar applications come to mind. The P3D spacecraft uses an array of six patch antennas for 70 cm operations. For an excellent introduction to patch antenna design see S. Wood and D. Jansson, "AMSAT Phase 3D Antenna Design Review: Phase 3D HF/UHF/Microwave Antennas," *The AMSAT Journal*, Mar/Apr 1993, pp 18-22. Patch antennas are also frequently used to receive signals from the Global Positioning Satellite (GPS) system from cars. See H. Ward, "A Patch Antenna for the Global Positioning System," *QST*, Oct 1995, pp 44-45.

ANTENNA SYSTEMS

An antenna system consists of several components in addition to the antenna itself. We'll look at these components briefly.

Feed LInes and Connectors

Satellite radio links generally use VHF and higher frequencies. In this part of the spectrum, RF power losses associated with both feed lines and connectors are a major concern. Since most ground stations use one or more coax feed lines and several connectors, it's important that selections be made to minimize losses.

All coaxial cable produces some attenuation. Typical losses for 100 foot runs of some common cables are shown in Table 10.9. The values quoted are for new, high-quality line; losses increase with age and exposure to the elements. The attenuation of bargain cable is often significantly greater. Measuring cable loss is relatively simple if you have access to a wattmeter, and doing so is good insurance! (See Figure 10.27.)

Radio-frequency power attenuation is directly proportional to the coaxial cable's length. Doubling the length doubles the attenuation. To compute the loss expected from a given length of cable at a particular frequency use Table 10.9 or your own measured attenuation value per hundred feed) and the formula

$$A_L = \frac{1}{100} A_o \qquad \text{[Eq 10.4]}$$

where

A_L = attenuation [in dB] of cable of length L
L = length [in feet] of cable
A_o = attenuation [in dB] of 100 feet of cable

Coaxial connectors may also cause losses. Amateurs

working at HF often use the so-called UHF series of connectors (PL-259 plug and SO-239 receptacle) with RG-8/U and RG-213 cable. *UHF connectors should never be used at UHF frequencies; they produce intolerable losses.* In fact, this misnamed series shouldn't even be used at 146 MHz unless losses are of little concern. At 146, 435 and 1260 MHz, the Type N series of connectors (UG-21 plug and UG-58 receptacle) may be used with RG-8 sized cable. Though RG-58 can be used for very short jumper cables, there are several better choices, short pieces of which are often available through surplus channels. These include semi-rigid Uniform Tubing UT-141; RG-142, which features Teflon dielectric, double shielding, and a silver-plated center conductor; and the more common RG-141, RG-223 and RG-55. All these cables can be used with BNC, TNC and SMA connectors, which give excellent results up to 4 GHz at low power levels. E. F. Johnson produces a widely available series of low-cost SMA-compatible connectors (JCM type) which are justifiably popular with amateur microwave experimenters. Most Hardline cables have matching low-loss connectors that mate to the Type N series. Since Hardline connectors are relatively expensive, some amateurs have devised makeshift connectors by combining Type N connectors and standard plumbing fittings. Table 10.10 lists several references that contain practical information on interfacing Hardline at amateur stations.

Delay and Phasing Lines

Short sections of coax cable are often used as delay lines or matching transformers in antenna feed harnesses. Numerous examples were given earlier in this and the preceding chapter. In many antenna systems the electrical length of these devices is critical. Because signals travel slower in a cable than in free space, the measured and electrical lengths of a cable are not equal. Assume that measured length and electrical length are specified in terms of wavelength at a specific frequency. The velocity factor of a cable is equal to the ratio of its measured length to its electrical length:

Table 10.9

Approximate Attenuation Values for Coaxial Lines

	Power Loss Per 100 Feet (dB)			
Cable	*29.5 MHz*	*146 MHz*	*435 MHz*	*1260 MHz*
RG-58 series	2.5	6.5	12	22
RG-58 foam	1.2	4.5	8	15
RG-8/M foam	1.3	3.2	7.2	13
RG-8 and RG-213	1.2	3.1	5.9	11
RG-8 foam	0.9	2.1	3.7	6.3
RG-17		1.0	2.3	
1/2" Hardline	0.4	1.0	1.8	3.4
3/4" Hardline	0.3	0.8	1.6	3.0
7/8" Hardline	0.3	0.7	1.3	2.5

Note: Attenuation values for old or bargain cable may be much higher.

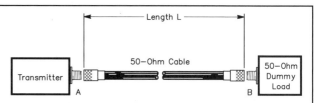

Method. Insert wattmeter at A (meter reads P_A) then adjust transmitter for proper operation. Now move meter to B and read P_S without touching transmitter adjustments. Cable attenuation, in dB, will equal $10 \log(P_A/P_S)$ This value can be scaled to 100 feet as follows:

$A_O = (100/L)(A_L)$

where

A_O = attenuation per 100 feet at test frequency

A_L = measured attenuation

Compare the value obtained to the value listed in Table 10.9 to determine if cable is performing up to specifications. Although it's best to make measurements at the satellite link frequency you'll be using, a test setup at 2 m will give a good indication of cable quality.

Figure 10.27—Experimental setup for measuring attenuation of a random length of cable. This approach is not designed for high accuracy, but it is useful for rough estimates and comparative measurements.

$$\text{velocity factor} = \frac{\text{measured length}}{\text{electrical length}}$$

Published values for velocity factor are generally in the range 0.66 (regular cable) to 0.80 (foam dielectric cable). Random measurements, however, show that these values vary by as much as 10% from cable to cable, or up to a few percent along the length of a given spool of cable. Although an error of a few percent may not be important, a 10% error can have a significant effect on antenna system performance. Therefore, it's best to cut all delay and matching lines about 10% long and then prune them to frequency using the dip-meter approach (Figure 10.28).

As an illustration, suppose we need a half-wavelength (electrical length) section of foam-dielectric coax line for 146 MHz. Assuming that our foam dielectric coax has a velocity of 0.80 as advertised, we can compute the measured length using Eq 10.4:

Measured length = (1/2) (0.80) = 0.40 wavelength

The free space wavelength (in inches) associated with a specific frequency, f, is given by 11,810/f. At 146 MHz this is 80.9 inches. The measured length will therefore be (0.40) (80.9) = 32.4 inches. A piece about 10% larger than this value should be cut and then trimmed to length using one of the methods shown in Figure 10.28.

Rotators (Azimuth and Elevation Control)

If you're using a beam to access amateur satellites, you generally have to reorient it as the satellite moves across the sky. The systems being used by amateurs to accomplish this task can be categorized as follows:

1) Azimuth rotator, fixed elevation angle
2) Azimuth rotator, manual elevation control
3) Azimuth and Elevation rotation
   a) Combination rotators

Table 10.10

Articles Containing Practical Information on Interfacing Hardline

C. J. Carroll, "Matching 75-Ohm CATV Hardline to 50-Ohm Systems," *Ham Radio*, Sep 1978, pp 31-33.

D. DeMaw, P. O'Dell, "Connectors for CATV 'Hardline' and Heliax," Hints and Kinks, *QST*, Sep 1980, pp 43-44.

J. H. Ferguson, "CATV Cable Connectors," *Ham Radio*, Oct 1979, pp 52-55.

L. T. Fitch, "Matching 75-ohm hardline to 5-ohm systems," *Ham Radio*, Oct 1982, pp 43-45.

J. Mathis, "7/8-inch Hardline Coax connectors," *Ham Radio*, Sep 1988, pp 95-97.

B. Olson, "Using surplus 75-ohm Hardline at VHF," *QEX*, Mar 1988, pp 12-13.

D. Pochmerski, "Hardline Connectors and Corrosion," Technical Correspondence, *QST*, May 1981, p 43.

M. D. Weisberg, "Hardline Coaxial Connectors," *Ham Radio*, Apr 1980, pp 32-33.

G. K. Woods, "75-Ohm Cable in Amateur Installations," *Ham Radio*, Sep 1978, pp 28-30.

J. R. Yost, "Plumber's Delight Coax Connector," *Ham Radio*, May 1981, pp 50-51.

b) Separate rotators,

c) Azimuth rotator and elevation drive.

System 1 is essentially the normal HF/VHF/UHF terrestrial setup with the antenna tilted up at roughly 25°. If you're operating on a tight budget and using a beam with modest gain, this is a reasonable way to go. Of course, when the

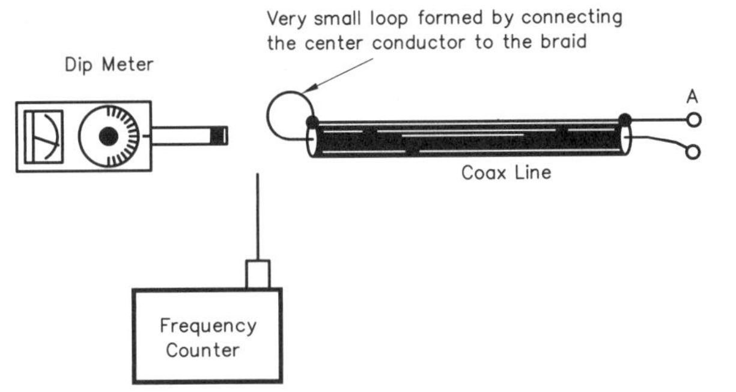

Method I. End A open
Lowest resonant frequency seen on dip meter corresponds to four times electrical length of line. Small pieces of coax are usually cut from end A until desired frequency is reached.
To cut a λ/4 line trim until lowest dip meter frequency = antenna design frequency.
To cut a λ/2 line trim until lowest dip meter frequency = 1/2 antenna design frequency.

Method II. End A shorted
Lowest resonant frequncy seen on dip meter coresponds to two times electrical length of line. A pin may be repeatedly inserted near end A until the desired frequency is reached.
To cut a λ/4 line adjust until dip meter frequency = 2 times antenna design frequency.
To cut a λ/2 line adjust until dip meter frequency = antenna design frequency.

Reference formulas

$$\text{free space wavelength in inches} = \frac{11,810}{\text{frequency}(\text{MHz})}$$

physical length of coax = (velocity factor) (electrical length)
velocity factor of regular coax = 0.66 (approx)
velocity factor of foam coax = 0.80 (approx)

Figure 10.28—Two methods for using a dip meter to prune a section of coaxial line to a specific electrical length. For additional details, see: G. Downs, "Measuring Transmission-Line Velocity Factor," *QST*, Jun 1979, pp 27-28; and A. E. Popodi, "Measuring Transmission Line Parameters," *Ham Radio*, Sep 1988, pp 22-25.

satellite elevation is less than 10° or more than 40°, performance may be poor.

Since the elevation angle of a Phase 3 satellite often stays within a narrow range (say 20°) for a long time interval, it's possible to devise an antenna mount incorporating a heavy-duty door or gate hinge making it possible to set the antenna elevation before operation begins. A visit to a sailboat supply house and/or a hardware store will provide the rope, pulleys, cleats and other hardware needed. A flagpole rigging kit will contain many useful parts.

Most amateurs prefer to control both elevation and azimuth from the operating position. Three rotators currently available combine the functions of azimuth and elevation control into a single housing—the Kenpro KR5400, the Dynetic Systems DR10, the Yaesu G-5400B and G-5600B, the Emotator EV700D5X and the M² OR-2800/MT-3000A. Rotators of this type greatly simplify system assembly since the user only has to provide a mast and a cross boom. Another approach is to use separate rotators for each function. Azimuth rotators are widely available in models varying from light to heavy duty. Because the weatherproofing, lubrication and internal thrust bearings are designed for a vertical mast, you're likely to run into trouble if you try to use them for elevation control. However, the Alliance U110, the design of which allows the mast to go completely through the rotator, has proven to be reliable as an elevation rotator if it's crudely sheltered from the elements by an umbrella type arrangement and if the antenna load is arranged so that all static twisting forces are minimized. The light-duty Blonder-Tongue PM-2 can also be used to control elevation. There are several rotators specifically designed for elevation control, including the Kenpro KR500 and the Yaesu G-500A. When using separate azimuth and elevation rotators, you'll need a fitting that will allow you to mount the elevation rotator directly to the top of the azimuth rotator or mast. If your rotators come from different manufacturers you'll probably have to jury rig something from U bolts and a plate of heavy plywood, aluminum or steel.

Elevation control can also be accomplished by employing a hinged plate and a positioning controller like those used on 4 GHz satellite TV dishes. These positioners can often be acquired at modest cost. As they're designed to operate outdoors, reliability should be high. Figure 10.29 shows a possible arrangement. Some amateurs have built positioners from stock threaded rod driven by a motor designed to operate an automobile windshield wiper or power window. If you go this route it helps to have access to welding equipment, an automobile graveyard, a tractor parts dealer and a good hardware store.

Since most amateurs use small computers to obtain tracking information and then manually adjust their antenna controllers, the idea of eliminating the middle man and having the computer directly control the antennas has occurred to many. It's certainly possible to have a small computer take care of antenna pointing chores, but it's questionable whether the result is worth the effort. With slowly moving Phase 3 satellites tracking is a minor chore. And, with Phase 2 satellites it's probably simpler and cheaper to use an omnidirectional antenna and invest part of the money saved in a good preamp and/or a 6-8 dB amp for the transmitter. Nevertheless, having the computer take care of antenna pointing is the ultimate convenience. An automated azimuth/elevation aiming system requires (1) appropriate software for your computer (both tracking software and control software), (2) a computer and hardware interface

board, or a dedicated hardware controller and (3) compatible rotators. Getting everything to work together is a major project, as a review of the literature in Table 10.11 will show. Unless you're a software and hardware design expert with lots of time to devote to development, it's best to acquire a set of components (software, hardware, and rotators) that are known to work together. In a 1988 article in *QEX*, Peter Prendergast (KC2PH) discussed the merits of six automated antenna aiming systems he had tested. Systems covered included two for the IBM PC and clones (*The Kansas City Tracker* and *The Mirage Tracking Interface*), two for the Commodore C64 (*Phase IV Systems Controller* and *Encomm KR-001*), *Autotrak* for the C64 or Timex 1000, and *The ARRL Automatic Antenna Controller*. Information can be obtained from the manufacturers listed in Table 10.11.

Radome Material

Most amateurs will not be constructing radomes to house their antenna systems. However, there are situations where you might wish to weatherproof part of an antenna system. For example, you may wish to seal the front of a coffee can dish feed, keep ice from building up on a gamma match, or cover a preamp. When choosing materials for these applications it's helpful to know how some common substances affect radio waves. Transmission attenuation is a good

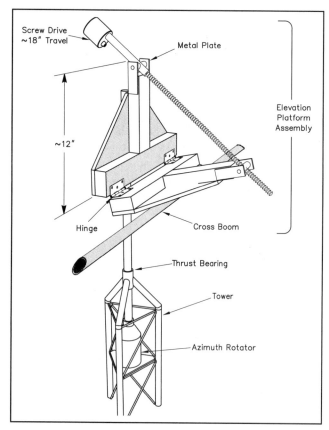

Figure 10.29—Az-el mount with homemade elevation platform assembly using "dish" positioner, wood and stock hardware items. This unit is suitable for the antenna shown in Figure 9.13. Mast and cross-boom are connected to platform assembly with U bolts and shear pins. Hardware for connecting screw drive to elevation platform should be chosen to match mechanical design of drive.

Table 10.11

Automated Antenna Controller Information Sources

Manufacturers and Distributors

Kansas City Tracker
L. L. Grace Communications Products
PO Box 1345
Voorhees, NJ 08043
609-751-1018
FAX: 609-751-9705

ARRL Controller
A & A Engineering
2521 W LaPalma, Unit K
Anaheim, CA 92801
714-952-2114
FAX: 714-952-3280

TRAKBOX
TAPR
8987-309 Tanque Verde Rd. #337
Tucson, AZ 85749
817-383-0000
FAX: 817-566-2544
http://www.tapr.org/tapr/html/trakbox.html

Articles

J. Barger, "Improvements for the Kansas City Tracker/Tuner," *The AMSAT Journal*, Mar/Apr 1992, pp 19-23.
P. Prendergast, "Automatic Antenna Controllers," *QEX*, Aug 1988, pp 8, 14.
J. Bloom, "An Automatic Rotator Controller," *QST*, Sep 1986, pp 40-46.

measure of how "invisible" a material is to RF radiation. J. DuBois (W1HDX) has measured the attenuation of a number of substances of interest. Though the measurements were made near 1.7 GHz they should be valid across the VHF/UHF spectrum. The results are listed in Table 10.12.

Calculating EIRP

To design the uplink side of a ground station, you usually aim at a specific EIRP (effective isotropic radiated power). This is the power that, if fed to an isotropic antenna, would provide the desired signal level at the spacecraft. Let's consider Mode L on OSCAR 13 for an example. The recommended EIRP was 3 kW. Assume our ground station transmitting system has the following characteristics:

Power output = 50 watts (P_o)

Antenna gain = 23.5 dBi (5-foot-diameter parabolic dish—see Figure 10.22)

Feed-line loss = 3 dB (50 feet of RG-8 foam—see Table 10.9)

Coax connector loss = 0.5 dB (two sets of Type N connectors)

Our calculation would proceed as follows:

Step I: Find G (gain, or loss, of entire feed and antenna system expressed in dBi)

G = 23.5 dBi – 3 dB – 0.5 dB = 20 dBi

Step II: Convert gain G (in dBi) to gain G (pure number)

$G = 10^{G/10} = 10^{20/10} = 10^2 = 100$

Step III: Calculate EIRP

EIRP = G   = (100) (50 watts) = 5000 watts

The results indicate that the EIRP is slightly higher than necessary. However, it's likely that our estimate of the parabolic antenna gain may be 1 or 2 dB high, so we're probably close to the desired level. In any event, keep in mind that published EIRP targets are only guidelines relating to performance under good conditions. To allow for poor squint angles and other factors that may degrade link performance, it's best to have a transmitting setup having more power than required and to include provisions for quick and easy reduction of the power level. If your station is in this category, it's critically important that you periodically compare your downlink signal level to that of the spacecraft general beacon. If you're louder than the beacon, you're running too much power!

Closing Hints

Having come this far, some brief final suggestions focusing on antenna systems seem in order. First, start simple and then make improvements where they most affect your operating needs. For example, with Phase 2 satellites try a groundplane or a Lindenblad before you decide that a circularly polarized beam with azimuth and elevation rotators is

Table 10.12

Measured Transmission Attenuation Characteristics of Common Materials

Material	dB Attenuation
0.005 in. plastic film bag	<0.1
0.05 in. Tupperware (cloudy)	<0.1
0.06 in. Rubbermaid (opaque)	<0.1
0.0625 in. Vector perfboard	<0.1
0.125 in. Plexiglas	<0.1
2.0 in. styrofoam	<0 1
20 lb bond paper	<0 1
cotton cloth	<0.1
0.07 in. Rubbermaid (cloudy)	0.2
0.125 in. ABS plastic	0.2
bubble pack, 0.25 in. bubbles	0.2
0.125 in. linen phenolic	0.5
0.375 in. dry plywood	1.0
0.70 in. Plexiglas	1.2
0.25 in. solid phenolic	1.5
0.750 in. dry plywood	3.0
0.01 in. brass shim stock	>50
0.050 in. rubber sheet	2

See: J. Dubois, "Radome Materials for 1500-1800 MHz," *Journal of the Environmental Satellite Amateur Users' Group*, Vol 89, no. 1, Spring 1989.

necessary. With Phase 3 satellites, listen to the 146 MHz downlink with a homebuilt, linearly polarized Quagi before deciding that you need full circular polarization on both links.

Second, don't get caught in the trap of thinking that you need one ultimate array. Often, it's more convenient and effective to have access to several simple antennas set up so that you can quickly switch to the one that produces the best results. Consider Phase 2 satellites again. The multiple antenna approach is most effective when the antennas are complementary in either (1) azimuth response (for example, two horizontal 29-MHz dipoles at right angles), (2) elevation response (for example, a 2-meter T-R array for high elevation angles and a beam aimed at the horizon for low elevation angles) or (3) polarization (for example, dipoles and a ground plane for 29 MHz).

Third, be sure to consider how the satellite of interest and your particular location affect antenna selection. A station at 50°N latitude interested in working with Mode B on AMSAT-OSCAR 10 might, after studying typical passes on the computer, decide that rotators are an unnecessary expense. A fixed-elevation array set at 20° and a manually adjustable azimuth control might be perfectly satisfactory. In many cases the operator could set azimuth prior to a pass and not need to adjust it any further.

Chapter 11

Receiving And Transmitting

11 Receiving and Transmitting

This chapter focuses on the transmitting and receiving equipment radio amateurs need to communicate via satellite. Coverage includes equipment for CW/SSB communications via the linear transponders that have been in orbit since 1965, and gear for packet communications using digital transponders of the type that first appeared on Fuji-OSCAR 12 in 1986. We'll be looking at receiving equipment for 29.5, 146, 435 and 2400 MHz, and transmitting equipment for 146, 436 and 1269 MHz.

If you're interested in telemetry reception, the information on receivers in this chapter will be helpful. You may also need special modems and software, however. Information on telemetry reception can be found in Chapter 14 and Appendix C.

In 1983, when OSCAR 10 was launched, very little commercial CW/SSB equipment was available for 2 m, 70 cm and higher frequencies. Even if an amateur used commercial equipment to set up a station, key building blocks were often missing so assembling a Mode B or L station involved a considerable amount of effort and expertise. The situation has changed considerably in recent years. Today, amateurs interested mainly in operating can purchase everything needed—transmitters, receivers, antennas and accessories—to put a station on any analog or digital mode currently used on amateur satellites. This approach can be expensive. If you're willing to invest some time in shopping and some effort in modifying and/or converting used equipment, it's possible to cut the cost substantially.

We begin by considering SSB and CW communications. The equipment needed to access satellites is essentially indistinguishable from gear built for terrestrial use at the same frequencies and power levels. Thus, the existing amateur literature on VHF and UHF construction is directly applicable to our needs. References to useful articles in various radio amateur publications are given throughout this chapter. Our main concern will be to describe several practical approaches to assembling a ground station by systematically evaluating the trade-offs involved in various choices.

RECEIVING

A CW/SSB receiver is a central component of the satellite ground station set up for either CW/SSB communica-

tions via a linear transponder or for 1200 baud packet communicating via a digital transponder. The receiver must meet certain minimal criteria with respect to sensitivity, stability, selectivity and freedom from overload or spurious responses. Anyone with hands-on HF experience knows roughly what these terms mean, and for our purposes we won't need to quantify most of them. Sensitivity, however, deserves special attention because downlink reception is often the limiting factor in the satellite communications chain.

At all radio frequencies, noise arriving by way of the antenna ultimately limits our ability to receive weak signals. Over a considerable range of the VHF, UHF and microwave spectrum, the dominant source of external noise is cosmic in origin. Figure 11.1 shows the background noise levels observed at various frequencies. The dip in the central section shows that the absolute level of this noise is very low at 146 and 435 MHz, making it possible, theoretically, to discern very weak signals. In practice, noise generated in the receiving system itself often masks these weak sources. Our ultimate goal in designing a ground-station receiver is to reduce the internally generated noise to a level below that of the incoming cosmic noise. In reality we usually don't reach this goal, but new receiver technology continually makes it easier and less expensive for us to approach it.

A receiver can be depicted as a chain of individual stages (Figure 11.2), each characterized by two properties: *gain* and *noise factor* (or noise figure), a quantity related to the amount of noise the stage introduces. Noise factor is a dimensionless number greater than or equal to one (noise figure is given in decibels). The lower the noise factor, the better the performance. In a receiver, the noise contribution of each stage acts to reduce the overall system signal-to-noise ratio. The impact of a particular stage on total receiver noise factor depends on the gain prior to the stage and the noise factor of the stage.

A mathematical analysis of receiver noise (Figure 11.3) shows that the first few stages in a receiver dominate overall performance. Therefore, it is important to use very-low-noise devices in the first stage or two of a receiver and to avoid runs of lossy feed line in front of active devices. Once you grasp this basic point, you're well on your way to designing an effective receive system. Though many readers may prefer to skip the computations, anyone interested in putting together a high-performance system should look at the sample calculations in Figure 11.3 to see the consequences of the various trade-offs.

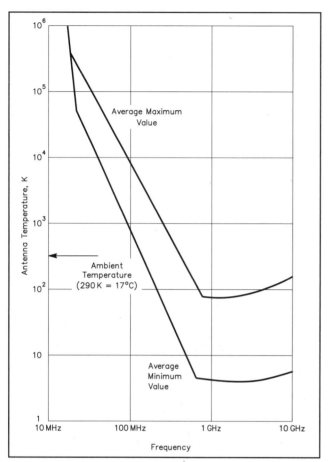

Figure 11.1—The sky noise arriving at an Earth-based antenna depends on several factors, including (1) the portion of the galaxy being observed, (2) the elevation angle of the antenna and (3) to a lesser extent, the water-vapor content of the atmosphere. Average values of the upper and lower limits on sky noise are shown in the graph. For details, see J. D. Kraus, *Radio Astronomy* (New York: McGraw-Hill, 1966), p 237, and D. Emerson, "The Radio Sky," *QST*, *Part 1*, June 1996, pp 32-35, *Part 2*, July 1996, pp 28-31.

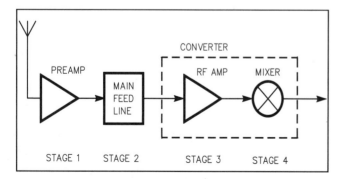

Figure 11.2—To analyze weak-signal performance, a receiver is pictured as consisting of a series of individual stages in the signal path.

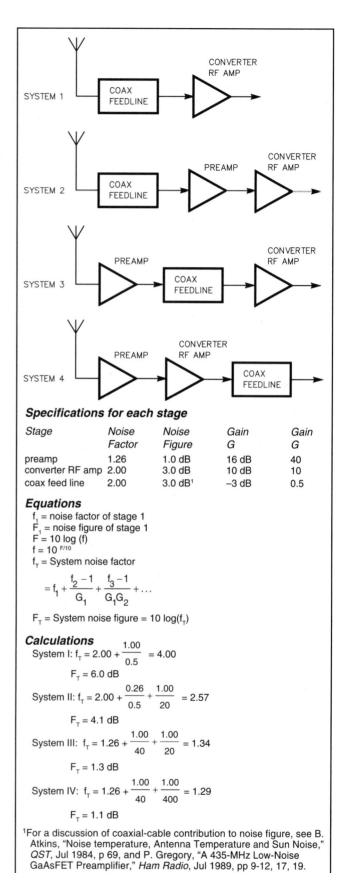

Specifications for each stage

Stage	Noise Factor	Noise Figure	Gain G	Gain G
preamp	1.26	1.0 dB	16 dB	40
converter RF amp	2.00	3.0 dB	10 dB	10
coax feed line	2.00	3.0 dB[1]	−3 dB	0.5

Equations

f_1 = noise factor of stage 1
F_1 = noise figure of stage 1
$F = 10 \log (f)$
$f = 10^{F/10}$
f_T = System noise factor

$$= f_1 + \frac{f_2 - 1}{G_1} + \frac{f_3 - 1}{G_1 G_2} + \cdots$$

F_T = System noise figure = $10 \log(f_T)$

Calculations

System I: $f_T = 2.00 + \dfrac{1.00}{0.5} = 4.00$

$F_T = 6.0$ dB

System II: $f_T = 2.00 + \dfrac{0.26}{0.5} + \dfrac{1.00}{20} = 2.57$

$F_T = 4.1$ dB

System III: $f_T = 1.26 + \dfrac{1.00}{40} + \dfrac{1.00}{20} = 1.34$

$F_T = 1.3$ dB

System IV: $f_T = 1.26 + \dfrac{1.00}{40} + \dfrac{1.00}{400} = 1.29$

$F_T = 1.1$ dB

[1]For a discussion of coaxial-cable contribution to noise figure, see B. Atkins, "Noise temperature, Antenna Temperature and Sun Noise," *QST*, Jul 1984, p 69, and P. Gregory, "A 435-MHz Low-Noise GaAsFET Preamplifier," *Ham Radio*, Jul 1989, pp 9-12, 17, 19.

Figure 11.3—Comparing noise figures of four systems. Reference: J. R. Fisk, "Receiver Noise Figure and Sensitivity and Dynamic Range," *Ham Radio*, Oct 1975, pp 8-25. This article also contains a good discussion of noise temperature. Also see: B. Atkins, "Calculating System Noise Temperature," *QST*, Jan 1982, p 80.

RECEIVING SYSTEMS FOR 28, 146, 435 AND 2400 MHz

29 MHz

Any HF communications receiver covering the 29.0-29.5 MHz range can be used to monitor Mode A downlinks (Figure 11.4). A good low-noise preamp will, in many cases, improve reception. This is true even with expensive receivers, because they've been designed to satisfy the less-stringent sensitivity requirements (noise factor) for terrestrial communication. Although mounting the preamp at the antenna always provides the best performance, the difference is often small at 29 MHz so many operators give in to convenience and place the preamp at the receiver. When a receiver has a "hot" 10-meter front end the preamp may not be needed. If in doubt give it a try without the preamp—you can always add one later.

146, 435, 2400 MHz

For receiving at VHF and UHF, we generally have a choice of either using a converter in conjunction with an HF receiver or acquiring a single band multimode transceiver. If you already own an HF receiver, the converter approach is substantially cheaper. If you have a need for the transmitting capabilities provided by the transceiver, however, its real cost is substantially reduced. For example, a 435 MHz transceiver acquired for 1200 baud PACSAT reception provides the ability to transmit on Mode B. Multimode transceivers are available for the 2-m, 70-cm and 23-cm bands. The receive sensitivity of these units is generally marginal as far as the needs of the satellite operator

are concerned. It is therefore important to plan on using an external preamp with them.

Crystal-controlled converters using an HF receiver as a tunable IF are used at a great many satellite ground stations for reception at 2 m, 70 cm, and 13 cm (Figure 11.5). A good HF receiver coupled with a well designed converter will provide state-of-the-art receive capabilities. Most modern converters for 2 m and 70 cm use 28.000 to 30.000 MHz as the IF range. If you have a 70 cm converter that covers 435.000 to 437.000 MHz and you wish to monitor 435.300 to 435.500 MHz, you just tune the HF receiver between 28.300 and 28.500 MHz. Well designed converters for 13 cm generally use 2 m or 70 cm as an IF. This reduces problems related to image rejection and spurious responses, both of which can degrade the converter's effective sensitivity.

Characteristics that distinguish a good converter from a mediocre performer include low noise figure, freedom from spurious responses, low susceptibility to IMD (intermodulation distortion) and gain compression, high frequency stability and low susceptibility to burnout. Although noise figure is important, it shouldn't be of overriding concern. Once you commit to placing a good (noise figure less than 1.5 dB at 145 MHz, 1.0 dB at 435 MHz and higher frequencies) preamp with moderate gain (16 dB) at the antenna, whether the converter noise figure is 3 dB or 4 dB makes little difference.

It's difficult to improve a converter that performs poorly with respect to deficiencies in the other important characteristics. Spurious responses are often caused by poor interstage filtering in the RF and local-oscillator circuits or instability (undesired oscillations) anywhere in the converter. IMD and gain compression can arise from poor choices of mixer injection power, bias levels or gain distribution. Poor stability is usually the result of cost-cutting shortcuts such as using cheap crystals and heavily loaded oscillators. Overcoming these problems can require re-engineering the entire converter.

Burnout is primarily associated with the first RF stage in converters or preamps. High-power transmitters and transients related to lightning, relay switching or other sources can destroy expensive RF devices even when extensive precautions are taken. If you build a preamp, don't skimp by omitting the recommended protection circuits. For a detailed analysis of converter design and hints for improving performance, see J. Reisert, "Low-Noise Re-

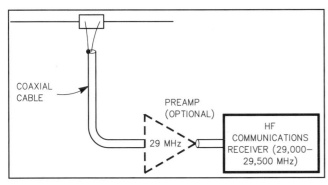

Figure 11.4—Basic receive system for Mode A reception.

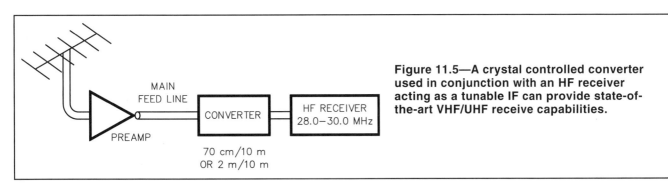

Figure 11.5—A crystal controlled converter used in conjunction with an HF receiver acting as a tunable IF can provide state-of-the-art VHF/UHF receive capabilities.

ceiver Update," Part I, *Ham Radio*, Nov 1987; Part II, Dec 1987.

If the cost of a modern, well-engineered, low-noise-figure converter is an obstacle, you can often obtain excellent performance using an older, well-engineered unit, even if it falls short in the noise-figure department; you need only add a good preamp. Several well-designed converters manufactured in the mid and late 1960s used Nuvistors, miniature tube-type devices typified by the 6CW4, in the front end. The better units had a noise figure in the 3.0 to 3.5 dB range at 2 meters and in the 4 to 5 dB range at 70 cm. Converters of this type can often be found at hamfests at very attractive prices. A number of operators actually prefer these older converters in situations where IM distortion, gain compression or burnout have been problems. In any event, avoid poorly engineered units, no matter how impressive the noise-figure specifications may seem.

Many operators experience receiver performance degradation (desense) whenever the transmitter is keyed. This problem is especially prevalent when operating Mode J, since the third harmonic of the 2 meter transmitter is very close to the 70 cm receive frequency. This problem makes spotting the downlink frequency and evaluating uplink performance difficult, if not impossible. Amateurs have tried a number of approaches to remedy the problem. These include (1) adding filters between the transmitter and its feed line, and between the receiver and its feed line, (2) separating transmit and receive antennas and feed lines physically and (3) replacing modern solid-state converters with older-type Nuvistor units. Several cases have been reported where serious overload, intermodulation or other receive problems that didn't respond to filters or physical displacement were cured by switching to a tube-type converter. Nonetheless, good filtering and adequate antenna and feed-line separation should also be pursued. One receive filter is shown in Figure 11.6.

Another feature that you may want in a converter is coverage of more than a 2-MHz segment of a band, 144 to

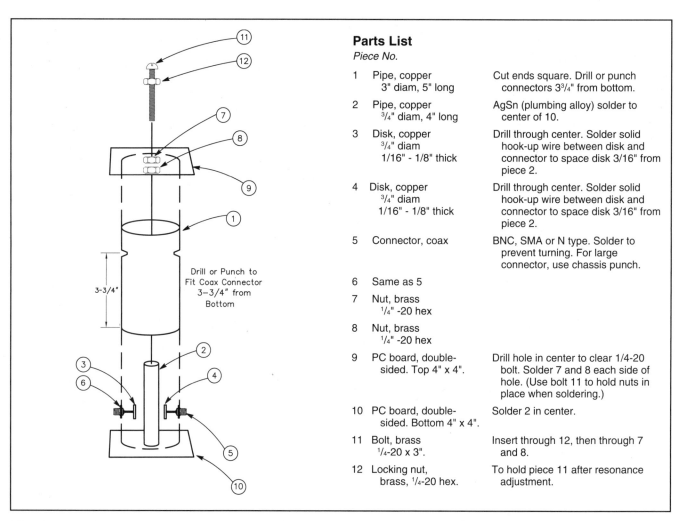

Parts List

Piece No.

1	Pipe, copper 3" diam, 5" long	Cut ends square. Drill or punch connectors 3¾" from bottom.
2	Pipe, copper ¾" diam, 4" long	AgSn (plumbing alloy) solder to center of 10.
3	Disk, copper ¾" diam 1/16" - 1/8" thick	Drill through center. Solder solid hook-up wire between disk and connector to space disk 3/16" from piece 2.
4	Disk, copper ¾" diam 1/16" - 1/8" thick	Drill through center. Solder solid hook-up wire between disk and connector to space disk 3/16" from piece 2.
5	Connector, coax	BNC, SMA or N type. Solder to prevent turning. For large connector, use chassis punch.
6	Same as 5	
7	Nut, brass ¼" -20 hex	
8	Nut, brass ¼" -20 hex	
9	PC board, double-sided. Top 4" x 4".	Drill hole in center to clear 1/4-20 bolt. Solder 7 and 8 each side of hole. (Use bolt 11 to hold nuts in place when soldering.)
10	PC board, double-sided. Bottom 4" x 4".	Solder 2 in center.
11	Bolt, brass ¼-20 x 3".	Insert through 12, then through 7 and 8.
12	Locking nut, brass, ¼-20 hex.	To hold piece 11 after resonance adjustment.

Figure 11.6—A 435-MHz cavity filter can significantly improve reception when front-end overload by out of band signals is a problem. Don't expect this filter to have much effect on the third harmonic of a 2-meter transmitter when operating Mode J, since the 3-dB bandwidth is generally about 15 MHz. This third harmonic should be removed at the transmitter by using a band-pass filter. For additional information see: D. Jansson, "The 4×3×5 Filter—Revisited," *QEX*, Sep 1992, pp 17-19 and "The 4×3×5 Filter for Mode J," *The 1997 ARRL Handbook*, p 23.39.

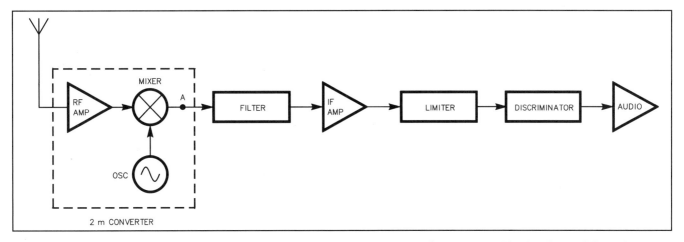

Figure 11.7—A block diagram of a typical 2-meter FM receiver. The section enclosed in the dashed lines forms a 2-meter converter. It's usually possible to pick off a portion of the RF signal at point A without impairing 2-meter FM operation. The frequency at point A varies from receiver to receiver, for example ICOM 211 (10.7 MHz), Clegg FM-28 (16.9 MHz) and GE Progline (8.7 MHz).

148 MHz on 2 m, or 432 to 434, 435 to 437, and 436 to 438 MHz on 70 cm, for example. If so, look for provisions for switching crystals in the injection chain.

Since many modern converters have noise figures under 2 dB you might consider eliminating the preamp. To take full advantage of the converter's noise figure, however, it has to be mounted remotely at, or very close to, the antenna so that most feed-line losses will occur after the point in the system where the noise figure is established. This approach generates many problems relating to weatherproofing, en-

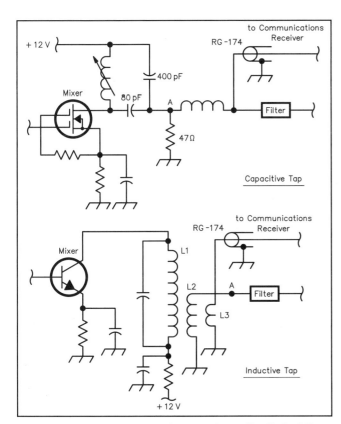

Figure 11.8—Techniques for tapping off a little RF from a 2-meter FM receiver.

vironmental temperature extremes, oscillator drift, switching the frequency range and adjusting the converter gain. Some of these problems are difficult to overcome. If you're considering remote converter mounting be sure to check whether the converter is suited to the planned environment. In most cases at frequencies below 3 GHz you'll have fewer headaches if you keep the converter in the shack and place a good preamp at the antenna.

Many HF operators don't realize that they already have a good 2 m or 70 cm converter at the operating position: the receiver front end in an FM transceiver (Figure 11.7). It's usually a simple matter to "steal" a little of the signal from the FM transceiver and feed it into the communications receiver that is then used as a tunable IF. This gives full CW/SSB capabilities. If you're considering this approach dig out the instruction manual for the FM transceiver and find the frequency of the first IF (point A in Figure 11.7). Next, determine whether the HF receiver following the converter can be adjusted to tune this range. If you have a modern continuous coverage receiver (0.5 to 30 MHz) this shouldn't be a problem since the FM transceiver IF is almost always in this range. With older receivers using plug-in crystals, like the Drake R4 series, one can order an appropriate crystal, or in many cases a standard crystal can be utilized by tuning the preselector to an image frequency. Modifying some receivers to cover the proper range may involve more work or expense than is justified.

To pick off the signal, check the transceiver schematic for an easily accessible low-impedance point between the mixer and filter (or between the first mixer and second mixer in double-conversion units) and then try either a capacitive or inductive probe (Figure 11.8). Use a heavily shielded cable and keep the exposed ends short to minimize IF feedthrough. A little experimentation with the point where the pick-off probe is attached may lead to significantly improved performance. If IF feedthrough is a problem you might try attaching the probe after the transceiver IF filter. This will make tuning somewhat less convenient since the HF receiver can be used only to cover a 20 kHz segment of the band. Additional segments are covered by switching channels on the transceiver.

Instead of using a probe to steal some signal from an operating VHF or UHF FM transceiver it may be preferable to salvage the front end of an inoperative unit obtained at low cost.

PREAMPS

At 146 MHz and above a good preamp mounted at the antenna almost always significantly improves downlink reception. Even at 29 MHz, an antenna-mounted preamp often provides noticeable improvement. The required preamp gain and noise figure depend on sky noise seen by the antenna, feed line length, noise figure of following stages, and so on. For most installations a gain of about 15 is reasonable. If you keep lowering the noise figure of a receiving system you'll eventually reach a point where further reduction provides no discernible improvement in performance. This is because noise arriving by the antenna has become the limiting factor. The target noise figure depends on frequency. At 29 MHz it's about 2.0 dB and at 146 MHz about 1.5 dB. At 435 MHz, it's desirable to aim as low as

---

Table 11.1

Some Manufacturers and Distributors of VHF/UHF Preamps, Receive Converters, Transverters, Transmit Converters, Power Amplifiers and Multimode Transceivers

Advanced Receiver Research, Box 1242, Burlington, CT 06013; 860-485-0310

Alinco, 438 Amapola Ave. #130, Torrance, CA 90501; 310-618-8616

Alpha/Power, Inc, 14440 Mead Ct, Unit B, Longmont, CO 80504; 970-535-4173

Angle Linear, PO Box 35, Lomita, CA 90717; 310-539-5395

Communications Concepts, Inc., 508 Millstone Dr, Beavercreek, OH 45434; 937-426-8600

Down East Microwave, 954 Rte 519, Frenchtown, NJ 08825; 908-996-3584

Encomm, 1506 Capitol Ave, Plano, TX 75074

Hamtronics, Inc., 65-Q Moul Rd, Hilton, NY 14468; 716-392-9430

ICOM America, Inc., 2380 116th Ave NE, Bellevue, WA 98004; 425-454-8155

Kenwood Communications Corp, PO Box 22745, 2201 East Dominguez St., Long Beach, CA 90801; 310-639-5300

Landwehr (Henry Radio) 310-820-1234

Microwave Components of Michigan, PO Box 1697, Taylor, MI 48180; 313-753-4581

Microwave Modules, ART House, 71 Leysholme Crescent, Wortley, Leeds, LS12 4HH, England. In US contact PX Shack or Spectrum International.

Mirage Communications, 300 Industrial Park Rd, Starkville, MS 39759; 601-323-8287

Radiokit, PO Box 973, Pelham, NH 03076; 603-635-2235

RF Concepts (Division of Kantronics), 1202 E 23rd St, Lawrence, KS 66046-5099; 913-842-7745

SSB Electronic, 124 Cherrywood Dr, Mountaintop, PA 18707; 570-868-5643

Spectrum International, PO Box 1084, Concord, MA 01742; 508-263-2145

Ten-Tec Inc, 1185 Dolly Parton Pkwy, Sevierville, TN 37862; 865-453-7172

TE Systems, PO Box 25845, Los Angeles, CA 90025; 310-478-0591

Yaesu USA, 17210 Edwards Rd, Cerritos, CA 90703; 562-404-2700

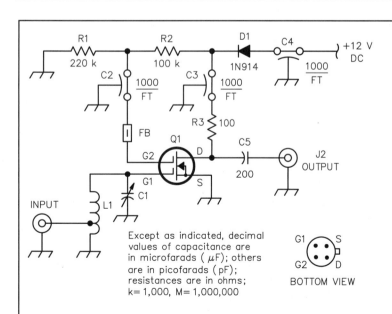

Figure 11.9—28-MHz dual-gate MOSFET preamplifier. Resistors are 1/4-W carbon types (see *The 1991 ARRL Handbook*, p 31-1).

C1—15 to 60-pF ceramic trimmer, Erie 538-002F.
C2, C3—500 to 1000-pF feedthrough capacitor, solder-in type preferred.
C4—500 to 1000-pF feedthrough capacitor.
C5—100 to 200-pF silver mica or ceramic capacitor.
J1, J2—Female chassis-mount RF connectors, BNC preferred.
L1—17 turns no. 28 enam on Amidon T-50-6 core. Tap at 6 turns from front end.
Q1—Dual gate MOSFET such as 3SK51 or 3N204.

Table 11.2
Construction Articles: Preamps and Receive Converters (10 meters to 3 cm)

1991 ARRL Handbook

Dual-Gate MOSFET Preamplifiers for 28, 50, 144 and 220 MHz, pp 31-1,2. Designs by Kent Britain, WA5VJB

Dual-Gate GaAsFET Preamplifiers for 28, 50, 144 and 220 MHz, pp 31-3,4. Designs by Kent Britain, WA5VJB

GaAsFET Preamplifiers for 144 and 220 MHz, pp 31-5,6. Designs by Kent Britain, WA5VJB

Dual-Gate GaAsFET Preamplifiers for 432 MHz, pp 32-1,2. Designs by Kent Britain, WA5VJB

GaAsFET Preamplifier for 70 cm, pp 32-3,4. Design by Chip Angle, N6CA

Periodicals

R. Bertelsmeier, "PHEMT Preamp for 13 cm," *QEX*, Oct 1995, pp 7-11.

G. Ehrler and J. DuBois, "A Very High Performance LNA for 1500-1750 MHz," *Journal of the Amateur Satellite User's Group*, Vol. 89-1, Spring 1989.

P. Gregory, "A 435-MHz Low-Noise GaAsFET Preamplifier," *Ham Radio*, July 1989, pp 9-12, 17, 18.

Z. Lau, "A VHF+ Preamp Design Technology Update and A 2.3 GHz Preamp Project," *QEX*, Mar 1996, pp 25-28.

Z. Lau, "Mode S Receive Converter," *QEX*, July 1994, pp 25-30. (13 cm) Also see "Mode-S Receive Converter," *The 1997 ARRL Handbook*, pp 23.41 - 23.44.

Z. Lau, "Designing a High-Performance 13-cm Preamp," *QEX*, Nov 1993, pp 20-23.

Z. Lau, "Home-Brewing a 10-GHz SSB/CW Transverter," *QST*, May 1993, pp 21-28.

Z. Lau, "The Quest for 1 dB NF on 10 GHz," *QEX*, Dec 1992, pp 16-19.

J. Reed, "Hearing Strange UHF Signals Lately?" *QEX*, Dec 1994, pp 13-16. (70-cm filter/preamp)

J. Reisert, "Low-Noise GaAsFET Technology," *Ham Radio*, Dec 1984, pp 99, 101, 103-106, 108, 111-112

J. Reisert, "Low-Noise Receiver Update: Part 1," *Ham Radio*, Nov 1987, pp 77; Part 2, Dec 1987, pp 72-76, 79-81

H. P. Shuch, "A Low-Noise Preamp for Weather Satellite VISSR Reception," *QEX*, Feb 1989, pp 3-9. (An excellent design for 1.7 GHz that can be adapted for 13 cm.)

A. Ward, "Simple Low-Noise Microwave Preamplifiers," *QST*, May 1989 pp 31-36, 75. (Includes designs for 13 cm.)

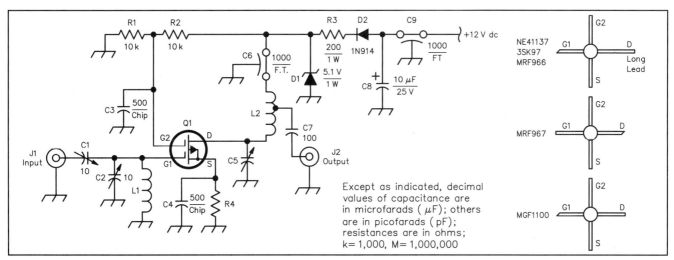

Figure 11.10—144-MHz dual-gate GaAsFET preamplifier. Resistors are 1/4-W carbon-composition types unless otherwise noted. (See 1991 *ARRL Handbook*, p 31-3.)

C1, C2—10-pF (max) ceramic or piston trimmer capacitor.
C3, C4—200 to 1000-pF ceramic chip capacitor or leadless disc-ceramic capacitor.
C5—For 144 MHz: 20-pF trimmer capacitor. For 220 MHz: 10-pF trimmer capacitor.
C6, C9—400 to 1000-pF feedthrough capacitor.
C7—50 to 100-pF silver-mica capacitor.
C8—1 to 25-µF, 25-V electrolytic capacitor.
D1—5.1-V, 1-W Zener diode (1N4733 or equiv).
D2—1N914, 1N4148 or any diode with ratings of 25 PIV and 50 mA or greater.
J1, J2—Female chassis-mount BNC or type-N connector.
L1—See Note.
L2—See Note.
Q1—NEC NE41137, Motorola MRF966/967, Mitsubishi MGF 1100 or 3SK97 dual-gate GaAsFET.

R1—For NE41137, MGF1100, 3SK97: 10 kΩ; for MRF966/967: 4.7 kΩ.
R2—10 kΩ for all devices.
R3—150 to 250 Ω, 1 or 2-W resistor.
R4—For NE41137, MGF1100, 3SK97: 47 Ω; for MRF966/967: 100 Ω.

Note:

L1 and L2 Values

Device	L1	L2
NE41137	7 turns	7 turns, tap at 2 turns
3SK97 and MGF1100	5 turns	7 turns, tap at 2 turns
MRF966/967	12 turns	8 turns, tap at 2 turns

All coils are no. 20 to 24 wire, 3/16-inch ID, spaced one wire diameter.

you can go—0.7 dB is not too difficult to achieve. Since system noise figure will always be greater than preamp noise figure (see Figure 11.3), preamp noise figure targets should be slightly below the levels specified.

Ready-made preamps are available from a number of manufacturers (see Table 11.1). One manufacturer (Hamtronics) sells a barebones kit (no case, no connectors) for under $30 that meets our requirements at 29 MHz and 146 MHz and is close to our objectives at 435 MHz.

A number of good preamp designs are available. See Table 11.2 for designs covering 10 meters to 13 cm. If you enjoy homebrewing, a simple preamp is a good project.

At 29 MHz a dual gate MOSFET will provide about 20-dB gain with a noise figure under 1.5 dB. A 10 meter preamp designed by Kent Britain, WA5VJB, is shown in Figure 11.9.

At 146 MHz suitable preamps may be built from transistors based on silicon or gallium-arsenide technology. In the 1970s and earlier it was extremely difficult to obtain noise figures under 2.0 dB at frequencies above 144 MHz. In about 1978, when GaAsFETs (Gallium-Arsenide Field Effect Transistors) became available to radio amateurs, it quickly became apparent that they would revolutionize preamp performance. Initially, these devices were extremely expensive but today you can purchase a dual-gate GaAsFET that will provide 20 dB gain with a noise figure under 1 dB at 146 MHz for less than $5. A typical circuit, again by WA5VJB, is shown in Figure 11.10.

GaAsFETs are hardy once they're installed in a preamp but they are static sensitive and they can be easily destroyed if not handled properly while the preamp is under construc-

tion. For this reason some amateurs prefer to use silicon devices. At 146 MHz this is possible. The preamp shown in Figure 11.11, modeled after a design by C. E. Scheideler, W2AZL, uses an inexpensive silicon JFET in a grounded gate configuration. The noise figure is 1.5 dB. The gain is only about 10 dB so this circuit is suitable only if feed line losses are relatively low and the following converter has a noise figure under 3.5 dB.

At 435 MHz and higher frequencies GaAs technology is the way to go, the main choice is whether to opt for a preamp using low cost dual gate devices or for one using a slightly more expensive, and better performing, single gate device. The 146 MHz dual gate GaAsFET preamp (Figure 11.10) also works at 435 MHz if the tuned circuits are changed. At 435 MHz it provides a noise figure under 0.9 dB with 22+ dB of gain. The single gate GaAsFET preamp shown in Figure 11.12 was designed by Chip Angle, N6CA. The noise figure is less than 0.7 dB and gain is about 13 dB. When working at these extremely low noise figures impedance matching of antenna, preamp input, and any band-pass filter connected between antenna and preamp, becomes important if the overall system is to perform as expected (Z. Lau, "Matching Receivers to Transmission Lines," *QST*, Sep 1988, p 46).

The N6CA circuit is slightly more complex than some other designs because it uses source feedback to keep the input impedance close to 50 Ω. As a result, the full effect of the low noise figure can be realized. In addition, the possibility of parasitic oscillations is greatly reduced and excellent performance is readily obtained. When tweaking a test unit in the ARRL Laboratory it was noted that no adjustment (C2 and/or expansion/contraction of L3 and L5) caused the gain to dip below 12 dB or the noise figure to rise above 0.65 dB. As a result, you can build this preamp without any test equipment. Simply tune it for maximum gain, and be reasonably sure of obtaining excellent performance.

One additional preamp design for 435 MHz deserves mention. The circuit shown in Figure 11.13, based on silicon bipolar transistor technology, was designed by Joe Reisert, W1JR. It has a noise figure of 1.5 to 2.0 dB and a gain of 12-14 dB. Note the simple design and the fact that there are no tuning adjustments. Because the noise figure of this preamp does not approach that of a GaAsFET design, it's not suitable for antenna mounting. If you're using a relatively low gain GaAsFET preamp like the N6CA design at the antenna in conjunction with a converter having a poor noise figure, however, you might see a substantial improvement in system performance if you place this preamp directly at the converter input. This preamp should not be used in urban environments where very high power TV stations and pagers operate at nearby frequencies.

The 13 cm downlink on OSCAR 40 is heavily used. Before 1988, building a preamp for 2.4 GHz was a difficult undertaking but thanks to the efforts of several radio amateurs it's now as easy, perhaps even easier, to build one at this frequency than at the lower end of the spectrum. The reason for this somewhat paradoxical situation is that at

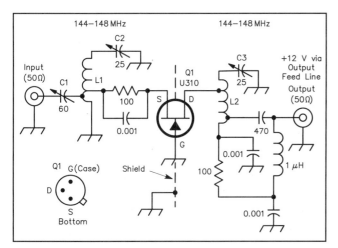

Figure 11.11—144-MHz JFET preamp. Noise figure: ~1.5 dB. Gain: ~10 dB. Q1: Siliconix U310 or 2N5397. See *The 1985 ARRL Handbook*, p 18-25, for additional information. A similar design by C. E. Scheideler with detailed construction information appeared in "A Preamplifier for 144-MHz EME," *EME Notes*, AS-49-9, Eimac Division of Varian Associates, 301 Industrial Way, San Carlos, CA. L1 has 5 turns of no. 20 wire, $^3/_4$ inch (19 mm) long, with an ID of $^1/_4$ inch (6.3 mm). C1 tap approx $^1/_2$ turn from ground, Q1 tap approx 1 turn from ground. L2 has same dimensions except for Q1 tap, which is approx 1 turn from C3 end.

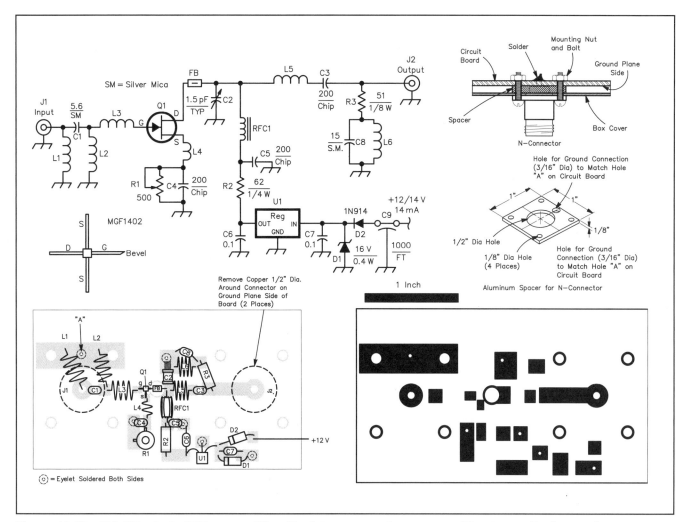

Figure 11.12—435-MHz GaAsFET preamplifier. Resistors are carbon-composition types. Resistor values are given in ohms; capacitor values are given in pF. This design, by E. R. "Chip" Angle, first appeared in the *432 and Above EME News*, Vol 9, no. 7, June 1981. Noise figure: 0.5 dB. Gain: ~16 dB.

C1—5.6-pF silver-mica capacitor, or same as C2.
C2—0.6 to 6-pF ceramic piston trimmer capacltor (Johnson 5700 series or equiv).
C3, C4, C5—200-pF ceramic chip capacitor.
C6, C7—0.1-µF disc-ceramic capacitor, 50 V or greater.
C8—15-pF silver-mica capacitor.
C9—500 to 1000-pF feedthrough capacitor.
D1—16 to 30-V, 500-mW Zener diode (1N966B or equiv).
D2—1N914, 1N4148 or any diode with ratings of at least 25 PIV at 50 mA or greater.
J1, J2—Female chassis-mount type-N connectors, PTFE dielectric (UG-58 or equiv).
L1, L2—3 turns # 24 tinned wire, 0.110 inch ID, spaced 1 wire diameter.

L3—5 turns # 24 tinned wire, 3/16 inch ID, spaced 1 wire diameter or closer. Slightly larger diameter (0.010 inch) may be required with some FETs.
L4—1 turn # 24 tinned wire, 1/8 inch ID.
L5—4 turns # 24 tinned wire, 1/8 inch ID, spaced 1 wire diameter.
L6—1 turn # 24 tinned wire, 1/8 inch ID.
Q1—Mitsubishi MGF 1402.
R1—200 or 500-Ω cermet potentiometer set to midrange initially.
R2—62-Ω, 1/4 W resistor.
R3—51-Ω, 1/8 W carbon-composition resistor, 5% tolerance.
RFC1—5 turns # 26 enam wire on a ferrite bead.
U1—5-V, 100-mA 3-terminal regulator (LM78L05 or equiv; TO-92 package).
For reference see *1997 ARRL Handbook* pp 17.38-39.

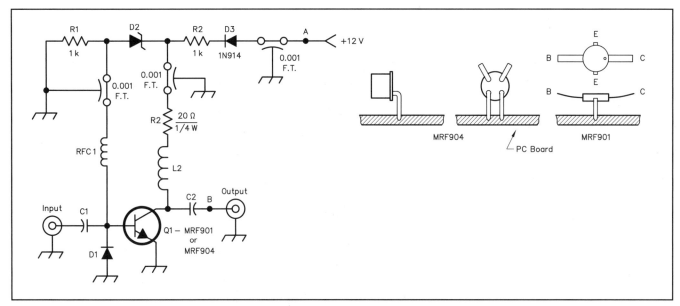

Figure 11.13—435-MHz preamp. Noise figure: 1.5-2.0 dB. Gain: 12-14 dB. Q1: MRF 901 or MRF 904. This design first appeared in J. Reisert, "An Inexpensive AMSAT-OSCAR Mode J Receive Preamplifier," *AMSAT Newsletter*, Vol X, no. 2, June 1978, pp 10-11. For additional information on this preamp, see: J. Reisert, "Ultra Low-noise UHF Preamplifier," *Ham Radio*, Mar 1975, pp 8-19. The complete absence of adjustments makes this design a pleasure to replicate.

C1—50 pF dipped mica.
C2—5.0 pF dipped mica.
D1—Hewlett-Packard 5082-2810 or equiv hot carrier diode.
D2—6.2 volt Zener diode, 1N4735 or equiv.
D3—1N914 or equiv.
L1—Deleted.
L2—3 turns #24 on $1/10$ inch ID space wire diameter.

RFC 1—0.47 µH Nytronics deciductor on 15 turns #32 AWG enamel covered copper wire on $1/10$" ID spaced wire diameter.
R2—20 Ω, $1/4$ W.

Note: Mount transistor as shown with leads just touching PC board.

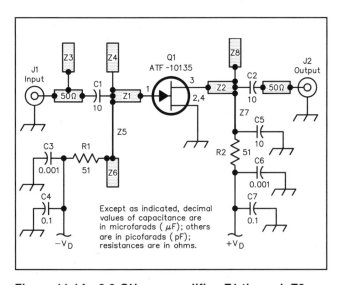

Figure 11.14—2.3-GHz preamplifier. Z1 through Z8 are microstriplines etched on the PC board. Shaded rectangles marked "50 Ω" are 50-Ω transmission lines etched on the PC board. All resistors and capacitors are chip types. C1, C2 and C5 can be 0.05 or 0.1-in. square. C4 and C7 enhance low-frequency bypassing. J1 and J2 are SMA female connectors. See *QST*, May 1989, pp 31-36, 75.

frequencies between 1 and 10 GHz it becomes practical to use microstrip lines for impedance matching and to replace lumped circuit inductors. With microstrip design, construction of prototypes may be time consuming, but duplication of a successful model is relatively simple. A typical circuit, designed by Al Ward, WB5LUA, is shown in Figure 11.14. Note that the circuit has *no* tuning adjustments. At this frequency extra gain is often needed to overcome feed line losses. Paul Shuch, N6TX, has demonstrated that bipolar monolithic microwave integrated circuits (MMICs) are ideal for this application since they have a reasonably low noise figure, are extremely stable, and are inexpensive (see Table 11.2). Since it's also possible to produce band-pass filters using stripline technology at these frequencies (R. Campbell, "A Clean, Low-Cost Microwave Local Oscillator," *QST*, July 1989, pp 15-21) one can build an entire 2.4 GHz converter that does not have any RF adjustments.

If you compare prices of commercial preamps you'll see a very wide range. To a large extent, this reflects what's being included. The preamp itself just consists of a few components mounted on a small circuit board in a box with connectors. Quality connectors and a good box make a big impact on cost. So does the inclusion of a couple of coax relays for transit/receive switching. After you take these factors into account, most of the remaining cost differential reflects the price of the active device being used.

MOUNTING PREAMPS AT THE ANTENNA

Three practical problems are encountered when mounting a preamp at the antenna: supplying power to the unit, weatherproofing the installation and switching the preamp out of the line if it's desired to use the antenna for transmitting.

Let's look at power first. Most solid-state units require a single positive supply of about +12 V dc. Batteries are inappropriate because they won't last long and the location may be difficult to access. The simplest method of supplying power to the preamp is to run a separate lead up to the antenna from a +12-V power supply in the shack and use the outer braid of the coaxial cable as the power-supply ground return. A more elegant solution eliminates the need for any extra wires running to the antenna by using the coax feed line to carry both dc power and RF signals. Measurements reveal no discernible RF losses when this technique is used.

Figure 11.15 shows two junction boxes that can be used with most preamps to accomplish this goal. One junction box mounts at the preamp, the other at the converter in the shack. In many cases it's possible to eliminate one or both junction boxes by incorporating the components directly into the preamp and converter. This has been done in the preamp pictured in Figure 11.11. If this feature is incorporated in a preamp it can, at the user's discretion, be utilized or ignored. The capacitors C1 and C3 shown in Figure 11.15 can be omitted if neither the preamp-exit or converter-entry point is at ground potential. Note that the alternate input circuit for Figure 11.9 and the output circuit for Figure 11.12 do not satisfy this requirement. To protect against possible accidents it's best to include these capacitors in all designs.

My limited personal experience is that weatherproofing a preamp is not a serious problem. One common technique is to enclose the preamp in a double plastic bag and mount it under a cover that protects against direct exposure to the elements. The rain cover may be plastic, glass, or aluminum. Most plastics tend to deteriorate when exposed to sunlight but enclosures cut from large plastic soda bottles seem to hold up well (this is why their large scale production causes serious environmental problems). Plastic bags may be gathered together using a twist tie; cables should be routed as shown (Figure 11.16) to discourage seepage.

No attempt should be made to seal the unit. Seals eventually fail and lead to problems with condensation. How well does this approach to weatherproofing work? Many years ago I placed a microwave converter in a double plastic bag and set it out on the deck of my house where it was fully exposed to the weather. Several years later the deck had to be rebuilt so the experiment was terminated. The converter was working fine. Dick Jansson, WD4FAB, and John DuBois, W1HDX, report similar results.

If you wish to use the antenna for transmitting, the preamp must be switched off line. The recommended switching circuit requires the installation of two SPDT coax switches between the antenna and preamp. The first one toggles the antenna between a transmission line to the trans-

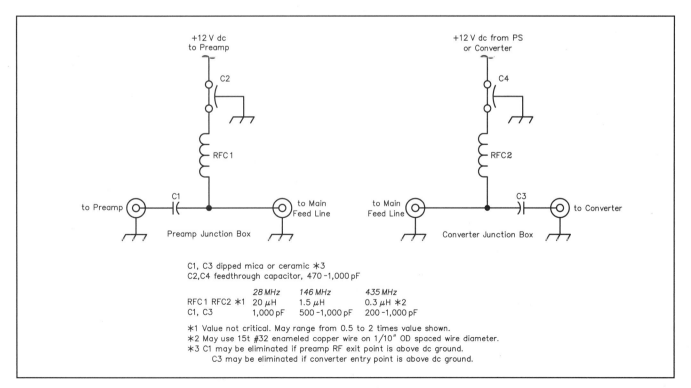

Figure 11.15—Junction boxes that can be used to provide dc power to a remote preamp via the RF feed line. See accompanying text for details.

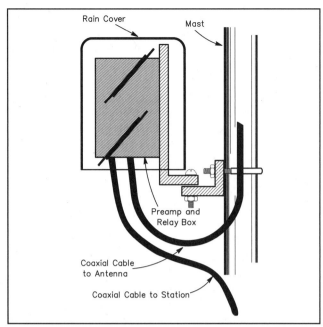

Figure 11.16—Protection for tower-mounted equipment need not be elaborate. Be sure to dress the cables as shown so that water drips off the cable jacket before it reaches the enclosure.

mitter and a jumper to the second relay. The second relay switches the preamp input between the jumper and a 50 ohm resistor to ground. This switching circuit requires two transmission lines, one for the receiver and one for the transmitter. Some commercial preamps use PIN diode switching to automatically bypass the preamp when transmitter power is sensed. PIN diode switching systems appear to be reliable when transmitter power limitations (generally on the order of 25 to 100 W) are adhered to.

Picture a crossed Yagi for 70 cm used for both transmitting (Mode B) and receiving (Mode L). The antenna system includes a phasing harness, polarity switcher, preamp, and relays for bypassing the preamp. Because of weight, wind load, and possible antenna pattern distortion it's best to mount all these components in a weatherproof enclosure attached to the mast and to run a short length of coax from the enclosure to the antenna.

All these relays, connectors, and lengths of coax will add some loss to the receiving system and degrade overall performance. One way of avoiding a significant part of this loss is to use a dedicated receiving antenna but the expense of this approach is generally prohibitive. 70 cm is the worst case situation. Antennas for 23 cm and 13 cm are only used to uplink or downlink, so preamp bypassing circuitry is not required. The polarity switcher shouldn't be needed for working with OSCAR 40 since the off axis polarity sense reversals encountered with earlier Phase 3 spacecraft should not occur (discussed in Chapter 9). And, at 2 meters the preamp bypassing system can usually be omitted since it is generally preferable to use a small beam or omnidirectional antenna to transmit on a Mode A or Mode J rather than a high gain 2 meters antenna intended for Mode B reception.

TRANSMITTING

All radio amateurs using the transponders on OSCAR satellites must share the available power and bandwidth. Cooperation is essential. Stations employing too high an EIRP will use more than their share of spacecraft energy and may even activate automatic-gain control circuitry, making it impossible for low-power ground stations to be heard. See comments in Chapters 4, 5 and 6 concerning cooperation and Appendix C for recommended EIRP levels.

RF Power Safety

Amateur Radio is basically a safe activity but accidents can always occur if we don't use common sense. Most of us know enough not to place an antenna where it can fall on a power line, insert our hand into an energized linear amplifier, or climb a tower on a windy day.

RF energy can also be dangerous. Large RF fields can cause damage in people by heating tissues. The magnitude of the effect depends on the wavelength, incident energy density of the RF field, exposure duration, and other factors such as polarization. It's especially important to be aware of the threat posed by RF fields because they're invisible and, the most susceptible parts of the body, the tissues of the eyes and gonads, don't have heat-sensitive receptors to warn us of the danger before damage occurs. Symptoms of overexposure may not appear until after irreversible damage has been done.

With the launch of OSCAR 40 radio amateurs operating in the Amateur Satellite Service are transmitting from 21 MHz to 5.7 GHz. It is extremely important that every individual operating a transmitter takes steps to assure that no one is exposed to excessive amounts of RF energy. The FCC has released Regulations discussing how this should be done. The FCC RF-Exposure Regulations require that amateur operators not categorically excluded perform a routine analysis of compliance with the MPE limit (Table 11.3).

RF RADIATION AND ELECTROMAGNETIC FIELD SAFETY

Amateur Radio is basically a safe activity. In recent years, however, there has been considerable discussion and concern about the possible hazards of electromagnetic radiation (EMR), including both RF energy and power-frequency (50-60 Hz) electromagnetic (EM) fields. FCC regulations set limits on the maximum permissible exposure (MPE) allowed from the operation of radio transmitters. These regulations do not take the place of RF-safety practices, however. This section deals with the topic of RF safety.

This section was prepared by members of the ARRL RF Safety Committee and coordinated by Dr. Robert E. Gold, WBØKIZ. It summarizes what is now known and offers safety precautions based on the research to date.

All life on Earth has adapted to survive in an environment of weak, natural, low-frequency electromagnetic fields (in addition to the Earth's static geomagnetic field).

Natural low-frequency EM fields come from two main sources: the sun, and thunderstorm activity. But in the last 100 years, man-made fields at much higher intensities and with a very different spectral distribution have altered this natural EM background in ways that are not yet fully understood. Researchers continue to look at the effects of RF exposure over a wide range of frequencies and levels.

Both RF and 60-Hz fields are classified as *nonionizing radiation,* because the frequency is too low for there to be enough photon energy to ionize atoms. (*Ionizing radiation,* such as X-rays, gamma rays and even some ultraviolet radiation has enough energy to knock electrons loose from their atoms. When this happens, positive and negative ions are formed.) Still, at sufficiently high power densities, EMR poses certain health hazards. It has been known since the early days of radio that RF energy can cause injuries by heating body tissue. (Anyone who has ever touched an improperly grounded radio chassis or energized antenna and received an *RF burn* will agree that this type of injury can be quite painful.) In extreme cases, RF-induced heating in the eye can result in cataract formation, and can even cause blindness. Excessive RF heating of the reproductive organs can cause sterility. Other health problems also can result from RF heating. These heat-related health hazards are called *thermal effects.* A microwave oven is a positive application of this thermal effect.

There also have been observations of changes in physiological function in the presence of RF energy levels that are too low to cause heating. These functions return to normal when the field is removed. Although research is ongoing, no harmful health consequences have been linked to these changes.

In addition to the ongoing research, much else has been done to address this issue. For example, FCC regulations set limits on exposure from radio transmitters. The Institute of Electrical and Electronics Engineers, the American National Standards Institute and the National Council for Radiation Protection and Measurement, among others, have recommended voluntary guidelines to limit human exposure to RF energy. The ARRL has established the RF Safety Committee, consisting of concerned medical doctors and scientists, serving voluntarily to monitor scientific research in the fields and to recommend safe practices for radio amateurs.

THERMAL EFFECTS OF RF ENERGY

Body tissues that are subjected to *very high* levels of RF energy may suffer serious heat damage. These effects depend on the frequency of the energy, the power density of the RF field that strikes the body and factors such as the polarization of the wave.

At frequencies near the body's natural resonant frequency, RF energy is absorbed more efficiently, and an increase in heating occurs. In adults, this frequency usually is about 35 MHz if the person is grounded, and about 70 MHz if insulated from the ground. Individual body parts may be resonant at different frequencies. The adult head, for example, is resonant around 400 MHz, while a baby's smaller head resonates near 700 MHz. Body size thus de-

termines the frequency at which most RF energy is absorbed. As the frequency is moved farther from resonance, less RF heating generally occurs. *Specific absorption rate (SAR)* is a term that describes the rate at which RF energy is absorbed in tissue.

Maximum permissible exposure (MPE) limits are based on whole-body SAR values, with additional safety factors included as part of the standards and regulations. This helps explain why these safe exposure limits vary with frequency. The MPE limits define the maximum electric and magnetic field strengths or the plane-wave equivalent power densities associated with these fields, that a person may be exposed to without harmful effect—and with an acceptable safety factor. The regulations assume that a person exposed to a specified (safe) MPE level also will experience a safe SAR.

Nevertheless, thermal effects of RF energy should not be a major concern for most radio amateurs, because of the power levels we normally use and the intermittent nature of most amateur transmissions. Amateurs spend more time listening than transmitting, and many amateur transmissions such as CW and SSB use low-duty-cycle modes. (With FM or RTTY, though, the RF is present continuously at its maximum level during each transmission.) In any event, it is rare for radio amateurs to be subjected to RF fields strong enough to produce thermal effects, unless they are close to an energized antenna or un- shielded power amplifier. Specific suggestions for avoiding excessive exposure are offered later in this chapter.

ATHERMAL EFFECTS OF EMR

Research about possible health effects resulting from exposure to the lower level energy fields, the athermal effects, has been of two basic types: epidemiological research and laboratory research.

Scientists conduct laboratory research into biological mechanisms by which EMR may affect animals including humans. Epidemiologists look at the health patterns of large groups of people using statistical methods. These epidemiological studies have been inconclusive. By their basic design, these studies do not demonstrate cause and effect, nor do they postulate mechanisms of disease. Instead, epidemiologists look for associations between an environmental factor and an observed pattern of illness. For example, in the earliest research on malaria, epidemiologists observed the association between populations with high prevalence of the disease and the proximity of mosquito infested swamplands. It was left to the biological and medical scientists to isolate the organism causing malaria in the blood of those with the disease, and identify the same organisms in the mosquito population.

In the case of athermal effects, some studies have identified a weak association between exposure to EMF at home or at work and various malignant conditions including leukemia and brain cancer. A larger number of equally well designed and performed studies, however, have found no association. A risk ratio of between 1.5 and 2.0 has been observed in positive studies (the number of observed cases of malignancy being 1.5 to 2.0 times the "expected" number in the population). Epidemiologists generally regard a risk ratio of 4.0 or greater to be indicative of a strong association between the cause and effect under study. For example, men who smoke one pack of cigarettes per day increase their risk for lung cancer tenfold compared to non-smokers, and two packs per day increases the risk to more than 25 times the nonsmokers' risk.

Epidemiological research by itself is rarely conclusive, however. Epidemiology only identifies health patterns in groups—it does not ordinarily determine their cause. And there are often confounding factors: Most of us are exposed to many different environmental hazards that may affect our health in various ways. Moreover, not all studies of persons likely to be exposed to high levels of EMR have yielded the same results.

There also has been considerable laboratory research about the biological effects of EMR in recent years. For example, some separate studies have indicated that even fairly low levels of EMR might alter the human body's circadian rhythms, affect the manner in which T lymphocytes function in the immune system and alter the nature of the electrical and chemical signals communicated through the cell membrane and between cells, among other things. Although these studies are intriguing, they do not demonstrate any effect of these low-level fields on the overall organism.

Much of this research has focused on low-frequency magnetic fields, or on RF fields that are keyed, pulsed or modulated at a low audio frequency (often below 100 Hz). Several studies suggested that humans and animals can adapt to the presence of a steady RF carrier more readily than to an intermittent, keyed or modulated energy source.

The results of studies in this area, plus speculations concerning the effect of various types of modulation, were and have remained somewhat controversial. None of the research to date has demonstrated that low-level EMR causes adverse health effects.

Given the fact that there is a great deal of ongoing research to examine the health consequences of exposure to EMF, the American Physical Society (a national group of highly respected scientists) issued a statement in May 1995 based on its review of available data pertaining to the possible connections of cancer to 60-Hz EMF exposure. This report is exhaustive and should be reviewed by anyone with a serious interest in the field. Among its general conclusions were the following:

1. The scientific literature and the reports of reviews by other panels show no consistent, significant link between cancer and power line fields.

2. No plausible biophysical mechanisms for the systematic initiation or promotion of cancer by these extremely weak 60-Hz fields has been identified.

3. While it is impossible to prove that no deleterious health effects occur from exposure to any environmental factor, it is necessary to demonstrate a consistent, significant, and causal relationship before one can conclude that such effects do occur.

In a report dated October 31, 1996, a committee of the National Research Council of the National Academy of Sciences has concluded that no clear, convincing evidence exists to show that residential exposures to electric and magnetic fields (EMFs) are a threat to human health.

A National Cancer Institute epidemiological study of residential exposure to magnetic fields and acute lymphoblastic leukemia in children was published in the *New England Journal of Medicine* in July 1997. The exhaustive, seven-year study concludes that if there is any link at all, it is far too weak to be concerned about.

Readers may want to follow this topic as further studies are reported. Amateurs should be aware that exposure to RF and ELF (60 Hz) electromagnetic fields at all power levels and frequencies has not been fully studied under all circumstances. "Prudent avoidance" of any avoidable EMR is always a good idea. Prudent avoidance doesn't mean that amateurs should be fearful of using their equipment. Most amateur operations are well within the MPE limits. If any risk does exist, it will almost surely fall well down on the list of causes that may be harmful to your health (on the other end of the list from your automobile). It does mean, however, that hams should be aware of the potential for exposure from their stations, and take whatever reasonable steps they can take to minimize their own exposure and the exposure of those around them.

SAFE EXPOSURE LEVELS

How much EM energy is safe? Scientists and regulators have devoted a great deal of effort to deciding upon safe RF-exposure limits. This is a very complex problem, involving difficult public health and economic considerations. The recommended safe levels have been revised downward several times over the years —and not all scientific bodies agree on this question even today. An Institute of Electrical and Electronics Engineers (IEEE) standard for recommended EM exposure limits was published in 1991 (see Bibliography). It replaced a 1982 American National Standards Institute (ANSI) standard. In the new standard, most of the permitted exposure levels were revised downward (made more stringent), to better reflect the current research. The new IEEE standard was adopted by ANSI in 1992.

The IEEE standard recommends frequency-dependent and time-dependent maximum permissible exposure levels. Unlike earlier versions of the standard, the 1991 standard recommends different RF exposure limits in *controlled environments* (that is, where energy levels can be accurately determined and everyone on the premises is aware of the presence of EM fields) and in *uncontrolled environments* (where energy levels are not known or where people may not be aware of the presence of EM fields). FCC regulations also include controlled/occupational and uncontrolled/general population exposure environments.

The graph in Fig 11.17 depicts the 1991 IEEE standard. It is necessarily a complex graph, because the standards differ not only for controlled and uncontrolled environments but also for electric (E) fields and magnetic (H)

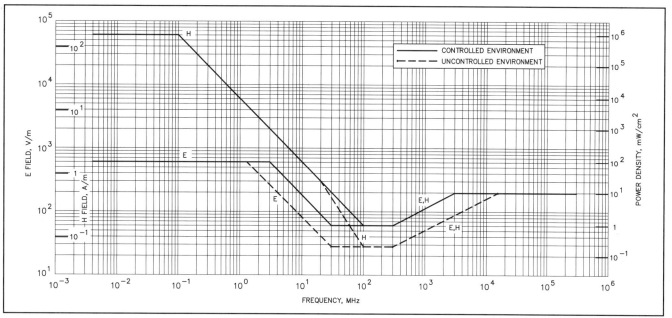

Figure 11.17—1991 RF protection standard for body exposure of humans. It is known officially as the "IEEE Standard for Safety Levels with Respect to Human Exposure to Radio Frequency Electromagnetic Fields, 3 kHz to 300 GHz."

fields. Basically, the lowest E-field exposure limits occur at frequencies between 30 and 300 MHz. The lowest H-field exposure levels occur at 100-300 MHz. The ANSI standard sets the maximum E-field limits between 30 and 300 MHz at a power density of 1 mW/cm² (61.4 V/m) in controlled environments—but at one-fifth that level (0.2 mW/cm² or 27.5 V/m) in uncontrolled environments. The H-field limit drops to 1 mW/cm² (0.163 A/m) at 100-300 MHz in controlled environments and 0.2 mW/cm²

Table 11.3

Typical 60-Hz Magnetic Fields Near Amateur Radio Equipment and AC-Powered Household Appliances

Values are in milligauss.

Item	Field	Distance
Electric blanket	30-90	Surface
Microwave oven	10-100	Surface
	1-10	12"
IBM personal computer	5-10	Atop monitor
	0-1	15" from screen
Electric drill	500-2000	At handle
Hair dryer	200-2000	At handle
HF transceiver	10-100	Atop cabinet
	1-5	15" from front
1-kW RF amplifier	80-1000	Atop cabinet
	1-25	15" from front

Source: Measurements made by members of the ARRL RF Safety Committee

(0.0728 A/m) in uncontrolled environments. Higher power densities are permitted at frequencies below 30 MHz (below 100 MHz for H fields) and above 300 MHz, based on the concept that the body will not be resonant at those frequencies and will therefore absorb less energy.

In general, the 1991 IEEE standard requires averaging the power level over time periods ranging from 6 to 30 minutes for power-density calculations, depending on the frequency and other variables. The ANSI exposure limits for uncontrolled environments are lower than those for controlled environments, but to compensate for that the standard allows exposure levels in those environments to be averaged over much longer time periods (generally 30 minutes). This long averaging time means that an intermittently operating RF source (such as an Amateur Radio transmitter) will show a much lower power density than a continuous-duty station—for a given power level and antenna configuration.

Time averaging is based on the concept that the human body can withstand a greater rate of body heating (and thus, a higher level of RF energy) for a short time than for a longer period. Time averaging may not be appropriate, however, when considering nonthermal effects of RF energy.

The IEEE standard excludes any transmitter with an output below 7 W because such low-power transmitters would not be able to produce significant whole-body heating. (Recent studies show that hand-held transceivers often produce power densities in excess of the IEEE standard within the head.)

There is disagreement within the scientific community about these RF exposure guidelines. The IEEE standard is still intended primarily to deal with thermal effects, not

FCC RF-Exposure Regulations

FCC regulations control the amount of RF exposure that can result from your station's operation (§§97.13, 97.503, 1.1307 (b)(c)(d), 1.1310 and 2.1093). The regulations set limits on the maximum permissible exposure (MPE) allowed from operation of transmitters in all radio services. They also require that certain types of stations be evaluated to determine if they are in compliance with the MPEs specified in the rules. The FCC has also required that five questions on RF environmental safety practices be added to Novice, Technician and General license examinations.

These rules went into effect on January 1, 1998 for new stations or stations that file a Form 605 application with the FCC. Other existing stations have until September 1, 2000 to be in compliance with the rules.

The Rules

Maximum Permissible Exposure (MPE)

All radio stations regulated by the FCC must comply with the requirements for MPEs, even QRP stations running only a few watts or less. The MPEs vary with frequency, as shown in **Table A**. MPE limits are specified in maximum electric and magnetic fields for frequencies below 30 MHz, in power density for frequencies above 300 MHz and all three ways for frequencies from 30 to 300 MHz. For compliance purposes, all of these limits must be considered *separately*. If any one is exceeded, the station is not in compliance.

The regulations control human exposure to RF fields, not the strength of RF fields. There is no limit to how strong a field can be as long as no one is being exposed to it, although FCC regulations require that amateurs use the minimum necessary power at all times (§97.311 [a]).

Environments

The FCC has defined two exposure environments — *controlled* and *uncontrolled*. A controlled environment is one in which the people who are being exposed are aware of that exposure and can take steps to minimize that exposure, if appropriate. In an uncontrolled environment, the people being exposed are not normally aware of the exposure. The uncontrolled environment limits are more stringent than the controlled environment limits.

Although the controlled environment is usually intended as an occupational environment, the FCC

Table A—(From §1.1310) Limits for Maximum Permissible Exposure (MPE)

(A) Limits for Occupational/Controlled Exposure

Frequency Range (MHz)	Electric Field Strength (V/m)	Magnetic Field Strength (A/m)	Power Density (mW/cm^2)	Averaging Time (minutes)
0.3-3.0	614	1.63	(100)*	6
3.0-30	1842/f	4.89/f	(900/f^2)*	6
30-300	61.4	0.163	1.0	6
300-1500	—	—	f/300	6
1500-100,000	—	—	5	6

f = frequency in MHz
* = Plane-wave equivalent power density (see Note 1).

(B) Limits for General Population/Uncontrolled Exposure

Frequency Range (MHz)	Electric Field Strength (V/m)	Magnetic Field Strength (A/m)	Power Density (mW/cm^2)	Averaging Time (minutes)
0.3-1.34	614	1.63	(100)*	30
1.34-30	824/f	2.19/f	(180/f^2)*	30
30-300	27.5	0.073	0.2	30
300-1500	—	—	f/1500	30
1500-100,000	—	—	1.0	30

f = frequency in MHz
* = Plane-wave equivalent power density (see Note 1).

Note 1: This means the equivalent far-field strength that would have the E or H-field component calculated or measured. It does not apply well in the near field of an antenna. The equivalent far-field power density can be found in the near or far field regions from the relationships: $P_d = |E_{total}|^2 / 3770$ mW/cm^2 or from $P_d = |H_{total}|^2 \times 37.7$ mW/cm^2.

---

exposure to energy at lower levels. A small but significant number of researchers now believe athermal effects also should be taken into consideration. Several European countries and localities in the United States have adopted stricter standards than the recently updated IEEE standard.

Another national body in the United States, the National Council for Radiation Protection and Measurement (NCRP), also has adopted recommended exposure guidelines. NCRP urges a limit of 0.2 mW/cm^2 for nonoccupational exposure in the 30-300 MHz range. The NCRP guideline differs from IEEE in two notable ways: It takes into account the effects of modulation on an RF carrier, and it does not exempt transmitters with outputs below 7 W.

The FCC MPE regulations are based on parts of the 1992

Table B—Power Thresholds for Routine Evaluation of Amateur Radio Stations

Wavelength Band	Evaluation Required if Power* (watts) Exceeds:
MF	
160 m	500
HF	
80 m	500
75 m	500
40 m	500
30 m	425
20 m	225
17 m	125
15 m	100
12 m	75
10 m	50
VHF (all bands)	50
UHF	
70 cm	70
33 cm	150
23 cm	200
13 cm	250
SHF (all bands)	250
EHF (all bands)	250
Repeater stations (all bands)	*non-building-mounted antennas*: height above ground level to lowest point of antenna < 10 m *and* power > 500 W ERP *building-mounted antennas*: power > 500 W ERP

*Transmitter power = Peak-envelope power input to antenna. For repeater stations **only,** power exclusion based on ERP (effective radiated power).

has determined that it generally applies to amateur operators and members of their immediate households. In most cases, controlled-environment limits can be applied to your home and property to which you can control physical access. The uncontrolled environment is intended for areas that are accessible by the general public, such as your neighbors' properties.

The MPE levels are based on average exposure. An averaging time of 6 minutes is used for controlled exposure; an averaging period of 30 minutes is used for uncontrolled exposure.

Station Evaluations

The FCC requires that certain amateur stations be evaluated for compliance with the MPEs. Although an amateur can have someone else do the evalua-tion, it is not difficult for hams to evaluate their own stations. The ARRL book *RF Exposure and You* contains extensive information about the regulations and a large chapter of tables that show compliance distances for specific antennas and power levels. Generally, hams will use these tables to evaluate their stations. Some of these tables have been included in the FCC's information — *OET Bulletin 65* and its *Supplement B*. If hams choose, however, they can do more extensive calculations, use a computer to model their antenna and exposure, or make actual measurements.

Categorical Exemptions

Some types of amateur stations do not need to be evaluated, but these stations must still comply with the MPE limits. The station licensee remains responsible for ensuring that the station meets these requirements.

The FCC has exempted these stations from the evaluation requirement because their output power, operating mode and frequency are such that they are presumed to be in compliance with the rules.

Stations using power equal to or less than the levels in **Table B** do not have to be evaluated. For the 100-W HF ham station, for example, an evaluation would be required *only* on 12 and 10 meters.

Hand-held radios and vehicle-mounted mobile radios that operate using a push-to-talk (PTT) button are also categorically exempt from performing the routine evaluation. Repeater stations that use less than 500 W ERP or those with antennas not mounted on buildings, if the antenna is at least 10 meters off the ground, also do not need to be evaluated.

Correcting Problems

Most hams are already in compliance with the MPE requirements. Some amateurs, especially those using indoor antennas or high-power, high-duty-cycle modes such as a RTTY bulletin station and specialized stations for moonbounce operations and the like may need to make adjustments to their station or operation to be in compliance.

The FCC permits amateurs considerable flexibility in complying with these regulations. As an example, hams can adjust their operating frequency, mode or power to comply with the MPE limits. They can also adjust their operating habits or control the direction their antenna is pointing.

More Information

This discussion offers only an overview of this topic; additional information can be found in *RF Exposure and You* and on *ARRLWeb* at **http://www.arrl.org/news/rfsafety/**. *ARRLWeb* has links to the FCC Web site, with *OET Bulletin 65* and *Supplement B* and links to software that hams can use to evaluate their stations.

IEEE/ANSI standard and recommendations of the National Council for Radiation Protection and Measurement (NCRP). The MPE limits under the regulations are slightly different than the IEEE/ANSI limits. Note that the MPE levels apply to the FCC rules put into effect for radio amateurs on January 1, 1998. These MPE requirements do not reflect and include all the assumptions and exclusions of the IEEE/ANSI standard.

CARDIAC PACEMAKERS AND RF SAFETY

It is a widely held belief that cardiac pacemakers may be adversely affected in their function by exposure to electromagnetic fields. Amateurs with pacemakers may ask whether their operating might endanger themselves or visitors to their shacks who have a pacemaker. Because of this, and similar concerns regarding other sources of electromagnetic fields, pacemaker manufacturers apply design methods that for the most part shield the pacemaker circuitry from even relatively high EM field strengths.

It is recommended that any amateur who has a pacemaker, or is being considered for one, discuss this matter with his or her physician. The physician will probably put the amateur into contact with the technical representative of the pacemaker manufacturer. These representatives are generally excellent resources, and may have data from laboratory or "in the field" studies with specific model pacemakers.

One study examined the function of a modern (dual chamber) pacemaker in and around an Amateur Radio station. The pacemaker generator has circuits that receive and process electrical signals produced by the heart, and also generate electrical signals that stimulate (pace) the heart. In one series of experiments, the pacemaker was connected to a heart simulator. The system was placed on top of the cabinet of a 1-kW HF linear amplifier during SSB and CW operation. In another test, the system was placed in close proximity to several 1 to 5-W 2-meter hand-held transceivers. The test pacemaker was connected to the heart simulator in a third test, and then placed on the ground 9 meters below and 5 meters in front of a three-element Yagi HF antenna. No interference with pacemaker function was observed in these experiments.

Although the possibility of interference cannot be entirely ruled out by these few observations, these tests represent more severe exposure to EM fields than would ordinarily be encountered by an amateur—with an average amount of common sense. Of course prudence dictates that amateurs with pacemakers, who use hand-held VHF transceivers, keep the antenna as far as possible from the site of the implanted pacemaker generator. They also should use the lowest trans-mitter output required for adequate communication. For high power HF transmission, the antenna should be as far as possible from the operating position, and all equipment should be properly grounded.

LOW-FREQUENCY FIELDS

Although the FCC doesn't regulate 60-Hz fields, some recent concern about EMR has focused on low-frequency energy rather than RF. Amateur Radio equipment can be a significant source of low-frequency magnetic fields, although there are many other sources of this kind of energy in the typical home. Magnetic fields can be measured relatively accurately with inexpensive 60-Hz meters that are made by several manufacturers.

Table 11.4 shows typical magnetic field intensities of Amateur Radio equipment and various household items. Because these fields dissipate rapidly with distance, "prudent avoidance" would mean staying perhaps 12 to 18 inches away from most Amateur Radio equipment (and 24 inches from power supplies with 1-kW RF amplifiers).

DETERMINING RF POWER DENSITY

Unfortunately, determining the power density of the RF fields generated by an amateur station is not as simple as measuring low-frequency magnetic fields. Although sophisticated instruments can be used to measure RF power densities quite accurately, they are costly and require fre-

---

Table 11.4

Typical RF Field Strengths Near Amateur Radio Antennas

A sampling of values as measured by the Federal Communications Commission and Environmental Protection Agency, 1990

Antenna Type	Freq (MHz)	Power (W)	E Field (V/m)	Location
Dipole in attic	14.15	100	7-100	In home
Discone in attic	146.5	250	10-27	In home
Half sloper	21.5	1000	50	1 m from base
Dipole at 7-13 ft	7.14	120	8-150	1-2 m from earth
Vertical	3.8	800	180	0.5 m from base
5-element Yagi at 60 ft	21.2	1000	10-20	In shack
			14	12 m from base
3-element Yagi at 25 ft	28.5	425	8-12	12 m from base
Inverted V at 22-46 ft	7.23	1400	5-27	Below antenna
Vertical on roof	14.11	140	6-9	In house
			35-100	At antenna tuner
Whip on auto roof	146.5	100	22-75	2 m from antenna
			15-30	In vehicle
			90	Rear seat
5-element Yagi at 20 ft	50.1	500	37-50	10 m from antenna

quent recalibration. Most amateurs don't have access to such equipment, and the inexpensive field-strength meters that we do have are not suitable for measuring RF power density.

Table 11.4 shows a sampling of measurements made at Amateur Radio stations by the Federal Communications Commission and the Environmental Protection Agency in 1990. As this table indicates, a good antenna well removed from inhabited areas poses no hazard under any of the IEEE/ANSI guidelines. However, the FCC/EPA survey also indicates that amateurs must be careful about using indoor or attic-mounted antennas, mobile antennas, low directional arrays or any other antenna that is close to inhabited areas, especially when moderate to high power is used.

Ideally, before using any antenna that is in close proximity to an inhabited area, you should measure the RF power density. If that is not feasible, the next best option is make the installation as safe as possible by observing the safety suggestions listed in Table 11.5.

It also is possible, of course, to calculate the probable power density near an antenna using simple equations. Such calculations have many pitfalls. For one, most of the situations where the power density would be high enough to be of concern are in the near field. In the near field, ground interactions and other variables produce power densities that cannot be determined by simple arithmetic. In the far field, conditions become easier to predict with simple calculations.

The boundary between the near field and the far field depends on the wavelength of the transmitted signal and the physical size and configuration of the antenna. The boundary between the near field and the far field of an antenna can be as much as several wavelengths from the antenna.

Computer antenna-modeling programs are another approach you can use. *MINI-NEC* or other codes derived from *NEC* (Numerical Electromagnetics Code) are suitable for estimating RF magnetic and electric fields around amateur antenna systems.

These models have limitations. Ground interactions must be considered in estimating near-field power densities, and the "correct ground" must be modeled. Computer modeling is generally not sophisticated enough to predict "hot spots" in the near field—places where the field intensity may be far higher than would be expected, due to reflections from nearby objects. In addition, "nearby objects" often change or vary with weather or the season, so the model so laboriously crafted may not be representative of the actual situation, by the time it is running on the computer.

Intensely elevated but localized fields often can be detected by professional measuring instruments. These "hot spots" are often found near wiring in the shack, and metal objects such as antenna masts or equipment cabinets. But even with the best instrumentation, these measurements also may be misleading in the near field.

One need not make precise measurements or model the exact antenna system, however, to develop some idea of the relative fields around an antenna. Computer modeling using close approximations of the geometry and power input of

Table 11.5
RF Awareness Guidelines

These guidelines were developed by the ARRL RF Safety Committee, based on the FCC/EPA measurements of Table 11.4 and other data.

- Although antennas on towers (well away from people) pose no exposure problem, make certain that the RF radiation is confined to the antennas' radiating elements themselves. Provide a single, good station ground (earth), and eliminate radiation from transmission lines. Use good coaxial cable or other feed line properly. Avoid serious imbalance in your antenna system and feed line. For high-powered installations, avoid end-fed antennas that come directly into the transmitter area near the operator.
- No person should ever be near any transmitting antenna while it is in use. This is especially true for mobile or ground-mounted vertical antennas. Avoid transmitting with more than 25 W in a VHF mobile installation unless it is possible to first measure the RF fields inside the vehicle. At the 1-kW level, both HF and VHF directional antennas should be at least 35 ft above inhabited areas. Avoid using indoor and attic-mounted antennas if at all possible. If open-wire feeders are used, ensure that it is not possible for people (or animals) to come into accidental contact with the feed line.
- Don't operate high-power amplifiers with the covers removed, especially at VHF/UHF.
- In the UHF/SHF region, never look into the open end of an activated length of waveguide or microwave feed-horn antenna or point it toward anyone. (If you do, you may be exposing your eyes to more than the maximum permissible exposure level of RF radiation.) Never point a high-gain, narrow-beamwidth antenna (a paraboloid, for instance) toward people. Use caution in aiming an EME (moonbounce) array toward the horizon; EME arrays may deliver an effective radiated power of 250,000 W or more.
- With hand-held transceivers, keep the antenna away from your head and use the lowest power possible to maintain communications. Use a separate microphone and hold the rig as far away from you as possible. This will reduce your exposure to the RF energy.
- Don't work on antennas that have RF power applied.
- Don't stand or sit close to a power supply or linear amplifier when the ac power is turned on. Stay at least 24 inches away from power transformers, electrical fans and other sources of high-level 60-Hz magnetic fields.

the antenna will generally suffice. Those who are familiar with *MININEC* can estimate their power densities by computer modeling, and those who have access to professional power-density meters can make useful measurements.

While our primary concern is ordinarily the intensity of the signal radiated by an antenna, we also should remember that there are other potential energy sources to be considered. You also can be exposed to RF radiation directly from a power amplifier if it is operated without proper shielding. Transmission lines also may radiate a significant amount of energy under some conditions. Poor microwave waveguide joints or improperly assembled connectors are another source of incidental radiation.

FURTHER RF EXPOSURE SUGGESTIONS

Potential exposure situations should be taken seriously. Based on the FCC/EPA measurements and other data, the "RF awareness" guidelines of Table 11.5 were developed by the ARRL RF Safety Committee. A longer version of these guidelines, along with a complete list of references, appeared in a *QST* article by Ivan Shulman, MD, WC2S ("Is Amateur Radio Hazardous to Our Health?" *QST*, Oct 1989, pp 31-34).

In addition, the ARRL has published a book, *RF Exposure and You*, that is helping hams comply with the FCC's RF-exposure regulations. The ARRL also maintains an RF-exposure news page on its Web site. See **http://www.arrl.org/news/rfsafety**. This site contains reprints of selected *QST* articles on RF exposure and links to the FCC and other useful sites.

Transmitting Equipment

Amateurs use several methods for obtaining CW/SSB RF power at 146, 435 and 1269 MHz. The deluxe approach is to purchase a multimode-mode transceiver for the desired uplink frequency. Output powers are generally in the range 10 to 40 W.

Other approaches to producing an uplink signal include modifying FM equipment (commercial, amateur or military surplus), using a transverter in conjunction with an existing lower frequency transmitter, exciting a varactor multiplier with an appropriate source, etc. Power amplifiers are often used to boost the output power of these devices.

Transverter. A transmit converter works very much like a receive converter. Two RF sources are injected into a mixer that produces sum and difference frequencies. One source is a CW/SSB transmitter and the other a fixed frequency local oscillator. See Figure 11.18 for an example of a unit designed to generate a 435 MHz CW/SSB signal using a 28-30 MHz transmitter and a 407 MHz fixed frequency oscillator. Almost all commercial transmit converters use a mixer that operates at very low (fraction of a watt) power levels. A unit will generally include one or more stages of linear amplification to bring the output signal up to the 0.5 to 10 watt range.

Adding a receive converter to a transmit converter takes a minimal number of parts since the local oscillator signal is already available. A combined transmit/receive converter sharing a common local oscillator is often called a *transverter*. Many amateurs use the term transverter to refer to a transmit converter. When the distinction is important (as when you're purchasing one), however, make sure you know how the term is being used. Transverters designed for 146 and 435 MHz usually employ a 28-30 MHz IF. Units for 1269 MHz generally are designed to operate with a 146 MHz IF to minimize the need for filtering image and local oscillator frequencies from the output.

High-level mixing can also be used in a transmit converter. This is not a very efficient approach if one is designing a unit from scratch but it does lead to a relatively simple method for converting older tube type high band

commercial FM (420 or 460 MHz) transmitter strips to CW/SSB transverters for 435 MHz. With 20 W of drive from an HF transmitter, such a transverter will provide about 10 W output.

The conversion of an FM unit to a transmit converter can be accomplished by modifying the final amplifier to act as a mixer. A typical final amplifier circuit is shown in Figure 11.19. Injecting the 28 MHz signal into the cathode is usually the simplest approach. Figure 11.19 suggests two possible circuits for accomplishing this. If the cathode is initially grounded try (A). (B) can be used if the unmodified transmitter includes R_0 and L_0 in the cathode circuit. The tank circuit L1, C1 is resonant at 10 meters. The RFC prevents C_0 from detuning the tank circuit. It should have a broad peak at 10 meters (about 15 μH).

Before any modifications are attempted, the FM strip should be tuned up and checked out at either 465 or 407 MHz. (If these frequencies are out of the tuning range you can select frequencies that require 21 MHz drive from the HF transmitter.) Once everything is working correctly modify the 5894 cathode circuit, activate the transverter and the HF transmitter (use CW), and retune the output circuit to 435 MHz. Switch the HF transmitter to SSB and adjust the drive level for the cleanest sounding signal. Since the 5894 output tank circuit provides only minimal attenuation at the image and local oscillator frequencies you should include additional filtering before the antenna.

Varactor Multiplier. A power varactor is a type of semiconductor diode whose properties make it an efficient frequency multiplier in the 1 to 100 watt range. Although varactors can be used as doublers, triplers, quintuplers and higher-order multipliers, their most common application is tripling. Amateurs have used them to triple from 145 MHz to 435 MHz and from 420 MHz to 1260 MHz. The efficiency (output RF power × 100% / input RF power) is generally in the 50% to 60% range. A varactor multiplier does *not* require any dc power for operation so it's possible to mount one remotely at the antenna. One serious limitation of varactor multipliers is that they produce severe distortion and spurious signals if used on SSB. Therefore they're

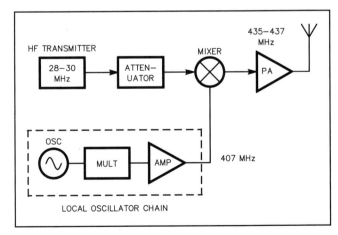

Figure 11.18—Block diagram of typical 10 meter to 70 cm transmit converter.

suitable only for CW. In recent years varactor multipliers have not been very popular. But situations may arise where their unique features make them an appropriate choice for producing an uplink signal. For example, a relatively inexpensive way of generating a 1269 MHz CW signal is to use a varactor tripler in conjunction with the transmitter strip from a commercial 420 MHz FM transceiver. At least one manufacturer, Microwave Modules, has produced units for 145/435 MHz and 420/1260 MHz in the recent past.

The remarkable efficiencies exhibited by varactor multipliers are the result of an interesting design concept. The

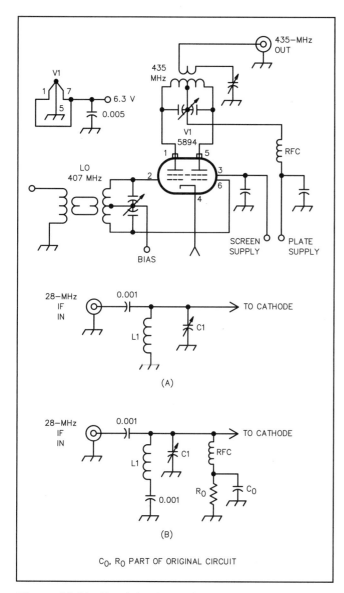

Figure 11.19—Partial schematic of a 70-cm mixer, built from a converted FM transmitter. The original oscillator-multiplier-driver stages of the unit now provide LO injection. A filter should be used at the output of the mixer to prevent radiation of spurious products. See R. Stevenson, *QST*, Hints and Kinks, Mar 1976, p 40; and R. Stevenson, "SSB on Mode B, Using Modified FM Equipment," *AMSAT Newsletter*, Dec 1975, p 10. Reference: See *The 1990 ARRL Handbook*, p 11-7.

tripler, for example, can be thought of as simultaneously operating as a doubler and a high-level mixer. The mixer combines the fundamental frequency and the doubled frequency to produce a signal at 3× the input frequency. Table 11.6 contains an extensive list of articles on varactor operation and construction.

Converting Commercial FM or Military Surplus Equipment. Old tube-type commercial FM gear designed for the land mobile service (130 to 160 MHz and 420 to 460 MHz) is widely available at modest cost at hamfests. Amateurs have successfully converted FM transmitter strips into CW transmitters, transmit converters for CW/SSB operation, and linear amplifiers for 146 and 435 MHz. (The receiver front ends can also be modified to make excellent receiver converters). Conversion may involve: (1) constructing an appropriate ac power supply, (2) retuning resonant circuits and cavities to the correct frequencies, (3) adding provisions for keying (producing a stable, chirp-free signal at 435 MHz can be challenging) and (4) changing power amplifier biasing to AB1 or AB2 linear operation. Transmitter strips that are rated at 15 to 60 W output in commercial service can safely provide 50% more power for amateur operation. A crystal-controlled 435 MHz transmitter can usually be pulled enough to give a 75-kHz tuning range. An annotated list of conversion articles is contained in Table 11.7.

In recent years the military surplus market has been a very minor source for equipment. The technically astute amateur with access to a nearby surplus dealer warehouse will sometimes come across a desirable piece of equipment, but gear is generally not available in the quantities needed to stimulate the dissemination of conversion information. One desirable piece of gear that is at times available on the surplus market is the AN/UPX-6, which can be turned into a linear amplifier that will provide about 50 W output at 1269 MHz when driven with a few watts. For information on the AN/UPX-6, see the article by R. Stein referenced in Table 11.6.

Modifying Amateur 2-Meter FM Transceiver. This approach to producing an uplink signal will mainly appeal to beginners who are interested in gaining temporary access to Mode A. Most amateur 2-meter FM transceivers can be modified easily for CW operation on the Mode A uplink frequencies currently used by the RS satellites. Modification may be as simple as tuning to the correct frequency, removing the mike element and keying the push-to-talk switch. Of course, it's far better to change the push-to-talk circuitry so the unit can be left in transmit while only the driver and final amplifier are keyed. Amateur FM equipment produced in the mid '70s is often available at very low cost at hamfests. If the price is right it may pay to cannibalize a rig to acquire a 10 W CW transmitter for Mode A. The receiver front end can often be put to use as a converter for listening to Mode B.

Construction of Transmitting Equipment from Scratch. Collecting components, building and debugging equipment can involve a relatively large amount of time and expense. However, the educational rewards and the intrinsic satisfaction derived by constructing one's own equip-

Table 11.6
Varactor Multipliers

H. H. Cross, "Frequency Multiplication with Power Varactors at U.H.F.,"*QST*, Oct 1962, pp 60-62. This pioneering article describes a 144/432-MHz tripler that uses conventional inductors. The unit yields 40% efficiency at 20 W input with a Microwave Associates MA-4060A diode. The article gives lots of good practical advice.

D. Blakeslee, "Practical Tripler Circuits," (*QST*, Mar 1966, pp 14-19. Contains a practical tripler that incorporates a strip-line output filter. The unit yields 60% efficiency, at 20 W input with an Amperex H4A (1N4885) diode. The basic design was reprinted in several editions of *The Radio Amateur's Handbook* in the late '60s and early '70s.

D. DeMaw, "Varactor Diodes in Theory and Practice," *QST*, Mar 1966, pp 11-14. Contains a thorough and understandable discussion of basic varactor doubler and tripler design considerations.

The Radio Amateur's VHF Manual, ARRL, 3rd edition, 1972. 144/432 tripler using H4A, pp 289-290; 432/1296 tripler using MA4062D, pp 292-293 (out of print).

D. S. Evans and G. R. Jessop, *VHF-UHF Manual*, 3rd edition, RSGB, London, 1976 (available from ARRL). Contains general information (pp 5.20-5.21), a 145/435-MHz tripler (pp 5.21- 5.23) that uses 1N4387 (40 W in/25 W out) or BAY 96 (15 W in/9 W out) and a 384/1152-MHz tripler (pp 5.70-5.71) using BXY 35A (30 W in).

FM and Repeaters, 2nd edition, ARRL, 1978. Contains a practical design for a 145/435-MHz tripler that uses an H4A (pp 49-50). (Out of print.)

D. R. Pacholok, "Microwave-Frequency Converter for UHF Counters," *Ham Radio*, Jul 1980, pp 40-47. Describes how transistor collector-base junction can be used as varactor. As a result, a bipolar transistor can be used simultaneously to amplify at the input frequency and multiply using efficient varactor effect.

Complete triplers for 145/435 MHz and 420/1260 MHz are available from Microwave Modules at several power levels.

Note: In most cases, the varactors specified are interchangeable as long as power dissipation is taken into account. A summary of the varactors used in various amateur construction projects and the maximum RF power input follows

Device	Max recommended Input Power	Manufacturer
MA-4060A	20 watts	Microwave Associates
H4A (1N4885)	20 watts	Amperex
BAY 66	12 watts	Mullard
BAY 96	40 watts	Mullard
1N4387	40 watts	Motorola
BXY35A	30 watts	Mullard
MA4062D		Microwave Associates

Table 11.7
Sources of Information on Converting Commercial FM Transmitting Equipment for Satellite Ground Station Use

FM and Repeaters, 2nd edition, ARRL, Newington, 1978. The chapter on surplus FM equipment contains a great deal of useful general information. (Out of print.)

D. P. Clement, "Using the Motorola TU-110 Series Transmitters on 420 MHz," *QST*, Sep 1971, pp 39-41, 45. Contains detailed information on converting the TU-110 to a 20-W-output CW transmitter. Treats such topics as obtaining a stable, chirp-free signal.

R. McLeod, Jr, "ATV with the Motorola T44 UHF Transmitter," Part I, *QST*, Dec 1972, pp 28-32, Part II, *QST*, Feb 1973, pp 36-43. These articles are very useful to anyone wishing to put the widely available T44 on 435 MHz.

R. Stevenson, "SSB on Mode B, Using Modified FM Equipment," *AMSAT Newsletter*, Dec 1975, p 10. Shows how an RCA CMU-15 designed for 460 MHz can be converted to a 435-MHz transverter. Conversion involves modifying the 5894 power amplifier to operate as a high-level mixer as shown in Figure 9-19. This information was also published in *QST*, Hints & Kinks, Mar 1976, p 40.

W. R. Gabriel, "A 70-cm Linear Amplifier from a Motorola T44," *AMSAT Newsletter*, March 1977, pp 45. Illustrates how the 2C39 output stage of a Motorola T44 can be used as a 435-MHz linear amplifier. Specific power levels aren't given, but the design should provide 6-10 dB of gain at up to 40 W output.

ment continue to appeal to many amateurs. Excellent plans exist for most any piece of equipment required at a ground station. See Table 11.8 for a list.

In 1993, Rick Campbell, KK7B, introduced the R2 receiver incorporating an image rejecting mixer and the T2 transmitter based on the phasing method of SSB genera-tion to the amateur community. Both of these units could be set up from HF to 500 MHz (and with modifications at higher frequencies). They provided excellent performance at modest cost in an easily replicable design. Campbell later published an article demonstrating how no-tune transverter technology could be coupled with the R2/T2

Table 11.8
Articles: Constructing VHF and UHF Transmitting Equipment

(Amplifiers over 100 W are tube designs, others are solid state. All units are linear unless specified otherwise).

General

B. Olson, W3HQT, "RF Hybrid Modules: Building with Bricks," *QEX*, July 1988, pp 13-14.

J. Reisert, W1JR, "VHF/UHF Exciters," *Ham Radio*, April 1984, pp 84-88.

J. Reisert, W1JR, "Medium Power Amplifiers," *Ham Radio*, Aug 1985, pp 39-42, 45-46, 51-54.

145 MHz

D. DeMaw, W1FB, "Some Basics of VHF Design and Layout," *QST*, Aug 1984, pp 18-22. (146 MHz, Class-C, 2 W / 15 W). Feedback, Oct 1984, p 42.

L. Leighton, WB6BPI, "Two-Meter Transverter Using Power FETs," *Ham Radio*, Sep 1976, pp 10-15. (Contains linear amplifier: 2 W/10 W).

B. Lombardi, WB4EHS, "A High-Performance 2-Meter Transverter; *Ham Radio*, July 1989, pp 68-72, 75, 77. (Contains linear amplifier: .25 W / 4 W)

D. Mascaro, WA3JUF "25-Watt Linear Amplifiers for 144 and 220 MHz," *QST*, August 1988, pp 15-21. (2 W / 25 W)

R. S. Stein, W6NBI, "Solid-State Transmitting Converter for 144-MHz SSB," *Ham Radio*, Feb 1974, pp 6-18. (contains 2 linear amplifiers: .5 W / 6 W, 6 W / 30 W)

"A Medium-Power 144-MHz Amplifier," 1989 *ARRL Handbook*, Chapter 31, 39-45. Design by Clarke Greene, W1JX, construction by Mark Wilson, AA2Z. (10 W / 300 W).

"Linear Transverters for 144 and 220 MHz," 1989 *ARRL Handbook*, Chapter 31, 17-29. Design and construction by P. Drexlex, WB3JYO. Includes design for 1 W / 10 W linear amplifier.

435 MHz

J. Buscemi, K2OVS, "A 60-Watt Solid-State UHF Linear Amplifier," *QST*, July 1977, pp 42-45. (Contains two stage amplifier: 2 W / 60 W).

E. Krome, "A High-Performance, Easy-to-Build 432-MHz Transverter - Part 1," *QST*, Aug 1991, pp 19-23, Part 2, *QST*, Sep 1991, pp 18-21. (includes 5 mW / 10 W, linear AB amp)

R. K. Olson, WA7CNP, "100-Watt Solid-State Power Amplifier for 432 MHz," *Ham Radio*, Sept 1975, pp 36-43. (10 W/100 W)

J. C. Reed, W6IOJ, "A UHF Amplifier-from Scratch," *QST*, Aug 1987, pp 24-27. (2 W / 45 W, Class C).

J. C. Reed, W6IOJ, "A Simple 435-MHz Transmitter," *QST*, May 1985, pp 14-18, 45. (15 W, VXO controlled CW transmitter.)

F. Telewski, WA2FSQ, "A Practical Approach to 432-MHz SSB," *Ham Radio*, June 1971, pp 6-21. Contains an extensive review of tube-type mixers and linear amplifiers at all power levels for 432 MHz. Since vacuum tube techniques have remained relatively stagnant over the last two decades the information here is still valuable for anyone working with 6939 mixers and the 2C39 family of amplifiers.

L. Wilson, WB6QXF, "Solid-State Linear Power Amplifier for 432 MHz," *Ham Radio*, Aug 1975, pp 30-35. (1 W/ 10 W)

1.2 GHz

Though most of the units referenced were built for 1296 MHz, they'll work equally well at 1269 MHz.

E. R. Angle, N6CA, "A Quarter Kilowatt 23-cm Amplifier," Part I, *QST*, March 1985, pp 14-20; Part II, *QST*, April 1985, pp 32-37. Reprinted in 1989 *ARRL Handbook*, Chapter 32, pp 41-54.

B. Atkins, KA1GT, "The New Frontier: 1296-MHz Bibliography," *QST*, Aug 1985, p 68.

B. Olson, W3HQT, "Focus on Technology above 50 MHz," *QEX*, June 1987, pp 11-15. 23-cm amplifier, 8 W / 33 W.

R. S. Stein, W6NBI, "Converting Surplus AN/UPX-6 Cavities," *Ham Radio*, March 1981, pp 12-17. Describes a 3-stage amplifier that produces 40-W output for 100-mW drive using 2C39 tubes.

A. Ward, WB5LUA, "1296-MHz Solid-State Power Amplifiers," *QST*, Dec 1985, pp 41-44. (2 units, 1.5 W / 6 W, 5 W / 18 W). Reprinted in 1989 *ARRL Handbook*, Chapter 32, pp 37-40.

"1296- to 144-MHz Transverter," 1989 *ARRL Handbook*, Chapter 32, pp 24-37. Design and construction by A. Ward, WB5LUA. Complete transmit and receive converter. 250 mW transmitter.

"1296-MHz Transverter," 1989 *ARRL Handbook*, Chapter 32, pp 14-23. Design and construction by D. Eckhardt, W6LEV. Complete transmit and receiver converter, 28 MHz IF. 250 mW transmitter.

design to produce high performance microwave SSB/CW transceivers. Figure 11.20 shows a ground station designed around the R2 and T2 units.

Purchasing New or Used Amateur Equipment. Several major Japanese manufacturers supplying the amateur community now offer multimode transceivers for 2 m, 70 cm and 23 cm. Some of these transceivers will operate on 2 or more bands. Earlier, we mentioned that it was extremely important for a CW or SSB ground station to be able to transmit and listen simultaneously so that the downlink can be monitored. Most multiband, multimode transceivers have this capability but it's important to check. A few smaller specialty manufacturers are producing transverters (see Table 11.1).

Solid state power amplifiers that can raise the typical transceiver power output (10 to 30 W) to up to 160 W are widely available. If you plan to operate SSB you'll need an amplifier that operates in a linear mode. Many older models were designed for Class C operation, which is fine for CW or FM, but not for SSB. Some power amplifiers contain a preamp and automatic RF switching. Naturally the cost is higher but this feature can be a great convenience if you're setting up a ground station to operate several satellite modes.

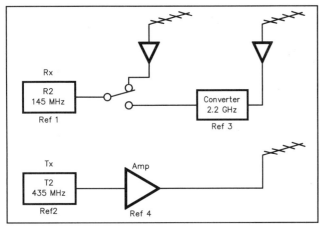

Figure 11.20—High performance, moderate cost ground station for Mode B (70 cm/2 meter) and Mode S (70 cm/13 cm) operation with AMSAT-OSCAR 40.

References
1) 145 MHz Receiver: R. Campbell, "High-Performance, Single-Signal Direct-Conversion Receivers," *QST*, Jan 1993, pp 32-40. Also discussed in "The R2: An Image-Rejecting D-C Receiver," *ARRL Handbook*, 1997, pp 17.72-79.
2) 3 mW 70 cm Transmitter: R. Campbell, "A Multimode Phasing Exciter for 1 to 500 MHz," *QST*, April 1993, pp 27-31; "Single-Conversion Microwave SSB/CW Transceivers," *QST*, May 1993, pp 29-34.
3) 13 cm to 2 meter Receive Converter: J. Davey, "A No-Tune Transverter for the 2304-MHz Band," *QST*, Dec 1992, pp 33-39.
4) 10 W, 30 dB gain, 70 cm transmit linear amplifier: E. Krome, "A High-Performance, Easy-to-Build 432-MHz Transverter—Part 2," *QST*, Sep 1991, pp 18-21.

Several excellent, though long discontinued 2-m transmitters and transverters sometimes appear on the used-equipment market at very reasonable prices. Many of the items use tube technology so replacement parts may be a problem. Some of the older gear is useless but age is not always a reliable indicator of quality. Many old tube-type transmitters (including some designed for AM/CW operation) and transverters are still providing good service. For example the AMECO TX-62 40-W transmitter and gear by Clegg can be used on CW. And transverters by Drake and Collins have a reputation for being reliable. Old receive converters by Parks and Tapetone are often seen going for peanuts at hamfests. With a good preamp these units provide excellent service. Table 11.9 contains a list of *QST* equipment reviews of "old" (and some not so old) equipment that may prove helpful if you're considering purchasing used gear.

TRANSMITTING POWER REQUIREMENTS

It's difficult to specify absolute power requirements for each satellite mode for several reasons. First, a mode may be used on several spacecraft operating at different altitudes. Second, the important parameter is EIRP, not power, so it's important to consider the entire transmitting station including antennas and transmission line losses when selecting an appropriate uplink power. Third, though a given power level may be sufficient 98% of the time there will always be instances where the satellite is just outside your access circle or someone is desensing the spacecraft transponder and a little extra power would be useful. Despite these problems it is possible to suggest power levels that will provide good performance more than 90% of the time when used in conjunction with a typical antenna system. Keep in mind that the levels specified are guidelines taking into account several satellites and may have to be modified to allow for your special needs. Specific EIRP recommendations for each mode aboard each satellite are contained in Appendix C: *Spacecraft Profiles*.

146 MHz. This band is used as an uplink with several low altitude spacecraft. The relevant modes are A, J, and JD. 40 to 80 W to an omnidirectional antenna should provide excellent performance. 20 W to a rotatable 3-el beam set at a fixed elevation angle of 20° will also work well. When transponder loading was light many amateurs have communicated via Mode A using less than a watt to an omnidirectional antenna.

435 MHz. This band is currently used as an uplink for OSCAR 10 and OSCAR 40. A transmitter putting out 40 W in conjunction with an antenna having about 13 dBic gain will produce good downlink signals on OSCAR 10. OSCAR 40 provides a similar downlink signal with about 6 dB less power.

1269 MHz. This band was used as an uplink on OSCAR 13 Mode L. A survey of stations operating Mode L in 1988 showed that the great majority were using from 10 to 40 W with beams averaging 20 dBi gain. Solid state devices are generally used to produce powers up to the 20-30 W level. Above this point cavity amplifiers employing

Table 11.9

QST **Equipment Reviews**

The following product reviews may prove useful if you're considering purchasing used equipment for your satellite ground station. Much of the equipment listed is no longer manufactured.

(*Manufacturer, item, initial page, month, year*)

Advanced Receiver Research: MML 144VDG preamp and TRS04VD TR sequencer, 39, Feb 1987

Ameco: CN-144 2-m converter, 42, Sep 1962

Angle Linear: VHF/UHF preamps, 36, Aug 1978

ARCOS: 432 MHz transmit converter and PA, 40, Aug 1976

Braun: TTV 1270 144/435 MHz varactor tripler and 435/144 MHz receive converter, 52, Jul 1971

Clegg: 22'er CW/am transceiver, 38, Apr 1965; AB-144 HF to 2-m receive converter, 44, Oct 1980
Zeus VHF transmitter, 55, Sep 1961

Collins: 62S-1 VHF converter, 52, Nov 1963

Down East Microwave: 432PA 432-MHz Amplifier Kit, 66, Mar 1993
DEM 432 No-Tune 432-MHz Transverter, 64, Mar 1993
DEM SHF-2400 2.4 GHz Satellite Down-converter, 69, Feb 1994

Drake: VHF converters, 51, Feb 1968

Gonset: Sidewinder 2-m transverter, 64, Mar 1965;
903A and 913A VHF PAs, 74, Aug 1965

Hallicrafters: HA-2 2-m transverter, 43, Sep 1962

Hamtronics: VX-4 70-cm transmit converter, 43, Jan 1982;
XV-2 2-m transmit converter, 46 Feb 1979;
70-cm converter kit, 29, Jul 1978
P8 VHF preamp, 47, May 1977

Heath: VL-1180, 2-m PA, 38, May 1982;
VL-2280 2-m PA, 48, Jun 1982;
SB-500 2-m transverter, 43, Sep 1970

ICOM: IC-275A 2-m multimode transceiver, 32, Oct 1987;
IC-290H 2-m multimode transceiver, 36, May 1983;
IC-471A 70-cm multimode transceiver, 38, Aug 1985;
IC-271A 2-m multimode transceiver, 40, May 1985;
IC-211 2-m multimode transceiver, 30, Dec 1978
IC-820H 2-m/70-cm multimode transceiver, 80, Mar 1995
IC-821H 2-m/70-cm multimode transceiver, 70, Mar 1997

Janel Laboratories: 432CA 70-cm converter, 40, Dec 1975

Johnson: Viking 6N2 transmitter (2 m), 46, Mar 1957;
6N2 Converter, 45, Nov 1959;
6N2 VFO, 43, Oct 1959;
6N2 Thunderbolt PA, 46, Jan 1960

Kenwood: TR-9000 2-m multimode transceiver, 49, Dec 1981;
TS-700A 2-m multimode transceiver, 38 Mar 1976;
TR-751A 2-m multimode transceiver, 41 Mar 1987
TS-700S 2-m multimode transceiver, 31, Feb 1978
TS-790A multimode transceiver, 39, Apr 1991
TM-255A 2-m multimode transceiver, 66, Jun 1995

Klitzing: 70CM10W60 70-cm PA, 38, Jun 1979

KLM: 2M-22C and 435-40 crossed Yagis, 43, Oct 1985
PA 15-80BL 2-m PA, 43, Sep 1979

LMW Electronics: 1296TRV1k 23-cm transverter kit, 39, Dec 1987;
2304TRV2, 13-cm transverter, 37, Dec 1987

Microwave Modules, Ltd: MMt432 70-cm transverter, 43, Sep 1977;
MMv1296 435/1296 MHz varactor tripler, 41, Dec 1977

Mirage Communications: B215 2-m PA, 40, Feb 1985
D1010 70-cm PA, 42, Jan 1984;
B108 2-m PA, 41, May 1979

PacComm PSK-1T Satellite Modem and TNC, 46, Jul 1993

Parks: 144-1 2-m converter, 85, Jul 1964;
432-3 70-cm converter, 44, Oct 1966

RF Concepts: RFC-2-23 2-m PA, 37, Mar 1988;
RFC 2-317 2-m PA, 34, Oct 1987

SSB Electronic: SP-70 Mast-Mount Preamplifier, 63, Mar 1993;
UEK-2000S 2.4 GHz Satellite Down-converter, 69, Feb 1994

Tapetone: 2-m converter, 42, Jul 1957;
TC-432 70-cm converter, 46, Feb 1961

Telco: 125 2-m PA, 40, Mar 1978

Ten-Tec: 2510 70 cm transmitter and 2-m converter, 41, Oct 1985

Trio-Kenwood: see Kenwood

VHF Engineering: BLE 10/40 70-cm PA, 33, Sep 1978

Yaesu: FTV-901R VHF/UHF transverter, 48, Feb 1982
FT-726R VHF/UHF multimode transceiver, 40, May 1984
FT-480R 2-m multimode transceiver, 46, Oct 1981
FT-736R, 30, May 1990

---

the 2C39 tube are popular. The P3D uplink at this frequency should require about 6-8 dB less power.

DIGITAL COMMUNICATIONS

For 9600 baud digital satellite communications a ground station must use an FM transmitter and receiver. To operate the 1200 baud digital PACSATs a ground station needs an FM transmitter and an SSB receiver. Equipment designed for terrestrial FM communications will generally work fine

although minor modifications may be needed for digital operations. Requirements were discussed in Chapter 5.

The modifications basically revolve around the fact that modulation must be applied to the transmitter directly at the frequency determining element (after any audio shaping circuitry) and modulation must be extracted from the receiver directly at the detector (before any audio shaping circuitry). Modifications widening the receiver IF shaping filter are sometimes desirable. And, it's very important

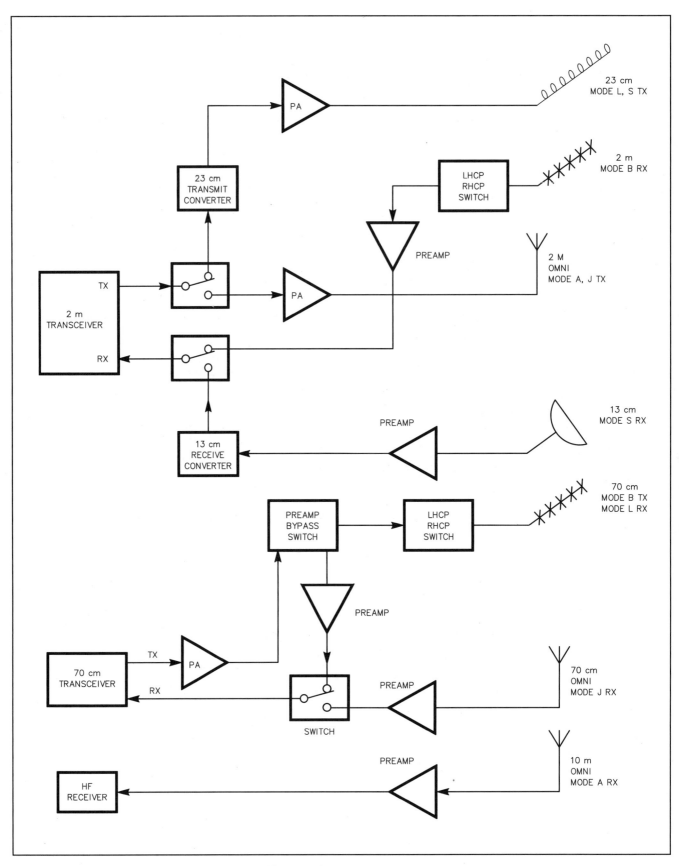

Figure 11.21—Deluxe ground station for multiple modes.

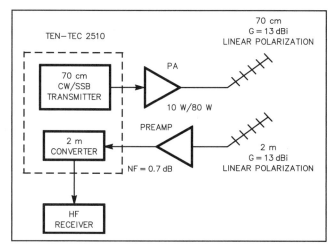

Figure 11.22—Modest Mode B ground station.

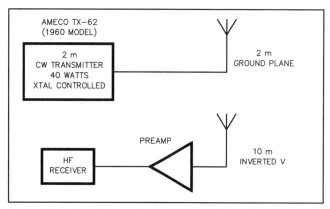

Figure 11.23—Simple Mode A ground station.

that transmit deviation be kept to 3.5 kHz for both 1200 baud and 9600 baud operation.

Although the information presented earlier in this chapter was directed at analog communications modes, comments concerning preamps, receive converters and transmit converters are directly applicable to FM communications links.

OVERALL STATION DESIGN

Figure 11.21 shows a relatively complex satellite ground station designed for analog communications using Modes A, B, J, L and S. Block diagrams of ground stations for digital communications were presented in Chapter 5. Figure 11.22 shows a relatively modest station capable of excellent performance on Mode B. Adding a 2.3 GHz receive converter would enable this station to step up to Mode S operation. A simple beginner's station for Mode A operation is shown in Figure 11.23. It happens to be the station I used back in the early '70s on OSCAR 6. The gear, which still works fine, is put on the air aperiodically for demonstrations.

Satellite Orbits

12 Satellite Orbits

Using the step-by-step techniques of Chapter 7, radio amateurs can track OSCAR spacecraft without needing to know the basic physics of satellite motion or how a satellite moves in space. This chapter is for those amateurs interested in "why" as well as "how." Here we'll examine satellite motion from a more detailed physical/mathematical point of view.

Several of the topics we look at in this chapter are usually found in texts designed for graduate-level scientists and engineers. These texts, rigorous and generalized, are often incomprehensible to readers who don't have an advanced mathematical background. Yet most of the ideas and results can be expressed in terms that someone with a solid background in algebra, plane trigonometry and analytic geometry can understand. We'll keep the mathematics in this chapter as simple as possible, but—face it—mathematics is a key element in understanding satellite motion. Study the solved *Sample Problems* scattered throughout this chapter to see how key formulas are applied. As they also form the basis for later work, the problems may be the most valuable part of the chapter.

At several points we had to raise the mathematical level slightly higher than desired to avoid obscuring potentially useful information. Much of the material in this chapter is not serial in nature, however, so you can skip big chunks and still follow later sections. By now, you should realize that this chapter is not for the faint-hearted. If you elect to plow through, reviewing the tracking material of Chapter 7 before beginning will make the path a little easier. Also note that Table 12.1 summarizes repeatedly used symbols. Good luck!

The objectives of this chapter are:

1) to introduce the satellite-orbit problem (from a scientific point of view);

2) to provide the reader with an overview of satellite motion (including both an understanding of important parameters and an ability to visualize the motion in space and with respect to Earth);

3) to summarize the important equations needed to compute orbital parameters so that these equations will be easily accessible when needed.

BACKGROUND

The satellite-orbit problem (determining the position of a satellite as a function of time and finding its path in space) is essentially the same whether we are studying the motion of the planets around the Sun, the Moon around the Earth, or artificial satellites revolving around either. The similarity arises from the nature of the forces affecting an orbiting body that doesn't have a propulsion system. In the early 17th century Kepler discovered some remarkable properties of planetary motion; they have come to be called *Kepler's Laws*.

I) Each planet moves around the Sun in an ellipse, with the Sun at one focus (motion lies in a plane);

II) The line from the Sun to planet (radius vector, r) sweeps across equal areas in equal intervals of time;

III) The ratio of the square of the period (T) to the cube of the semi-major axis (a) is the same for all planets in our solar system. (T^2/a^3) is constant.

These three properties summarize observations; they say nothing about the forces governing planetary motion. It remained for Newton to deduce the characteristics of the force that would yield Kepler's Laws. The force is the same one that keeps us glued to the surface of the Earth—good old gravity.

Newton showed that Kepler's Second Law would result if the planets were being acted on by an attractive force always directed at a fixed central point: the Sun (central force). To satisfy the First Law, this force would have to vary as the inverse square of the distance between planet and Sun $(1/r^2)$. Finally, if Kepler's Third Law were to hold, the force would have to be proportional to the mass of the planet. Actually, Newton went a lot further. He assumed that not only does the Sun attract the planets in this manner, but that every mass (m_1) attracts every other mass (m_2) with a force directed along the line joining the two masses and having a magnitude (F) given by

$$F = \frac{Gm_1 m_2}{r^2} \quad \text{(Universal Law of Gravitation)} \quad \text{[Eq 12.1]}$$

where G is the Universal Gravitational Constant.

THE GEOMETRY OF THE ELLIPSE

As Kepler noted in his First Law, ellipses take center stage in satellite motion. A brief look at the geometry of the ellipse is therefore in order (see Figure 12.1). The lengths a, b and c shown in Figure 12.1 are not independent. They're related by the formula

Table 12.1

Symbols Used in This Chapter

Note: Abbreviations used only in computer programs are marked (*)

a	— primary: semi-major axis of ellipse (secondary: side of spherical triangle)
A	— angle in spherical triangle
b	— primary: semi-minor axis of ellipse (secondary: side of spherical triangle)
B	— angle in spherical triangle
c	— primary: distance between center of ellipse and focal point (secondary: side of spherical triangle)
C	— angle in spherical triangle
e	— eccentricity of ellipse
E	— eccentric anomaly (angle)
EA	— eccentric anomaly (*)
ETY	— eccentricity (*)
G	— gravitational constant
h	— satellite height above surface of Earth
h_a	— satellite height above surface of Earth at apogee
h_p	— satellite height above surface of Earth at perigee
i	— orbital inclination
$\bar{I}$	— longitude increment (rough estimate)
I	— estimated longitude increment
m	— primary: mass of satellite (secondary: abbreviation for meter)
M	— mass of Earth
MM	— mean motion
m/s	— meters per second
r	— satellite-geocenter distance
r_a	— satellite-geocenter distance at apogee
r_p	— satellite-geocenter distance at perigee
R	— mean radius of Earth = 6371 km satellite-geocenter distance
R_{eq}	— mean equatorial radius of Earth = 6378 km
s	— seconds
SMA	— semi-major axis (of ellipse) (*)
t	— elapsed time since last ascending node (circular orbits) or last perigee (elliptical orbits)
T	— period of satellite
v	— magnitude of satellite velocity with respect to static Earth
w	— argument of perigee
$\dot{w}$	— rate of change of argument of perigee
θ	— polar angle in orbital plane
φ	— latitude
λ	— longitude
Ω	— right ascension of ascending node
$\dot{\Omega}$	— rate of orbital-plane precession about Earth's N-S axis

$$c^2 = a^2 - b^2 \quad \text{or} \quad c = \sqrt{\left(a^2 - b^2\right)} \qquad \text{[Eq 12.2]}$$

Using Eq 12.2, any one of the parameters a, b or c can be computed if the other two are known. In essence, it takes two parameters to completely describe the shape of an ellipse. One could, for example, give the semi-major and semi-minor axes (a and b), the semi-major axis and the distance from the origin to one focus (a and c), or the semi-minor axis and the distance from the origin to one focus (b and c).

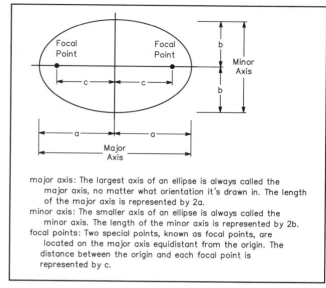

major axis: The largest axis of an ellipse is always called the major axis, no matter what orientation it's drawn in. The length of the major axis is represented by 2a.

minor axis: The smaller axis of an ellipse is always called the minor axis. The length of the minor axis is represented by 2b.

focal points: Two special points, known as focal points, are located on the major axis equidistant from the origin. The distance between the origin and each focal point is represented by c.

Figure 12.1–Geometry of the ellipse.

There's another convenient parameter, called eccentricity (e), for describing an ellipse. Eccentricity may be thought of as a number describing how closely an ellipse resembles a circle. When the eccentricity is 0, we've got a circle. The larger the eccentricity, the more elongated the ellipse becomes. To be more precise, eccentricity is given by

$$e^2 = 1 - (b/a)^2 \quad \text{or} \quad e = \sqrt{1 - (b/a)^2} \qquad \text{[Eq 12.3]}$$

Because of its mathematical definition, e must be a dimensionless number between 0 and +1. Using Eqs 12.2 and 12.3, we can derive another useful relationship:

$$c = ae \qquad \text{[Eq 12.4]}$$

As stated earlier, it always takes two parameters to describe the shape of an ellipse. Any two of the four parameters, a, b, c or e, will suffice.

Figure 12.2 shows the elliptical path of a typical Earth satellite. Since the Earth is located at a focal point of the ellipse (Kepler's Law 1), it is convenient to introduce two additional parameters that relate to our Earth-bound vantage point: the distances between the center of the Earth and the "high" and "low" points on the orbit. Figure 12.2 summarizes several useful relations and definitions. Note especially

apogee distance: $r_a = a(1 + e)$ [Eq 12.5a]

perigee distance: $r_p = a(1 - e)$ [Eq 12.5b]

We now have six parameters, a, b, c, e, r_a and r_p, any two of which can be used to describe an ellipse. With the information we've learned so far, many practical satellite problems can be solved. (See Sample Problem 12.1.)

When the major and minor axes of an ellipse are equal, the ellipse becomes a circle. From Eq 12.2 we see that setting a = b gives c = 0. This means that in a circle, both focal points coalesce at the center. Setting a = b in Eq 12.3 yields e = 0, as we stated earlier.

Since the circular orbit is just a special case of the elliptical orbit, the most general approach to the satellite orbit problem would be to begin by studying elliptical orbits. Circular orbits, however, are often simpler to work with, so we'll look at them separately whenever it makes our work easier.

Our approach to the satellite-orbit problem involves first determining the path of the satellite in space and then looking at the path the sub-satellite point traces on the surface of the Earth. Each of these steps is, in turn, broken down into several smaller steps.

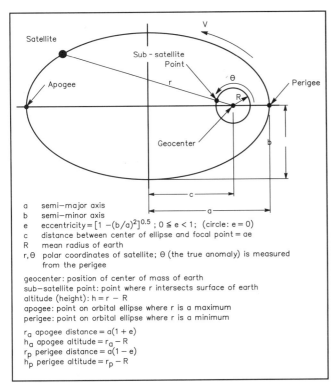

a   semi-major axis
b   semi-minor axis
e   eccentricity = $[1 - (b/a)^2]^{0.5}$; $0 \leq e < 1$; (circle: e = 0)
c   distance between center of ellipse and focal point = ae
R   mean radius of earth
r,θ polar coordinates of satellite; θ (the true anomaly) is measured from the perigee

geocenter: position of center of mass of earth
sub-satellite point: point where r intersects surface of earth
altitude (height): h = r − R
apogee: point on orbital ellipse where r is a maximum
perigee: point on orbital ellipse where r is a minimum

r_a apogee distance = a(1 + e)
h_a apogee altitude = r_a − R
r_p perigee distance = a(1 − e)
h_p perigee altitude = r_p − R

Figure 12.2—Geometry of the orbital ellipse for an Earth satellite.

Sample Problem 12.1

AMSAT-OSCAR 10 has an apogee distance (r_a) of 6.57R and a perigee distance (r_p) of 1.62R. Specify the orbit in terms of the semi-major axis (a) and eccentricity (e). (**Note**: In studying Earth satellites, distances are sometimes expressed in terms of R, the mean radius of the Earth).

Solution

(Given r_a and r_p, solve for a and e)
Subtracting Eq 12.5b from Eq 12.5a we obtain:

$$r_a - r_p = 2ae \quad \text{or} \quad e = \frac{r_a - r_p}{2a}$$

Adding Eq 12.5a to Eq 12.5b gives

$$r_a + r_p = 2a; \quad a = 4.10R$$

$$\text{so,} \quad e = \frac{r_a - r_p}{r_a + r_p} = \frac{6.75R - 1.62R}{6.75R + 1.62R} = 0.604$$

SATELLITE PATH IN SPACE

The motion of an object results from the forces acting on it. To determine the path of a satellite in space, we will (1) make a number of simplifying assumptions about the forces on the satellite and other aspects of the problem, taking care to keep the most important determinants of the motion intact; (2) solve the simplified model; and then (3) add corrections to our solution, accounting for the initial simplifications.

Simplifying Assumptions

We begin by listing the assumptions usually employed to simplify the problem of determining satellite motion in the orbital plane.

1) The Earth is considered stationary and a coordinate system is chosen with its origin at the Earth's center of mass (geocenter).

2) The Earth and satellite are assumed to be spherically symmetric. This enables us to represent each one by a point mass concentrated at its center (M for the Earth, m for the satellite).

3) The satellite is subject to only one force, an attractive one directed at the geocenter; the magnitude of the force varies as the inverse of the square of the distance separating satellite and geocenter ($1/r^2$).

The model just outlined is known as the two-body problem, a detailed solution for which is given in most introductory physics texts.[1,2] Some of the important results follow.

Solution to the Two-Body Problem

Initial Conditions. Certain initial conditions (the velocity and position of the satellite at the instant the propulsion system is turned off) produce elliptical orbits ($0 \leq e < 1$). Other initial conditions produce hyperbolic (e > 1) or parabolic (e = 1) orbits, which we will not discuss.

The Circle. For a certain subset of the set of initial conditions resulting in elliptical orbits, the ellipse degenerates (simplifies) into a circle (e = 0).

Satellite Plane. The orbit of a satellite lies in a plane that always contains the geocenter. The orientation of this plane remains fixed in space (with respect to the fixed stars) after being determined by the initial conditions.

Period and Semi-major Axis. The period (T) of a satellite and the semi-major axis (a) of its orbit are related by the equation

$$T^2 = \frac{4\pi^2}{GM} a^3 \qquad \text{[Eq 12.6a]}$$

where M is the mass of the Earth and G is the Universal Gravitational Constant. For computations involving a satellite in Earth orbit, the following equations may be used (T in minutes, a in kilometers).

$$T = 165.87 \times 10^{-6} \times a^{3/2} \qquad \text{[Eq 12.6b]}$$

$$a = 331.25 \times T^{2/3} \qquad \text{[Eq 12.6c]}$$

Note that the period of an artificial satellite that is orbiting the Earth depends only on the semi-major axis of its orbit. For a circular orbit, a is equal to r, the constant satellite geocenter distance. Sample Problems 12.2 and 12.3 show how Eq 12.6 is used.

A graph of period vs height for low-altitude spacecraft in circular orbits is shown in Figure 12.3. In Figure 12.4 we plot period vs semi-major axis. Both of these plots were obtained from Eq 12.6b. The *mean motion*, MM, was defined in Chapter 7 as the number of revolutions (perigee to perigee) completed by a satellite in a solar day (1440 minutes). A satellite's mean motion is related to its period by Eq 12.7. (MM in revolutions per solar day, T in minutes.)

$$MM = 1440/T \qquad \text{[Eq 12.7]}$$

Since many sources of orbital elements provide the mean motion, it is often necessary to compute period and semi-major axis from it. A short BASIC program that does this is shown in Table 12.2.

Velocity. The magnitude of a satellite's total velocity (v) generally varies along the orbit. It's given by

$$v^2 = GM\left(\frac{2}{r} - \frac{1}{a}\right) = 3.986 \times 10^{14}\left(\frac{2}{r} - \frac{1}{a}\right) \qquad \text{[Eq 12.8]}$$

where r is the satellite-geocenter distance, r and a are in meters, and v is in meters/sec (see Figure 12.2). Note that for a given orbit, G, M and a are constants, so that v depends only on r. Eq 12.8 can therefore be used to compute the velocity at any point along the orbit if r is known. The range of velocities is bounded: The maximum velocity occurs at perigee and the minimum velocity occurs at apogee. The direction of motion is always tangent to the orbital ellipse. For a circular orbit r = a and Eq 12.8 simplifies to (r in meters, v in m/s)

Sample Problem 12.2

Given that RS-10/11 is in a circular orbit at a height of 1003 km, find its period.

Solution

Eq 12.6b provides the period when the semi-major axis is known. To obtain the orbital radius (geocenter-satellite distance) we have to add the radius of the Earth to RS10/11's altitude: r = 6371 + 1003 = 7374 km. Plugging this value into Eq 12.6b yields a period of 105.0 minutes:

$$T = 165.87 \times 10^{-6} \times (7374)^{3/2} = 105.0 \text{ minutes.}$$

Sample Problem 12.3

Shortly after launch, OSCAR 13's orbit was characterized by an apogee height (h_a) of 36,265 km and a perigee height (h_p) of 2545 km. What was its period?

Solution

R = radius of Earth = 6371 km

r_a = 36,265 + 6371 = 42,636 km

r_p = 2545 + 6371 = 8916 km

2a = r_a + r_p (see Sample Problem 12.1)

2a = 51,552 km; a = 25,776 km

Applying Eq 12.6b we obtain

$$T = 165.87 \times 10^{-6} \times (25,776)^{3/2} = 686.4 \text{ minutes}$$
$$= 11 \text{ hours } 26.4 \text{ minutes}$$

$$v^2 = \frac{GM}{r} = \left(3.986 \times 10^{14}\right)\left(\frac{1}{r}\right)$$

Note that for circular orbits, v is constant. Sample Problems 12.4 and 12.5 illustrate the use of Eq 12.8.

Position. Figure 12.2 shows how the satellite position is specified by the polar coordinates r and θ. Note that θ is measured counterclockwise from perigee. Often, it's necessary to know r and θ as a function of the elapsed time, t, since the satellite passed perigee (or some other reference point when a circle is being considered).

For a satellite in a circular orbit moving at constant speed:

$$\theta\,[\text{in degrees}] = \frac{t}{T}(360°) \quad \text{or}$$

$$\theta\,[\text{in radians}] = 2\pi \frac{t}{T} \qquad \text{[Eq 12.9]}$$

and the radius is fixed.

The elliptical-orbit problem is considerably more involved. We know (Eq 12.8) that the satellite moves much more rapidly near perigee. The relation between t and g can be derived from Kepler's Law II. For details of the derivation, see Notes 3, 4, 5 and 6.

In an elliptical orbit, time from perigee, t, is given by

$$t = \frac{T}{2\pi}[E - e \sin E] \qquad \text{[Eq 12.10]}$$

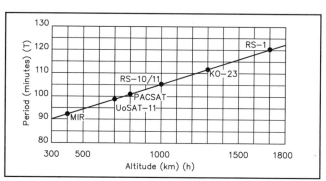

Figure 12.3—Period vs altitude for satellites in low-altitude circular orbits.

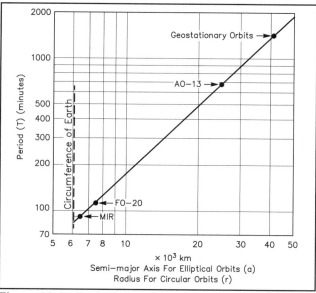

Figure 12.4—Period vs semi-major axis.

where the angle E, known as the eccentric anomaly, is defined by the associated equation

$$E = 2 \arctan\left[\left(\frac{1-e}{1+e}\right)^{0.5} \tan\frac{\theta}{2}\right] + 360°\,n \qquad \text{[Eq 12.11]}$$

$$n = \begin{cases} 0 \text{ when } -180° \leq \theta \leq 180° \\ 1 \text{ when } 180° < \theta \leq 540° \end{cases}$$

Eq 12.11 may also appear in several alternate forms:

$$E = \arcsin\left[\frac{\left(1-e^2\right)^{0.5} \sin\theta}{1+e\cos\theta}\right] \quad \text{or}$$

$$E = \arccos\left[\frac{e+\cos\theta}{1+e\cos\theta}\right]$$

Note that here, "anomaly" just means angle. Eqs 12.10 and 12.11, taken together, are commonly referred to as Kepler's Equation. Figure 12.5 shows the position of a satellite in an elliptical orbit (similar to those used for Phase 3 spacecraft) as a function of time. It should give Kepler's Equation some physical meaning.

There are two common mistakes that people frequently make the first time they try to solve Eqs 12.10 and 12.11. Eq 12.10 contains the first pitfall. Since the expression e sin E is a unitless number, the E term standing by itself inside the brackets *must* be given in *radians*. The second pitfall is encountered when working with the various forms of Eq 12.11. Although all inverse trigonometric functions are multi-valued, computers and hand calculators are pro-grammed to give only principal values. For example, if sin θ = 0.99, then θ may equal 82° or 98° (or either of these two values ± any integer multiple of 360°), but a calculator only lights up 82°. If the physical situation requires a value outside the principal range, appropriate adjustments must be made. Eq 12.11 already includes the adjustments needed so it can be used for values of θ in the range −180° to +540°. If the alternate forms of Eq 12.11 are used, it's up to you to select the appropriate range. A few hints may help: (1) E/2 and θ/2 must always be in the same quadrant; (2) as θ increases, E must increase; (3) adjustments to the alternate

Table12.2

Program to Calculate Period and Semi-major Axis from Mean Motion
Language: BASIC

```
100  ' Program to calculate period and semimajor
110  '    axis, SMA, from mean motion, MM
120 INPUT "mean motion (rev/day) = ? ", MM
130 PERIOD = 1440/MM          ' See Eq. 12.7
140 PRINT "Period (minutes) ="; PERIOD
150 SMA = 331.25 * PERIOD^(2/3)   ' See Eq. 12.6c
160 PRINT "semimajor axis (km) ="; SMA
170 END
```

Sample Problem 12.4

A satellite is in a circular orbit at a height of 2545 km. What is its velocity?

Solution

In a circular orbit we can use the simplified form of Eq 12.8.

$$v^2 = \frac{GM}{r} = \left(3.986 \times 10^{14}\right)(1/r)$$

$$r = 2545\,\text{km} + 6371\,\text{km} = 8.916 \times 10^6\,\text{m}$$

$$v^2 = \frac{3.986 \times 10^{14}}{8.916 \times 10^6} = 0.4471 \times 10^8\,(\text{m/s})^2$$

$$v = 0.6686 \times 10^4 = 6686\,\text{m/s}$$

Sample Problem 12.5

Shortly after launch, OSCAR 13 had an apogee height (h_a) of 36,265 km and a perigee height (h_p) of 2545 km. What was its velocity at apogee? At perigee? Compare the perigee velocity of OSCAR 13 (h_p=2545 km) to that of a satellite in a circular orbit at a height of 2545 km.

Solution

(See Sample Problem 12.3)

a = 25,776 km
r_a = 42,636 km
r_p = 8916 km

Use Eq 12.8: $v^2 = 3.986 \times 10^{14}\left(\frac{2}{r} - \frac{1}{a}\right)$

At Apogee

$$v^2 = 3.986 \times 10^{14}\left(\frac{2}{42,636,000} - \frac{1}{25,776,000}\right)$$

$$= 3.2338 \times 10^6\,(\text{m/s})^2$$

$$v = 1798\,(\text{m/s})$$

At Perigee

$$v^2 = 3.986 \times 10^{14}\left(\frac{2}{8,916,000} - \frac{1}{25,776,000}\right)$$

$$= 73.948 \times 10^6\,(\text{m/s})^2$$

$$v = 8599\,\text{m/s}$$

At perigee, OSCAR 13 is moving about 28% faster. Doppler shift (see Chapter 8) on OSCAR 13 near perigee is therefore about 28% greater.

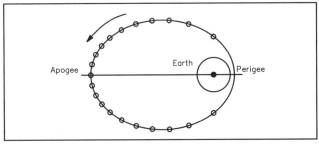

Figure 12.5—This orbital plane diagram shows the position of a satellite in a 12-hour elliptical orbit at half-hour intervals. Note that near apogee the satellite moves relatively slowly.

forms of Eq 12.11 occur when the term in brackets passes through ±1.

We now have a procedure for finding t when θ is known: Plug θ into Eq 12.11 to compute E, then plug E into Eq 12.10 to obtain t. The reverse procedure, finding θ when t is known, is more complex. The key step is solving Eq 12.10 for E when t is known. Unfortunately, there isn't any way to neatly express E in terms of t. We can, however, find the value of E corresponding to any value of t by drawing a graph of t vs θ, then reading it "backwards," or by using an iterative approach. An iterative technique is just a systematic way of guessing an answer for E, computing the resulting t to determine how close it is to the desired value, then using the information to make a better guess for E. Although this procedure may sound involved, it's actually simple. The iterative technique usually employed to solve Kepler's Equation is known as the Newton-Raphson method. A BASIC language subroutine that calculates θ when t is known is shown in Table 12.3. Most modern introductory calculus texts explain how the Newton-Raphson method is used.

We now turn to r, the satellite-to-geocenter distance. Rather than attempt to express r as a function of t, it's simpler and often more useful just to note the relation between r and θ.

$$r = \frac{a(1-e^2)}{1+e\cos\theta}$$ [Eq 12.12]

Now try Sample Problem 12.6.

Corrections to the Simplified Model

Now that we've looked at the solutions to the two-body problem (the simplified satellite-orbit model), let's examine how a more detailed analysis would modify our results.

1) In the two-body problem, the stationary point is the center of mass of the system, not the geocenter. The mass of the Earth is so much greater than the mass of an artificial satellite that this correction is negligible.

2) Treating the Earth as a point mass implicitly assumes that the shape and the distribution of mass in the earth are spherically symmetrical. Taking into account the actual asymmetry of the Earth (most notably the bulge at the equator) produces additional central force terms acting on the satellite. These forces vary as higher orders of l/r (for example, $1/r^3$, $1/r^4$, and so on). They cause (i) the major axis of the orbital ellipse to rotate slowly in the plane of the satellite and (ii) the plane of the satellite to rotate about the Earth's N-S axis. Both of these effects are observed readily,

---

Table 12.3

Program to Calculate True Anomaly and Satellite-Geocenter Distance when Time from Perigee is Given

Illustrates Newton-Raphson method of solving Kepler's Equation.

Language: BASIC

```
100    ' Program to calculate true anomaly (THETA) and satellite-
110    ' geocenter distance (R) for OSCAR 13 when time from perigee
120    ' is given.  For other satellites change lines 150 & 160.
130    ' EA = Eccentric Anomaly: SMA = semimajor axis; ETY = eccentricity
140    PI=3.14159
150    ETY=.6541
160    PERIOD=686.4  ' minutes
170    SMA=331.25*PERIOD^(2/3)                    ' See Eq. 12.6c
180    INPUT "minutes after perigee = ? ", TIME
190    EAINIT = 2*PI*TIME/PERIOD                  ' Initial estimate for EA
200    EA = EAINIT
210    For I = 1 to 20                            ' Loop to improve estimate for EA
220       CORRECTION = (EA-EAINIT-ETY*SIN(EA))/(1-ETY*COS(EA))
230       EA = EA-CORRECTION
240       IF ABS(CORRECTION) < .0001 THEN GOTO 270
250    NEXT I
260    PRINT "Loop did not converge." : STOP
270    PRINT "Iterations = "; I
280    IF ABS(EA-PI) < .0001 THEN THETA = PI : GOTO 310
290    THETA = 2*ATN(SQR((1+ETY)/(1-ETY))*TAN(EA/2)) ' Eq. 12.11 inverted
300    IF THETA < 0 THEN THETA = THETA + 2*PI
310    R = SMA*(1-ETY*ETY)/(1+ETY*COS(THETA))         ' Eq. 12.12
320    PRINT "theta (degrees) ="; THETA*180/PI
330    PRINT "Satellite-geocenter distance (km) ="; R
340    END
```

Sample Problem 12.6

Consider the OSCAR 13 orbit shortly after launch (see Sample Problem 12.3)

r_a = 42,636 km
r_p = 8916 km
a = 25,776 km
T = 686.4 minutes

(a) Compute the satellite altitude (h) when θ = 108°
(b) How long after perigee does this occur?

Solution

(a) *Step 1*: Solve for the eccentricity
(see Sample Problem 12.1)

$$e = \frac{r_a - r_p}{2a} = 0.6541$$

Step 2: Solve for r using Eq 12.12

$$r = \frac{a\left(1 - e^2\right)}{1 + e \cos \theta} = 18,484 \text{ km}$$

$$h = r - R = 18,484 \text{ km} - 6371 \text{ km} = 12,113 \text{ km}$$

(b) *Step 3*: Compute the eccentric anomaly using Eq 12.11

$$E = 2 \arctan\left[\left(\frac{1-e}{1+e}\right)^{0.5} \tan\frac{\theta}{2}\right]$$

$$= 2 \arctan\left[\left(\frac{1-0.6541}{1+0.6541}\right)^{0.5} \tan 54°\right]$$

E = 64.37° = 1.123 radians

Step 4: Compute t from Eq 12.10

$$t = \frac{T}{2\pi}[E - e \sin E]$$

$$= \frac{686.4}{2\pi}\left[1.123 - (0.6541) \sin (64.37°)\right]$$

$$= 58.3 \text{ minutes}$$

and we'll return to them shortly.

3) The satellite is affected by a number of other forces in addition to gravitational attraction by the Earth. For example, such forces as gravitational attraction by the Sun, Moon and other planets; friction from the atmosphere (atmospheric drag); radiation pressure from the Sun, and so on enter into the system. We turn now to the effects of some of these forces.

Atmospheric Drag. At low altitudes the most prominent perturbing force acting on a satellite is drag caused by collisions with atoms and ions in the Earth's atmosphere. Let us consider the effect of drag in two cases: (i) elliptical orbits with high apogee and low perigee and (ii) low-altitude circular orbits. In the elliptical-orbit case, drag acts mainly near perigee, reducing the satellite velocity and causing the altitude at the following apogee to be lowered (perigee altitude initially tends to remain constant). Atmospheric drag therefore tends to reduce the eccentricity of elliptical orbits having a low perigee (makes them more circular) by lowering the apogee.

In the low-altitude circular orbit case, drag is of consequence during the entire orbit. It causes the satellite to spiral in toward the Earth at an ever-*increasing* velocity. This is not a misprint. Contrary to intuition, drag causes the velocity of a satellite to *increase*. As the satellite loses energy through collisions it falls to a lower orbit; Eq 12.8 shows that velocity increases as the height decreases.

A satellite's lifetime in space (before burning up on re-entry) depends on the initial orbit, the geometry and mass of the spacecraft, and the composition of the Earth's ionosphere (which varies a great deal from day to day and year to year). Figure 12.6 provides a very rough estimate of the lifetime in orbit of a satellite similar in geometry and mass to AMSAT-OSCAR 7 or 8 as a function of orbital altitude.[7] As the altitudes of LEO AMSAT-OSCAR communication spacecraft are greater than 800 km, their lifetimes in orbit should not be a serious concern.

Solar activity has a very big effect on the composition of the Earth's atmosphere at altitudes between 300 and 600 km. High solar activity results in increased atmospheric density and greater drag on spacecraft. The effect was clearly visible on OSCAR 9. See Figure 12.7. Early predictions, for a satellite lifetime of three to five years, had to be revised because of the very low level of solar activity recorded during the 1984-87 time period. Reentry occurred in October 1989 with spacecraft electronics subsystems fully functional until the final orbits.

Gravitational Effects. Gravitational attraction by the Sun and Moon can affect the orbit of Earth satellites that have a large (roughly greater than one Earth radii) apogee distance such as those in the Phase 3 series. In many cases these small perturbations (forces) average out to zero over long time periods so their impact is minor. However, in some instances these forces tend to exert their effects during the same part of the orbit for months or even years. In such cases the effects do not average out—they are cumulative. The result, called a resonant perturbation, can produce major changes in an orbit. An effect of this type caused OSCAR 13 to reenter after about 8.5 years in orbit.

In the mid 1980s, when possible orbits for OSCAR 13 were being evaluated, the existing small computers that AMSAT engineers had access to didn't have the power to

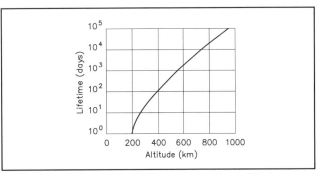

Figure 12.6—Satellite lifetime in circular LEO for spacecraft geometry and mass similar to AMSAT-OSCARs 7 and 8.

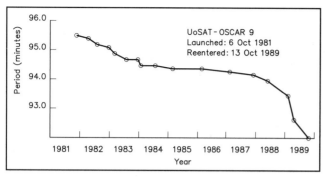

Figure 12.7—The orbital decay of UoSAT-OSCAR 9.

fully investigate the long term effects that slightly different launch times or initial orbits would have on the spacecraft. Today we have access to far more powerful computers and, thanks to the development work of James Miller, G3RUH, and others, the analysis software needed to prevent another OSCAR 13 type scenario. Table 12.4 shows the relative strengths of selected perturbing forces. Now that the motion of the satellite in space has been described, we turn to the problem of relating this motion to an observer on the surface of the Earth.

SATELLITE MOTION VIEWED FROM EARTH

Terrestrial Reference Frame

To describe a satellite's movement as seen by an observer on the Earth, we have to establish a terrestrial reference frame. Once again we simplify the situation by treating the Earth as a sphere. The rotational axis of the Earth (N-S axis) provides a unique line through the geocenter that intersects the surface of the Earth at two points that are designated the *north* (N) and *south* (S) geographic *poles*. The intersection of the surface of the Earth and any plane containing the geocenter is called a *great circle*. The great circle formed from the *equatorial plane*, that plane containing the geocenter that also is perpendicular to the N-S axis, is called the *equator*. The set of great circles formed by planes containing the N-S axis are also of special interest. Each is divided into two *meridians* (half circles), connecting north and south poles.

Table 12.4

The Approximate Magnitudes of Various Forces Acting on Two Identical Satellites

Source of perturbing force	Relative force on satellite at specified height	
	Satellite I (h = 370 km)	Satellite II (h = 37,000 km)
Sun	7×10^{-4}	3×10^{-2}
Moon	4×10^{-6}	1×10^{-4}
Earth's oblateness	1×10^{-3}	4×10^{-6}

$$\text{Relative force} = \frac{\text{Average force exerted by perturbation}}{\text{Force exerted by symmetrical Earth}}$$

Points on the surface of the Earth are specified by two angular coordinates, *latitude* and *longitude*. As an example, the angles used to specify the position of Washington, DC, are shown in Figure 12.8.

Latitude. Given any point on the surface of the Earth, the latitude is determined by (i) drawing a line from the given point to the geocenter, (ii) dropping a perpendicular from the given point to the N-S axis and (iii) measuring the included angle. A more colloquial, but equivalent, definition for latitude is the angle between the line drawn from the given point to the geocenter and the equatorial plane. To prevent ambiguity, an N or S is appended to the latitude to indicate whether the given point lies in the Northern or Southern Hemisphere. The set of all points having a given latitude lies on a plane perpendicular to the N-S axis. Although these latitude curves form circles on the surface of the Earth, most are *not* great circles. The equator (latitude = 0°) is the only one to qualify as a great circle, since the equatorial plane contains the geocenter. The significance of great circles will become apparent later in this chapter when we look at spherical trigonometry. Better models of the Earth take the equatorial bulge and other asymmetries into account when latitude is defined. This leads to a distinction between geodetic, geocentric and astronomical latitude. We won't bother with such refinements.

Longitude. All points on a given meridian are assigned the same longitude. To specify longitude one chooses a reference or "prime" meridian (the original site of the Royal Greenwich Observatory in England is used). The longitude of a given point is then obtained by measuring the angle between the lines joining the geocenter to (i) the point where the equator and prime meridian intersect and (ii) the point where the equator and the meridian containing the given point intersect. For convenience, longitude is given a suffix, E or W, to designate whether one is measuring the angle east or west of the prime meridian.

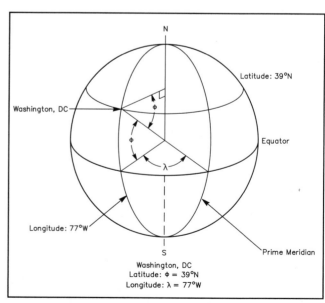

Figure 12.8—The location of Washington, DC, on the Earth can be described by giving its latitude and longitude coordinates.

Inclination

As the Earth rotates about its N-S axis and moves around the Sun, the orientation of both the plane containing the equator (*equatorial plane*) and, to a first approximation, the plane containing the satellite (*orbital plane*) remain fixed in space relative to the fixed stars. Figure 12.9(A) shows how the orbital plane and equatorial plane are related. The line of intersection of the two planes is called the *line of nodes*, since it joins the ascending and descending nodes. The relative orientation of these two planes is very important to satellite users. It is partially specified by giving the inclination. The *inclination*, i, is the angle between the line joining the geocenter and north pole and the line through the geocenter perpendicular to the orbital plane (to avoid ambiguity, the half-line in the direction of advance of a right-hand screw following satellite motion is used). An equivalent definition of the inclination, the angle be-tween the equator and the sub-satellite path on a static (nonrotating) Earth as the satellite enters the Northern Hemisphere, is shown in Figure 12.9(B).

The inclination can vary from 0° to 180°. To first order, none of the perturbations to the simplified model we discussed earlier cause the inclination to change, but higher-order effects result in small oscillations about a mean value. Diagrams of orbits having inclinations of 0°, 90° and 135° are shown in Figure 12.10. A quick analysis of these three cases yields the following information. When the inclination is 0°, the satellite will always be directly above the equator. When the inclination is non-zero the satellite passes over the equator twice each orbit, once heading north and once heading south. When the inclination is 90°, the satellite passes over the north pole and over the south pole during each orbit.

Orbits are sometimes classified as being polar (near polar) when their inclination is 90° (near 90°), or equatorial (near equatorial) when their inclination is 0° (near 0° or 180°). The maximum latitude (ϕ_{max}), north or south, that the sub-satellite point will reach equals (i) the inclination when the inclination is between 0° and 90° or (ii) 180° less the inclination when the inclination is between 90° and 180°. This can be seen from Figure 12.11.

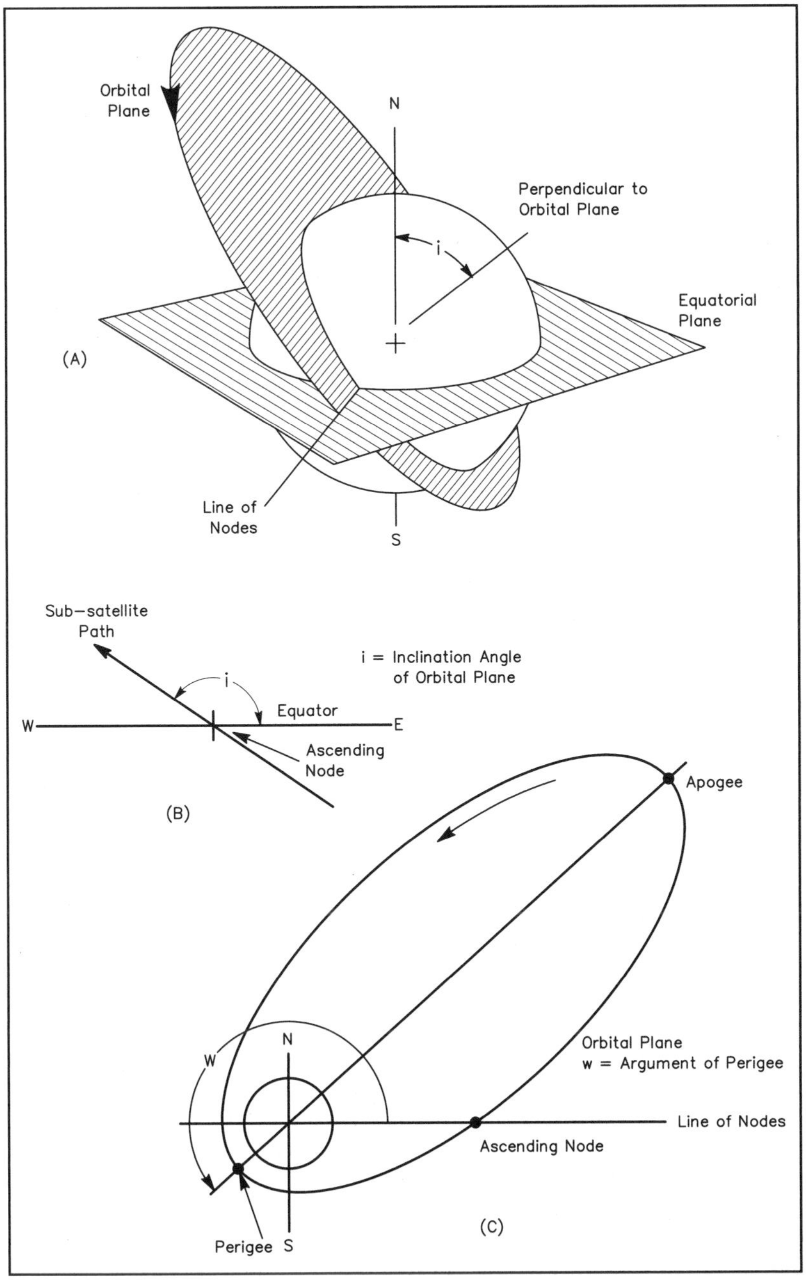

Argument of Perigee

The angle between the line of nodes (the segment joining the geocenter to the ascending node) and the major axis of the ellipse (the segment joining the geocenter and perigee) is known as the argument of perigee. Figure 12.9(C) shows how the argument of perigee serves to locate the perigee in the orbital plane. In the simplified two-body model of satellite motion, the argument of perigee is constant. In reality however, it does vary with time, mainly as a result of the Earth's equatorial bulge. The rate of precession (variation) is given by

$$\dot{w} = 4.97 \left(\frac{R_{eq}}{a} \right)^{3.5} \frac{\left(5\cos^2 i - 1 \right)}{\left(1 - e^2 \right)^2} \qquad \text{[Eq 12.13a]}$$

where
　$\dot{w}$ = rate of change of argument of perigee in degrees per day
　R_{eq} = mean equatorial radius of Earth in same units as a
　a = semi-major axis
　i = inclination
　e = eccentricity

Figure 12.9—The orientation of the orbital plane relative to the equatorial plane is given by i, the inclination angle. The position of the perigee in the orbital plane is given by w, the argument of perigee.

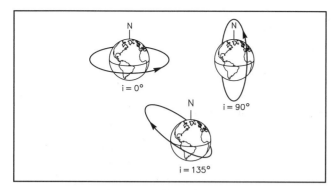

Figure 12.10—Satellite orbits with inclination angles of 0°, 90° and 135°. Orbits with 0<i<90° are called prograde or direct. Orbits with 90°<i≤180° are called retrograde.

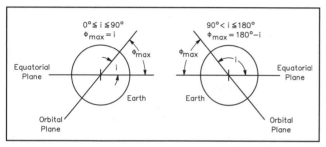

Figure 12.11—The maximum latitude reached by the subsatellite point depends only on the inclination angle of the orbital plane. The cross sections shown in the diagram are edge views of the orbital and equatorial planes.

Sample Problem 12.7

a) Calculate the rate of change of argument of perigee for OSCAR 13 shortly after launch.
b) Given that the argument of perigee was 198.6° on day 40 of 1989, when will the apogee occur at the northernmost point on the orbit? (When will argument of perigee = 270°?)

a = 25,776 km (semi-major axis)
i = 57.37° (inclination)
e = 0.654 (eccentricity)
R_{eq} = 6378 km (equatorial radius of Earth)

Solution

a) Use Eq 12.13a

$$\dot{w} = 4.97 \left(\frac{R_{eq}}{a}\right)^{3.5} \frac{\left(5\cos^2 i - 1\right)}{\left(1 - e^2\right)^2}$$

$$= 0.0519°/\text{day} = 18.953°/\text{year}$$

b) The required change in argument of perigee is
270°−198.6° = 71.4°
This will take 71.4/0.0519 = 1376 days =
  3 years + 280 days
Northernmost apogee will occur 1992 day 320.

Note: The northernmost apogee actually occurred in Nov 1991 due to the resonant behavior of the orbit. This is what caused OSCAR 13 to reenter in late 1996.

Focusing on the $(5\cos^2 i - 1)$ term, we see that no matter what the values of a and e, when $i = 63.4°$ the argument of perigee will be constant. The position of the perigee rotates in the same direction as the satellite when $i < 63.4°$ or $i > 116.6°$, and in the opposite direction when $63.4° < i < 116.6°$.

Let w_o represent the value of w at a specific time. Future values of w can be obtained from

$$w(t) = w_o + \dot{w}t \qquad \text{[Eq 12.13b]}$$

where t is the elapsed time in days.

In Sample Problem 12.7 we calculate the rate of change of argument of perigee for OSCAR 13. The daily rate of change of the argument of perigee as a function of inclination angle for a typical Phase 3 orbit (h_a = 35,800 km, h_p = 1500 km) is shown in Figure 12.12.

Nodal vs Anomalistic Period

Once we've seen how the earth's Equatorial bulge affects the argument of perigee, we have to introduce a new term, *nodal period*, to refer to the elapsed time as a satellite travels from one ascending node to the next. The period that we've been referring to up to this point in this chapter is the *anomalistic period* (elapsed time from perigee to perigee). The adjectives "nodal" and "anomalistic" are often omitted in technical literature and conversation when the meaning is clear from the context. For example, when we discussed the various graphic tracking devices back in Chapter 7, the term period referred to nodal period since we considered an orbit to begin at one ascending node and end at the next. In the equations in this chapter, we'll be explicit when we refer to nodal period. The term period by itself will refer to anomalistic period.

The numerical differences between anomalistic period and nodal period are generally quite small. However, if one is making long-term predictions using the wrong period, the error is cumulative. After a few weeks, the predictions

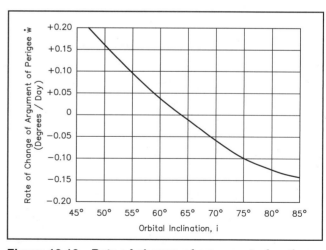

Figure 12.12—Rate of change of argument of perigee vs orbital inclination for Phase 3-type elliptical orbit (h_a =35,800 km, h_p =1500 km). See Eq 12.13. When $\dot{w}$ is positive, the argument of perigee rotates in the same direction as the satellite. When $\dot{w}$ is negative, the argument of perigee rotates in the opposite direction.

will be useless. As a result, it's sometimes necessary to calculate nodal period from the information distributed with classical orbital elements which refers to anomalistic period. An example showing how this is done can be found in Sample Problem 12.8.

Solar and Sidereal Time

Living on earth we quite naturally keep time by the sun. So when we say the earth undergoes one complete rotation about its N-S axis each day, we're actually referring to a mean solar day, which is arbitrarily divided into exactly 24 hours (1440 minutes). Figure 12.13 illustrates how a solar day can be measured. The time interval known as the *solar day* begins at A, when the Sun passes our meridian, and ends at C, when the Sun next passes our meridian. Note that, because of its motion about the Sun, the Earth rotates slightly more than 360° during the solar day. The number is calculated in Sample Problem 12.9. The time for the Earth to rotate exactly 360° is known as the *sidereal day*. When the word "day" is used by itself, solar day is meant. For example, orbital elements distributed by NASA give the units for mean motion as revolutions/day. The day referred to is the solar day of 1440 minutes.

Precession: Circular Orbits

Figure 12.14 shows a satellite whose orbital plane is fixed in space as the Earth moves about the Sun. In the illustration, the satellite closely follows the terminator

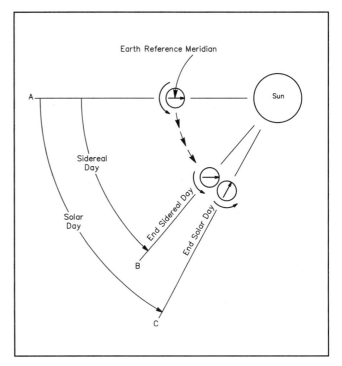

Figure 12.13—The figure shows the relation between the solar day and the sidereal day from the vantage point of an observer on the North Star. The measured day begins at A as the reference meridian aligns with the Sun. The sidereal day ends at B when the reference meridian rotates 360°. The solar day ends at C when the reference meridian again aligns with the Sun. (Not to scale.)

Sample Problem 12.8

Calculate the nodal period for RS-10/11 given the following classical orbital elements and constants.

MM = 13.71883140 (mean motion)
i = 82.9265° (inclination)
e = 0.0010301 (eccentricity)
R_{eq} = 6378 km (equatorial radius of Earth)

Solution

First calculate the anomalistic period using Eq 12.7
Anomalistic period = 1440/MM = 104.9652086 minutes
Next calculate the semi-major axis using Eq 12.6c
SMA = 331.25 × (anomalistic period)$^{2/3}$ = 7370.88 km
Now calculate the rate of change of argument of perigee using Eq 12.13a

$$\dot{w} = 4.97 \left(\frac{R_{eq}}{a}\right)^{3.5} \frac{\left(5\cos^2 i - 1\right)}{\left(1 - e^2\right)^2}$$

$$\dot{w} = -2.76816° \, / \, day$$

Divide this by the mean motion to obtain the total precession during one orbit = −0.201778°
The negative sign means the rotation is opposite to that of the satellite. During one anomalistic period the satellite will therefore rotate 360 − 0.201778 = 359.798°.
The following proportion yields the nodal period

$$\frac{359.798°}{104.965 \, \text{min}} = \frac{360°}{\text{nodal period}}$$

Nodal period = 105.024 minutes

Sample Problem 12.9

(a) How many degrees does the Earth rotate in one solar day?
(b) How many minutes are there in a sidereal day?

Solution

The difference between the solar day and sidereal day occurs because of the Earth's rotation about the Sun. To an observer off in space viewing a scene like that in Figure 12.13, the yearly circuit about the Sun is equivalent to adding 360° of extra axial rotation to the Earth each year. Since there are approximately 365.25 days per year, the Earth's movement about the Sun adds

$$\frac{360°}{365.25 \, \text{days}} = 0.98563° / day$$

to the Earth's axial rotation. The Earth therefore rotates 360.98563°/day on the average. To find the number of minutes in a sidereal day, we set up a proportion

$$\frac{\text{number of minutes in sidereal day}}{360°} = \frac{\text{number of minutes in solar day}}{360.98563°}$$

Solving, we obtain approximately 1436.07 minutes for the sidereal day.

(day-night line) in summer. As a result, passes accessible to a ground station will be centered near 6 AM and 6 PM each day. Three months later, the satellite passes over the center of the day and night regions. Accessible passes now occur near 3 AM and 3 PM each day.

Although the two-body model predicts that the orbital plane will remain stationary, we've already noted that when the Earth's equatorial bulge is taken into account, the plane precesses about the Earth's N-S axis. Figure 12.15 shows an example of such precession. For circular orbits the precession is given by

$$\dot{\Omega} = -9.95 \left(\frac{R_{eq}}{r} \right)^{3.5} \cos i \qquad \text{[Eq 12.14]}$$

(circular Earth orbits only)

where
$\dot{\Omega}$ = orbital plane precession rate in °/day. A positive precession is shown in Figure 12.15 (counterclockwise as seen from the North Star).
R_{eq} = mean equatorial radius of Earth = 6378 km
r = satellite-geocenter distance in same units as R_{eq}
i = orbital inclination

Sun Synchronous Orbits

By choosing the altitude and inclination of a satellite, we can vary $\dot{\Omega}$ over a considerable range of values. Looking at the example of Figure 12.15, you may have noted that the orbital plane precessed exactly 360° in one year. As a result, the satellite followed the terminator the entire time. An orbit that precesses very nearly 360° per year is called Sun-synchronous. Such orbits pass over the same part of the Earth at roughly the same time each day, making communication and various forms of data collection con-

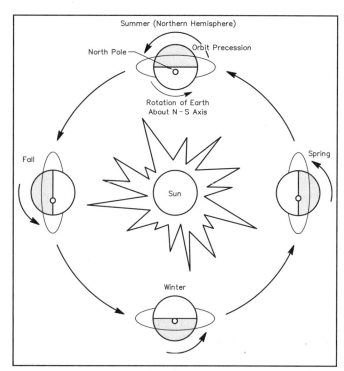

Figure 12.15—Sun-synchronous orbit like the one chosen for OSCARs 6-9, 11 and 14-19. The view of the Sun-Earth satellite system is from the North Star. Note how the orbital precession can keep the satellite near the twilight line year-round when total precession for a year is 360°.

venient. They can also provide nearly continuous sunlight for solar cells or good Sun angles for satellite photos. Because of all these factors, orbits are often carefully designed to be Sun-synchronous.

To obtain an orbital precession of 360° per year, we need a precession rate of 0.986°/day (360°/365.25 days). Substituting this value in Eq 12.14 and solving for i we obtain

$$i* = \arccos \left[-(0.09910) \left(\frac{r}{6378} \right)^{3.5} \right] \qquad \text{[Eq 12.15]}$$

where i* is the inclination needed to produce a Sun-synchronous circular orbit. In this form, we can plug in values of r and calculate the inclination which will produce a Sun-synchronous orbit. Graphing Eq 12.15 (Figure 12.16), we see that for low-altitude satellites Sun-synchronous orbits will be near polar. You may have noted that the 0.986°/day precession rate needed to produce a Sun-synchronous orbit exactly corresponds to the amount in excess of 360° that the Earth rotates each solar day (Sample Problem 12.9). This is no accident; the precession rate was chosen precisely for this purpose.

Precession: Elliptical Orbits

The precession of the orbital plane about the Earth's N-S axis for elliptical orbits is given by

$$\dot{\Omega} = -9.95 \left(\frac{R_{eq}}{a} \right)^{3.5} \frac{\cos(i)}{\left(1-e^2\right)^2} \qquad \text{[Eq 12.16]}$$

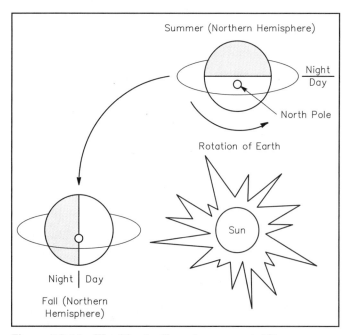

Figure 12.14—The illustration shows a satellite whose orbital plane is fixed in space. The view is that of an observer looking down from the North Star.

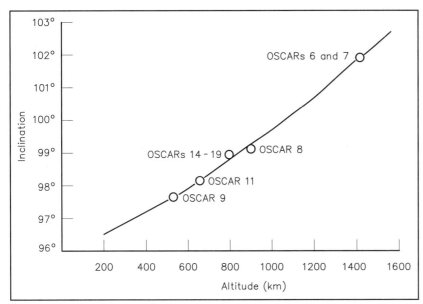

Figure 12.16—This graph shows the inclination value that results in a Sun-synchronous circular orbit.

$$\bar{I} = (T/1440)\,(-360.98563°E) \quad [\text{Eq } 12.18a]$$

$$\bar{I} = -(0.250684°E)\,T \quad [\text{Eq } 12.18b]$$

The period, T, must be in minutes; the negative sign means that each succeeding node is further west; and 360.98563° is the angular rotation of the Earth about its axis during a solar day (1440 minutes) From Eq 12.18b we see that it's easy to get a quick estimate of I by computing T/4 and expressing the result in degrees west per revolution.

The value for the orbital increment provided by Eq 12.18 can be improved by taking into account the fact that the precession of the orbital plane (Eq 12.14 or Eq 12.16) will affect the apparent rotation of the Earth during one solar day. The result is given in Eq 12.19.

$$\bar{I} = (T/1440)(-360.98563 + \dot{\Omega}) \quad [\text{Eq } 12.19]$$

Sample Problem 12.10 illustrates how calculations involving the longitude increment proceed.

Once the increment is known we can compute the longitude of any ascending node, λ_m, given the longitude of any other ascending node, λ_n. The orbit reference integers, m and n, may either be the standard ones beginning with the first orbit after launch, or any other convenient serial set.

$$\lambda_m = \lambda_n + (m - n)\,I \quad [\text{Eq } 12.20]$$

This formula works either forward or backward in time. When future orbits are being predicted, m > n. The right side of Eq 12.20 must be brought into the range of 0-360° by successive subtractions or additions of 360° if necessary (see Sample Problem 12.11).

GROUND TRACK

To study the ground track, we have to (1) look at the geometry involved when the orbital plane intersects the surface of the Earth, (2) consider the motion of the satellite about its orbit and (3) take into account the rotation of the Earth. The best way to handle complex problems of this type is to use mathematical objects known as vectors. All advanced texts in orbital mechanics proceed in this manner. However, many simple problems can be treated using spherical trigonometry. If you have a reasonable background in plane trigonometry, a brief introduction to spherical trigonometry will provide you with all the information needed to understand how the ground-track equations are derived. Since many more readers have experience with trigonometry than with vectors, we'll use the spherical trigonometry approach.

A barebones introduction to spherical trigonometry follows. The results for circular orbits are then generalized and summarized. (Readers who just need access to the ground-track equations for programming a computer can skip the spherical trigonometry and derivation sections and jump right to the summary.) We then go on to derive and summarize the ground-track equations for elliptical orbits.

If a = r and e = 0 (that is, when the ellipse becomes a circle), Eq 12.16 simplifies to Eq 12.14.

Longitude Increment

We now know how the satellite moves in the orbital plane and how the orientation of the orbital plane changes with time. Our next objective is to relate this information to the longitude increment. The *longitude increment* (I), or simply increment, is defined as the change in longitude between two successive ascending nodes. In mathematical terms

$$I = \lambda_{n+1} - \lambda_n \quad [\text{Eq } 12.17]$$

where λ_{n+1} is the longitude at any ascending node in degrees east of Greenwich [°E], λ_n is the longitude at the preceding ascending node in °E, and I is in degrees east per revolution [°E/rev].

In Chapter 7 we saw that the increment is an important parameter to those working with the OSCARLOCATOR and similar tracking aids. There are two ways to obtain the increment: experimentally by averaging observations over a long period of time, or theoretically by calculating it from a model. Though the best numbers are obtained experimentally, the calculation approach is needed; we, after all, want a value for I before a spacecraft is launched, and in the early weeks or months of its stay in orbit when observations haven't accumulated over a long time period.

The computations that follow will use the sign convention specified with Eq 12.16. However, when convenient, the final result may be expressed in degrees west by simply changing the sign.

If we neglect precession of the orbital plane, the increment can be estimated by computing how much the Earth rotates during the time it takes for the satellite to complete one revolution from ascending node to ascending node. (In this section, period refers to nodal period.)

Sample Problem 12.10

About four weeks after the launch of the Soviet RS-1, observations had yielded the nodal period to six significant digits, T = 120.389 minutes, and had confirmed the TASS and NASA reports that gave i as 82.6° (i is not very critical in $\dot{\Omega}$ computations). Using this data, compute the longitudinal increment.

Solution

Step 1. Compute r from the period using Eq 12.6c.

$$r = 331.25 \times T^{2/3} = 8076 \text{ km}$$

Step 2. Calculate $\dot{\Omega}$ using Eq 12.14.

$$\dot{\Omega} = -9.95 \left(\frac{6378}{8076}\right)^{3.5} \cos(82.6) = -0.5610°\text{E/day}$$

Step 3. Calculate I from Eq 12.19

$$I = \frac{120.389}{1440}(-360.9856 - 0.5610)$$
$$= -30.227°\text{E / rev}$$
$$= 30.227°\text{W / rev}$$

Note: Observations of RS-1 over several months yielded the same value for I.

Sample Problem 12.11

A satellite we're interested in has an increment of I = −28.75°E/rev. If the longitude of the ascending node on orbit number 1256 is 237°E, find the longitude of the ascending node on (a) the next orbit and (b) orbit number 1337.

Solution

(a) For the next orbit (number 1257)

$$\lambda_{1257} = \lambda_{1256} + (1257 - 1256)\ I \qquad \text{[see Eq 12.20]}$$

$$= 237°\text{E} + (1 \text{ rev}) (-28.75°\text{E/rev})$$

$$= 208.25°\text{E}$$

$$\lambda_{1257} = 360 - 208.25 = 151.75°\text{W}$$

(b) For orbit number 1337

$$\lambda_{1337} = \lambda_{1256} + (1337 - 1256)\ I$$

$$= 237°\text{E} + (81 \text{ rev}) (-28.75°\text{E /rev})$$

$$= -2091.7°\text{E}$$

Add 360° to this value six times to put λ_{1337} in the correct range.

$$\lambda_{1337} = 68.25°\text{E}$$

$$\lambda_{1337} = 360 - 68.25 = 291.75°\text{W}$$

This section on spherical trigonometry will also be referred to in the next chapter when we discuss terrestrial distance, bearing and "spiderwebs."

Spherical Trigonometry Basics

A triangle drawn on the surface of a sphere is called a spherical triangle *only* if all three sides are arcs of great circles. A great circle is formed *only* when a plane containing the center of a sphere intersects the surface. The Earth's equator is a great circle; other latitude lines are not. The intersection of a satellite's orbital plane and the surface of a static (nonrotating) Earth is a great circle. Range circles drawn around a ground station are not great circles.

Spherical trigonometry is the study of the relations between sides and angles in spherical triangles. The notation of spherical trigonometry closely follows that of plane trigonometry. Surface angles and vertices in a triangle are labeled with capital letters A, B and C, and the side opposite each angle is labeled with the corresponding lower-case letter, as shown in Figure 12.17. Note that the arc length of each side is proportional to the central angle formed by joining its end points to the center of the sphere. For example, side b is proportional to angle AOC. The proportionality constant is the radius of the sphere, but because it cancels out in the computations we'll be interested in, the length of a side will often be referred to by its angular measure.

The rules governing the relationships between sides and angles in spherical triangles differ from those in plane triangles. In spherical trigonometry, the internal angles in a triangle do not usually add up to 180° and the square of the hypotenuse does *not* generally equal the sum of the squares of the other two sides in a right triangle.

A spherical triangle that has at least one 90° angle is called a right spherical triangle (see Figure 12.17).

Recall how in plane trigonometry the rules for right triangles were simpler than those for oblique triangles. In spherical trigonometry the situation is similar: The rules for right spherical triangles are simpler than those for general spherical triangles. Fortunately, since the spherical triangles we'll be working with have at least one right angle, we need only consider the laws for right spherical triangles. A convenient method for summarizing these rules, developed by Napier, is shown in Figure 12.18. Sample Problem 12.12 illustrates how Napier's Rules can be applied.

Two major pitfalls await newcomers attempting to apply spherical trigonometry for the first time. The first pitfall, the degree-radian trap, comes from overlooking the fact that angles must be expressed in units appropriate to a given equation *and* a given computing machine. For example, focus on the angle θ = 30° = π/6 radians. Consider the machine-dependent aspect first. To evaluate sin(θ) on most simple scientific calculators, you must input "30" since the calculator expects θ to be in degrees unless you've been instructed otherwise. To evaluate sin(θ) in BASIC on a computer, you must input π/6 (or 0.52360), because the BASIC language expects θ to be in radians. In some situations, especially in cases where θ is *not* the argument of a

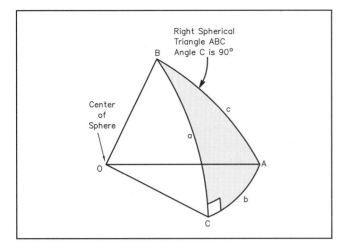

Figure 12.17—Right spherical triangle ABC lies on the surface of a sphere. The three sides are formed from segments of great circles.

trigonometric function, the form of the equation determines whether θ must be in degrees or radians. Consider a radio station at 30° N latitude trying to use the equation S = Rθ to find the surface distance (S) along a meridian (Earth radius = R) to the equator. The equation only holds for θ in radians, so the input must be π/6.

The second trap awaiting spherical trigonometry novices is using a latitude line as one side of a spherical triangle. The only latitude line that will serve in this manner is the equator. All other latitude lines do not work, since they are not arcs of great circles.

Circular Orbits: Derivation

The most important step in deriving the ground-track equations for circular orbits is drawing a clear picture. In

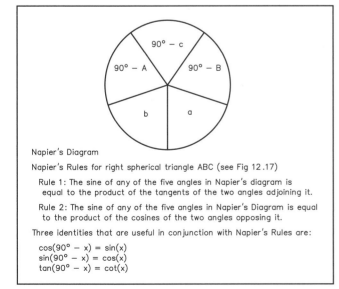

Napier's Diagram

Napier's Rules for right spherical triangle ABC (see Fig 12.17)

Rule 1: The sine of any of the five angles in Napier's diagram is equal to the product of the tangents of the two angles adjoining it.

Rule 2: The sine of any of the five angles in Napier's Diagram is equal to the product of the cosines of the two angles opposing it.

Three identities that are useful in conjunction with Napier's Rules are:

$\cos(90° - x) = \sin(x)$
$\sin(90° - x) = \cos(x)$
$\tan(90° - x) = \cot(x)$

Figure 12.18—Napier's Rules and this diagram provide an easy way to remember and apply the rules for right spherical triangles.

Sample Problem 12.12

Given a right spherical triangle like the one in Figure 12.16, assume that A and c are known. (a) First solve for a in terms of A and c. (b) Then solve for b in terms of a and c.

Solution

(a) To find a, apply Napier Rule II to the indicated segment of the Napier diagram

$\sin(a) = \cos(90°-c) \cos(90°-A)$

Using the identity for $\cos(90°-x)$

$\sin(a) = \sin(c) \sin(A)$

$a = \arcsin[\sin(c) \sin(A)]$

(b) To find b apply Napier Rule II again, this time to the segment shown

$\sin(90°-c) = \cos(a) \cos(b)$

Using the identify for $\sin(90°-c)$

$\cos(c) = \cos(a) \cos(b)$

$\cos(b) = \dfrac{\cos(c)}{\cos(a)}$

$b = \arccos\left[\dfrac{\cos(c)}{\cos(a)}\right]$

Figure 12.19 we've chosen to show i between 90° and 180° and a satellite headed north in the Northern Hemisphere. Our object is to compute the latitude and longitude of the subsatellite point (SSP)—ϕ_s and λ_s —when the spacecraft reaches S, t minutes after the most recent ascending node. We assume that the period T, orbit inclination i, and the longitude of the ascending node, λ_o, are known.

Since arc AS, along the actual ground track, is not a section of a great circle, we first consider the situation for a static Earth (one not rotating about its N-S axis). On such an Earth, the SSP would be at point B at t minutes after the ascending node. Triangle ABC is a right spherical triangle. Angle A is given by 180° – i. Arc AB (side c of the spherical triangle) is a section of the circular orbit with

$$c = 2\pi \frac{t}{T} \qquad \text{[see Eq 12.9]}$$

By definition, the latitude of point B is equal to a.

The problem of finding the latitude of point B, ϕ_B, in terms of i, t and T is identical to the problem of finding a in terms of A and c. This was solved in Sample Problem 12.12 where we found that

$a = \arcsin[\sin(c) \sin(A)]$

Substituting the variables ϕ_B, T, i and t we obtain

$$\phi_B = \arcsin\left[\sin\left(2\pi \frac{t}{T}\right)\sin(180° - i)\right]$$

Using the symmetry of the sine function, this simplifies to

$$\phi_B = \arcsin\left[\sin\left(2\pi \frac{t}{T}\right)\sin(i)\right] \qquad \text{(nonrotating Earth)}$$

If for computations we wish to specify c in degrees, we would replace

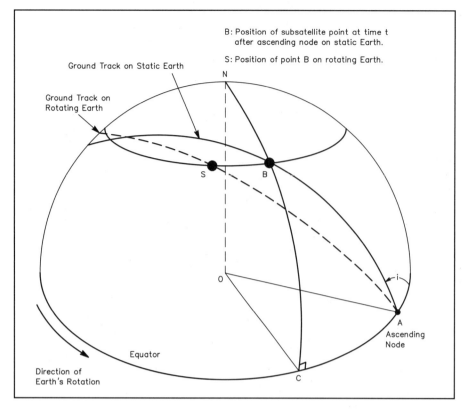

B: Position of subsatellite point at time t after ascending node on static Earth.

S: Position of point B on rotating Earth.

Figure 12.19—Illustration for applying the principles of spherical trigonometry to the circular-orbit ground track problem.

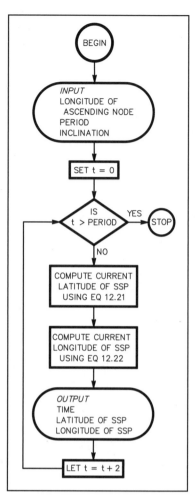

Figure 12.20—Flow chart for circular-orbit ground-track program.

$2\pi \dfrac{t}{T}$ by $360° \dfrac{t}{T}$

To solve for the longitude at B, λ_B, we note that $b = \lambda_o - \lambda_B$. So, our problem of solving for λ_B in terms of ϕ_B, t and T is equivalent to solving for b in terms of a and c. This was also done in Sample Problem 12.12 where we found that

$$b = \arccos\left[\frac{\cos(c)}{\cos(a)}\right]$$

Making the appropriate substitutions, this yields

$$\lambda_o - \lambda_B = \arccos\left[\frac{\cos(2\pi t / T)}{\cos(\phi_B)}\right]$$

(nonrotating Earth)

The effect of the Earth's rotation is to move the SSP from B to S. The latitude remains constant ($\phi_s = \phi_B$); only the longitude changes. The longitude change is simply the angular rotation of the Earth during the time t. To a first approximation, the rotation rate of the Earth is 0.25°/ minute, so if we measure t in minutes, $\lambda_s = \lambda_B - t/4$. For long-term predictions a more accurate figure for the Earth's rotation should be used (as we saw when the longitude increment was discussed). This value is 0.25068°/minute. (See Eq 12.18b.)

This completes the derivation for the case illustrated. A more complete derivation would consider several additional cases: satellites in the southern hemisphere, inclination be-

tween 0° and 90°, spacecraft headed south, and so on. As the approach is similar, we'll just summarize the results in the next section.

Circular Orbits: Summary

Latitude of SSP:

$$\phi(t) = \arcsin[\sin(i)\sin(360° t / T)] \qquad \text{[Eq 12.21]}$$

Note: "$\phi(t)$" should be read "latitude as a function of time"; it does *not* mean ϕ times t.

Longitude of SSP:

$$\lambda(t) = \lambda_o - (0.250684)T + (S1)(S2)\arccos\left[\frac{\cos(360° t / T)}{\cos(\phi(t))}\right]$$

[Eq 12.22]

$$S1 = \begin{cases} +1 \text{ when } 0° \leq i \leq 90° \\ -1 \text{ when } 90° < i \leq 180° \end{cases}$$

$$S2 = \begin{cases} +1 \text{ when } \phi(t) \geq 0° \text{ (Northern Hemisphere)} \\ -1 \text{ when } \phi(t) < 0° \text{ (Southern Hemisphere)} \end{cases}$$

SIGN CONVENTIONS

Latitude
   North: positive
   South: negative

Longitude
   East: positive
   West: negative

All angles are in degrees and time is in minutes
   i = inclination of orbit
   T = period
   t = elapsed time since most recent ascending node
   λ_o = longitude of SSP at most recent ascending node

COMMENTS

1) Please note the sign conventions for east and west longitudes. Most maps used by radio amateurs in the US are labeled in degrees west of Greenwich. This is equivalent to calling west longitudes positive. Because there are important computational advantages to using a right-hand coordinate system, however, almost all physics and mathematics books refer to east as positive, a custom that we follow for computations. When calculations are completed it's a simple matter to re-label longitudes in degrees west. This has been done for all user-oriented data in this book.

2) Eq 12.22 should only be applied to a single orbit. At the end of each orbit, the best available longitude increment should be used to compute a new longitude of ascending node. Eq 12.22 can then be reapplied.

3) Eq 12.21 and Eq 12.22 can be solved at any time, t, if i, λ_o and T are known. In other words, it takes four parameters to specify the location of the SSP for a circular orbit. The four we've used are known as the "classical orbital elements." They were chosen because each has a clear physical meaning. There are several other sets of orbital elements that may also be employed.

4) If you have a microcomputer or programmable hand calculator, you can use Eqs 12.21 and 12.22 to run your own predictions, either to follow a particular satellite pass or to produce data for an OSCARLOCATOR ground-track overlay. The flow chart of Figure 12.20 outlines one simple approach. All sorts of refinements can be added, but it's best to get the basic program running first. You might, for example, input the time increment instead of using a fixed value of two minutes. Or you might add a time delay to the loop to produce a real-time display.

Elliptical Orbits: Derivation

Now that we've seen how the ground-track equations for a circular orbit are derived, we go on to look at the additional parameters and steps required for elliptical orbits.

Once again, a clear diagram is essential. In Figure 12.21 we've chosen an inclination between 90° and 180°, a satellite perigee in the northern hemisphere, and the spacecraft headed north in the northern hemisphere. A diagram of the orbital plane (Figure 12.22) is also very helpful.

We assume that the following parameters are known: T (period in minutes), i (inclination in degrees), λ_p (SSP longitude at perigee), w (argument of perigee) and e (eccentricity). Our object is to solve for the latitude and longitude of the SSP—$\phi(t)$ and $\lambda(t)$—at any time t. We will measure t from perigee.

The actual ground track is not a great circle, so our strategy will again be to focus first on a static earth model where the principles of spherical trigonometry can be applied. The results will then be adjusted to take into account the rotation of the Earth. In Figure 12.19, which was drawn for circular orbits, we elected to let the static-Earth ground track coincide with the true ground track at the ascending node. In Figure 12.21 we've chosen to let the two ground tracks coincide at perigee.

Step 1. Our object here is to relate our perigee-based parameters to the ascending node. More specifically, we wish to calculate (a) elapsed time as the satellite moves from D to P, (b) the latitude at perigee and (c) the longitude at the ascending node.

1a) Consider the static-Earth model and focus on spherical triangle CPD. From Figure 12.22 we see that arc PD is, by definition, equal to the argument of perigee, w. Using Kepler's Equation (Eqs 12.10 and 12.11), we can plug the value of w in for θ and calculate the elapsed time between perigee and the ascending node, which we call t_p.

1b) The latitude at perigee is, by definition, the length of arc PC. Angle PDC is equal to 180°–i. Knowing angle PDC

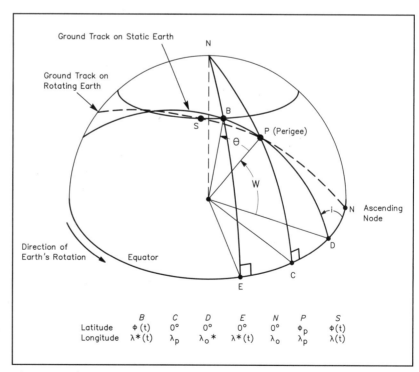

Figure 12.21—Illustration for applying the principles of spherical trigonometry to the elliptical-orbit ground-track problem.

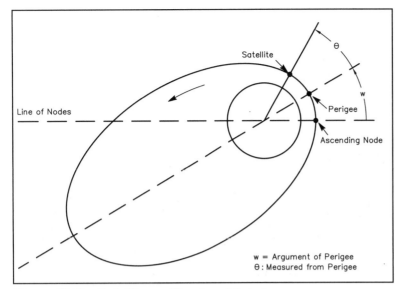

Figure 12.22—Satellite position in orbital plane.

w = Argument of Perigee
θ: Measured from Perigee

and arc PD, we use Napier Rule II to solve for arc PC.

$$\phi_p = \arcsin\left[\sin(i)\sin(w)\right]$$

1c) To obtain the longitude at point D, we again apply Napier Rule II.

$$\lambda_o^* = \lambda_p + \arccos\left[\frac{\cos(w)}{\cos(\phi_p)}\right]$$

1d) The actual longitude at the ascending node is found by computing how far the earth rotated as the satellite traveled from the ascending node to perigee and adding this to the preceding static-earth result. To simplify the following equations we approximate the rotation of the Earth by 0.25°/min.

$$\lambda_o = \lambda_p + \arccos\left[\frac{\cos(w)}{\cos(\phi_p)}\right] + \left|t_p\right|/4$$

Step 2. We now turn to the problem of locating the SSP at S, any time, before or after perigee. We again begin by focusing on the static-Earth mode to find the latitude and longitude of point B. To do this we use spherical triangle BDE.

2a) Comparing Figures 12.21 and 12.22, we see that arc BD is equal to (θ + w). To emphasize that θ changes with time, we write this term as (θ(t) + w). Using Napier Rule II we obtain the latitude of point B, which is also the actual latitude of SSP at S.

$$\phi(t) = \arcsin\left[\sin(i)\sin(\phi(t) + w)\right] \qquad \text{[Eq 12.23]}$$

2b) Applying Napier Rule II once again we obtain the longitude of point B.

$$\lambda^*(t) = \lambda_o^* - \arccos\left[\frac{\cos(\theta(t) + w)}{\cos(\phi(t))}\right]$$

2c) Finally, correcting for the rotation of the Earth we obtain the actual longitude of the SSP at S.

$$\lambda(t) = \lambda_o - \arccos\left[\frac{\cos(\theta(t) + w)}{\cos(\phi(t))}\right] - t/4 - t_p/4$$

[Eq 12.24]

Eq 12.24 only gives the correct results when the spacecraft is in the northern hemisphere, θ > w, and both are less than 90°, as shown in Figure 12.21.

RIGHT ASCENSION DECLINATION COORDINATE SYSTEM

We've now discussed all classical orbital elements except for the term *right ascension*. Calculations by astronomers and those working with satellites are best carried out in an inertial coordinate system (one that has fixed directions with respect to the distant stars). The right ascension-declination coordinate system is often used for this purpose. The position of the center of the system isn't important. For convenience we take it to be the geocenter. We now imagine a sphere of infinite radius, called the *celestial sphere*, surrounding the Earth. When the Earth's equatorial plane is extended in all directions, it becomes the celestial equator. When the Earth's North-South axis is extended, it become the celestial polar axis. See Figure 12.23. To locate points in the right ascension-declination coordinate system, we need a set of three perpendicular axes. The extended north polar axis is one. The other two lie in the equatorial plane. We take one of these to be parallel to the directed line from the center of the Sun to the geocenter on the first day of spring. This is frequently referred to as the direction of the vernal equinox or first point of Aries. The position of an object in space is described by the two angles, called right ascension and declination (see Figure 12.23) and, if necessary, its distance from the Earth.

This coordinate system is particularly convenient for keeping track of the orientation of a satellite's orbital plane

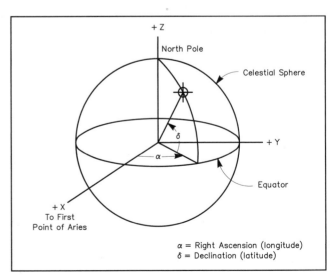

α = Right Ascension (longitude)
δ = Declination (latitude)

Figure 12.23—Celestial sphere and Right Ascension-Declination coordinate system.

as, the plane rotates slowly about the celestial spheres polar axis. Let Ω_o be the angle (at a particular time) in the celestial equator between (1) the line from the geocenter to the vernal equinox and (2) the line from the geocenter to the ascending node of a satellite orbital plane. This angle is referred to as the right ascension of ascending node (RAAN) at the epoch time. When Ω_o is known, we can predict the RAAN at any future time with the equation

$$\Omega(t) = \Omega_o + \Omega t \qquad \text{[Eq 12.25]}$$

By adopting the right ascension-declination coordinate system, we can separate the problems of keeping track of (1) the direction of the line of nodes and (2) the position of a terrestrial observer, as the Earth rotates about its polar axis and revolves around the Sun. At any time these two pieces of information can be combined with the location of the spacecraft in the orbital plane to give the longitude of the SSP.

BAHN LATITUDE AND LONGITUDE

The orientation of a satellite in its orbital plane is specified by two angles, *Bahn latitude* and *Bahn longitude*. Bahn latitude is the angle between the spacecraft + Z axis and the orbital plane. Suppose we rotate the spacecraft through this angle so that the Z axis is now in the orbital plane (Figure 12.24) and then rotate the spacecraft a second time so that its + Z axis is aligned with the directed line running from the geocenter to the spacecraft at apogee. This second rotation angle is the Bahn longitude.

To understand why the terms "latitude" and "longitude" are used, refer to Figure 12.23 and note the connection to the ascension and declination coordinates. Declination, rotation of a line into a plane, is essentially a latitude. Ascension, rotation in a plane, is essentially a longitude.

ORBITAL ELEMENTS

The parameters used to describe the position and motion of a satellite, rocket, planet or other heavenly body are called orbital elements. There's a lot of flexibility in selecting particular parameters to serve as orbital elements. The choice depends on the characteristics of the problem being examined, the information available and the coordinate system being used. If we focus our attention on satellites that do not contain propulsion systems and are not affected by atmospheric drag, we find that it requires a set of six parameters specified at a particular time (called the epoch time) to specify the current spacecraft location and to accurately predict its future positions (the basic satellite tracking problem).

From a computational viewpoint, a desirable set of six elements consists of three position coordinates and three velocity components expressed in an inertial Cartesian coordinate system. One shortcoming of this set of elements is that it doesn't provide any immediate clues as to what the orbit looks like. In contrast, classical orbital elements, which involve parameters like eccentricity, inclination, argument of perigee, mean motion (or semi-major axis), RAAN and time since last perigee are extremely helpful for

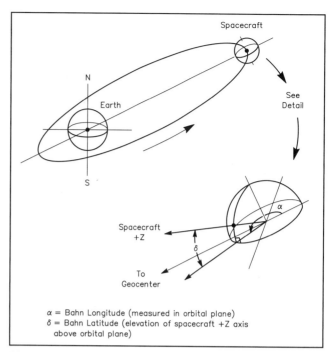

Figure 12.24—Geometry used to define Bahn latitude and Longitude, the angles that specify the orientation of a Phase 3 spacecraft.

visualizing an orbit.

The orbital elements used by amateurs in tracking problems (see Chapter 7) are almost always a variation of the classical set. In many instances, more than six parameters are provided by the source (or requested by the program) at a particular epoch time. One reason that many programs require more than six elements is that they do more than solve the basic problem. For example, they may take drag into account or keep track of the spacecraft orientation in the orbital plane so that squint angle can be determined. Some element distributors provide redundant data to allow for the fact that one tracking program may, for example, request mean motion as an input while another might request semi-major axis. In any event, a set of orbital elements must include at last six parameters specified at a particular time.

THE OBLATE EARTH

As a first approximation, it is reasonable to treat the Earth as a sphere having a mean radius of 6371 km. A model of satellite motion based on a spherical Earth predicts that the orientation (right ascension and inclination) of a satellite's orbital plane will remain fixed in space and that the position of a satellite's perigee in the orbital plane (argument of perigee) will not change. Such a model might be acceptable for a single orbit, but it is not adequate for long-term predictions.

In order to obtain equations for important factors such as rate of change of perigee (Eq 12.13) and precession of the line of nodes (Eq 12.16), one has to adopt a more complex model. The next step in complexity is to use an ellipsoidal Earth (an ellipse rotated about the polar axis). Higher-order models are possible, but it turns out that an oblate Earth model based on the ellipse gives very good results. The semi-major axis of the ellipse is the equatorial radius of the Earth: 6378 km; the semi-minor axis is the polar radius: 6357 km; and the Earth's eccentricity is 0.08182. (For more precise numbers see Appendix E.)

An oblate Earth model enters our calculations two ways. First, it affects the motion of the satellite in space. We have taken these effects into account by our use of Eqs 12.13 and 12.16. Second, it affects calculations that involve the position of a ground station on the surface of the Earth, such as antenna aiming parameters and range, which we'll be considering in the next chapter. If one compares antenna pointing predictions (azimuth and elevation) using a spherical Earth model to those using an oblate Earth model, the differences turn out to be small fractions of a degree, an amount that will never be visible with any amateur antenna. Using an oblate Earth model for these calculations does lead to complications, such as a need to distinguish between geocentric latitude, geodetic latitude and astronomical latitude.

A reasonable approach to designing tracking programs for amateurs would therefore be to incorporate the oblate Earth by using Eqs 12.13 and 12.16, but to treat the Earth as a sphere for calculations involving range and antenna aiming. This would suffice for 99.9% of amateur needs. However, for the critical orbit determination process leading to the rocket burns used to boost Phase 3 satellites from a transfer orbit to an operating orbit, it's desirable to use the most accurate model possible. Since key early tracking programs were specifically developed for the orbit transfer process, they incorporated an oblate Earth model at all steps. This refinement is included in most programs being distributed today. For a discussion of the mathematics involved, see Notes 3, 4, 5 and 6.

SPECIAL ORBITS

With at least four parameters to vary—eccentricity, inclination, semi-major axis and argument of perigee—there are many possible ways of classifying orbits. We've already paid considerable attention to low Earth circular orbits with inclinations near 90°. We've also discussed the special characteristics of Sun-synchronous orbits. In this section, we briefly look at two additional types of orbits of special interest to radio amateurs.

The Geostationary Orbit

A satellite launched into an orbit with an inclination of zero degrees will always remain directly above the equator. If such a satellite is in a circular orbit (constant velocity), traveling west to east, at a carefully selected height (35,800 km), its angular velocity will equal that of the Earth about its axis (period = 24 hours). As a result, to an observer on the surface of the Earth the spacecraft will appear to be hanging motionless in the sky. Satellites in such orbits are called *geostationary* (or stationary for short).

The geostationary orbit has a number of features that make it nearly ideal for a communications satellite. Of prime importance, Doppler shift on the radio links is non-

existent, and ground stations can forget about orbit calendars and tracking. These features have not gone unnoticed—so many commercial spacecraft are spaced along the geostationary arc above the equator that a severe "parking" problem exists. From an Amateur Radio point of view, a geostationary satellite is not without problems. The biggest shortcoming is that a single spacecraft can only serve slightly less than half the Earth. It's sometimes stated that a geostationary satellite provides poor east-west communications coverage to radio amateurs at medium to high latitudes. This may be true when Molniya-type orbits (see next section) are the standard of comparison, but take a good look at the map shown in Figure 12.25 before adopting an opinion.

If the orbital inclination of a satellite is not zero, the spacecraft cannot appear stationary; stationary satellites can only be located above the equator. A 24 hour-period circular orbit of non-zero inclination will have a ground track like a symmetrical figure eight (see Figure 12.26). Note that the ascending and descending nodes of such an orbit coincide and the longitude of ascending node is constant (the increment is nearly zero). The 24-hour circular path is known as a *synchronous orbit*. The geostationary orbit is a special type of synchronous orbit, one with a zero-degree inclination.

Note that some authors apply the term synchronous (or geosynchronous) to other types of orbits, ones that are circular or elliptical with periods that are an exact divisor of 24 hours, such as 8 hours or 12 hours. Because this might lead to unnecessary confusion, we'll avoid this use of the term synchronous.

Molniya Type Orbit

Looking at elliptical orbits earlier in this chapter, we noted that the position of the perigee in the orbital plane (the argument of perigee) changes from day to day at a rate

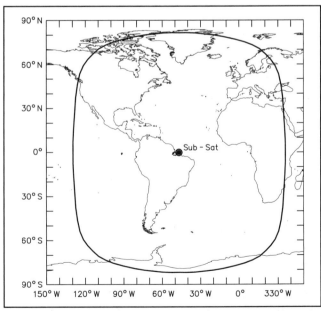

Figure 12.25—Coverage provided by a geostationary satellite at 0°N, 47°W. The access region corresponds to 0° elevation angle at ground station.

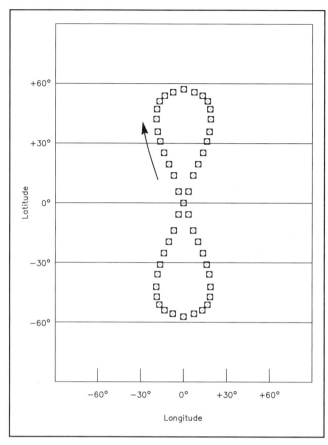

Figure 12.26—Ground track for satellite in circular orbit with a period of 24 hours and an inclination of 57°. Position shown at 0.5-hour intervals.

geometry for two consecutive orbits, with apogees occurring 180° apart in the longitude. In reality, the orbit remains fixed as the Earth rotates, so don't take the illustration too literally. Notice how in the Eurasian circuit there's a second good four- to five-hour Washington-Moscow window. A single spacecraft is accessible to the Washington station about 16 hours per day, and simultaneously to both stations about 12 hours each day. Thus, a three-satellite Molniya system can provide a reliable Washington-Moscow link 24 hours a day.

From an Amateur Radio point of view, the Molniya-type orbit has a number of attractive features. The orbits selected for Phase 3 spacecraft have been variations on the Molniya theme.

There has been a great deal of discussion as to the specific orbit desired. Some amateurs preferred an orbit with i = 63.4°. With this inclination, the apogee can be set to favor the northern hemisphere continuously. Other amateurs preferred a different value of inclination, since a changing argument of perigee eventually gives one access to a considerably larger portion of the world. Thinking in terms of a long-term Phase 3 system, such a satellite would begin to favor the southern hemisphere six or seven years after launch as the apogee drifted south of the equator. A new spacecraft would then be launched to take over in the northern hemisphere.

Meanwhile, spacecraft design engineers must also investigate the trade-offs involving the thrust required to reach a high inclination orbit and the Sun angles the spacecraft would encounter during the year. The Sun-angle numbers have a big impact on the transmitter power available on the spacecraft.

When compared to a geostationary orbit, the Molniya-type orbit has several advantages, which we've been focusing on, and several shortcomings.

Most of the shortcomings are minor. Greater attention must be given to antenna aiming and Doppler shifts, but to

(the argument of perigee) changes from day to day at a rate given by Eq 12.13. An interesting feature of this equation is that when i=63.4°, the argument of perigee remains constant regardless of the values of the period and eccentricity. as a consequence, the argument of perigee, period and eccentricity can be chosen independently to satisfy other mission requirements.

Orbits with i=63.4°, eccentricities in the 0.6 to 0.7 range and periods of 8 to 12 hours have a number of features that make them attractive communications satellites. Spacecraft in the Russian Molniya series were designed to take advantage of this type of orbit.

Let's take a brief look at a Molniya II series communications satellite of the type once used for the Moscow-Washington Hotline. (The Hotline used redundant Molniya and Intelsat links.) The spacecraft is maintained in an orbit with an inclination of 63.4°, and argument of perigee constant at 270° and a period of 12 hours. Because of the 12 hour period, the ground track tends to repeat on a daily basis (there is a slow drift in the longitude of ascending node). Apogee, where the satellite moves slowly, always occurs over 63.4° N latitude. At apogee nearly half the Earth, most in the northern hemisphere, is in view. A typical Molniya-orbit ground track is shown in Figure 12.27. The primary Washington-Moscow mutual visibility window lasts 8 to 9 hours. Figure 12.28 represents the orbit

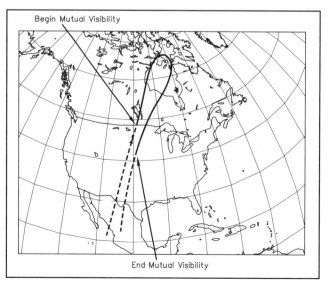

Figure 12.27—Typical Molniya II ground track with apogee over North America. The mutual visibility window is for the Washington, DC-to-Moscow path.

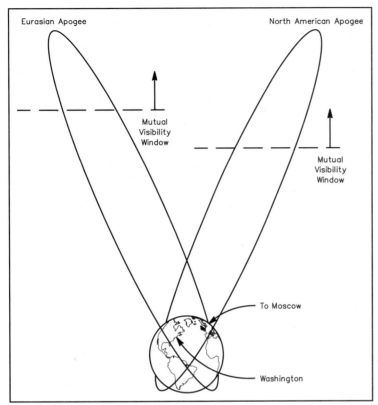

Figure 12.28—The relative positions of two successive Molniya II apogees. In actuality, the orbit plane remains fixed in space while the Earth rotates. The mutual visibility windows shown are for the Washington, DC-to-Moscow path.

ing of the computer chip is necessary, but this shielding increases the weight, restricting access to desirable orbits.

The trade-off involved here is so important that AMSAT undertook a special research program to look into the effects of radiation on the RCA CMOS integrated circuits used on OSCAR 10. Chips of the type which were to be flown were exposed to radiation under conditions that simulated the anticipated space environment. These failure-rate studies, performed at Argonne and Brookhaven National Laboratories, used various amounts and types of shielding. The results provided the data used to design OSCAR 10. Using every option possible, the engineers were able to project a three- to five-year lifespan for the spacecraft computer. The projections were remarkably accurate. When OSCAR 13 was built, integrated circuits having a much higher resistance to radiation damage were available. With respect to radiation damage, OSCAR 13 had a projected lifetime of nearly a century.

Notes

[1]Halliday, D. and Resnick, R., *Physics for Students of Science and Engineering Part I* 2nd Ed. (New York: John Wiley & Sons, 1962) Chap 16.

[2]Symon, K. R., Mechanics, 3rd Ed. (Reading, Mass: Addison-Wesley, 1971).

[3]Bate, R., Mueller, D. and White, J., *Fundamentals of Astrodynamics* (New York: Dover Publications, 1971). In addition to being an excellent book, this text is a bargain. If you're interested in additional information on astrodynamics, this is the first book to buy. Dover Publications, 31 East 2nd St, Mineola, NY 11501.

[4]Escobal, P., *Methods of Orbit Determination*, New York: John Wiley & Sons, 1976. This text is also an excellent introduction to astrodynamics. The price is typical for technical books at this level, about five times that of Reference 3.

[5]Larson, W. J. and James R. Wertz (Eds.), *Space Mission Analysis and Design*, 2nd Ed., 1992, Microcosm, Inc and Kluwer Academic Publishers.

[6] J. J. Sellers, *Understandinq Space, An Introduction to Astronautics*, McGraw-Hill, 1994.

[7]Kork, J., "Satellite lifetimes in elliptic orbits," *J Aerospace Science*, Vol 29, 1962, pp 1273-1290.

[8]Corliss, W. R., *Scientific Satellites* (NASA SP133), National Aeronautics and Space Administration, Washington, DC, 1967, p 104.

a lesser degree than with low-altitude spacecraft.

The major problem is one for the AMSAT spacecraft engineers. A satellite in a Moloiya orbit traverses the Van Allen radiation belts twice each orbit, subjecting many of the onboard electronic subsystems, especially those associated with the central computer, to damage from the high-energy particles that may be encountered. Extensive shield-

Chapter 13

Tracking

$\mathbf{13}$ Tracking

Chapter 7 showed that it's possible to track satellites without concern for the basic science involved. If you are interested in the mathematics and physics that form the basis of tracking, however, you'll find this information in Chapters 12 and 13. Chapter 12 described satellite motion in the orbit plane and related this information to satellite height and subsatellite point (SSP) location at any time.

In this chapter we show how the information provided in Chapter 12 (satellite height and SSP location) can be combined with ground station location to provide us with (1) the information needed to aim an antenna at the spacecraft (azimuth and elevation) and (2) data on satellite-ground station range. We also discuss the mathematics of a closely related problem, obtaining data for drawing spiderwebs around any ground station location. Finally, we look at some additional ways of providing satellite coverage information that are of interest to users—total coverage factor (TCF) and average daily access time (ADAT). TCF and ADAT are very important to those selecting orbits for future spacecraft as well as those using them.

COVERAGE

Consider two points on the surface of the Earth, one a ground station and the other an SSP. The surface distance between them, s, is defined as the distance along the arc of the great circle that they lie on. The geometry is shown in Figure 13.1.

The figure contains three important parameters: s (surface distance or arc length), β (central angle), and R (radius of Earth). The relation between these parameters is given by Eq 13.1.

Surface Distance

$$s = R\beta \qquad \text{(Eq 13.1)}$$

In this formula, β must be expressed in *radians*. The lengths R and s can use any convenient units as long as they're both the same. We'll generally use kilometers.

Because the radio frequencies used in conjunction with most spacecraft normally propagate over line-of-sight paths, radio amateurs generally consider a satellite to be

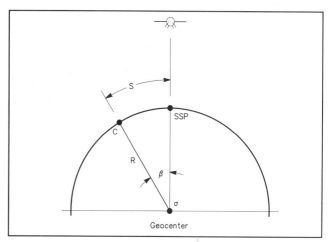

Figure 13.1—Distance between subsatellite point (SSP) and ground station (C).

within range whenever the elevation angle at the ground station is greater than zero degrees. We'll begin with this assumption. Later, we'll see how the definition of "in range" can be modified to accommodate some other elevation angle. For example, many commercial satellite users specify an elevation angle of +5° for the cutoff point.

To study satellite coverage at a particular point in time we consider the locus of all lines radiating from the satellite, which are tangent to the Earth. These lines form a cone (*coverage cone*). The plane through this cone containing the geocenter, SSP and satellite is shown in Figure 13.2.

The intersection of the coverage cone with the surface of the Earth is a circle (*access circle*) whose center lies on the line through the satellite, SSP and geocenter. Any ground station inside the circle has access to the satellite. Any two suitably equipped ground stations inside the circle can communicate via the satellite.

To compute the maximum terrestrial distance (between ground station and SSP) at which one can hear signals from the satellite, s_0, we pick a point on the edge of the access circle. See C in Figure 13.2, for example. Since this is a two-dimensional problem, s can be calculated using plane trigonometry. Because line AC is tangent to the earth, triangle AOC is a right triangle. Therefore

$$\cos\beta = \frac{R}{R+h} \qquad \text{(Eq 13.2)}$$

The maximum access distance, s_o, can be expressed using inverse trigonometric functions.

Maximum Access Distance

$$s_o = R\beta = R\arccos\left[\frac{R}{R+h}\right] \qquad \text{(Eq 13.3)}$$

Satellite users are naturally interested in the maximum distance apart that two ground stations can be and still be able to communicate. The maximum communications distance is simply twice s_o. See, for example, stations B and C in Figure 13.2.

Maximum Communications Distance:

$$2s_o = 2R\beta = 2R\arccos\left[\frac{R}{R+h}\right] \qquad \text{(Eq 13.4)}$$

A graph showing how maximum communications distance depends on satellite height can be produced from Eq 13.4. See Figure 13.3. Sample Problem 13.1 illustrates how Equations 13.1 through 13.4 are applied.

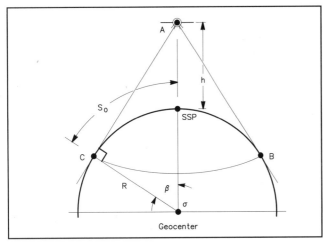

Figure 13.2—Cross-section of satellite-coverage cone.

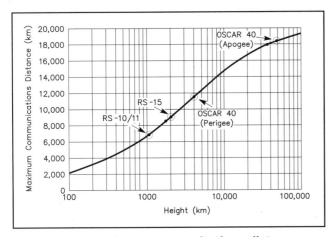

Figure 13.3—Maximum communications distance vs instantaneous satellite altitude.

ELEVATION AND SLANT RANGE

The previous discussion focused on a ground station at the edge of the coverage circle where the elevation angle was zero. We now look at the more general problem where the ground station sees the satellite at an elevation angle (ε) and slant range (ρ). The relevant geometry, shown in Figure 13.4, is again two dimensional so the problem can be solved using plane trigonometry.

Elevation

Our first objective is to express the satellite's elevation angle in terms of its height, h, and either s or β. Compare Figure 13.4 to Figure 13.2. Now, looking at Figure 13.4, focus your attention on triangle AOC formed by the satellite, the geocenter and the ground station.

Sample Problem 13.1

Find the maximum communications distance for RS-10/11, RS-15 and OSCAR 40 (at apogee and at perigee) given the following information

RS-10/11:	h =	1,003 km
RS-15:	h =	2,030 km
OSCAR 40 at perigee:	h =	4,000 km
OSCAR 40 at apogee:	h =	47,700 km

SOLUTION

Plugging the given values for h into Eq 13.4 and using R = 6371 (spherical Earth model) we obtain for

RS-10/11:	$2s_o$	= 6,724 km
RS-15:	$2s_o$	= 9,046 km
OSCAR 40 at perigee:	$2s_o$	= 11,586 km
OSCAR 40 at apogee:	$2s_o$	= 18,510 km

If your answers don't agree you probably forgot to convert the arccos[R/(R+h)] term into radians (see comment accompanying Eq 13.1) before multiplying by 2R.

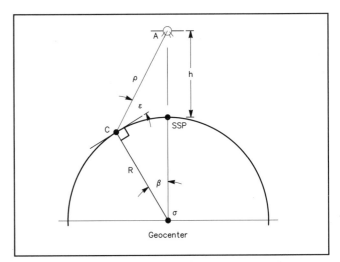

Figure 13.4—Diagram for determining satellite elevation angle and slant range as a function of height and distance to subsatellite point.

Since the angles in a plane triangle must add up to 180°, the included angle at the satellite is:

$$A = 180° - \beta - (\varepsilon + 90°) = 90° - \beta - \varepsilon$$

Applying the Law of Sines to sides R and R+h we get

$$\frac{R+h}{\sin(\varepsilon + 90°)} = \frac{R}{\sin(90° - \beta - \varepsilon)}$$

Using the trigonometric identity $\sin(90° \pm x) = \cos(x)$, this simplifies to

$$\frac{R+h}{\cos(\varepsilon)} = \frac{R}{\cos(\varepsilon + \beta)}$$

Next, applying the addition formula for the cosine function,

$\cos(x+y) = \cos(x)\cos(y) - \sin(x)\sin(y)$, we obtain

$$\frac{R+h}{\cos(\varepsilon)} = \frac{R}{\cos(\varepsilon)\cos(\beta) - \sin(\varepsilon)\sin(\beta)}$$

Finally, isolating all terms containing e on the left-hand side, we arrive at the desired formula

Elevation Angle

$$e = \arctan\left[\frac{(R+h)\cos(\beta) - R}{(R+h)\sin(\beta)}\right] \qquad \text{(Eq 13.5a)}$$

Using Eq 13.1, we can rewrite the elevation-angle formula in terms of surface distance:

Elevation Angle

$$\varepsilon = \arctan\left[\frac{(R+h)\cos(s/R) - R}{(R+h)\sin(s/R)}\right] \qquad \text{(Eq 13.5b)}$$

Note that the arguments of the angles in Eq 13.5b are given in radians.

Slant Range

To obtain an expression for ρ, the satellite/ground station distance, we again consider triangle AOC in Figure 13.4. Applying the Law of Cosines to this triangle we obtain

Slant Range

$$\rho = [(R+h)^2 + R^2 - 2R(R+h)\cos(s/R)]^{1/2} \qquad \text{(Eq 13.6)}$$

Elevation angle (Eq 13.5) and slant range (Eq 13.6) depend only on (1) the height of the satellite and (2) the surface distance between SSP and ground station. As a result, both of these equations are valid for elliptical as well as circular orbits. Sample Problems 13.2, 13.3 and 13.4 illustrate some important applications.

Elevation Circle Area

When planning the antenna system for a ground station, it's often useful to know the percentage of time a satellite will be viewable between certain elevation angles while it is in range. The relevant calculations require that we know the areas of various circular regions on the surface of the Earth. The necessary formulas are derived in most introductory calculus texts. Results are given here for reference. The surface area inside a given elevation angle circle is

$$\text{area [circle]} = 2\pi R^2[1 - \cos(s/R)] \qquad \text{(Eq 13.7)}$$

where s is the surface distance between the ground station and the elevation circle and R is the radius of the Earth. The

---

Sample Problem 13.2

A ground station is going to be using a beam antenna with a fixed elevation angle. A set of graphs of elevation angle vs. surface distance will be prepared for several satellites of interest to help determine surface distances at which the antenna will be useful. On a single set of axes, prepare graphs for RS-10/11, RS-15, OSCAR 40 at perigee and OSCAR 40 at apogee.

SOLUTION

Use Eq. 13.5b in conjunction with the following values
R = 6,371 km
RS-10/11:   h =   1,003 km
RS-15:   h =   2,030 km
OSCAR 40 at perigee: h =   4,000 km
OSCAR 40 at apogee: h = 47,700 km

The results are shown in Figure 13.5.
Note that the curve for OSCAR 40 at apogee is nearly a straight line. As a result, the following approximate expression

$\varepsilon = 90° - 0.1s$

where ε is in degrees, s is in km

can be used for determining satellite elevation during about eight hours centered on apogee.

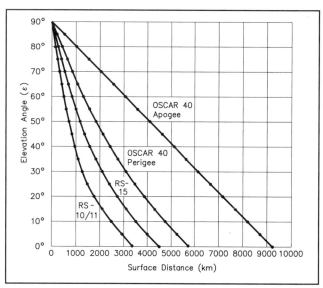

Figure 13.5—Elevation angle as a function of surface distance for several satellites (see Eq 13.5b and Sample Problem 13.2).

Sample Problem 13.3

The concentric circles that form a spiderweb are iso-elevation curves. Find an expression that gives the surface distance, s, corresponding to a given elevation angle, ε, for a satellite at height h.

Solution

To solve this problem we rearrange Eq 13.5b to obtain s as a function of e and h. This is easier said than done. The result is

$$s = R\left[\arccos\left(\left[\frac{R}{R+h}\right][\cos\varepsilon]\right) - \varepsilon\right] \qquad \text{(Eq 13.15)}$$

Again, it's important to pay attention to units; the arccos term and the isolated ε must be expressed in radians. Data for several satellites of interest are included in Table 13.1.

Table 13.1
Terrestrial Distance for Drawing Elevation Circles

Satellite	Mean Altitude (km)	Surface Distance (km) at Elevation Angle					
		0°	15°	30°	45°	60°	75°
Mir	395	2187	1062	596	361	212	99
AMSAT-OSCAR 16	800	3038	1766	1078	676	403	189
RS-10/11	1003	3362	2050	1286	817	490	231
RS-15	2030	4523	3102	2106	1397	858	409
OSCAR 40 at perigee	4000	5793	4292	3097	2140	1346	650
OSCAR 40 at apogee	47,700	9255	7612	6020	4472	2960	1473

Note how the 0° elevation curve gives the same results as Sample Problem 13.1 and that Eq 13.15 simplifies to Eq 13.3 when ε = 0°.

---

surface area between two elevation circles is given by

$$\text{area [ring]} = 2\pi R^2[\cos(s_2/R) - \cos(s_1/R)] \qquad \text{(Eq 13.8)}$$

where s_1 corresponds to the lower elevation angle (larger distance) and s_2 corresponds to the higher elevation angle (smaller distance).

BEARING AND SURFACE DISTANCE

The basic navigation problem on the surface of the Earth involves finding the great circle distance between two points, and the bearing (azimuth angle) of one point from the other. This problem is also fundamental to our tracking efforts since, as we've just seen, we can compute the elevation angle and range if we know the surface distance between our ground station and the SSP. And, the bearing provided by the navigation problem is identical to the azimuth data needed for antenna pointing. Although the navigation problem can be solved using the information on spherical trigonometry presented in Chapter 12, an approach using vectors is more efficient. Since the derivation is widely available we'll just present the results for reference.

We begin by defining variables and specifying sign conventions.

Let

R = radius of Earth (we'll use a spherical Earth model, which is more than adequate for most radio amateur needs)

β = central angle at geocenter in *radians*. $0 \le \beta \le \pi$ (smaller angle between line segments joining the geocenter to the two points on the surface of the Earth)

s = surface distance between two points

ϕ_1, λ_1 = latitude and longitude of point 1 (primary ground station)

ϕ_2, λ_2 = latitude and longitude of point 2 (SSP or second ground station)

Our sign conventions are:
Latitude: north (positive), south (negative)
Longitude: east (positive), west (negative)

The cosine of the central angle between the two points is

$$\cos\beta = \sin\phi_1 \sin\phi_2 + \cos\phi_1 \cos\phi_2 \cos(\lambda_1 - \lambda_2) \qquad \text{(Eq 13.9a)}$$

and, using Eq 13.1, the surface distance is

Surface Distance

$$s = R\beta = R\left(\arccos\left[\sin\phi_1 \sin\phi_2 + \cos\phi_1 \cos\phi_2 \cos(\lambda_1 - \lambda_2)\right]\right) \qquad \text{(Eq 13.9b)}$$

The azimuth of point 2 as seen from point 1 can be obtained from the formula

Azimuth Parameter

$$\cos(A) = \left[\frac{\sin\phi_2 - \sin\phi_1 \cos\beta}{\cos\phi_1 \sin\beta} \right] \qquad \text{(Eq 13.10)}$$

where A is the azimuth parameter. To obtain the azimuth of point 2 as seen from point 1, measured clockwise from north, we must account for the fact that the inverse cosine function returns a value only between 0° and +180°. To do this we check to see if $\left(\lambda_1 - \lambda_2\right)$ is between −180° and +180°. If not, add or subtract 360° to bring it into this range. If the resulting value of $\left(\lambda_1 - \lambda_2\right)$ is

1) negative or zero, then azimuth is given by A;
2) positive, then azimuth is given by 360°−A.

SPIDERWEB COMPUTATION

A set of range circles about a specific location on the Earth, and a set of azimuth curves that radiate outward from it are commonly referred to as a *spiderweb*. Spiderwebs are often an effective way to present information on satellite azimuth and elevation. To draw a spiderweb about a specific location on a map we need to find the coordinates for a large set of points on each elevation circle and azimuth line. The key generating equations were presented in the previous section when we covered bearing and surface distance. Using the same notation with point 1 being our ground station and point 2 being one of the outlying points, our job is to reorganize Eqs 13.9 and 13.10 to provide the latitude and longitude of each point on the spiderweb.

For the spiderweb calculation we assume that the latitude and longitude of point 1 (our ground station) and the appropriate value for the elevation (ε) and azimuth (A_z) for each point on the spiderweb are known. Three steps are involved; they must be done in order since each step uses the results of the previous one. The first step is to find the appropriate surface distance (s or β) for each elevation circle. Sample Problem 13.3 illustrates how this is accomplished. For convenience, temporarily set λ_1 equal to zero. This is equivalent to calculating our spiderweb for a point on the Greenwich Meridian. After we finish we just add the longitude of the actual central point to the longitude of all points on the spiderweb.

The second step is to revamp Eq 13.10, solving for θ_2. The result is

$$\phi_2 = \arcsin\left[\left(\sin\phi_1\right)\left(\cos\beta\right) + \left(\cos A_z\right)\left(\sin\beta\right)\left(\cos\phi_1\right)\right] \text{(Eq.13.11)}$$

The third step is to rearrange Eq 13.9. Recall that we let $\lambda_1 = 0$ and that $\cos(-\lambda_2) = \cos(\lambda_2)$.

$$\lambda_2 = \arccos\left[\frac{\cos\beta - \left(\sin\phi_1\right)\left(\sin\phi_2\right)}{\left(\cos\phi_1\right)\left(\cos\phi_2\right)}\right] \qquad \text{(Eq 13.12)}$$

For additional details concerning spiderweb calculations see Note 1.

Sample Problem 13.4

This problem involves Chapters 12 and 13. Consider a satellite in a highly elliptical orbit as used by the Phase 3 series. As the satellite moves around its orbit its height, and consequently the maximum access distance, is changing. Using the following notation

r = radial distance (geocenter to satellite) in satellite plane
θ = polar angle locating satellite in satellite plane
e = eccentricity of orbit
a = semi-major axis of orbit
s_0 = maximum access distance

find a formula that gives the polar angle, θ, corresponding to a particular value for the maximum access distance, s_0.

Solution

The relevant geometry is shown in Figure 12.2. The radial distance, r, is given by Eq 12.2.

$$r = \left[\frac{a\left(1 - e^2\right)}{1 + e\cos\theta}\right]$$

Also note Eq 13.3 for maximum access distance,

$$s_0 = R \arccos[R/(R+h)]$$

Combining these equations to eliminate r we obtain

$$\cos\left(\frac{s_0}{R}\right) = \frac{R}{R+h} = \frac{R}{r} = \left[\frac{R\left(1 + e\cos\theta\right)}{a\left(1 - e^2\right)}\right]$$

Finally, solving for θ

$$\theta = \arccos\left[\left(\frac{1}{e}\right)\left(\frac{a}{R}\right)\left(1 - e^2\right)\cos\left(\frac{s_0}{R}\right) - 1\right]$$

ORBIT SELECTION

Any radio amateur with some experience in satellite communications realizes that certain satellites are more useful than others. What are the characteristics of an orbit that cause this to happen? And, do amateurs at other latitudes evaluate the situation the same way? While these questions are posed from the viewpoint of individual users they are clearly also important to those selecting orbits for future missions.

Prior to 1975, orbit engineering was a minor concern of those designing OSCARs. When a launch opportunity arose the main question to be considered was whether the target orbit was minimally acceptable for real-time communications via an analog transponder. The construction of the Phase 3A spacecraft with its attitude control system and solid propellant kick motor altered this situation. Even though P3A ended up in the Atlantic Ocean, its design forever changed the way amateurs thought about orbit selection.

For simplicity, radio amateurs still often accept being dropped off in an orbit convenient to the launch agency.

The ability to move from a transfer orbit to a targeted orbit has been demonstrated on several occasions (OSCAR 10, OSCAR 13, OSCAR 40), however. In the course of doing this amateurs have gained experience with solid propellant kick motors capable of a single burn, liquid propellant engines capable of several burns and low thrust ion jet engines of the type flown on OSCAR 40. The potential usefulness of water-powered engines and solar sails has also been investigated.

In order to compare and rate orbits we need some quantitative measures of the coverage they provide. In this section we'll introduce two such performance measures, *Total Coverage Factor* (TCF) and *Average Daily Access Time* (ADAT).[2]

Total Coverage Factor

TCF represents the total *quantity* of coverage available without specifying how it's distributed. TCF is essentially a normalized average coverage area. The normalization process involves dividing the average coverage area by the surface area of the Earth. The process gives a unitless number between 0 and 1.00. Some examples might be helpful here. A TCF of 1.00 means that everyone on the Earth has access to the satellite 24 hours per day. (This is impossible for a single satellite but possible when using a constellation of spacecraft.) A TCF of 0.25 can refer to any one of an infinite variety of situations falling between the extremes: (1) 25% of the Earth has access 24 hours per day, (2) 100% of the Earth has access 6 hours (25%) of each day. The orbit selection process often involves varying orbital elements to try to arrive as closely as possible to the second case where all users receive an equal dose of access time.

Consider a satellite at a height h. Eqs 13.2 and 13.7 can be combined to provide the area of the coverage circle where R is the radius of the Earth.

Area of Coverage Circle

$$2\pi R^2[h/(R+h)] \qquad \text{(Eq 13.13)}$$

For circular orbits TCF is obtained by dividing the area of the coverage circle by the surface area of the Earth, $4\pi R^2$.

Total Coverage Factor

$$TCF = (1/2)\left[\frac{h}{R+h}\right] \qquad \text{(Eq 13.14)}$$

For elliptical orbits TCF is defined as the instantaneous TCF averaged with respect to 360 equal time intervals.

Table 13.2
Total Coverage Factor (TCF) for Selected Spacecraft

Spacecraft	Apogee Height (km)	Perigee Height (km)	Maximum Coverage	Minimum Coverage	TCF
Mir	395	—	—	—	0.029
AO-16	800	—	—	—	0.056
RS-10/11	1003	—	—	—	0.068
RS-15	2030	—	—	—	0.121
AO-13	36,333	2491	0.425	0.140	0.376
OSCAR 40	47,700	4027	0.440	0.194	0.401
P4	35,870	—	—	—	0.425

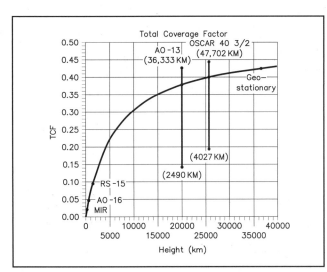

Figure 13.6—Total Coverage Factor (TCF) vs spacecraft height for circular orbits. The vertical lines representing the two elliptical orbits show TCF at apogee, TCF at perigee and average TCF.

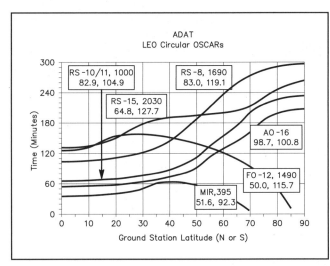

Figure 13.7—Average Daily Access Time (ADAT) vs ground station latitude for several OSCAR spacecraft in low Earth circular orbits. [Spacecraft name, height (km), inclination (degrees), period (minutes)].

Figure 13.6 shows the relation between TCF and satellite height. Satellites in elliptical orbits are represented by a vertical line that shows TCF and normalized coverage areas at apogee and perigee. Table 13.2 contains TCF data for several satellites of interest.

As a result of the steep slope of the TCF curve at low heights (see Figure 13.6), a small increase in height can produce a significant increase in coverage. This illustrates one reason for the significant differences in service provided by different Low Earth Orbit spacecraft. A satellite at a height of 1000 km (RS-12/13) provides only 56% of the coverage of one at 2030 km (RS-15). In other words, RS-15 provides nearly as many access hours to users as RS-10/11 and RS-12/13 combined! While TCF describes the total quantity of coverage it tells us nothing about how this coverage is distributed. The measure that does this is Average Daily Access Time (ADAT).

Average Daily Access Time

A satellite is accessible to each ground station a specific amount of time each day. We can compute an average access time for each ground station. In most cases (if satellite ascending nodes are uniformly distributed with respect to longitude) the result depends only on the ground station's latitude. Although ADAT data can be obtained via direct computation[3] it is most easily obtained via computer simulations.

To use the simulation approach one chooses a particular ground station latitude (since the results are independent of longitude placing the station at the Greenwich Meridian simplifies the calculations) and then randomly selects perhaps 100,000 satellite positions along the orbit and, for each position, determines if the satellite is in range. The total number of in range occurrences divided by 100,000 gives the percentage of the day that the satellite will be in range. For example, if one observes 8000 in range occurrences in 100,000 tries the spacecraft will be in range 8,000/100,000 or 8% of each day. This amounts to about 115 minutes. By repeating this procedure for other ground station latitudes one obtains the data needed to prepare a graph of ADAT vs ground station latitude.

Figure 13.7 shows ADAT data for several low altitude spacecraft. Compare, for example, the performance of RS-10/11 to RS-15 from the point of view of a ground station at 70°N latitude, and then again from the point of view of a ground station at 40°N latitude. Although the RS-15 is superior in both cases the difference is more significant at 40°N. Figure 13.8 uses the RS-8 orbit (circular, h = 1690 km) to show how changes in satellite inclination angle affect ADAT. Note that all curves in this figure reflect the same total coverage—it's just being distributed different ways.

Figure 13.9 shows ADAT data for OSCAR 40. Curves

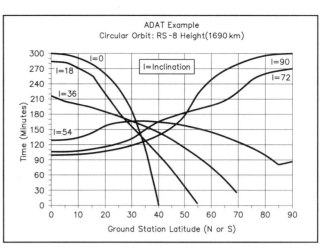

Figure 13.8—Average Daily Access Time vs ground station latitude for spacecraft in circular orbit (height = 1690 km).

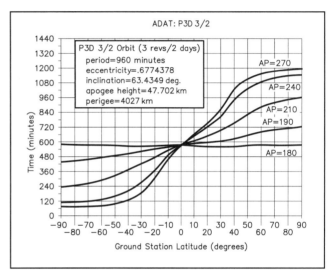

Figure 13.9—Average Daily Access Time vs ground station latitude for an OSCAR 40 orbit (3 revolutions in 2 days). Performance is shown for several values of argument of perigee.

are given for several different positions of the OSCAR 40 apogee so that users can predict behavior over the entire operational lifetime of the spacecraft.

Notes
[1] D. Zachariadis, "Spiderweb—The Range Circle Calculation," *QST*, Feb 1986, pp 36-38.
[2] M. Davidoff, "Selecting Orbits for Radio Amateur Satellite Missions," *Proceedings of the Sixth AMSAT-UK Colloquium*, 1991, pp 1-16.
[3] M. Davidoff, "An Efficient Method For Calculating Average Daily Access Time," *Proceedings of the Fifth AMSAT-UK Colloquium*, 1990, pp 57-63; updated in *AMSAT Journal*, Nov 1990, pp 22-26.

Satellite Systems

14 Satellite Systems

Even a simple satellite is a complex collection of hardware (and possibly software). To manage the design and construction of communications and scientific satellites, it's convenient to think of a spacecraft as being built from a standard set of subsystems, each with a specific function.[1,2] See Table 14.1. This makes it possible to parcel out the tasks of analyzing and optimizing each subsystem. Several design objectives almost always apply: minimizing weight and cost, maximizing reliability and performance, and ensuring compatibility.

These aims often result in conflicts. On OSCAR 10, for example, radiation shielding of the central computer was desired but the total amount carried was limited by weight constraints. Even when designers focus on a single subsystem they must keep in mind how it impacts on other subsystems. For example, a small reduction in transponder power-amplifier efficiency may have little effect on downlink signal strength but it might completely upset spacecraft thermal design.

In this chapter we'll look at each of the systems listed in Table 14.1. Various methods of accomplishing system objectives will be discussed. Methods that were used on OSCAR satellites and those suitable for future missions will be emphasized.

Table 14.1
Satellite Subsystems: Emphasis OSCAR

Subsystem	Function	OSCAR Series Equipment
Attitude control	To modify and stabilize satellite orientation	Phase 2: magnet, gravity boom, torquing coils Phase 3: torquing coils, reaction wheels
Central computer	To coordinate and control other subsystems; provides memory, computation capability	Digital logic, microprocessor, D/A converter, command decoder
Communications	To receive uplink commands and transmit downlink telemetry	Command receiver, transmitters (beacons), antennas
Energy supply	To provide power for all onboard subsystems	Batteries, solar cells, conditioning electronics
Engineering telemetry	To measure operating status of onboard subsystems	Electronic sensors, telemetry encoders
Environment control	To regulate temperature levels, provide electromagnetic shielding, provide height-energy particle shielding	Mechanical design, thermal coatings
6Guidance and Control	To interface computer with sensors, attitude-control and propulsion subsystems	Hard-wired electronics, sun and Earth sensors, GPS unit
Mission-unique equipment	To accomplish objectives	Transponders, scientific and educational instruments
Propulsion	To provide thrust for orbit changes	Phase 2: none Phase 3: solid-fuel kick motor, arc-jet
Structure	To provide support and packaging function, thermal control, protect modules from stress of launch, mate to launch vehicle	Mechanical structure, aluminum sheet wherever possible to minimize machining

COMMUNICATIONS, ENGINEERING AND MISSION SUBSYSTEMS

The communications subsystem provides ground stations a direct link to a satellite. It enables us to observe what's happening inside the spacecraft, often as it happens, and to modify the operation of the spacecraft. Three communications links are of interest: (1) downlink beacons providing telemetry (TTY), (2) uplink telecommand and (3) communications links supported by transponders. For the first quarter century of amateur satellite operation these functions were distinct. In recent years downlink TTY and digital communications modes are often combined.

Beacons: Function

The beacons aboard the OSCAR satellites serve a number of functions. In the *telemetry mode* they convey information about onboard satellite systems (solar cell panel currents, temperatures at various points, storage battery condition, and so on); in the *communications mode* they can be used for store-and-forward broadcasts; in either mode they can be used for tracking, for propagation measurements and as a reference signal of known characteristics for testing ground station receiving equipment. Beacon functions are summarized in Table 14.2.

Beacon telemetry. Amateurs have used several telemetry encoding methods. From the user's point of view, each method can be characterized by the data transfer rate and the complexity of the decoding equipment required at the ground station. To a large extent, there's a trade-off between these two factors (see Table 14.3).

Table 14.2
Beacon Functions

1) Telemetry
   a) Morse code
   b) Radioteletype (RTTY)
   c) Advanced encoding techniques
   d) Digitized (digitally synthesized) speech
2) Communications
   a) Store and forward broadcasts
3) Miscellaneous
   a) Tracking
   b) Propagation measurements
   c) Reference signal

Each OSCAR includes some, but not necessarily all, of the telemetry options listed.

Beacon characteristic. The method first used to encode telemetry on an amateur satellite was to vary the speed of OSCAR I's CW "HI" in response to a temperature sensor. Absolute temperature data, collected while the spacecraft was in sunlight and in shadow, provided information on reflective and emissive performance of thermal coatings. Rate of change of temperature data as the spacecraft passed from sunlight to shadow provided data on thermal conductivity of structural elements. Note that measurement of a single characteristic can provide a great deal of information since we can record both absolute value and rate of change under various stable and changing conditions.

Morse code telemetry. The Morse code telemetry systems employed on OSCARs 6, 7 and 8 (and on most RS spacecraft) have made these satellites very valuable to educators and amateur scientists.[3] In the CW telemetry mode data measurements at several key points on the spacecraft are downlinked in Morse code. Restricting the code to a numbers-only format, usually at either 25 or 50 numbers/minute (about 10 or 20 words/minute), enables individuals with little or no prior training to learn to decode the contents relatively quickly. As a result of the design of the telemetry processing equipment aboard the satellite, ground stations do not need any specialized decoding electronics. The information capacity of this mode is inherently limited in that any attempt to speed up the Morse code transmission would interfere with the ability of untrained users to decode it without special equipment.

Radioteletype telemetry. During the mid 1970s, as OSCAR spacecraft grew more complex it became necessary to adopt higher speed telemetry methods. Since many amateurs owned radioteletype equipment, this mode was adopted and flown on OSCAR 7. The information provided by the RTTY system was especially valuable to the advanced experimenter, to stations that were responsible for managing the satellite and to the engineers and scientists who would design and build future AMSAT spacecraft.

Advanced encoding techniques. A number of factors have acted to displace radioteletype as a primary means for downlinking satellite data. Recall that radioteletype was chosen for the convenience of users in the mid 1970s. A careful analysis shows that RTTY is relatively inefficient when considered in terms of data rate per unit of power. With Phase 3 satellites and the UoSAT series it became

---

Table 14.3
Telemetry Encoding Methods: Ground Station Complexity vs Data Rate

Telemetry Encoding Method	Relative Ground Station Complexity	Telemetry Data Rate	First OSCAR Utilization
Beacon characteristic	Low	Very low	OSCAR I
Digitized speech	Very low	Very low	OSCAR 9
Morse code	Low	Low	OSCAR 6
Radioteletype	Mooderate	Moderate	OSCAR 7
Advanced encoding techniques	High	High	OSCARs 9, 10

---

apparent that a higher speed, more power efficient, link was required. This need arose at the same time that microcomputers were becoming commonplace at ground stations. Since the new series of spacecraft would be controlled by onboard computers it was natural to switch to encoding techniques suitable for computer to computer communications. Once a ground station uses a microcomputer to capture telemetry it's only a small step to have the computer process the raw telemetry, store it, automatically check for values that indicate developing problems, graph data over time, and so on. Both the UoSAT and Phase 3 series used ASCII encoding but different modulation schemes were adopted. Designers of early low altitude UoSAT spacecraft, with their powerful beacons, selected a 1200 bps system that permitted the use of standard Bell 202 Modems. Power efficiency was much more important with Phase 3 series spacecraft so a special 400 bps optimized system was developed. Neither of these systems is compatible with the modems used for normal terrestrial packet operation, PACSAT communications or RUDAK operation. Later UoSAT spacecraft used a 9600 baud telemetry system for telemetry and communications. As a result, amateurs who desire access to all these systems need multiple modems.

Two projects currently underway may alleviate this situation. One involves the development of a device known as a digital signal processor (DSP). A DSP modem will (if appropriate software is available) replace a pile of existing discrete modems and handle new modes through software updates. A DSP unit will also decode Weather Satellite APT pictures, dig weak EME signals out of the noise, copy slow-scan TV, and so on.

A DSP unit is a very powerful microprocessor controlled analog-to-digital and digital-to-analog converter optimized for signal processing and designed to run under the control of an external computer. Software commands will permit the operator to reconfigure the DSP to serve the various functions mentioned. The DSP project is being sponsored by AMSAT and TAPR. Its eventual impact will be felt far beyond the amateur satellite service. For up-to-date information see the TAPR Web site.

While a number of commercial multimode DSP modems have become available and work on the elegant DSP approach goes forward, another group of amateurs believe it's more cost effective to implement DSP functions using the powerful new computers and 32 bit sound cards entering the mass consumer marketplace in the late '90s.

Digitized speech mode. In the digitally synthesized speech mode telemetry is simply spoken. This produces the ultimate simplicity in ground station decoding requirements (assuming the telemetry is being spoken in a language you're familiar with). Spoken telemetry is excellent for demonstrations involving general audiences and for educational applications at lower grade levels, but the extremely low data rate (about 1 baud!) makes it unsuitable for real communications needs. Digital speech telemetry systems have been used on OSCARs 9 and 11. These led to more sophisticated digital speech synthesizers capable of

storing and playing back natural sounding speech that could be used for broadcasts and store-and-forward communications. Devices of this type were carried on DO-17, RS-14/AO-21, AO-27 and FO-29.

Beacon communication mode. As just mentioned, beacons can also be used for store-and-forward communications or broadcasts. On early missions messages were loaded via the command link. Nowadays many beacon functions are being absorbed by digital transponders, however. With P3D message broadcasting, telemetry and digital communications will be integrated into a single system capable of handling CW, digital modes, or speech.

Beacon: Miscellaneous functions. In either the telemetry or store-and-forward broadcast modes, a beacon with stable intensity and frequency can serve a number of functions. For example, it can be used for Doppler shift studies, propagation measurements and testing ground-based receiving equipment. In addition, stations communicating via a satellite transponder can use the beacon to adjust their uplink power properly by comparing the strength of their downlink signal to that of the beacon.

Beacons: Design

Beacon power levels are chosen to provide adequate signal-to-noise ratios at well-equipped ground stations. Overkill (too much power) serves only to decrease the power available for other satellite subsystems, reduce reliability and cause potential compatibility problems with other spacecraft electronics systems. Typical power levels at 146 and 435 MHz are 40 to 100 mW on low-altitude spacecraft and 0.5 to 1.0 W on high-altitude spacecraft. As with all spacecraft subsystems, high power efficiency is essential. Phase 3 spacecraft have tended to use two beacons, a relatively high power unit called the *engineering beacon*, which is mainly operated when the omni antenna is used at high altitudes (during the early orbit transfer stages or in case of emergency) and the *general beacon*, which is operated continuously. The frequencies of these two beacons sandwich the passband of a primary transponder. This position is convenient both to users (the same ground-station receiving system can be used for both transponder and beacon downlinks) and satellite designers (the same satellite antennas can serve both systems).

Since the telemetry system is a key diagnostic tool for monitoring the health of a spacecraft, redundant beacons, often at different frequencies, are generally flown to enhance reliability. This approach has paid off in a number of instances. Beacon failures occurred on OSCARs 5 and 6 but neither mission was seriously affected since both spacecraft carried alternate units. Beacon power output is usually one of the readings sampled by the telemetry system.

Command Links

OSCAR spacecraft are designed so that authorized volunteer ground stations with the necessary equipment can command them. The first OSCAR satellite with a command link was OSCAR 5. OSCARs 5-8 responded to a relatively limited set of commands. More recent spacecraft, those controlled by onboard computers, can accept programs via the command link. As a result the number of possible operating states is very great. Satellite commandability is a necessity for several reasons. First, it's a legal requirement of spacecraft operating in the Amateur Satellite Service. Regulations state that, should the situation arise, we must be able to turn off a malfunctioning transmitter causing harmful interference to other services. Second, it would be impossible to accomplish the orbital change or attitude adjustment procedures critical to the existence of the Phasc 3 system without the ability to uplink software.

The capabilities of today's sophisticated Phase 2 spacecraft are also critically dependent on our ability to transmit software to the satellite via a command channel. Even with relatively simple satellites the existence of a command link can mean the difference between an operative mission and a failure. A constant stream of commands sent to OSCAR 6 turned a marginally usable spacecraft (one that was continually shutting itself down) into a reliable performer. Via the command system one can turn off malfunctioning subsystems, adjust operating schedules to meet changing user needs, employ attitude-control systems that require periodic adjustment, turn subsystems on/off to adjust spacecraft operating temperature, and so on. Command stations are built and manned by dedicated volunteers. Though command frequencies, access codes and formats are considered confidential, they are available to responsible stations for projects approved by AMSAT.

Transponders

On most amateur spacecraft the primary mission subsystem is the transponder. Open access linear transponders were carried on OSCARs 3, 6, 7, 8, P3A, 10, 12, 13, 20, 24, 27 and 29, and RSs 1, 2, 5, 6, 7, 8, 10/11, 12/13, 14 and 15. Open access digital transponders were flown on OSCARs 12, 14, 16, 19, 20, 22, 23, 24, 25, 26, 28, 29 and RS-14.

Linear Transponders

A linear transponder receives signals in a narrow slice of the RF spectrum, shifts the frequency of the passband, amplifies all signals linearly, and then retransmits the entire slice. Total amplification is on the order of 10^{13} (130 dB). A linear transponder can be used with any type of signal when real time communication is desired. From the standpoint of conserving valuable spacecraft resources such as power and bandwidth, the preferred user modes are SSB and CW. Transponders are specified by first giving the approximate input frequency followed by the output frequency. For example, a 146/29-MHz transponder has an input passband centered near 146 MHz and an output passband centered near 29 MHz. The same transponder could be specified in wavelengths, as a 2/10-m unit.

Transponder design. Transponder design is, in many respects, similar to receiver design. Input signals are typically on the order of 10^{-13} W and the output level is several watts. A major difference, of course, is that the transponder output is at radio frequency while the receiver output is at audio frequency. A block diagram of a simple transponder is shown in Figure 14.1. For several reasons, flight-model transponders are more complex than the one shown. As with receiver design, such considerations as passband filter availability, image response, wide variations in input signal level and required overall gain often cause designers to use multiple-frequency conversions. A block diagram of the basic Mode A transponder used on OSCARs 6, 7 and 8 is shown in Figure 14.2.

In spacecraft applications a key characteristic of a linear amplifier is its overall efficiency (RF-output/dc-input). Once we reach power levels above a few watts the use of class A, AB or B amplifiers cannot be tolerated. Dr. Karl Meinzer, DJ4ZC and his coworkers at the University of Marburg in the Federal Republic of Germany have developed a series of special high-efficiency linear transponders. The first method, known as envelope elimination and restoration (EER) operates somewhat like a class D amplifier.[4] Although individual stages are not linear, the overall transponder is a linear device. This technique proved very successful on the Mode B transponder on OSCAR 7 but it wasn't suitable for scaling to the high power, wide bandwidth system needed for Phase 3 spacecraft. For Phase 3A a new system was developed that used EER and Doherty amplifiers.[5] This technique was later superseded by HELAPS (High Efficiency Linear Amplification by Parametric Synthesis).[6]

Transponder operating characteristics. The power and bandwidth of a transponder must be compatible with each other and with the mission. That is, when the transponder is fully loaded with equal-strength signals, each signal should provide an adequate signal-to-noise ratio at the ground. Selecting appropriate values accurately on a theoretical basis using only link calculations is error prone. Experience with a number of satellites, however, has provided AMSAT with a great deal of empirical data from which it's possible to extrapolate accurately to different orbits, bandwidths, power levels, frequencies and antenna characteristics.

In general, low-altitude (300 to 1600 km) satellites that use passive magnetic stabilization and omnidirectional antennas can provide reasonable downlink performance with from 1 to 10 W PEP at frequencies between 29 and 435 MHz, using a 50 to 100-kHz-wide transponder. A high-altitude (35,000 km) spin-stabilized satellite that used

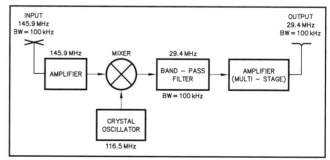

Figure 14.1–Block diagram: Simple Mode A transponder.

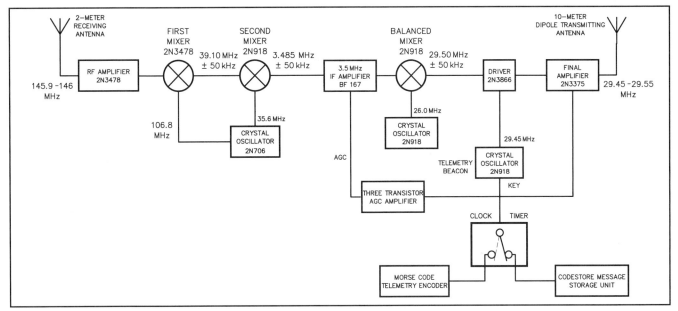

Figure 14.2–Block diagram: Mode A transponder used on OSCARs 6, 7, and 8.

modest (7 to 10 dB$_i$) gain antennas should be able to provide acceptable performance with 35 W PEP using a 300-kHz-wide transponder downlink at 146 or 435 MHz. Transponders are usually configured to be inverting in order to minimize Doppler shift.

Dynamic Range. The dynamic range problem for transponders is quite different from that for HF receivers. At first glance it may seem that the situation faced by satellite transponders is simpler. After all, an HF receiver must be designed to handle input signals differing in strength by as much as 100 dB, while a low-altitude satellite will encounter signals in its passband differing by perhaps 40 dB. Good HF receivers solve the problem by filtering out all but the desired signal before introducing significant gain. A satellite, however, has to accommodate all users simultaneously. The maximum overall gain can, therefore, be limited by the strongest signal in the passband.

Considering the state-of-the-art in transponder design and available spacecraft power budgets, an effective dynamic range of about 25 dB is about the most that can be currently obtained. Prior to OSCAR 40 satellite AGC was normally adjusted to accommodate the loudest user. As a result, stations 25 dB weaker were not able to put a usable signal through the spacecraft even though they might be capable of doing so when the AGC is not activated. In the ideal situation users would adjust uplink power so that spacecraft AGC is never activated.

The "power-hog" problem is a serious one. Karl Meinzer noted that during the first few years of OSCAR 10 operation the Mode B transponder gain was almost always reduced by approximately 15 dB. He stated ". . . if all stations would reduce their power by a factor of 30, their strength would not change one whit. Weaker stations would then also have a chance to use the transponder."

One approach to alleviating the high power problem is educational. Many users may not realize they're overloading the spacecraft or may not know the effects that such overloading produces (it doesn't necessarily increase the strength of their downlink; it often merely depresses the signal level of other stations). Education is very important but technical approaches to reducing the overload problem are also needed.

For several years designers considered dividing the transponder IF into a number of discrete channels, each with its own AGC system. An overloading signal would then only depress signal levels in one channel. This technique was never implemented, however.

A second approach, which has been implemented on OSCAR 40, is known as LEILA, for "LEIstungs Limit Anzeige" (Power Limit Indicator). LEILA operates as follows. A computer continuously monitors the 10.7 MHz transponder IF passband. When an uplink signal whose level exceeds a predetermined level is encountered the computer inserts a CW message over the offender's downlink. The message indicates to the transmitting station that the transponder is being overloaded. The station can then reduce power until the CW signal disappears. If the overloading signal continues, or exceeds an even higher preset level, LEILA activates a notch filter tuned to the offending station's frequency. LEILA is capable of handling several high power stations simultaneously.[7]

Redundancy. Since the transponder is the primary mission subsystem, reliability is extremely important. One way to improve system reliability is to include at least two transponders on each spacecraft; if one fails, the other would be available full time. There are significant advantages to *not* using identical units. Consider for example the Mode A, Mode B combination on OSCAR 7 and the Mode B, Mode L combination used on OSCARs 10 and 13. When OSCAR 7 was launched, not many amateurs had equipment to access Mode B so Mode A was scheduled the great majority of the time. However, Mode B's superior performance was very apparent and the number of users increased over the years. By OSCAR 7's third year in orbit Mode B was being scheduled nearly 70% of the time. The situation with OSCAR 13 was somewhat different. Because the spacecraft was generally available many hours each day, transponder scheduling was based on performance. Mode L was scheduled when it provided the best link, Mode B at other times. When Mode L failed it was replaced by Mode S.

Because of the large number of uplink and downlink frequencies available on OSCAR 40 the design team abandoned the concept of the hardwired transponder with specific input and output frequency bands. In its place they introduced a design consisting of discrete receiver front ends and transmitter mixer/power amplifiers all connected to a common IF. The Matrix IF operates at 10.7 MHz with input and output levels of −15 dBm, and it includes the LEILA unit. Instructions from the ground will direct the spacecraft computer to connect one or more receivers and one or more transmitters to the IF. The operating schedule is determined by an international operations committee. This approach is extremely flexible and can accommodate to equipment failures or degraded performance and to changes in user needs over the decade lifetime of the spacecraft design.

Digital Transponders

Digital transponders of the PACSAT or RUDAK type differ significantly from the linear transponders we've been discussing. A digital transponder demodulates the incoming signal. The data can be stored aboard the spacecraft (PACSAT Mailbox) or used to immediately regenerate a digital downlink signal (RUDAK digipeater). The mailbox service is best suited to low altitude spacecraft. Digipeating is most effective on high altitude spacecraft. Like linear transponders, digital units are downlink limited. A key step in the design procedure is to select modulation techniques and data rates to maximize the downlink capacity. Using assumptions about the type of traffic expected one then selects appropriate uplink parameters. An analysis of both PACSAT and RUDAK suggests that, due to collisions, the uplink data capacity should be about four or five times that of the downlink.

PACSAT Mailbox. For PACSAT Mailbox operation the designers decided to use similar data rates for the uplink and downlink and couple a single downlink with four uplinks. Fuji-OSCARs 12 and 20, and the MicroSat series ran both links at 1200 bps. These "pacsats" contain an FM receiver with a demodulator that accepts Manchester-encoded FSK on the uplink. To produce an appropriate uplink signal, the ground station uses an FM transmitter and a TNC-1 or TNC-2. However, minor modifications are necessary. The changes consist of extracting two signals from the host TNC—the TX data line and a 1200 Hz signal derived from the TX clock. These two signals are combined in an exclusive OR gate. The output of the OR gate is passed through a low pass filter and then to the transmitter mike input. Most ground station pacsat demodulators contain the simple circuitry needed to accomplish this.

The pacsat downlink uses binary phase-shift keying (BPSK) and can run either 1.5 or 4 W. This modulation method was selected because, at a given power level and bit rate, it provides a significantly better bit error rate than other methods that were considered. One way of receiving the downlink is to use an SSB receiver and pass the audio output to a PSK demodulator. The SSB receiver is just serving as a linear downconverter in this situation. Other methods of capturing the downlink are possible but the two proven systems now operating use this approach.

In Chapter 5 we discussed the pacsat modems currently available from TAPR and G3RUH. Both have been reproduced in significant numbers and are known to work well. The designs take different approaches to demodulating the signal. The G3RUH unit uses a limiter to immediately convert the received signal into a digital format so that all processing is digital. A block diagram of a pacsat transponder is shown in Figure 14.3.

RUDAK Digipeater. RUDAK is an acronym for *Regenerativer Umsetzer fur Digitale Amateurfunk Kommunikation* (Regenerative Transponder for Digital Amateur Communications).[8,9] Early RUDAK systems took a different approach to achieving the desired ratio of uplink to downlink capacity. The one flown on OSCAR 13 used one uplink channel and one downlink channel with the data rate on the uplink (2400 bps) roughly six times that on the downlink (400 bps). The 400 bps rate on the downlink was chosen because this is the standard that has been used for downlinking Phase 3 telemetry since the late 1970s so that users already capturing Phase 3 telemetry would be able to capture RUDAK transmissions from day one. The RUDAK unit on OSCAR 13 failed during launch.

A system known as RUDAK II was flown on RS-14/AO-21. It consisted of two units, one similar to the RUDAK flown on OSCAR 13 and the other a new experimental transponder using DSP technology. The latter, known as the RUDAK technology Experiment (RTX), was essentially a flying testbed for ideas being considered for future Phase 3 missions.[8]

The RUDAK-U system being flown on OSCAR 40 contains two CPUs, one 153.6 kbaud modem, 4 hardwired 9600 baud modems and 8 DSP modems capable of operating at speeds up to 56 kbaud. A block diagram and the operating strategy are discussed in Chapter 5 (see Figure 5.3).[9]

Engineering/Telemetry System

The function of a spacecraft engineering system is to gather information about all onboard systems, encode the data in a format suitable for downlinking (engineering subsystem) and then transmit the encoded data on the spacecraft beacons (communications subsystem). In this section we look at engineering aspects of the telemetry subsystem. A block diagram of a telemetry encoder of the type used on OSCARs 6, 7, and 8 is shown in Figure 14.4.

Each parameter of interest aboard the spacecraft is monitored by a sensor. The sensor output must be converted to a voltage proportional to the measured value. This voltage then goes to a variable-gain amplifier and then to an analog-to-digital converter. During prelaunch calibration the gain associated with each sensor is selected for optimum range

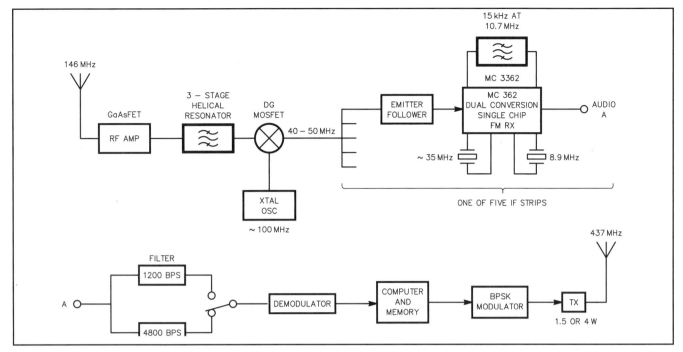

Figure 14.3–Block diagram: PACSAT transponder

and accuracy. The digital output is then converted to Morse code, RTTY or some other format for transmission via a beacon. Phase 2 satellites used hardwired logic to convert the output of the analog-to-digital converter to Morse code or RTTY. Phase 3 satellites are designed to perform the conversion with software in their onboard computers. Telemetry control logic (either hardwired or in software) selects the proper input sensor, chooses the appropriate amplifier gain and conducts other bookkeeping chores.

On early Phase 2 satellites sensors were sampled sequentially (*serial mode*) and the measurements were transmitted as they were made. Under flexible computer control, the sampling strategy can be modified by instructions on the command link. If the situation warrants, we can dwell on a particular sensor (*dwell mode*) or sample it frequently so short-term changes can be studied. It's also possible to store readings in the onboard computer. This is especially valuable with a low altitude spacecraft where one can collect data over one or more orbits and then

"dump" the information via the communications link while the satellite is in range. The *whole orbit data* (WOD) mode has been used extensively with OSCARs 9 and 11.

It's expected that future spacecraft will be controlled by onboard computers and that telemetry system operation will be controlled by software that's under ground control. As a result, AMSAT will have a great deal of flexibility in selecting channels, sampling strategies and encoding formats. For information on the telemetry capabilities of currently flying spacecraft see Appendix C: *Spacecraft Profiles*.

Morse Code Format. The hard wired Morse code telemetry systems aboard OSCARs 6, 7 and 8 had several features in common. The parameters being measured were sampled in a fixed sequence. One complete series of measurements was called a *frame*. The beginning and end of each frame were marked by a distinctive signal; the Morse code letters HI were used on OSCARs 6, 7 and 8. Each transmitted value consisted of three integers called a *channel*. To interpret a channel we needed to identify which

Table 14.4
A Morse Code Telemetry Frame with Nine Channels

Raw data	HI	142	116	178	239	202	216	392	352	365	HI
Channel ID		1A	1B	1C	2A	2B	2C	3A	3B	3C	

The top row is the actual data as received. The bottom row assigns a unique label to each channel. Channel 1A is the first one received, channel 1B is the second, 1C is the third, 2A is the fourth, and so on. Such data is sometimes written in the form of a 3x3 matrix, in which case the ID integer is a line number and the ID letter is a column label.

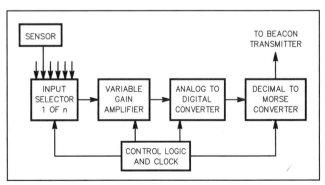

Figure 14.4—Block diagram: Typical early OSCAR Morse code telemetry encoder.

parameter was being monitored and obtain a raw data measurement that could be converted into a meaningful value. AMSAT used the first integer in a channel for parameter identification. When the number of channels is small (OSCAR 8 had six channels), a single digit can uniquely identify the parameter being measured. When the number of channels is large, the user must also note the order in which the channels are being sent in order to identify the particular parameter being sampled. Channel ID numbers are not needed since one can always count from the previous frame marker but the redundancy they provide is useful when QRM or QSB is present. Including channel ID information reduces the data rate, however.

As an example, a telemetry frame for an imaginary satellite using a nine channel system is shown in Table 14.4. The first digit in the channel contains ID information but it does not uniquely identify the channel. By noting the order in which the channels are received we can assign unique labels consisting of the ID number and a letter (not transmitted). Our labeling system is shown in the second row of Table 14.4. The last two digits in each channel represent the encoded information. To decode a channel one refers to published information about the specific satellite to determine which parameter is being measured and to obtain the simple algebraic equation needed to translate the raw data into a meaningful quantity. For example, a description of the imaginary satellite might tell us that channel 1A is total solar panel current, and that multiplying the raw data (42) by 30 will yield the value of total solar panel current in milliamperes, (1260 mA) at the time the measurement was taken. The procedure outlined here applies to OSCARs 6, 7 and 8 and, with minor modifications, to most RS satellites. (The RS spacecraft used one or two letters to identify each channel.)

Advanced Telemetry Formats. With the telemetry system in recent satellites being controlled by the onboard computer the traditional concept of a fixed telemetry frame is essentially obsolete. A frame may contain a fixed number of channels but the channels are selected by software. A channel generally consists of at least five integers, two or three to provide unique identification and three or more to encode the data to a high accuracy. The telemetry system on the MicroSats allows for 200 telemetry pick-off points. Ground station software is usually designed to identify the channel being sent, apply the correct equation to the raw data, and display the contents in a convenient format or save it for later analysis. In the future many of these chores may be handled by the spacecraft. For example, pacsat telemetry will consist of plain text packets similar to other mail packets.

Over the years a number of sophisticated encoding systems have been used to downlink telemetry data from amateur spacecraft. These include the 1200 bps Bell-202 system on early UoSATs, the 400 BPS BPSK system on OSCARs 10 and 13, the PACSAT 1200 baud BPSK system, and the UoSAT 9600 baud FSK system. Each required a different modem. In the future Digital Signal Processor or computer sound cards may eliminate this complication.

Table 14.5
Gain Pattern Simulation Equation Factors

n	Gain 2(n+1)	Gain dB$_i$	Half-power beamwidth
isotropic	—	0	—
0	2	3.0	180°
0.5	3	4.8	151°
1	4	6.0	120°
2	6	7.8	90°
3	8	9.0	74.9°
4	10	10.0	65.5°
6	14	11.5	54.0°
8	18	12.6	47.0°
12	26	14.1	38.6°
16	34	15.3	33.5°
20	42	16.2	30.0°
24	50	17.0	27.4°

The radiation pattern of a great many common beam antennas can be approximated by $2(n+1)\cos^n(\theta)$, where n is related to the maximum gain as specified in the table. (See Table 10.1.)

Antennas

Satellite antenna selection is closely linked to mission objectives, type of orbit, attitude stabilization, frequencies being used, desired coverage, spacecraft structure, launch-vehicle constraints and other factors. With low-altitude satellites (OSCARs 5-8, 12 and the PACSAT series) spacecraft designers were able to choose relatively omni-directional antennas and passive magnetic stabilization schemes, a combination that greatly simplified other aspects of satellite design. When mechanical considerations permitted, antennas that produced a circularly polarized wave such as the canted turnstile (a turnstile with drooping elements) were used. The advantages of circular polarization are only partially realized, however, since radiation from the canted turnstile is only fully circular along the main axis. At 29 MHz, mechanical constraints make it impossible to provide circular polarization on the spacecraft. Dipole antennas have been used at this frequency.

Since the relatively large 29 MHz antenna must be folded out of the way during launch, several schemes for antenna deployment have been tried (all successfully). With OSCARs 5 and 6, springy flexible elements made from metal similar to that used in a carpenter's rule was employed. The explosive bolts that released the satellite from the launch vehicle also released the folded antenna, allowing it to extend to its full, precut length.

On OSCAR 7 a different technique, producing a much stiffer antenna, was tried. Imagine a sheet of newspaper rolled into a two-inch diameter tube. Grab an inside corner and pull until the tube reaches about three times its original length. You've just modeled the OSCAR 7 29 MHz antenna elements. The design and fabrication of antenna elements of this type, using springy metals that self-deploy when released by explosive bolts, is a very difficult and specialized procedure. Commercial products are prohibitively expensive for most OSCAR applications.

The unit used on OSCAR 7 was a donation.

On OSCAR 8 yet another method was tried. The 29 MHz antenna consisted of motor-deployed concentric tubes much like the car radio antennas that automatically extend when the radio is turned on. Producing motors that work reliably in the vacuum and temperature extremes of space is also a tricky and expensive business. A lot of nail biting occurred during the hours between OSCAR 8's launch and the successful commanding of the 29 MHz antenna deployment mechanism. In sum, while all the approaches to 29 MHz dipole design for OSCAR spacecraft have worked, none of the methods are completely satisfactory with respect to cost, operation and reliability.

At 146 and 435 MHz, quarter-wavelength monopoles (frequently called stubs) can be formed from springy, whip-like material that is bent back against the spacecraft during launch and freed when the spacecraft is released from the launch vehicle. At 146 MHz and at higher frequencies the spacecraft structure has a major effect on antenna pattern so sophisticated theoretical models and empirical testing must be used to evaluate designs.

High altitude spacecraft require beam antennas. Because of its size, the 146 MHz antenna usually presents the biggest problem. The antenna selected for the 146 MHz link on OSCARs 10 and 13 was essentially an array of three Yagis. Each Yagi has a driven element and a director. The feed system introduces appropriate phase delays ($120°$ and $240°$) so that circular polarization is produced. The springy elements, which extend from each of the three arms on the satellite, are simply bent out of the way during launch.

The 70 cm antennas on OSCARs 10 and 13 can also be thought of as an array of three Yagis. Each Yagi consists of a driven element in front of a reflecting plate. Because of the position on the spacecraft the 70 cm antenna has a cleaner pattern. The phasing system produces circular polarization. At 23 cm and 13 cm single helix antennas have worked well. (The quadrifiliar helix isn't used because it doesn't have sufficient gain near apogee.) These spacecraft also include quarter wave 146 and 435 MHz monopoles for use near perigee and shortly after launch before the spacecraft has been properly oriented.

SELECTING ANTENNAS FOR PHASE 3 MISSIONS

When selecting an antenna for a Phase 3 spacecraft one must choose a radiation pattern that strikes a good balance between coverage and signal level at the ground. Consider the geometry shown in Figure 14.5. Because of the large slant range at apogee, we want a beam antenna on the spacecraft. But, for spin stabilized spacecraft like OSCARs 10 and 13, the narrow beamwidth of a high-gain antenna can lead to poor results when the satellite is away from apogee because ground stations will be far off to the side of the satellite antenna pattern (large squint angle). Let's look at one approach to modeling the situation.

J. Kraus has shown[10] that the radiation patterns of a great many common beam antennas can be approximated by the expression

$$2(n+1)\cos^n(\theta) \qquad \text{(Eq 14.1)}$$

In other words, the gain in a given direction can be calculated approximately using only θ and n, where θ is the angle between the antenna axis and the observer. The parameter n is chosen to produce the correct gain when θ is zero (on axis). See Table 14.5. With this formula and our knowledge of satellite orbits we can calculate the signal power at the subsatellite point (SSP) as the satellite travels around its orbit (see Figure 14.5). The results for beams having gains of 6 dB_i and 10 dB_i, and for an isotropic antenna, are shown in Figure 14.6.[11]

With Phase 3 OSCARs 10 and 13 a beam was used during the apogee portion of the orbit and a $1/4$-wavelength whip was switched to the point where it provided better signals. Radiation from a whip along the +Z axis spills over into the hemisphere centered about the –Z axis. As a crude approximation let's assume that the signal level from the whip is similar to that of the isotropic antenna. Referring to Figure 14.6, we see that the switch from beam to whip should be make when θ is approximately equal to $56°$ for the 10 dB_i beam and $76°$ for the 6 dB_i beam. Also, the 6 dB_i antenna begins to outperform the 10 dB_i beam when θ increases past $43°$. Each angle corresponds to a specific time from apogee. From Figure 14.6 we see that the 10-dB_i beam will provide superior performance (by 0 to 4 dB) during a 7.5-hour segment of each orbit (3.75 hours on either side of apogee). The 6-dB_i antenna will provide the best performance (by 0 to 3.5 dB) during 2.0 hours of each orbit (a one-hour segment centered at $\theta = +60°$ and a one-hour segment centered at $\theta = –60°$).

From the viewpoint of stations at the SSP, the 10-dB_i antenna appears preferable. In fact, you might wonder why we don't consider higher-gain antennas. A more careful analysis would take into account (1) signal levels at ground stations located away from the SSP and (2) the fact that its often necessary to align the spacecraft Z-axis in a slightly different orientation to account for poor sun angles on the solar panels. When this is done it makes higher gains less appealing. There is no clearcut "best" choice, but gains between 6 dB_i and 12 dB_i appear to be a good compromise for spin stabilized Phase 3 spacecraft. Mechanical constraints limit the amount of gain that can actually be ob-

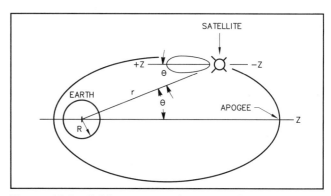

Figure 14.5—Orbit geometry for evaluating potential Phase 3 satellite antennas.

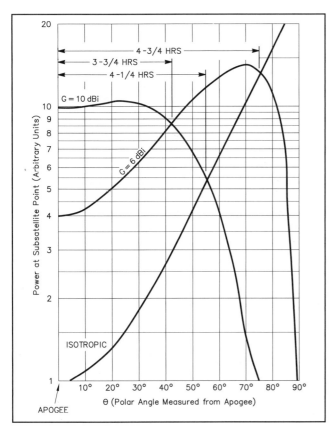

Figure 14.6—Graph: Relative power at SSP as function of Phase 3 satellite position in orbital plane.

tained aboard the spacecraft at 2 m. 23 cm and 13 cm links use higher gain but, as Figure 14.6 demonstrates, these modes only provide acceptable performance near apogee.

If antenna gain is too high (greater than about 18 dB$_i$ for OSCAR 13 apogee, 20 dB$_i$ for P3D apogee) the main lobe becomes so narrow that it no longer covers the entire Earth at apogee. Gains of this magnitude can be obtained at frequencies above about 1 GHz. This places an upper limit on the gain that can be used since whole Earth coverage is desired for amateur missions. Several approaches to antenna design are possible. One is to use a very high antenna near apogee and another lower gain antenna during other sections of the orbit. Another is to place an array of medium gain antennas on the spacecraft. By varying the phase of the power fed to each it's possible to synthesize an optimal pattern for each section of the orbit. Figure 14.7 shows what can be done with a spin stabilized spacecraft.

OSCAR 40 uses a three axis stabilization scheme. As a result, the spacecraft Z axis orientation can be adjusted throughout the orbit to continually point at the center of the Earth. This makes it possible to use higher gain antennas on all links. As a result of the increased antenna gain and the higher transmitter power OSCAR 40 provides at least 8 dB better performance on all links (up and down) that were used on OSCARs 10 and 13.

OSCAR 40 uses a variety of antennas including designs based on the whip, dipole, patch, parabolic dish, horn and

short back fire. Modeling software played a very prominent role in optimizing antenna designs. The OSCAR 40 antennas are described in detail in Appendix C.[12]

PREDICTING LINK RELATIVE SIGNAL LEVELS

Eq 14.1 can be used to construct a model predicting relative uplink or downlink signal levels for spin stabilized satellites if we replace θ with the squint angle Ψ. Link signal strength at time t will be proportional to

$$\frac{2\left(N+1\right)\cos^n\left(\Psi\right)}{\rho^2}$$

where ρ is the range.

For our reference signal level, S_o, we'll assume (1) the satellite is directly overhead at apogee and (2) the squint angle is zero. The ratio of signal level at time t, $S(t)$, to reference signal level is

$$\frac{S(t)}{S_o} = \frac{\left(r_o - R\right)^2}{\rho^2}\cos^n\left(\Psi\right) \qquad \text{(Eq 14.2)}$$

The predicted relative signal level (PRSL) in dB is then given by

$$PRSL = 20\log(r_o - R) - 20\log(\rho) + 10n\log[\cos(\Psi)]$$

$$\text{(Eq 14.3)}$$

As an example we apply Eq 14.3 to the OSCAR 13 Mode L uplink. Replace $r_o - R$ by the apogee height and use Table 14.5 and the published antenna gain (or halfpower beamwidth) of OSCAR 13's 23 cm helix antenna (12.2 dB$_i$) to select a value of 7.3 for n. For the OSCAR 13 Mode B downlink (with ρ in km)

$$PRSL \text{ [dB]} = 91.2 - 20\log(\rho) + 73\log[\cos(\Psi)] \qquad \text{(Eq 14.4)}$$

The two variables appearing on the right side of Eq 14.4, squint angle and range, are available in most tracking programs. Incorporating a value for PRSL in these programs is therefore relatively simple.

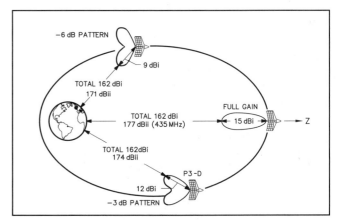

Figure 14.7—OSCAR 40 synthesized antenna patterns.

STRUCTURAL, ENVIRONMENTAL-CONTROL, AND ENERGY-SUPPLY SUBSYSTEMS

Structural Subsystem

The spacecraft structural subsystem, the frame that holds it all together, serves a number of functions including physical support of antennas, solar cells and internal electronic modules; protection of onboard subsystems from the environment during launch and while in space; conduction of heat into and out of the satellite interior; mating to the launch vehicle and so on. Structural design (size, shape and materials) is influenced by launch vehicle constraints, by the spacecraft's mission, and by the orbit and attitude stabilization system employed. OSCARs 6, 7 and 8 had masses in the 18 to 30 kg range. The larger early Phase 3 spacecraft containing either a kick motor or liquid fuel engine were in the 90 to 125 kg range at launch. Spacecraft in the MicroSat series have a mass of approximately 10 kg contained in a cube roughly 23 cm on edge. P3D will weigh approximately 400 kg at launch.

The prominent features one observes when looking at a satellite are the attach fitting used to mate the satellite to the launch vehicle, antennas for the various radio links, solar cells, the heat-radiative coating designed to achieve the desired spacecraft thermal equilibrium and, for Phase 3 the nozzle of the apogee kick motor. Insofar as possible, AMSAT satellite structures are fabricated from sheet aluminum to minimize the complexity of machining operations.

The MicroSat structure is unique. It consists of five modules (trays) formed into a composite stack held together with stainless steel tie bolts. See Figure 14.8. Each frame is approximately 210×210×40 mm. Aluminum side panels, about 5 mm thick, holding the solar panels cover the sides. The entire structure is a rectangular solid 230×230×213 mm. The trays form an extremely sturdy structure; no additional spacecraft frame is needed.

Each tray contains an electronic subassembly. The basic modules, needed by every MicroSat, are the (1) battery/BCR unit, (2) receiver unit, (3) CPU/RAM and (4) transmitter unit. The fifth module is the TSFR tray. TSFR stands for "this space for rent." The TSFR tray is essentially space set aside for experimental mission-specific subsystems. One significant aspect of the MicroSat structure is that, by its very nature, it invites small amateur groups around the world to build a TSFR module for inclusion on future spacecraft. It also establishes a standard structure that greatly simplifies the work of groups who wish to build their own MicroSat and reduces the cost of future MicroSats.

The OSCAR 40 structure was designed to accommodate to ESA requirements. When ESA launches two large primary satellites they are placed one above the other and separated by a conical adapter. The bottom of the lower satellite is attached to the rocket. The bottom of the upper satellite is attached to the adapter ring that is in turn at-

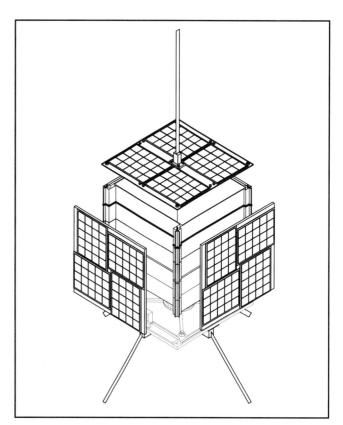

Figure 14.8—MicroSat structure.

tached to the top of the lower satellite. The adapter ring must therefore be capable of supporting the upper satellite during the entire launch phase. And, the upper spacecraft can weigh up to 10,350 pounds.

AMSAT studied the standard adapter ring to see if it could be incorporated into a P3 satellite spaceframe. However, this approach did not lead to promising results. In discussions with ESA AMSAT suggested an alternative approach that would use a cylindrical Specific Bearing Structure (SBS) as a spacer between the two primary spacecraft with the OSCAR 40 spaceframe contained inside the SBS. After extensive consultations, ESA agreed to the approach. The design, construction and testing of the SBS was a major technical accomplishment for AMSAT.

The spaceframe for OSCAR 40 has a completely different shape from that of previous Phase 3 spacecraft. It's the first AMSAT satellite to employ solar panels that extend out after launch. The central structure is hexagonal and weighs about 60 kg, nearly 10 times the weight of OSCARs 10 and 13. The entire spacecraft including the spaceframe, everything mounted to it, fuel and the SBS will weigh about 400 kg. Drawings of the OSCAR 40 spacecraft are contained in Appendix C.[13]

Environmental Control

The function of a spacecraft environmental control subsystem is to regulate temperatures at various points, shield against high-energy particles and protect the onboard electronics from RF interference. We'll focus on thermal control.

The temperature of a satellite is determined by the inflow and outflow of energy. More specifically, the satellite temperature will adjust itself so heat inflow equals heat outflow. Although we talk about the "temperature" of the satellite, different parts of a spacecraft are at different temperatures and these temperatures are constantly varying.

The goal of the spacecraft designer is to create a model of the spacecraft and its environment that will accurately predict the average and extreme temperatures that each unit of the spacecraft will exhibit during all phases of satellite operation. This includes prelaunch, where the satellite may sit atop a rocket more than a week baking under a hot tropical sun; the launch and orbit-insertion sequence of events; and the final orbit where, during certain seasons of the year, the spacecraft may go for months without any eclipse time. (An eclipse occurs when the Earth passes between the spacecraft and the sun. During other seasons it may be eclipsed for several hours each day.) Since excessive temperature extremes, either too hot or too cold, may damage the battery or electronic or mechanical subsystems permanently, the thermal design must keep the temperatures of susceptible components within bounds at all times.

Once the satellite is in the vacuum of space, heat is transferred only by radiation and conduction; convection need not be considered. The complete energy balance model of Phase 3A depicted the satellite as being composed of 121 subunits, each connected via conduction and radiation links to several other subunits. To solve the resulting energy-balance equations mathematically, the designers had to manipulate 121 nonlinear coupled equations, each consisting of about three or four terms. This was not a job for pad and pencil. A fairly large computer was needed. Even with sophisticated computer models, achieving a precision of ±10 K is difficult; commercial satellite builders usually resort to testing the thermal balance of full scale models in space simulators. The Phase 3A thermal design problem was handled by Dick Jansson, WD4FAB, using computer time donated by the Martin Marietta Corp.

Dick also handled the OSCAR 40 design. This time it was done on a powerful personal computer using a model involving 450 nodes (temperature points) and 3750 heat conduction links.[14]

Earlier OSCARs used a far simpler and less accurate approach to thermal design that nevertheless provided reasonable results. See, for example Figure 1.3 which shows the thermal behavior of OSCARs I and II. Since the details of the simple approach provide a good introduction to the science (art?) of thermal design, we'll go through an example.

Thermal Design: A Simple Example

The sun is the sole source of energy input to the satellite. Quantitatively we can write:

$$P_{in} = P_o <A> \alpha\beta \qquad \text{(Eq 14.5)}$$

where

P_{in} = energy input to the satellite

P_o = solar constant = incident energy per unit time on a surface of unit area (perpendicular to direction of radiation) at 1.49×10^{11} m (earth-sun distance) from the sun.

$P_o = 1380$ W/m^2

$<A>$ = effective capture area of the satellite for solar radiation

α = absorptivity (fraction of time satellite is exposed to the sun during each complete orbit)

β = eclipse factor (fraction of time satellite is exposed to the sun during each complete orbit)

Power output from the satellite consists of blackbody radiation at temperature T, and the radio emissions. Since blackbody radiation is very much greater than the radio emissions, we can ignore the latter.

$$P_o = A\sigma eT^4 \qquad \text{(Eq 14.6)}$$

where

P_{out} = energy radiated by satellite

A = surface area of satellite

σ = Stefan-Boltzmann constant = $\dfrac{5.67 \times 10^{-8} \text{ joules}}{k^4 m^2 s}$

e = average emissivity factor for satellite surface

T = temperature (K)

For equilibrium, incoming and outgoing radiation must balance,

$$P_{in} = P_{out} \quad \text{or}$$

$$P_o <A>\alpha\beta = A\sigma eT^4 \quad \text{(energy balance equation)} \qquad \text{(Eq 14.7)}$$

Solving for temperature, we obtain

$$T = \left(\frac{P_o^{ab} <A>}{\sigma e A} \right)^{1/4} \qquad \text{(Eq 14.8)}$$

Reasonable average values for the various parameters are $\sigma = 0.8$, $\beta = 0.8$ and $e = 0.5$. For AMSAT-OSCAR 7, A = 7770 cm^2 and $<A>$ = 1870 cm^2. Inserting these values in Eq 14.8 we obtain T = 294 K. This is equivalent to 21°C, which is close to the observed equilibrium temperature of OSCAR 7. Over the course of a year, as β varied from 0.8 to 1.0, the temperature of OSCAR 7 varied between 275 K and 290 K. The transponder final amplifier, of course, ran considerably hotter.

Passive methods used to achieve a desired spacecraft operating temperature include adjusting surface absorptivity (α) and emissivity (e) by roughening or painting and taking thermal conductivity of structural components into account when the spacecraft is designed. Active techniques for temperature control include fitting the spacecraft with shutters, or louvers, that are controlled by bimetallic strips or conducting pipes that can, by ground command, be filled with Helium gas or evacuated. To a certain extent active temperature control has been employed on OSCAR spacecraft; in several instances specific subsystems have been activated primarily because of their effect on spacecraft temperature.

Heat pipe technology is an important component in the design of OSCAR 40. A heat pipe consists of a long, thin evacuated tube partially filled with a liquid and a material that serves as a wick (supports capillary action). The fluid is vaporized at the hot end. The vapors flow through the hollow core of the heat pipe and condense at the cold end. The fluid then circulates back to the hot end via capillary action through the wicking material. A well designed heat pipe can, kg for kg, transport many times more heat than the best conducting materials. The process requires no power and works in a zero-gravity environment.

OSCAR 40 contains four heat pipes using anhydrous ammonia as the transport liquid. Each forms a hexagonal ring just inside the spacecraft structure.[7]

Energy-Supply Subsystems

Communications satellites can be classified as active or passive. An example of a passive satellite is a big balloon (Echo I, launched August 12, 1960, was 30 meters in diameter when fully inflated) coated with conductive material that reflects radio signals. Used as a passive reflector, such a satellite does not need any electronic components or power source. While such a satellite is appealingly simple, the radio power it reflects back to Earth is less, by a factor of 10 million (70 dB), than the signal transmitted by a transponder aboard an active satellite (assuming equal uplink signal strength and a comparison based on equal satellite masses in the 50-kg range).[15]

An active satellite (one with a transponder) needs power. The energy source supplying the power should be reliable, efficient, low-cost and long-lived. By efficient we mean that the ratio of available electrical power to weight and the ratio of available electrical power to waste heat should be large. We examine three energy sources that have been studied extensively: chemical, nuclear and solar.[16]

CHEMICAL POWER SOURCES

Chemical power sources include primary cells, secondary cells and fuel cells. Early satellites such as Sputnik I, Explorer I and the first few OSCARs were flown with primary cells. When the batteries ran down, the satellite "died." Spacecraft of this type usually had lifetimes of a few weeks, although Explorer I with low-power transmitters (about 70 mW total), ran almost four months on mercury (Hg) batteries. These early experimental spacecraft demonstrated the feasibility of using satellites for communications and scientific exploration and thereby provided the impetus for the development of longer-lived power systems. Today, batteries (secondary cells in this case) are used mainly to store energy aboard satellites to cushion against peak loads and to power the spacecraft during eclipse periods; they are no longer used as a primary power source. Table 14.6 provides a capsule history of OSCAR spacecraft power systems and their mission impact.

Batteries for early OSCAR missions were donated by companies or provided by government agencies from spares remaining when programs ended. In the early 1980s AMSAT realized that a more stable source was necessary to support the activities of the growing amateur program. AMSAT therefore initiated an ongoing battery qualification program to provide cells for future missions. Larry Kayser (VE3PAZ) looked into the procedures used to "space qualify" batteries. He concluded that carefully screened commercial grade NiCds were likely to perform as reliably. Kayser and a group of amateurs in Ottawa purchased a large supply of 6 Ah GE aviation NiCds and put them through a qualification procedure that involved X-raying to look for internal flaws and extensive computer controlled charge-discharge cycling with extremely detailed computer monitoring. All anomalous cells, whether better or worse than the others, were eliminated. The remaining cells were matched, potted, and stored in a freezer to prevent deterioration.

OSCAR 11 used cells from this batch and it has performed flawlessly since March 1984. The MicroSats and UoSATs launched in late 1989 were also powered by cells from this supply. AMSAT continues to monitor emerging technologies such as sealed nickel-hydrogen batteries that have energy densities about five times the value of NiCd cells. However, cost and reliability remain important selection criteria so there's good reason to stick to proven technology that's served us well in the past.

Another chemical power system, the fuel cell has been used as a source of energy on manned space missions where large amounts of power are required over relatively short time spans. Fuel cells do not appear to be appropriate for current OSCAR missions.

NUCLEAR POWER SOURCES

One nuclear power source to be flight-tested is the radioisotopic-thermoelectric power plant. In devices of this type, heat from decaying radioisotopes is converted directly to electricity by thermoelectric couples. Some early US Transit navigation satellites, the SNAP 3B and SNAP 9A (25 W), have flown generators of this type. The US is not currently using nuclear power in Earth orbit but development work on reactors for "Star Wars" related projects continues. The USSR currently flies nuclear reactors on Radar Ocean Reconnaissance Satellites (RORSATs). In 1989 some 34 deactivated but still radioactive reactors were orbiting the Earth.

Nuclear power sources have a high available-power-to-weight ratio, a very long operational lifetime and the ability to function in a high radiation environment. But they generate large amounts of waste heat and have a high hardware cost per watt because of the fuel. (They also have an extremely high cost due to related safety concerns and insurance). Nuclear power is most useful on missions where one of the following conditions holds: solar intensity is greatly reduced (deep-space), the radiation environment would quickly destroy solar cells (orbits inside the Van Allen Belts) or very large amounts of power are required.

There are strong pressures in the US and USSR to put an end to the use of nuclear power in Earth orbit. The primary

Table 14.6
OSCAR Satellite Power Systems

Satellite	Primary Power[1]	Secondary	Lifetime	Failure Mode
OSCAR I	Mercury battery	—	21 days	reentry
OSCAR II	Mercury battery	—	19 days	reentry
OSCAR III	Si solar cells (2.5 W)	Silver-zinc battery	several months	battery failure?
OSCAR IV	Si solar cells (10.0 W)	battery	85 days	? (partial launch failure)
OSCAR 5	Manganese alkaline battery	—	52 days	battery depletion
AMSAT-OSCAR 6	Si solar cells (5.5 W)	NiCd battery	4.5 years	battery failure
AMSAT-OSCAR 7	Si solar cells (15 W, 9%)	NiCd battery	6.5 years	battery failure
AMSAT-OSCAR 8	Si solar cells (15 W, 8%)	NiCd battery	5.3 years	battery failure
UoSAT-OSCAR 9	Si solar cells (17 W, 12.5%)	NiCd battery	—	battery failure
AMSAT-OSCAR 10	Si solar cells (50 W, 12.5%)	NiCd battery	8 years	reentry
UoSAT-OSCAR 11	Si solar cells (25 W)	NiCd battery[2]	—	—
Fuji-OSCAR 12	Si solar cells (8.5 W)	NiCd battery	3+ years	[3]
AMSAT-OSCAR 13	Si solar cells (50 W)	NiCd battery	—	—
UoSAT-OSCAR 14	Si and GaAs solar cells	NiCd battery[2]	—	—
UoSAT-OSCAR 15	Si, GaAs and InP solar cells	NiCd battery[2]	<1 day	unknown
Pacsat-OSCAR 16	Si solar cells (15 W, 15%)	NiCd battery[2]	—	—
DOVE-OSCAR 17	Si solar cells (15 W, 15%)	NiCd battery[2]	—	—
Webersat OSCAR-18	Si solar cells (15 W, 15%)	NiCd battery[2]	—	—
Lusat-OSCAR 19	Si solar cells (15 W, 15%)	NiCd battery[2]	—	—
Fuji-OSCAR 20	GaAs solar cells (13 W)	NiCd battery	—	—
OSCAR 40	Si solar cells (620 W, 14.3%)	NiCd battery		

Notes
[1]For solar cells power is specified with satellite in optimal orientation; beginning of life (BOL) efficiency is reported if known.
[2]Off-the-shelf commercial batteries space qualified by AMSAT.
[3]Operation terminated Nov 5, 1989 due to gradual decrease in power budget resulting from solar cell deterioration and reduced battery capacity.

reason is the danger of nuclear contamination in case of launch failure or satellite reentry.[17,18] Satellites with nuclear power are often placed in near Earth orbit with the intention of boosting them to a higher orbit when they reach the end of their useful life. However, many believe the likelihood of a spacecraft failure before the satellite is moved to a higher orbit is unacceptably high. This has been clearly demonstrated since three nuclear powered spacecraft have reentered and spewed radioactive material in either the atmosphere or on the ground (SNAP-9A [1964], COSMOS 954 [1978], COSMOS 1402 [1983]). The growing problem of space debris also poses a risk to these spacecraft. A second reason for outlawing nuclear powered spacecraft is that they cause severe gamma ray pollution and are having a serious impact on gamma-ray astronomy.[19]

Nuclear power is clearly out of the question for OSCAR satellites. If the previous facts don't convince you then practical concerns like the cost of insurance and the facilities, security precautions, and paperwork associated with handling nuclear material certainly will. This conclusion does not, of course, imply that nuclear power is not suitable for scientific deep-space missions. The Voyager mission to the outer planets would have been impossible without the 400 W nuclear generator aboard.

SOLAR POWER SOURCES

The third power source we consider is solar. The first solar cells were built in 1954 using silicon.[20] Solar cells quickly became the dominant supplier of power to space-craft. However, they are far from ideal for this application. They compete for mounting space on the outer surface of the satellite with antennas and heat-radiating coatings. Their efficiency decreases with time, especially when the satellite orbit passes through the Van Allen radiation belts (roughly at altitudes between 1600 and 8000 km). They work most efficiently below 0° C (most electronics systems perform best at about 10° C). They call for a spacecraft orientation that may conflict with mission objectives. Finally, they produce no output when eclipsed from the sun.

Despite these shortcomings, power sources that use solar cells to produce electrical energy and secondary cells to store energy are by far the simplest for long lifetime spacecraft. They're affordable; they generate little waste heat and they provide acceptable ratios of available-electric power to weight.

In Earth orbit a 1-meter-square solar panel, oriented perpendicular to incoming solar radiation intercepts about 1380 W. The amount of this power that can be used on a spacecraft depends on solar cell efficiency. The efficiency of cells used on OSCAR satellites has nearly doubled in the past 15 years. The silicon solar cells used on the initial group of MicroSats employed back-surface reflector technology to produce an efficiency of more than 15%. In the near future we'll probably use GaAs solar cells having even higher efficiencies. In 1988 researchers reported the production of two layer cells using Si and GaAs that had an efficiency of 31%.[21] While these are one of a kind laboratory devices they do demonstrate solar cell technology is continuing to move forward. A few years ago a satellite the size of a MicroSat would not have been capable of producing enough power to supply a useful mission.

Once a satellite is launched, its solar cell efficiency begins to decrease due to radiation damage. To minimize the rate of decrease the solar cells are usually covered by glass cover slides. These cover slides tend to reduce initial efficiency and increase spacecraft weight. One of the mission payloads on UoSAT E was the Solar-Cell Experiment designed to evaluate the long term performance of various new solar cell technologies in the space environment. Cells tested included: gallium arsenide, indium phosphide and new silicon designs. The study focused on issues related to radiation degradation over time using several cover slide geometries.

PRACTICAL ENERGY SUBSYSTEM

The typical AMSAT satellite energy system consists of a source, a storage device and conditioning equipment (shown in Figure 14.9). The source consists of silicon solar cells (future missions may use GaAs cells). A storage unit is needed because of eclipses (satellite in Earth's shadow) and the varying load; Nickel-Cadmium secondary cells are currently being used. The failure mode column of Table 14.6 points out the critical importance of the energy subsystem to long term mission success.

Power conditioning equipment typically flown on AMSAT spacecraft includes a battery charge regulator (BCR) and at least one instrument switching regulator (ISR) to provide dc-to-dc conversion with changes of voltage, regulation and protection. Because failures in the energy subsystem could totally disable the spacecraft, special attention is paid to ensuring continuity of operation. BCRs and ISRs usually are built as redundant twin units with switch-over between units controlled automatically, in case of internal failure, or by ground command.

Phase 3 spacecraft carry two separate batteries: a lower capacity backup capable of providing full operation through all but the longest eclipses, is kept in cold storage. Solar cell strings are isolated by diodes, so a failure in one string will lower total output capacity but will not otherwise affect spacecraft operation. These diodes also prevent the battery from discharging through the cells when the satellite is in darkness. The MicroSat approach to reliability does not include the use of redundant power systems.

The MicroSats use an interesting method for battery charge regulation. Spacecraft transmitters are designed to operate efficiently over a wide range of power levels running from a fraction of a watt up to about 4 W. The onboard computer selects a power level that places minimum strain on the battery system. Software is the key element in a feedback loop that operates in an overdamped condition. The software is periodically refined to maximize spacecraft longevity.

When the energy supply subsystem provides sufficient energy to operate a satellite's major systems on a continuous basis we say the spacecraft has a *positive power budget*. If some subsystems must be turned off periodically for the storage batteries to be recharged, we say the spacecraft has a *negative power budget*. An illustration of how spacecraft geometry can be taken into account when estimating the average power output of a solar cell array covering a spacecraft can be found in the references.[22] For information on the design and performance of the solar arrays used on a commercial spacecraft, INTELSAT IV-A, see reference 20.[23]

ATTITUDE-CONTROL AND PROPULSION SUBSYSTEMS

Attitude-Control Subsystem

The orientation of a satellite (its attitude) with respect to the Earth and sun greatly affects the effective antenna gain, solar cell power production, thermal equilibrium and scientific instrument operation. Attitude-control subsystems vary widely in complexity. A simple system might consist of a frame-mounted bar magnet that tends to align itself parallel to the Earth's magnetic field; a complex system might use cold gas jets, solid rockets and inertia wheels, all operating under computer control in conjunction with a sophisticated system of sensors. Attitude-control systems can be used to provide three-axis stabilization, or to point a selected satellite axis in a particular direction—toward the Earth, in a fixed direction in inertial space (with respect to the fixed stars), or parallel to the Earth's local magnetic field. Fixing a spacecraft's orientation in inertial space is generally accomplished by spinning the spacecraft about its major axis (spin-stabilized).

Attitude-control systems are classified as *active* or *passive*. Passive systems do not require power or sensor signals for their operation. Consequently, they are simpler and more reliable, but also less flexible. Some of the attitude-control systems in general use are described in the following paragraphs.

MASS EXPULSORS

Devices of this type are based on the rocket principle and are classified as active and relatively complex. Examples are cold gas jets, solid-propellant rockets and ion-thrust engines. Mass expulsors are often used to spin a satellite around its principal axis. The resulting angular momentum of the satellite is then parallel to the spin axis. As a result of conservation of angular momentum the spin axis will tend to maintain a fixed direction in inertial space.

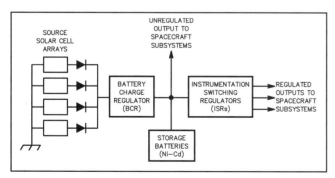

Figure 14.9—Block diagram: Satellite energy subsystem.

ANGULAR MOMENTUM RESERVOIRS

This category includes devices based on the inertia (fly) wheel principle. Assume that a spacecraft contains a flywheel as part of a dc motor that can be powered up on ground command. If the angular momentum of the flywheel is changed, then the angular momentum of the rest of the satellite must change in an equal and opposite direction (conservation of angular momentum). These systems are classified as active.

ENVIRONMENTAL-FORCE COUPLER

Every satellite is coupled to (affected by) its environment in a number of ways. In the two-body central force model (outlined in Chapter 12) the satellite and Earth were first treated as point masses at their respective centers of mass. Further analysis showed that the departure of the Earth from spherical symmetry causes readily observable perturbations of the satellite's path. The departure of the satellite's mass distribution from spherical symmetry likewise causes readily observable effects. An analysis of the mass distribution in the spacecraft defines a specific axis that tends to line up pointing toward the geocenter as a result of the Earth's gravity gradient. Gravity-gradient devices exploit this tendency. Anyone who's been on a sailboat, however, knows that gravity can produce two stable states. The gravity gradient effect is greatly accentuated when the spacecraft is in a very low orbit and if one of the satellite dimensions is much longer than the others. Attaching a long boom, with a weight at the far end, to the spacecraft is one way of achieving this configuration.

Another environmental factor that can be tapped for attitude control is the Earth's magnetic field. A strong bar magnet carried by the satellite will tend to align itself parallel to the local direction of this field (passive attitude control).

At any point in space the Earth's magnetic field can be characterized by its magnitude and direction. A simple model for the Earth's magnetic field employs a dipole offset somewhat from the Earth's rotational axis. The magnitude of a dipole field decreases as $1/r^3$, where r is the distance from the center of the Earth, so attitude control systems that depend on this field are most efficient at low altitudes. The direction of the magnetic field is often specified in terms of bearing and inclination (dip) angle. To describe bearing and dip we imagine a sphere concentric with the Earth drawn through the point of interest. Bearing and dip play the same role on this sphere that bearing and elevation play when describing a direction on the surface of the Earth. Figure 14.10 provides data on dip angle.

The Earth's magnetic field can also be exploited for attitude control via an active system based on electromagnets consisting of coils of wire. By passing current through these coils, one forms a temporary magnet. With proper timing, the coils can produce torques in any desired direction. Devices of this type are often called torquing coils.

Note that even if a satellite designer does not exploit magnetic or gravity-based environmental couplers for attitude control, these forces are always present and their ef-

fect on the satellite must be taken into account.

ENERGY ABSORBERS

Energy absorbers or dampers are used to convert undesired motional energy into heat. They are needed in conjunction with many of the previously mentioned attitude control schemes. For example, if dissipative forces did not exist, gravity gradient forces would cause the satellite's principal axis to swing pendulum-like about the local vertical instead of pointing toward the geocenter. Similarly, a bar magnet carried on a satellite would oscillate about the local magnetic field direction instead of lining up parallel to it. Dampers may consist of passive devices such as springs, viscous fluids or hysteresis rods (eddy-current brakes). At times, torquing coils are used to obtain similar results.

PRACTICAL ATTITUDE CONTROL

The attitude control systems that have been used on AMSAT spacecraft are summarized in Table 14.7. Passive magnetic stabilization was first tried on OSCAR 5 and it has since been used on numerous other Phase 2 spacecraft. When passive magnetic stabilization is used, Permalloy hysteresis damping rods are generally employed to reduce rotation about the spacecraft axis aligned parallel to the Earth's local magnetic field and to damp out small oscillations. Note that the principal axis of a spacecraft in a near polar orbit using this type of stabilization will rotate 720° in inertial space during each revolution of the Earth. By using Figure 14.10 and tracking software to observe the ground track of a satellite using passive magnetic stabilization you should be able to picture how the spacecraft antennas are oriented with respect to your location.

Because of temperature regulation concerns we don't want to allow one side of a spacecraft to face the sun for too long a time. Figure 14.11 shows the residual spin of OSCAR 7 for 15 months following launch. Part of this spin was introduced purposely for temperature regulation. The technique was a novel one wherein the elements of the canted turnstile antenna were painted with reflective paint on one side and absorbent paint on the other. Solar radiation pressure then produced a radiometer-like rotation

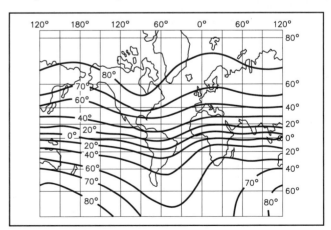

Figure 14.10—Inclination (dip) angle of Earth's magnetic field.

Table 14.7
OSCAR Satellite Attitude Control and Propulsion Systems

Satellite	Attitude Control System Design [propulsion system]
OSCAR I	None
OSCAR II	None
OSCAR III	None
OSCAR IV	Rocket ejection mechanism designed to provide initial spin stabilization
OSCAR 5	Permanent magnets, hysteresis damping rods
OSCAR 6	Permanent magnets, hysteresis damping rods
OSCAR 7	Permanent magnets, hysteresis damping rods, radiometer spin
OSCAR 8	Permanent magnets, hysteresis damping rods
Phase 3A	Spin stabilized, torquing coils, viscous liquid damping [solid propellent kick motor]
OSCAR 9	Gravity gradient boom and torquing coils
OSCAR 10	Spin stabilized, torquing coils, viscous liquid damping [liquid fuel kick motor]
OSCAR 11	Gravity gradient boom and torquing coils
OSCAR 12	Permanent magnets, hysteresis damping rods
OSCAR 13	Spin stabilized, torquing coils, liquid nutation dampers [liquid fuel kick motor]
OSCARs 14-17	Permanent magnets, hysteresis damping rods
OSCAR 40	Earth oriented, 3-axis stabilized using reaction control system and momentum storage, torquing coils and liquid nutation dampers [liquid fuel kick motor, arc-jet engine]

dubbed by users at the time as the "barbecue rotisserie" technique.

Because the camera on UoSAT must be pointed directly at the Earth, a passive magnetic stabilization system wasn't sufficient. To accomplish their mission objectives, UoSAT engineers chose a complex gravity-gradient stabilization system used in conjunction with torquing coils. Equipment modifications over the course of the UoSAT series, coupled with several generations of software optimization, have resulted in major performance improvements of this active control system. The evolution of the system hardware and control software represent an important contribution to spacecraft stabilization technology.

OSCARs 10 and 13 used spin stabilization (approximately 20 to 30 rpm). The spin axis is ideally aimed at the geocenter when the spacecraft is at apogee. However, for adequate spacecraft illumination the orientation must often depart from this ideal state. When the orbital inclination is near 57° these departures will be relatively small (on the order of 20°). The need for off-aiming occurs periodically. On average, a spacecraft like OSCAR 13 will need to have its attitude adjusted about every three months. Attitude information is obtained by sun and Earth sensors under the control of the spacecraft computer.

To produce attitude changes the torquing coils must be pulsed at precisely the correct time. Software loaded by a ground station directs the satellite computer to monitor sun and Earth sensors and pulse the torquing coils when the proper conditions are met. Because the magnitude of the Earth's magnetic field drops off as $1/r^3$ pulsing takes place near perigee to conserve satellite energy.

OSCARs 10 and 13 employed viscous fluid dampers to discourage nutation (small oscillations in the direction of the spin axis). These dampers consist of a mixture of glycerine and water (about 50/50) contained in thin tubes (about 0.2 cm in diameter and 40 cm long) that run along the far edge of each arm of the spacecraft.

The attitude control system on OSCAR 40 involves a number of major changes that allow this satellite to point the antennas directly at the center of the Earth throughout the entire orbit. It consists of a set of three magnetically suspended, orthogonally mounted reaction wheels, two torquing coils, and six nutation dampers. When outside forces are absent the angular momentum of the spacecraft remains constant but one can change the orientation of the body of the spacecraft by transferring momentum from one reaction wheel to another. The reaction wheels are magnetically suspended. Therefore there is no friction and no lubricants are needed. As a result, the estimated lifetime of this system is greater than the 10 to 15 year lifetime expected for the spacecraft. The torquing coils will be used to "dump" accumulated momentum so that the velocity of the reaction wheels can be kept in a desired range. The nutation dampers are similar

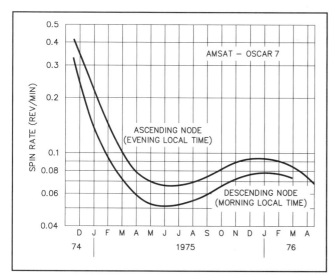

Figure 14.11—Graph: Spin rate of AMSAT-OSCAR 7 during the year following launch. (Data provided by John Fox, WØLER)

to those flown on OSCAR 10 and 13.

Propulsion Subsystem

The simplest type of space propulsion system consists of a small solid-propellant rocket which, once ignited, burns until the fuel is exhausted. Rockets of this type are often used to boost a satellite from a near-Earth orbit into an elliptical orbit with an apogee close to geostationary altitude (35,800 km) or to shift a satellite from this type of elliptical orbit into a circular orbit near geostationary altitude. Such rockets are known as "apogee kick motors" or simply "kick motors."

Liquid propellant motors are more complex to construct and they require on site fueling involving hazardous materials. However, they make multiple burns possible. This greatly increases mission planning flexibility.

Both kick motors and liquid propellant motors are extremely dangerous. Their use, handling, shipping and storage must conform to rigid safety procedures.

PHASE 3A: SOLID FUEL ROCKET

The only AMSAT satellite to use a kick motor was Phase 3A. The kick motor was intended to shift the spacecraft from the planned transfer orbit (roughly 300×35,800 km, 10° inclination) to the target operating orbit (1500×35,800 km, 57° inclination).

The kick motor was a solid-propellant Thiokol TEM 345-12 containing approximately 35 kg of a mixture of powdered aluminum and organic chemicals in a spherical shell (17 cm radius) with a single exit nozzle. See Figure 14.12. These units were originally designed as retro rockets for the Gemini spacecraft. The TEM 345 was capable of producing a velocity change of 1600 m/s during its single 20-second burn. Because of the launch failure this kick motor was never fired.

OSCARs 10, 13, 40: LIQUID FUEL ROCKET

OSCARs 10 and 13 used liquid-fuel rockets donated by the German aerospace firm Messerschmitt-Boelkow-Blohm. These units were significantly more powerful (400 N thrust) than the solid propellant motor used on P3A. The added thrust enabled AMSAT to fly a heavier spacecraft (thicker shielding, more electronics modules, and so on) and to compensate for the lower inclination and perigee of the transfer orbit being provided. The fuels used were Unsymmetrical DiMethyl Hydrazine (UDMH) and Nitrogen Tetroxide (N_2O_4). Both of these chemicals are extremely toxic. Those involved in loading fuel had to wear protective suits and breath filtered air. See Figure 14.13.

While the rocket motor and several of the associated valves were a donation much of the "plumbing" needed for the fuel system had to be devised and constructed by AMSAT personnel. The OSCAR 10 propulsion system is shown in Figure 14.14. Note the number of components required: filling valves, mixing valves, pressure regulators, check valves to prevent backflow, explosive (pyro) valves to prevent the system from accidentally firing be-

Figure 14.12—Photograph: Thiokol kick motor of type used on AMSAT Phase 3A spacecraft.

fore it was in orbit. Not shown in the figure is the Liquid Ignition Unit, the electronics module that directly controls the various valves and motor firing time. Construction of the two chamber fuel tank and the high pressure helium bottle presented significant challenges.

The orbit transfer strategy planned for OSCAR 10 included two burns. There were important advantages to a two burn transfer over a single burn maneuver. With a single burn transfer the spacecraft velocity passes through a danger zone where premature termination will cause the spacecraft to reenter at the next perigee. Another advantage of the two burn approach is that it gives AMSAT an opportunity to compensate for unexpected performance characteristics of the rocket unit; the initial burn serves in part as a calibration run. The first burn went relatively well — there was a small deviation from the expected burn duration that placed the spacecraft perigee somewhat higher than planned. However, the engine could not be reignited for a second burn due to the fact that a slow leak in the high pressure helium system during the week the spacecraft was being reoriented prevented the opening of valves feeding fuel to the thrust assembly.

OSCAR 13 used a liquid fuel kick motor similar to the one employed on OSCAR 10. MBB again agreed to donate a rocket but this time very little support hardware was available. For this mission AMSAT designed a new propellant

Figure 14.13—Photograph: Amateurs fueling OSCAR 13 rocket wearing protective suits.

flow/storage assembly that used available hardware and made the system more robust. A two burn strategy was again planned. This time the motor firings went perfectly. Each burn was accomplished exactly as planned. OSCAR 40 carries an updated liquid fuel motor.[24]

OTHER PROPULSION SYSTEMS

Water fuel rockets. AMSAT has evaluated the potential utility of a propulsion system using water as a fuel. The inherent safety of these systems is a key factor if AMSAT hopes to attain a useful orbit from a shuttle launch where it's unlikely that we could obtain permission to fly a solid fuel or chemical fuel kick motor. The problem with "water rockets" is that they take a considerable amount of time to affect orbit transfer. For example, its been estimated that it would require approximately one year to reach a Phase 3 type orbit from a shuttle launch. The economic consequences of the time involved in orbit change make water rockets impractical for commercial satellites so this method has never been developed. However, now that AMSAT is constructing spacecraft with long expected lifetimes, this approach may be well matched to our needs. There are two types of water rockets. Hughes Aircraft Company developed a working model of a rocket based on the electrolysis of water to produce hydrogen and oxygen. A second method involves the production of steam, which is released through a specially designed thruster. The steam method produces less impulse per unit of water than the electrolysis method but system complexity is extremely low and less external energy is required for operation. The reliability of such a system should therefore be extremely high.[25]

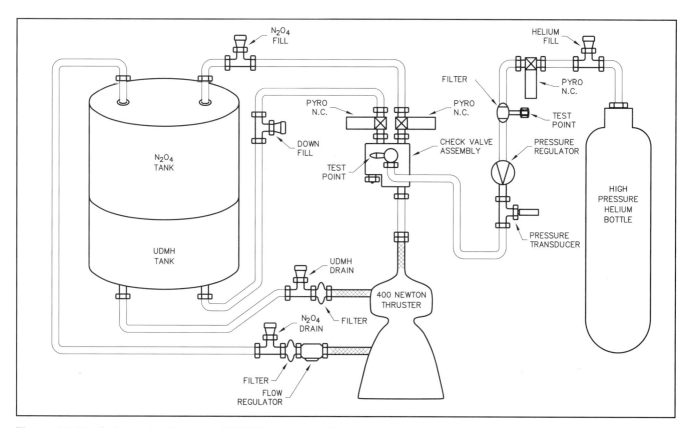

Figure 14.14—Schematic diagram: OSCAR 10 motor plumbing.

Arc-jet thruster. In addition to the main propulsion system, OSCAR 40 carries an arc-jet thruster (aka an ion-jet engine) to provide for station-keeping and minor adjustments once the spacecraft is in its near final orbit. Using ammonia as a fuel, the arc-jet can provide 100 milli-Newtons of thrust, far less than the 400 Newtons of the primary system. Operating the arc-jet requires about 1 kW of power to heat the ammonia. The system was designed at the University of Stuttgart.

COMPUTER AND GUIDANCE-AND-CONTROL SUBSYSTEMS

On OSCARs 5-8, hard-wired logic was used to interface the various spacecraft modules to both the telemetry system and the command system. As overall spacecraft complexity grows, at some point it becomes simpler and more reliable to use a central computing facility in place of hard-wired logic. Once the decision to incorporate a computer is made, the design of the spacecraft must be reevaluated totally to take advantage of the incredible flexibility provided by this approach.[26] Ground stations need no longer be located in position to send immediate commands; they uplink pretested computer programs. After correct reception is confirmed, these programs take control of the spacecraft and the uploaded directions are executed at designated times or when needed. Phase 3 spacecraft feed data from sun and Earth sensors to the computer. Using a simple model of the Earth's magnetic field the computer pulses the torquing coils at the appropriate times to maintain the correct spacecraft attitude. Firing the apogee kick motor on a Phase 3 spacecraft is also handled by the computer.

Computer programs control telemetry content and format. If we want to change the scale used to monitor a particular telemetry channel or to sample it more frequently, we simply add a couple of bytes to the computer program and it's done. Want to send out a daily Codestore message at 0000 GMT? No problem; uplink the message and control program whenever it's convenient and the message will be broadcast on schedule.

The Phase 3 Series IHU

Each Phase 3 satellite contains a module composed of a central processing unit (CPU) board, a random access memory (RAM) board, and a multiplexer (MUX) and command detector (CMD) board. The entire module is known as the Integrated Housekeeping Unit (IHU). The IHU combines a traditional multi-tasking computer (CPU and RAM) with a telemetry encoder and command decoder so that a single unit handles all guidance, control and telemetry functions.[27]

The CPU. The 8-bit RCA COSMAC CDP1802 microprocessor was selected for the Phase 3A CPU back in the mid 1970s for a simple reason. It was the only suitable device available when the spacecraft was being designed. The choice proved to be a good one since this processor has proved powerful and flexible enough to meet the more complex demands of later missions. A radiation hardened version (one more resistant to radiation damage) later became available.

A novel feature of the spacecraft 1802 CPU design is that it does not use any read-only-memory. This is considered an important attribute since radiation damage to ROM is considered a serious threat to spacecraft longevity. When the spacecraft IHU recognizes a particular sequence of bits on the command link a reset is sent to the computer. The next 128 bytes uplinked are fed into sequential locations in low memory. When the last of the 128 bytes are received the processor is automatically toggled into the run mode. A bootstrap loader contained in the 128 bytes then controls the loading of the rest of the operating system.

CPU Language. The CPU runs a high-level language called IPS (Interpreter for Process Structures), a threaded code language similar to Forth. IPS was developed by Dr. K. Meinzer, DJ4ZC, for multi-tasking industrial control type operations. IPS is fast, powerful, flexible, and extremely efficient in terms of memory usage. Some say it's also nearly incomprehensible for anyone not brought up using an HP Reverse Polish Notation hand calculator.[28] In any event, users are *not* required to know IPS to recover data from the downlink telemetry beacons.

RAM. Initial plans (1975) were to fly Phase 3A with 2 kbytes of NMOS RAM. By the time Phase 3A was flown it was possible to include 16 k. The unit flown on OSCAR 13 contained 32 k of radiation hardened CMOS RAM. This may not seem like much when compared to today's personal computers that typically contain 640 k or more of RAM. However, the *Voyager* mission to the outer planets ran fine using 32 k of memory and memory size didn't limit OSCAR 13 in any important way. Each byte of 8-bit memory is backed up by 4 additional bits in an error detection and correction (EDAC) arrangement. The CPU, as a background task, constantly cycles through RAM checking each memory cell. This is called a memory wash. If an error (radiation induced bit-flip) is detected it's corrected. The memory is thus protected against soft errors (radiation-induced bit-flips), provided that no more than one occurs in a byte in the time it takes for the CPU to check the entire memory, typically less than one minute. The EDAC circuitry is based on a Hamming code.[29]

MUX/CMD Board. The CMD unit just sits monitoring the uplink. When it identifies a unique bit sequence it passes data to the CPU. The MUX is an electronic 64 pole switch. When used in conjunction with the analog-to-digital converter on the CPU board it forms a 64 channel scanning voltmeter with a 0 to 2 V range. Each parameter to be measured must provide voltage in this range. Temperatures are measured using thermistors. An ingenious technique is used to measure currents without incurring the losses and reliability problems that series resistors would introduce. The system works as follows: A symmetrical low level ac signal is impressed on a coil wound on a small toroid. A dc measurement across the coil normally reads zero. If a wire carrying a dc current passes through the center of the toroid, however, a small dc offset voltage will be superimposed on the ac signal. The magnitude of the offset signal is proportional to the current flowing in the wire passing through the center. Small toroids are placed about each wire carrying a current to be measured.

Radiation Shielding. The integrated circuits comprising the electronics modules aboard the spacecraft are susceptible to radiation damage from high energy particles. This problem is especially acute with Phase 3 spacecraft because these craft make two passes through the Van Allen radiation belts during each orbit and the high energy particle density in these belts is a severe threat. Soft errors, ones that simply cause a bit-flip in a memory cell, are not a major problem. The EDAC circuitry will take care of these. The problem is hard errors — permanent destruction of a memory cell. When this occurs in RAM, sections can be placed off limits. However, if too many memory cells are eliminated, or if certain key cells are destroyed, the computer cannot be rescued. There are lots of strategies for minimizing the susceptibility of the spacecraft to such damage and AMSAT used them all: choosing chips with the best possible radiation properties, placing individual shields on chips, placing shields over groups of chips, and so on.

With OSCAR 10 susceptibility to radiation damage was the acknowledged Achilles heel. After slightly more than three years in orbit the IHU did succumb. When OSCAR 13 was being readied for launch, chips with a much higher resistance to radiation became available and these were used on the new spacecraft. Radiation damage was not a limiting factor on OSCAR 13. OSCAR 40 carries several computers including the old faithful 1802 and a complex local area network.

UoSAT Series IHU

Early UoSAT spacecraft were controlled by CDP1802 microprocessors running the IPS language. OSCAR 9 and OSCAR 11 supported the 1802 with 48 k of dynamic RAM and carried secondary computers. On OSCAR 9 the backup computer was a Ferranti 16-bit F100L supported by 32 k of static CMOS RAM. On OSCAR 11 it was an NSC-800 with 128 k of CMOS RAM used in the digital communications experiment. UoSAT D carries three computers (1802, 80C31, 80C186) and more than 4 Mbytes of RAM. More recent UoSAT spacecraft have used computers having architectures similar to the Intel 186 series for overall spacecraft and communications system control and transputer parallel processing microcomputers for image processing.

One of the primary objectives of the UoSAT series has been to test and evaluate new hardware and systems approaches. Since Phase 3A never attained orbit, OSCAR 9 gave amateurs their first opportunity to control a computer in space. Many of the techniques used for packet radio satellites were first tested on UoSAT spacecraft.[30,31]

MicroSat Series IHU

It has been said, somewhat seriously, that a MicroSat is a compact, low power IBM computer clone masquerading

as a spacecraft. The MicroSat CPU uses an NEC CMOS V-40 (similar to the 80C188) and 2 k of ROM for a bootstrap loader. EDAC is used for 256 k of memory that holds the operating system software. An additional 8 Megabytes of static RAM is used to hold messages. MicroSat software is written in assembler and Microsoft C, linked with Microsoft LINK.

The spacecraft computer control system on the MicroSats represented a significant change in direction over the 8-bit 1802 architecture running IPS used on early Phase 3 and UoSAT spacecraft. The reason for the change is straightforward. The development of the primary MicroSat mission subsystem (the mailbox) required a microprocessor more powerful than the 1802. It was decided to use one from the Intel series so that development work could be done on IBM clones that a great many amateurs have access to. The V-40 had the desired characteristics. It would have been possible to use an 1802 for overall spacecraft control and use the V-40 to manage the mailbox but this would require that extra circuitry be placed on the satellite and that the spacecraft command and development teams work in IPS in addition to the more familiar languages used for Intel microprocessors. It was simpler to place the V-40 in overall control and treat spacecraft management as one of many tasks the V-40 was responsible for.

A major innovation of the MicroSat series is the introduction of a standard spacecraft bus (interconnection scheme) for linking the onboard computer and the various electronic modules. In the past, each satellite required a unique and extremely elaborate wiring harness. These harnesses had to be designed and constructed to provide all the links needed between the various modules. As spacecraft became more complex the number of interconnections that the harness had to handle grew rapidly and construction difficulty increased at an even faster rate. This has a negative effect on spacecraft reliability. In the MicroSats the function of the wiring harness is mainly handled by a ribbon cable that plugs into each module. The setup is similar to a simple local area network with the on board computer (OBC) acting as the master and the modules as slaves. Each module contains an AART (Addressable Asynchronous Receiver/Transmitter) chip and associated components for communications with the OBC and telemetry sensor measurements.

The bus-communications orientation provides several additional advantages. With small engineering groups spread around the world, each working on a different spacecraft module, communication has always been a problem. A detailed bus definition greatly reduces this problem and facilitates distributed engineering. The bus orientation also makes it easier for new groups to become involved in spacecraft construction. Finally, it provides a design and control approach that can be efficiently applied to spacecraft of widely varying complexity and with all types of mission objectives.

Guidance and Control Subsystems

A satellite guidance and control subsystem includes

components and software involved in the measurement of spacecraft position and orientation, attitude adjustment and in control of all other onboard systems in response to orders issued by telecommand or the spacecraft computer. On OSCAR spacecraft the command receiver generally uses elements of the transponder (linear or digital) front end. A tap goes to a dedicated IF strip, demodulator and decoder. Data from the decoder is routed to the IHU. An active attitude control system requires sensors. Since most of the elements of the guidance and control subsystem, except for the sensors, have already been discussed we'll focus our attention on sensors. The sensors on OSCAR 13 serve as a good example.

OSCAR 13 contained three sets of sensors designed to provide attitude information: a sun sensor, an Earth sensor, and a top/bottom sensor. In the following discussion it will help to picture the shape of OSCAR 13 and the fact that it's rotating about its symmetry axis that is aligned in a fixed direction in space. The attitude determination strategy consists of first finding the relative orientation or the spacecraft with respect to two celestial bodies, the sun and Earth, whose positions are accurately known and then mathematically reducing this data to absolute orientation. When this is done there are frequently two solutions, only one of which is correct. The top/bottom sensor is used to eliminate the ambiguity.

The top/bottom sensor consists of a few solar cells mounted on the top and bottom of the spacecraft. When the spacecraft is in sunlight only one set will be illuminated. This provides a crude estimate of the satellite's orientation, sufficient to choose between the solutions provided by the sun and Earth sensors. The sun and Earth sensors are mounted at the end of arm two of the spacecraft as shown schematically in Figure 14.15.

Because the sun is extremely bright and virtually a point source, construction of the sun sensor is relatively simple. It consists of two slits and two photodiodes. Because of the satellite's spin the sun sensors will scan a region ±60° from the spacecraft's equator once each revolution (about 20 times per minute). If the sun is in this region we will get a "pip" from each photodiode. The time between these two pips and knowledge of which one pips first provide important information about satellite orientation. There are some real world complications to this simple model caused by the fact that extraneous pips may be introduced by sunlight reflecting off an antenna. For an excellent discussion of the mathematics involved in reducing this data see the article by J. Miller.[32] The primary reference used by professional satellite designers of attitude control systems is by J. Wertz.[33]

The second body we choose to focus on is the Earth. The Earth is rather dim and its diameter as seen from OSCAR 13 varies from about 18° at apogee to 90° at perigee. Light enters the Earth sensor through an anti-glare shield and is focused by a lens on a photodiode. The threshold sensitivity of the diode electronics is set so that a step-like change in output will occur when the diode field of view changes from dark space to sunlight reflected off the Earth. Tempo-

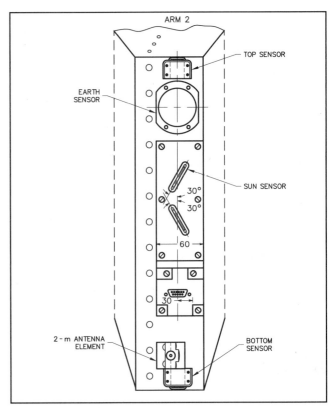

Figure 14.15—OSCAR 10 Sun and Earth sensors (end of arm 2).

rarily assume that the Earth is completely bathed in sunlight (of course this is impossible). During most of the satellite's orbit the Earth sensor will not scan through the Earth as the spacecraft rotates. However, there will be two periods, one slightly before perigee and one slightly after perigee, when the sensor will view the Earth. As we enter one of these periods the sensor will scan through the Earth very quickly, but the time during which the sensor is focused on the Earth will increase, reaching a maximum slightly further along the satellite's orbit, and then decrease back down to zero.

The mathematics needed to convert data from this simple model into information on satellite orientation is not too horrendous. However, there are complications. The most serious one occurs because only part of the Earth may be illuminated. The Earth sensors will therefore be reporting illuminated crescent acquisition and loss. Additional uncertainty is introduced by the fact that the transition from light to dark is not very sharp when the Earth is partially illuminated. To help with data interpretation the Earth sensor actually includes two photodiodes each having a beamwidth of about 2°. One points about 4° above the spacecraft's equator and the other points about 4° below.

Using OSCAR 13 telemetry values containing the sensor data, a personal computer can be used to determine the direction of the spacecraft spin axis to about 1°. The absolute spin angle (needed for determining when torquing coils should be pulsed) can be determined to within about 0.1°. This accuracy is completely adequate for orbital transfer maneuvers and for attitude adjustment via the torquing coils.

OSCAR 40 is actually the second OSCAR satellite to carry a Global Positioning Satellite receiver for use in orbit and attitude determination. The first such unit was on PoSAT but amateurs were not responsible for its construction or operation. However, OSCAR 40 is the first satellite in any service to experiment with the use of GPS in highly elliptical orbits. GPS receivers on OSCAR 40 are used to determine OSCAR 40's orbit (to within 20 meter accuracy) and back up the attitude determination system. OSCAR 40 carries eight GPS antennas. Information from the system is converted to Keplerian orbital elements on the satellite and made available to users on the downlink.

LAUNCH CONSIDERATIONS

Launch Sites

Launching a satellite takes a lot of energy. The amount depends on the final orbit, the location of the launch site and the mass of the satellite. Energy constraints related to launch and orbit transfer affect AMSAT's selection of orbits.

To place the largest possible payload in orbit using a specific rocket and launch site, the launch azimuth should be due east, taking full advantage of the relative "boost" given by the Earth's rotational velocity. When this is done the orbital inclination of the satellite will equal the latitude of the launch site. The coordinates of various launch sites are listed in Table 14.8. These locations were chosen for several reasons including safety (it's best to launch over water or very sparsely populated regions) and energy considerations. Looking at Table 14.8 it's clear that Plesetsk is nearly ideal for placing a payload into a Molniya (63° inclination) orbit, while Kourou is excellent for launch to geostationary orbit.

Changing the inclination of the orbital plane of a spacecraft takes a great deal of energy. If the initial launch azimuth is other that due east (or west), the orbital plane inclination will be *greater* than the launch site latitude. Note that it's impossible to place a payload directly into an orbit having an inclination lower than the launch site latitude unless the upper stages of the launch vehicle expend considerable energy to modify the initial trajectory.

Launch Opportunities

When AMSAT secures a ride into space, it must either accept the orbit provided or include a propulsion system on the spacecraft so a new orbit can be attained. The decision to include a propulsion system on a spacecraft is a major one since it requires not only a rocket but a complex support system of sensors, computer and physical structure, and a much higher level of coordination with the launch agency. With OSCAR 10 and OSCAR 13 AMSAT has clearly demonstrated its ability to maneuver a spacecraft.

The simplest type of propulsion system is a solid fuel kick motor that fires only once. With such a motor the perigee height of the final orbit can never be greater than the apogee height of the initial orbit. This is an important constraint when considering launches from the US Shuttle. AMSAT has experience with solid fuel and liquid fuel kick motors that can provide multiple burns. Because of safety concerns it's unlikely that kick motors of this type will be allowed to fly on the shuttle. AMSAT has therefore looked into ion propulsion motors using water as a fuel. Conceptual studies were very promising but development work has been temporarily suspended due to poor prospects for shuttle launch opportunities.

AMSAT continually explores launch possibilities with existing launch agencies and commercial groups planning to enter the launching business. Free or subsidized launches are becoming exceedingly rare but they are still possible if a government agency deems such a launch desirable for

---

Table 14.8
Major Launch Sites of the World

Launch Authority	Site Name	Latitude	Longitude
Brazil	Alcantara	2°S	316°E (44°W)
PR China	Shuang Ch'eng Tzu (Jiuquan)	40.4°N	99.7°E
PR China	Xichang (Chengdu)	27.9°N	102.3°E
ESA	Kourou	5.2°N	307.3°E (52.7°W)
India	ISRO Sriharikota	13.7°N	80.2°E
Italy	San Marco Platform	2.9°S	40.3°E
Japan	Tanegashima	30.4°N	131.0°E
Japan	Kagoshima	31.3°N	131.1°E
USSR	Kapustin Yar	48.3°N	45.9°E
USSR	Plesetsk	62.9°N	40.7°E
USSR	Tyuratam (Baikonur)	45.9°N	63.3°E
US	Cape Canaveral/Kennedy	28.5°N	279.5°E (80.5°W)
US	Vandenberg	34.6°N	239.4°E (120.6°W)
US	Wallops Island	37.9°N	284.5°E (75.5°W)

Sources

[1]S. B. Kramer, *The Satellite Sky*, Graphic Display Chart available from Smithsonian Air & Space Museum, Washington, DC 20560.
[2]*Jane's Spaceflight Directory 1986*, Jane's, London 1986, "World Space Centres," pp 345-353.
[3]*Aviation Week & Space Technology*, ongoing clipping file.

scientific reasons or to support science education activities. Another opportunity for low cost launches occurs when an agency is testing a new launch vehicle. Other opportunities may occur when we demonstrate how launch agencies can market new services or space (the MicroSats and OSCAR 40 use space that ESA has not previously thought of as being commercially marketable). Finally, we may have to consider paying the going rate for launches. If commercial launching develops into a viable business this approach may be feasible. Current estimates are that we could have a MicroSat launched into a useful orbit for about $60,000. The assistance of anyone associated with launch agencies or companies in identifying potential launches is always greatly appreciated by AMSAT.

Experience teaches us to expect the unexpected. If the Radio Amateur Space Program remains both flexible and vital, we'll be in an excellent position to take advantage of the launch opportunities that are sure to come.

Notes

[1]W. R. Corliss, *Scientific Satellites* (NASA SP-133), National Aeronautics and Space Administration, Washington, DC (1967), p 78.
[2]W. J. Larson and J. R. Wertz (Eds.), *Space Mission Analysis and Design, 2nd Ed.*, Kluwer Academic Publishers, 1993.
[3]P. Klein, J. Goode, P. Hammer and D. Bellair, "Spacecraft Telemetry Systems for the Developing Nations," 1971 IEEE *National Telemetering Conference Record*, April 1971, pp 118-129.
[4]K. Meinzer, "Lineare Nachrichtensatellitentransponder Durch Nichtlinear Signalzerlegung" (Linear Communications Satellite Transponder Using Non-linear Signal splitting), Doctoral Dissertation, Marburg University, Germany, 1974. K. Meinzer, "A Frequency Multiplication Technique for VHF and UHF SSB," *QST,* Oct 1970, pp 32-35.
[5]J. King, "The Third Generation," *Orbit*, Vol. 1, no. 4, Nov/Dec 1980, pp 12-18. Also see J. King, "Principles of HELAPS Transponder Amplifiers," *The AMSAT Journal*, Sept/Oct 1993, pp 27-31.
[6]G. Hardman, "A Novel Transponder for Mobile Satellite Service," *Telecommunications*, Feb 1986, Vol. 20, no. 2, pp 61-62.
[7]P3D Design Team, "Phase 3D, A New Era for Amateur Satellites," *The AMSAT Journal*, Mar/Apr 1995, pp 5-15.
[8]P. Guelzow, "RUDAK-II on AMSAT OSCAR-21, Full System Overview, Current Activities and Future Planning," *The AMSAT Journal*, Mar/Apr 1993, pp 14.16, 23-25. For more complete information see [in German] *AMSAT-DL Journal*, Marz/Mai 1990.
[9]H. Price, "Digital Communications with Phase 3D," *QEX*, Feb 1995, pp 24-27. Reprinted in *The AMSAT Journal*, Mar/Apr 1995, pp 29-31.
[10]J. Kraus, *Antennas*, New York: McGraw-Hill, 1950, Chapter 2.
[11]M. Davidoff, *Using Satellites in the Classroom: A Guide for Science Educators*, Catonsville Community College, 1978, pp 6.52-6.56. Out of print. Microfiche copies are available from: ERIC (Educational Resources Information Center), Computer Microfilm Corp., 3900 Wheeler Ave, Alexandria, VA 22304. Specify Document # ED 162 635.
[12]See Note 7.
[13]D. Jansson, "Mechanical and Thermal Design of the Phase 3D Spacecraft," *AMSAT-NA Technical Journal*, Jan/Feb 1996 pp 1, 4-7.
[14]D. Jansson, "Thermal Analytical Modeling of Phase 3D," *The AMSAT Journal*, Mar/Apr 1996, pp 10-11.
[15]G. Mueller and E. Spangler, *Communications Satellites*, New York: John Wiley & Sons, 1964, p 12.
[16]See Note 1, section 9.5.
[17]J. R. Primack, "Let's Ban Nuclear Reactors from Orbit," *Technology Review*, May/June 1989, pp 27-28.
[18]R. Leifer et al, "Detection of Uranium from Cosmos-1402 in the Stratosphere," *Science*, vol 238, Oct 23 1987, pp 512-514.
[19]T. Beardsley, *Scientific American*, Feb 1989, pp 15-16.
[20]D. Chapin, C. Fuller, and G. Pearson, "A New Silicon P-N Junction Photocell for Converting Solar Radiation into Electrical Power," *J. Applied Physics*, vol. 25, May 1954, p 676.
[21]H. M. Hubbard, "Photovoltaics Today and Tomorrow," *Science*, Vol. 244, 21 April 1989, pp 297-304.
[22]See Note 11 pp 6.24-6.31, 6.40-6.41.
[23]J. Lyons III and A. Ozkul, "In-orbit performance of INTELSAT IV-A spacecraft solar arrays," *COMSAT Technical Review*, Vol. 17, no. 2, Fall 1987, pp 403-419.
[24]See Note 7.
[25]J. King, "Using Water as a Primary Method of Propulsion for Spacecraft Modifying Standard STS Orbits," *Orbit*, no. 19, Nov/Dec 1984, pp 5-8.
[26]P. Stakem "One Step Forward — Three Steps Backup, Computing in the US Space Program," *BYTE*, Vol. 6, no. 9, Sept 1981, pp 112, 114, 116, 118, 122, 124, 126, 128, 130, 132-134, 138, 140, 142, 144.
[27]G. Hardman, "The Integrated Housekeeping Unit — A Method of Telemetry, Command and Control for Small Spacecraft," *AMSAT-NA Technical Journal*, Vol. 1, no. 2, Winter, 1987-88.
[28]K. Meinzer, "IPS, An Unorthodox High Level Language," *Byte*, Jan 1979, pp 146, 148-152, 154, 156, 158-159.
[29]R. J. McEliece, "The Reliability of Computer Memories," *Scientific American*, Jan 1985, pp 88-92, 94,95.
[30]T. Jeans and C. Traynar, "The Primary UoSAT Spacecraft Computer," *The Radio and Electronic Engineer*, Vol. 52, no. 8/9, Aug/Sept 1982, pp 385-390.
[31]C. Haynes, "A Low-Power 16-bit Computer for Space Application," *The Radio and Electronic Engineer*, Vol. 52, no. 8/9, Aug/Sept 1982, pp 391-397.
[32]J. Miller, G3RUH, "OSCAR-10 Attitude Determination," *Proceeding of the 4th Annual AMSAT Space Symposium*, Dallas, 1986, ARRL.
[33]J. R. Wertz, *Spacecraft Attitude Determination and Control*, Reidel Publishing Co. 1984. ISBN 90-277-1204-2.

Chapter 15

So You Want to Build a Satellite

CONSTRUCTION SUPPORT ACTIVITIES

SPACECRAFT HARDWARE

15 | So You Want to Build a Satellite

Many people view satellite construction as meticulously assembling a huge pile of mechanical and electrical components into an OSCAR. They're about 2% right. The visible part of the satellite program, the flight hardware, is only the tip of a massive iceberg. Without an effective support structure there wouldn't be any amateur spacecraft: no iceberg, no tip. A partial list of the countless necessary support activities that lead to a finished OSCAR is given in Table 15.1.

CONSTRUCTION SUPPORT ACTIVITIES

The radio amateur satellite program has been, and will always be, understaffed. AMSAT attracts people who are both doers and dreamers, doing the nearly impossible while dreaming about what they could accomplish if they only had access to a few more resources. If you share in the dream you'll probably want to help out in some way. Of the many avenues open to you, the first is to become an active AMSAT volunteer. If this appeals to you, the following steps are in order:

1) Learn all you can about the radio amateur space program.

2) Consider seriously how much time and effort you're willing to commit to satellite activities.

3) Pick an area where your personal skills and interests mesh with the needs of the program, identify an unmet need where you feel you can make a special contribution and then present your ideas to AMSAT.

Step 1 doesn't need much explanation. You'll be more of an asset than a drain if you know what's going on.

The importance of Step 2 cannot be overemphasized. Space activities have a certain aura of excitement that attracts many of us initially. But the kind of personal involvement AMSAT needs often leads to long hours of tedious work with hardly even a "thank you." For their efforts, most volunteers receive little more than indigestion, a continual drain on their petty cash, and an ever-growing sleep deficit! Seriously, you have to be the kind of person who can be satisfied simply with seeing than an important job gets done well and on schedule. If you're after glamour and personal recognition, you've probably chosen the wrong field. Bringing a new volunteer onboard involves a big investment of effort by current workers who are probably already up to their apogees in work. The decision to volunteer should be given very serious consideration.

Step 3 needs further explanation. In truth, many volunteers are attracted initially by the idea of designing and building flight hardware. After learning as much as possible about the OSCAR program, however, they may realize that contributing their special skills in other areas could make a more significant impact on amateur space efforts. While a few immediate needs are often announced on the AMSAT nets, many, many other important tasks go unadvertised. Why? Because long-term efforts to locate the right person to undertake them have been unsuccessful, or because the idea hasn't yet occurred to the AMSAT directors.

Some potential volunteers hesitate to step forward because they fear that their lack of special spacecraft expertise means there aren't any important jobs for them. Nothing could be further from the truth. A glance at Table 15.1 should make it clear that people with any one of a surprisingly large variety of skills, or areas of expertise, from graphic arts, writing and editing, language translation and videotape production, to accounting and law, can contribute significantly to the success of the satellite program. In fact, many tasks don't require specialized skills, but are nonetheless important to AMSAT's success. These are often the most difficult jobs to find volunteers for, since a person must be very committed to undertake them.

If, after due consideration you still want to become part of the team, it takes only an informal note or proposal to AMSAT to get started. Volunteers are usually amazed at how quickly they can take on major responsibilities.

When I asked several long-term workers if they'd like to pass along any hints to new volunteers, two closely related themes were repeated: don't be afraid to say "no," never agree to a schedule you feel isn't possible to meet and do everything possible to live up to any schedule you've committed to. It's often difficult, especially for a newcomer, to say "no" when asked to take on some extra assignment. Saying "no," however, is best for both the long-term satellite program and everyone involved—if saying "yes" would lead to unmet schedules or severe personal sacrifices that destroy the satisfaction that working for the program can provide. Since effective workers are likely to attract additional tasks, one either learns to say "no" or suffers early

Table 15.1

Support Activities Involved in the Production of an OSCAR

1) Design of flight hardware.

2) Construction of prototype hardware.

3) Construction of flight hardware:
   electrical
   modules and wiring, PCB layout
   mechanical
   machining; sheet metal work; potting, construction
   of handling fixtures and shipping crates.
4) Testing of flight hardware:
   Includes arranging for test facilities and people to
   oversee vibration, environmental, burn-in, and
   performance tests
5) Finished drafting:
   mechanical subsystems
   electrical subsystems
6) Interfacing with launch agency:
   providing documentation related to satellite/rocket
   attending coordination meetings as required
7) Identifying and procuring future launches.
8) Construction Management:
   parts procurement including locating special
   components and ensuring timely arrival of long-
   lead time items
   allocating financial and human resources
   locating volunteers with special expertise
9) Launch information nets.
10) Providing user information and membership services:
   production of periodical (at least bi-monthly)
   production of other written materials
   coordinate weekly AMSAT Nets (provide
   information)
   management of AMSAT Web site
   produce information programs (slide shows, video
   tapes)
   provide support to professional educators
   coordinate operating awards (ZRO tests, operating
   events)

area coordinator program
encourage and support production of texts and
   magazine articles
11) Fund raising:
   sales of QSL cards, software, T-shirts, patches, etc.
   handling special contribution campaigns
   artwork preparation for magazine ads, T-shirts, QSL
   cards, etc.
12) Coordination with international AMSAT affiliates.
13) Technical studies focusing on future spacecraft
   design:
   thermal design, orbit selection, orbit determination,
   attitude control, designs of all subsystems
14) Launch operations:
   travel to launch site, shipping satellite and rocket
   engine, interface satellite to launch vehicle,
   checkout
15) Command station network:
   arranging for construction and operation of
   worldwide network
   design of special hardware and computer programs
16) Miscellaneous needs:
   language translation: French, German, Italian,
   Japanese,Russian, Spanish and others
   legal: procurement contracts, trademark concerns,
   corporation papers
   insurance of various types
17) Financial and business:
   financial record keeping
   auditing as required
   maintaining membership files
   filing corporation reports as required
   estimating future needs and cash-flow situation
   international cash transfers
18) Maintaining historical records:
   general and spacecraft telemetry
19) Construction of test equipment and special test
   facilities

burnout. Only the individual knows where the critical overload point is.

The need to meet schedules is absolutely essential. Satellite construction is a team effort to meet deadlines imposed by a launch agency, by a laboratory providing special test facilities on certain dates or by another volunteer who has scheduled personal vacation time so it could be devoted to a specific AMSAT task. Under these circumstances, one person's late project can be disastrous.

One outstanding characteristic of almost all long-term AMSAT volunteers is the seriousness with which they accept commitments. Once they agree to a task or schedule they do everything possible to deliver as promised. Over the years this sense of commitment has led to a very special camaraderie, trust and respect among those involved. It's a spirit that I've never seen anywhere else in the academic, scientific, industrial or sports communities.

You don't have to have a formal title or be willing to invest a big chunk of time to be an AMSAT supporter. Everyone who helps a newcomer get started in satellite communications, provides information on the satellite program to other segments of the Amateur Radio community or makes a modest financial contribution to AMSAT is filling an important need. A great many people helping in a lot of small ways will keep the satellite program vital, so let's all try to be conscious of the little things. For example, if you need something from AMSAT headquarters or a volunteer worker, an SASE will save a few minutes as will a request phrased so it can be answered yes or no, or with an article reprint. Similarly, providing information by telephone requires only a fraction of the time that preparing a written answer does. The point is: to key AMSAT volunteers, time is a very valuable commodity, so small efforts by all of us to lighten their workload will pay off cumulatively.

By now you probably have some idea as to what level of support you'd be comfortable with. For those who are determined to become involved in flight, flight-related or ground-command hardware, we now look at the steps involved in the spacecraft-construction aspect of the OSCAR program.

SPACECRAFT HARDWARE

If you want to become directly involved in satellite construction one of your first steps should be to familiarize yourself with satellite system design. You don't have to become an expert in all areas but you do need a good practical understanding of the functions of the various subsystems, the trade-offs involved in their selection and how they affect each other. This chapter is a good starting point for obtaining this information.

From a project-management perspective, the construction of a satellite can be thought of as consisting of six major stages: (1) preliminary design, (2) system specification, (3) subsystem design and fabrication, (4) integration and testing, (5) launch operations and (6) information dissemination and post-launch management. The time frame for these activities is outlined roughly in Figure 15.1. Figure 15.2 presents the elapsed time, from commitment to spacecraft construction to launch, for an OSCAR spacecraft.

The preliminary-design stage involves feasibility studies of new approaches to satellite design. The availability of recently developed high performance, low cost components, launch access to unusual orbits, new sources of financial support and the like are always presenting new design options. In a long-term multi-satellite program, feasibility studies are continually taking place.

At some point, usually in response to a specific launch opportunity, the decision is made to construct a spacecraft. A set of system specifications must be agreed upon and the subsystem requirements defined. Initial system specifications include selecting a primary mission subsystem, determining the spacecraft size, shape and attitude stabilization system, estimating the available power and allocating this power to various subsystems. The design goes through a couple of iterations until everyone feels the system design is solid.

Subsystems are then designed, built, tested and refined. With AMSAT satellites, subsystem design and construction is usually handled by small core groups scattered around the world. An electronic subsystem is usually built in

a number of versions: an engineering development model, a flight prototype and flight unit. The flight unit uses the most reliable components available. Each subsystem must be tested thoroughly, under extreme conditions of temperature, over- and under-voltage, and intense RFI, so that potential weak spots can be identified and corrected.

Next, the subsystems are integrated into a spacecraft so that additional stress tests, operational checks and RF-compatibility tests can be performed. The electronic system stress test includes a burn-in period during which electrical parameters and temperatures are similar to those expected in space. The system is also tested at atmospheric pressure and in a vacuum chamber under temperatures considerably more severe than those expected in space. For example, between –20°C and +60°C. A vibration test is performed to ensure that the satellite will survive the launch. The objectives of the vacuum test include, (1) checking for material sublimation that could contaminate spacecraft systems, (2) testing for corona discharge and (3) verifying the predicted thermal behavior in the absence of convective heat flow. Vacuum and vibration tests are usually performed at large government or commercial laboratories that have the special facilities required.

The electrical testing strategy is based on the fact that high temperatures and overvoltages tend to compress the time scale of the failure curves for most electrical components. A typical curve is shown in Figure 15.3. Temperature cycling and vibration tests have a similar effect on mechanical components. Consequently, one month of actual testing might be equivalent to two years of testing under normal operating conditions. The aim of the testing program is to discover and correct all weak spots and then bring the spacecraft past the initial hump in the failure curve while it's still on the ground. NASA's experience has clearly proved the validity of this approach to ensuring reliability.

When the satellite has passed all tests, it is transported to the launch site, mated to the launch vehicle and checked out one last time. The project, however, doesn't end with the launch. Command stations must be available when and where they are needed, information must be disseminated to users, and data on spacecraft operation must be collected for both current and future operations. The entire procedure, from system specification to launch, can take anywhere from six months to five years, depending on the complexity of the spacecraft and the available resources.

Once you know something about satellite systems and the stages of satellite construction, it's time to pick a particular project, subsystem, or aspect of construction to focus on. This may involve refining a specific subsystem you're particularly knowledgeable about, such as analog/digital converter design or looking into spacecraft subsystems that appear to need improvement, even though you are not an expert. Perhaps you see a technique for accomplishing a spacecraft function that's simpler or more reliable than the approach currently being used. You'll probably be entering the construction cycle (Figure 15.1) at the preliminary design stage, so try to maintain a broad long-term perspective.

As a first project pick something modest with clearly defined interfaces. For example, you might elect to work on a

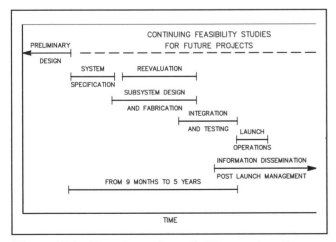

Figure 15.1—Time frame for satellite construction from project management perspective.

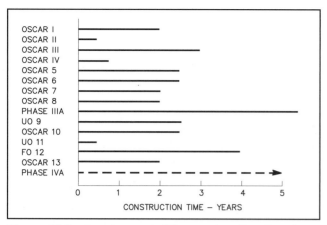

Figure 15.2—Amateur satellite construction time from commitment to launch. From *AMSAT Tech. Journal #2*, Winter 87/88.

high-efficiency linear Mode A/J transponder with a 146 MHz input and outputs at 29.5 and 435 MHz designed to fit the TSFR tray in a MicroSat. Initial objectives would probably be limited to producing and testing an engineering development model.

One important area of spacecraft construction that is frequently overlooked is the need for special test equipment and detailed procedures for satellite evaluation and checkout. If you're interested in this area, contact AMSAT to find out what's needed.

Once you identify a specific aspect of construction that you'd like to work on, send a brief memo to the person who is coordinating the core group currently handling that aspect. If you're not sure who to write contact one of the AMSAT directors. It's important to realize that AMSAT workers and directors don't see each other at the office each morning, they're spread around the world and most have full-time jobs. Circulating a letter can take months and the chances of its getting lost are, unfortunately, high. Therefore, the best strategy may be to make several copies and send one to each person you think may be interested. The object is to establish direct contact with the person or persons responsible for the work you're interested in. Because of AMSAT's geographical scatter, there are always problems in internal communication. It is best to establish a single point of contact, preferably with one person at one of the established AMSAT core groups. The choice can depend on geographical proximity, language skills, similarity of interests, access to communications channels (commercial or amateur), patterns of business travel and so forth. It's anticipated that PACSATs will take on a large part of our communications needs, so reading the mail on OSCAR 14 will give you a picture of who's working on what project. Setting up for PACSAT, either direct or via a gateway, may provide the communications links you need.

Before undertaking a major effort that will require significant assistance from AMSAT, you should plan to take on some simple tasks to demonstrate your competence and ability to adhere to schedules. Initiating a large project generally involves preparing a proposal that focuses on the concerns listed in Table 15.2. These are not formal guidelines; they're

merely suggestions. AMSAT is most definitely not a huge, faceless bureaucracy. Every proposal is treated individually. It's the content that counts.

When estimating the amount of time that a project is going to require, don't forget "paperwork." Communication is a two-way street. You must be willing to provide clear documentation to other groups that have an immediate need to know and eventually to users. You must also maintain good records relating to electronic design and testing and cost. Try to anticipate as many of these little loose ends as possible when estimating the total resources needed to accomplish a particular job. Frankly, no matter how thorough you think your estimates are, you'll probably grossly underestimate the real effort needed. Psychologically this might be a good thing, if we knew what we were really committing ourselves to, far fewer might volunteer.

Over the years several individuals in the academic and educational communities have been able to fuse their vocations with their satellite interests. Students in the undergraduate Electrical Engineering Technology program at Trenton State College (NJ) often chose senior projects, such as a 70 to 23-cm linear transponder satellite system. Key systems for OSCAR 15 (Webersat) and Phase 4A are being built by students and faculty at the Center for Aerospace Technology at Weber State College in Utah. Programs are also in place at the University of Surrey (England) and the University of Marburg (Germany.) Several students have received Master's and PhD degrees for projects that relate to OSCAR satellite design. Science and engineering educators have, at times, received government grants to work on particular aspects of the OSCAR program.

AMSAT has, on occasion, been able to sponsor an internship program. The object of the program is to train young radio amateurs who have strong backgrounds in science and engineering in all aspects of satellite construction. This is the wisest investment we can make to ensure the continuation of the radio amateur space program. Interns may be paid employees, but the wages are terrible and the hours ridiculous. Interns nonetheless receive invaluable experience in all phases of satellite design and construction involving a measure of responsibility usually achieved only by senior engineers. In return, AMSAT receives the services of very bright, committed scientists and engineers at modest cost. Internships are flexible, appointments can last from a few months to several years. Don't send for a formal application form—there aren't any. If you would like to apply, just submit a letter that details your background and explains why you feel you could contribute to the amateur space pro-

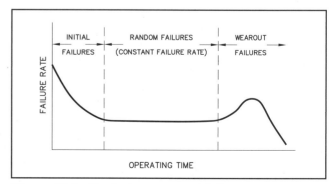

Figure 15.3—Typical component failure curve.

Table 15.2
Construction Project Proposals

Topics to be Addressed

1) *General Conceptual Plan:* A general description of the proposed subsystem or project.

2) *Trade-off Discussion:* A detailed discussion of the proposed subsystem including a candid evaluation of, (1) its advantages and disadvantages with respect to prior subsystems having a similar function and (2) its impact on other subsystems.

3) *Interface Considerations:* A detailed specification of how the proposed subsystem will interface with other subsystems.

4) *Environmental Design:*A discussion of how the experimenter will attempt to guarantee that the completed unit will perform satisfactorily under anticipated extremes of temperature, vacuum, power variation, radiation and the RF environment, including analysis of waste heat, potential RFI and steps taken to prevent RFI problems.

5) *Component Selection and Construction Techniques:* If the experimenter is planning to construct a flight unit, describe steps to be taken to ensure component and construction quality.

6) *Testing Program:* Detailed description of all tests to be performed on the completed unit.

7) *Required Support:* If the experimenter anticipates calling on AMSAT to provide assistance in financing, design or parts procurement, the required type and level of support should be specified.

8) *Experience of Project Personnel:* List the people expected to work on the project, and the expertise and the expected time commitment of each project member.

9) *Schedule and Delivery:* Set up a timetable for the project, indicating dates for milestones and specifying a realistic delivery date that includes allowances for unanticipated delays.

---

gram. Better yet, volunteer to spend a few weeks as an unpaid intern so that both you and the AMSAT team can better evaluate the desirability of making a longer-term commitment.

Most of the comments in this section have focused on building flight hardware. The construction of telecommand equipment and gateways may also offer a great deal of satisfaction, however. For instance the design of software for operating spacecraft and testing spacecraft during the design stages may be as satisfying as the hardware design. Many people working on today's spacecraft got their start by building telecommand stations. Most notable are: Larry Kayser, VE3PAZ, who almost single-handedly kept OSCAR 6 operating during its early days; A. Gschwindt, HA5WH, who set up a command station for OSCAR 6 and later built switching regulators for Phase 3A and OSCARs 10 and 13, and Martin Sweeting, G3YJO, who went from commanding OSCARs 6 and 7 to directing the University of Surrey Satellite Program where UoSAT-OSCARs 9 and 11 and UoSAT D and E were constructed.

Constructing a local satellite gateway is an excellent way to start a "career" in satellite hardware construction. The gateway might be designed to provide local 2-meter FM voice stations with access to a linear transponder on a high altitude spacecraft or to provide local 2-meter packet operators with access to the PACSAT system. In either case you'll be acquiring valuable design experience, generating new support for the OSCAR program, initiating a local support group and demonstrating your ability to oversee a project from conception to completion.

Another avenue for getting involved in the construction of flight hardware that has proven very effective in the past, is to organize balloon launches. The payload could consist of a digital or linear transponder or a FM or ATV repeater. Many of the design problems associated with balloon launchings are closely related to those involved in spacecraft construction. Of course, you also have to handle your own launch and recovery operations. Several AMSAT groups, in Germany, England, Holland, South Africa and the US, have engaged in this activity. These groups often go on to construct flight hardware. Karl Meinzer, DJ4ZC, a key designer of several AMSAT spacecraft, started this way nearly two decades ago.

If nothing short of building satellite hardware interests you, you're not shut out of the picture. MicroSat provides one possible path. If you construct a prototype experimental module for the MicroSat TSFR tray that's of interest to AMSAT you're likely to be able to find support for the construction of a flight model.

AMSAT is a flexible, vital organization. Its very informality—the lack of straightforward procedures for submitting proposals or volunteering—can make it difficult for a newcomer to become involved. The same lack of formal structure, however, makes it possible for the competent, committed individual to assume important responsibilities quickly. We'd like to hear from you.

APPENDIX

Amateur Spacecraft Statistics

(Listed by launch date)

Satellite Launch date Operating life	Launch Agency, Licensing Authority	Transponder input/output freq (bandwidth)	Beacon Frequencies	Transmitting Power (peak)	Apogee Height
OSCAR I 430 km Dec. 12, 1961 21 days	USA., USA	—		144.983 MHz	0.1 W
OSCAR II 390 km June 2, 1962 19 days	USA, USA	—		145.000 MHz	0.1 W
OSCAR III March 9, 1965 transponder: 18 days beacon: several months	USA, USA	145.10/145.90 MHz (50 kHz)	145.85 MHz 145.95[1]	1.0 W	940 km
OSCAR IV Dec. 21, 1965 85 days	USA, USA	144.100/431.938 MHz (10 kHz)	431.928 MHz	3.0 W	33,600 km
Australis-OSCAR 5 Jan. 23, 1970 52 days	NASA, USA	—	144.05 MHz 29.45 MHz	0.2 W	1480 km
AMSAT-OSCAR 6 Oct. 15, 1972 4.5 years	NASA, USA	145.95/29.50 MHz (100 kHz)	29.450 MHz 435.100 MHz	1.5 W	1460 km
AMSAT-OSCAR 7 Nov. 15, 1974 (operating 4/2003)	NASA, USA	145.90/29.45 MHz (100 kHz) 432.15/145.95 MHz (40 kHz)	29.502 MHz 145.972 MHz 435.100 MHz 2304.1 MHz[2]	8.0 W	1460 km
AMSAT-OSCAR 8 March 5, 1978 5.3 years	NASA, USA	145.90/29.45 MHz (100 kHz) 145.95/435.15 MHz (100 kHz)	29.402 MHz 435.095 MHz	1.5 W	910 km
RS-1, Oct. 26, 1978 several months	USSR, USSR	145.89/29.37 MHz (40 kHz)	29.401 MHz	1.5 W	1700 km
RS-2 Oct. 26, 1978 several months	USSR, USSR	145.89/29.37 MHz (40 kHz)	29.401 MHz	1.5 W	1700 km

Satellite Launch date Operating life	Launch Agency, Licensing Authority	Transponder input/output freq (bandwidth)	Beacon Frequencies	Transmitting Power (peak)	Apogee Height
AMSAT-Phase III-A May 23, 1980 launch failure	ESA, FRG	435.22/145.90 MHz (180 kHz) 435.22/145.90 MHz (180 kHz)	145.99 MHz 145.81 MHz	50 W	35,800 km (target)
UoSAT-OSCAR 9 Oct. 6, 1981 8+ years [3]	NASA, UK	—	145.825 MHz 435.025 MHz 7.050, 14.002 MHz 21.002, 29.510 MHz 2.401, 10.47 GHz	0.8 W	544 km
RS-3 Dec. 17, 1981 2 years	USSR, USSR	—-	29.321, 29.401 MHz	1.5 W	1690 km
RS-4 Dec. 17, 1981 2 years	USSR, USSR	—-	29.360, 29.403 MHz	1.5 W	1690 km
RS-5 Dec. 17, 1981 6.5 years	USSR, USSR	145.93/29.43 MHz (40 kHz) 145.826 MHz [4]	29.331, 29.452 MHz	1.5 W	1690 km
RS-6 Dec. 17, 1981 3 years	USSR, USSR	145.93/29.43 MHz (40 kHz)	29.411, 29.453 MHz	1.5 W	1690 km
RS-7 Dec. 17, 1981 6.5 years	USSR, USSR	145.98/29.48 MHz (40 kHz) 145.836 MHz [4]	29.341, 29.501 MHz	1.5 W	1690 km
RS-8 Dec. 17, 1981 4 years	USSR, USSR	145.98/29.48 MHz (40 kHz)	29.461, 29.502 MHz	1.5 W	1690 km
Iskra 2 May 17, 1982 53 days	USSR, USSR	21.25/29.60 MHz (40 kHz)	29.578 MHz	1.0 W	335 km
Iskra 3 Nov. 18, 1982 37 days	USSR, USSR	21.25/29.60 MHz (40 kHz)	29.583 MHz	1.0 W	335 km
AMSAT-OSCAR 10 June 16, 1983 OBC failure late 1986 transponder operating (9/2002)	ESA, FRG	435.103/146.901 MHz (152 kHz) 1269.45/436.55 MHz (800 kHz)	145.810 MHz 145.987 MHz 436.02 MHz 436.04 MHz	50 W	35,500 km
UoSAT-OSCAR 11 March 1, 1984 operating (4/2003)	NASA, UK	—	145.826 MHz 435.025 MHz 2401.5 MHz	1.0 W	690 km
Fuji-OSCAR 12 Aug. 12, 1986 3+years[5]	NASDA, Japan	145.95/435.85 MHz (100 kHz)	435.797 MHz 145.85, 145.87, 145.89, 145.91 MHz [7]	2.0 W	1510 km

Satellite Launch date Operating life	Launch Agency, Licensing Authority	Transponder input/output freq (bandwidth)	Beacon Frequencies	Transmitting Power (peak)	Apogee Height
RS-10/11 June 23, 1987 9.9 years	USSR, USSR	21.18/29.38 MHz (40 kHz) 21.18/145.88 MHz (40 kHz) 145.88/29.38 MHz (40 kHz) 21.18/29.38 and 145.88 MHz (40 kHz) 21.18 and 145.88/29.38 MHz (40 kHz) 21.120 and 145.820 MHz[4] 21.23/29.43 MHz (40 kHz) 21.23/145.93 MHz (40 kHz) 145.93/29.43 MHz (40 kHz) 21.23/29.43 and 145.93 MHz (40 kHz) 21.23 and 145.93/29.43 MHz (40 kHz) 21.130 and 145.830 MHz[4]	29.357, 29.403 MHz 145.857, 145.903 MHz 29.407, 29.453 MHz 145.907, 145.953 MHz	5 W	1000 km
AMSAT-OSCAR 13 June 15, 1988 8.5 years[6]	ESA, FRG	435.498/145.900 MHz (150 kHz) 1269.496/435.860 MHz (290 kHz) 144.448/435.965 MHz (50 kHz) 435.620/2400.729 MHz (36 kHz) 1269.710/435.677 MHz (RUDAK digital)	145.812 MHz 145.985 MHz 435.652 MHz 2400.664 MHz	50 W	36,265 km
UoSAT-OSCAR 14 Jan. 22, 1990 operating (4/2003)[8]	ESA, UK	145.975 MHz[7]	435.070 MHz	5 W	805 km
UoSAT-OSCAR 15 Jan. 22, 1990 several orbits	ESA, UK	—	435.120 MHz	5 W	805 km
Pacsat-OSCAR 16 Jan. 22, 1990 operating (4/2003)	ESA, USA	145.900, 145.920, 145.940, 145.960 MHz[7]	437.051 MHz 437.026 MHz 2401.143 MHz	4 W 4 W 1 W	805 km
DOVE-OSCAR 17 Jan. 22, 1990 8.8 years	ESA, USA	—	145.824 MHz 145.825 MHz 2401.221 MHz	4 W 4 W 1 W	805 km
Webersat-OSCAR 18 Jan. 22, 1990 operating (2/2000)	ESA, USA	Modes J,L (digital)[7]	437.102 MHz	4 W	805 km 437.075 MHz
Lusat-OSCAR 19 Jan. 22, 1990 operating (4/2003)	ESA, Argentina	145.840, 145.860, 145.880, 145.900 MHz[7]	435.154 MHz 435.126 MHz 437.127 MHz	4 W 4 W 0.8 W	805 km
Fuji-OSCAR 20 Feb. 7, 1990 operating (4/2003)	NASDA, Japan	145.950/435.850 MHz (100 kHz) 145.850, 145.870, 145.890, 145.910 MHz[7]	435.797 MHz	2.0 W	1745 km
RS-14/AO-21 Jan. 29, 1991 Sept. 16, 1994[9]	CIS, CIS	435.062/145.892 MHz (80 kHz) 435.083/145.906 MHz (80 kHz) 435.016, 435.041, 435.155, 145.952, .983 MHz, 145.838, .800 MHz, 435.193 MHz[7]	145.822 MHz 145.948 MHz	10 W	1000 km

Satellite Launch date Operating life	Launch Agency, Licensing Authority	Transponder input/output freq (bandwidth)	Beacon Frequencies	Transmitting Power (peak)	Apogee Height
RS-12/13 Feb. 5, 1991 10.5 years	CIS, CIS	21.23/29.43 MHz (40 kHz) 21.23/145.93 MHz (40 kHz) 145.93/29.43 MHz (40 kHz) 21.23/29.43 and 145.93 MHz (40 kHz) 21.23 and 145.93/29.43 MHz (40 kHz) 21.129 and 145.830 MHz[4]	29.408, 29.454 MHz 145.912, 145.959 MHz	5 W	1000 km
		21.28/29.48 MHz (40 kHz) 21.28/145.98 MHz (40 kHz) 145.98/29.48 MHz (40 kHz) 21.28/29.48 and 145.98 MHz (40 kHz) 21.28 and 145.98/29.48 MHz (40 kHz) 21.138 and 145.843 MHz[4]	29.458, 29.504 MHz 145.862, 145.908 MHz	5 W	
UoSAT-OSCAR 22 July 17, 1991 operating (4/2003)	ESA, UK	145.900, 145.975 MHz[7]	435.120 MHz	5 W	775 km
SARA July 17, 1991[20]	ESA/France	436.500 MHz[7] (command only)	145.955 MHz	0.5 W	780 km
KITSAT-OSCAR 23 Aug. 10, 1992 operating (10/2000)[21]	ESA, S. Korea	145.850, 145.900 MHz[7]	435.175 MHz	5 W	1515 km
Arsene-OSCAR 24 May 13, 1993 Sept. 9, 1993	ESA, France	435.050, 435.100, 435.150 MHz[7] 435.100/2446.540 MHz (16 kHz)	145.975 MHz	20 W	40,000 km
KITSAT-OSCAR 25 Sept. 26, 1993 operating (4/2003)	ESA, S. Korea	145.980, 145.870 MHz[7]	436.500, 435.175 MHz	5W	810 km
ITAMSAT-OSCAR 26 Sept. 26, 1993 operating (4/2003)	ESA, Italy	145.875, 145.900, 145.925, 145.950 MHz[7]	437.822, 435.867 MHz	4 W	810 km
AMRAD-OSCAR 27 Sept. 26, 1993 operating (4/2003)	ESA, USA	145.850/436.800 MHz FM	436.800 MHz	4 W	810 km
PoSAT-OSCAR 28 Sept. 26, 1993 operating (4/2003)[10]	ESA, Portugal	145.975, 145.925 MHz[7]	435.250, 435.275 MHz	4 W	810 km
RS-15 Dec. 16, 1994 operating (4/2003)	CIS, CIS	145.878/29.374 MHz (40 kHz)	29.353, 29.399 MHz	1 W	2030 km
UNAMSAT-A March 28, 1995 launch failure	CIS, Mexico	See Mexico-OSCAR 30			
TechSat-A March 28, 1995 launch failure	CIS, Israel	145.850, 145.890, 145.930 MHz 435.225, 435.325 MHz, 1269.700, 1269.800, 1269.900 MHz[7]		3 W	

Satellite Launch date Operating life	Launch Agency, Licensing Authority	Transponder input/output freq (bandwidth)	Beacon Frequencies	Transmitting Power (peak)	Apogee Height
Fuji-OSCAR 29 Aug. 17, 1996 operating (4/2003)	NASDA, Japan	145.950/435.850 MHz (100 kHz) 145.850, 145.870, 145.890, 145.910 MHz[7]	435.795 MHz 435.910 MHz	1 W	1020 km
Mexico-OSCAR 30 Sept. 5, 1996 several orbits	CIS, Mexico	145.815, 145.835, 145.855, 145.875 MHz[7]	437.206, 437.138 MHz	4 W[11]	1000 km
RS-16 Mar 4, 1997[12]	CIS, CIS	145.93/29.43 (30 kHz)	29.408, 29.451 MHz 435.504, 435.548 MHz	4 W	455 km
RS-17 (Sputnik-40) Nov 3, 1997 (Mir) Dec 30, 1997[13]	CIS/France	—	145.823 MHz	200 mW	390 km
TMSAT-OSCAR 31 Jul 10, 1998 operating (9/2001)[21]	CIS/Thailand	145.925 (Primary), 145.975 MHz[7]	436.925 (Primary), 436.900, 436.950, 436.975 MHz	2.0 W	826 km
Gurwin-OSCAR 32 Jul 10, 1998	CIS/Israel	145.850, 145.890, 145.930 MHz 1269.700, 1269.800, 1269.900 MHz[7]	435.325 (Primary), 435.225 MHz	3 W	826 km
SEDSAT-OSCAR 33 Oct 24, 1998[14]	NASA/USA	145.945/29.380 MHz (60 kHz) 1268.21 MHz[7]	437.91 MHz	3 W	1085 km
PANSAT-OSCAR 34 Oct 30, 1998 (STS)[16]	NASA/USA	436.5 MHz[15]	435.5 MHz[15]	2.0 W	570 km
RS-18 (Sputnik-41) Nov 10, 1998 Dec 11, 1998[17]	CIS/France	—	145.812 MHz	150 mW	370 km
SUNSAT-OSCAR 35 Feb 23, 1999 23 months	NASA/S. Africa	145.825, 145.850, 145.900, 145.950 MHz 436.291, 436.250 MHz,[7] 13 cm[18] 23 cm[18]	145.825 MHz 436.250, 436.300 MHz	10 W	871 km
UoSAT-OSCAR 36 Apr 21, 1999 operating (7/2001)[21]	CIS/UK	2 m, 23 cm[7, 18]	437.400, 437.025 MHz 2401.0 MHz	50 W	666 km
JAWSAT (WO-38) Jan 27, 2000 operating (2/2000)[21]	Commercial/USA	145.860 MHz[7]	437.070, 437.175 MHz 2403.2 MHz	8 W	814 km
ASUSat (AO-37) Jan 27, 2000 ~ 1 day	Commercial/USA	145.820, 145.990 MHz[7]	436.500, 436.700 MHz	2 W	814 km
OPAL (OO-38) Jan 27, 2000 operating (3/2001)[21]	Commercial/USA	2 meters[7, 18]	437.100 MHz	—	814 km
StenSat Feb 11, 2000[19, 20]	From OPAL	145.840 MHz[7]	436.625 MHz	250 mW	814 km
Artemis JAK Feb 11, 2000[19, 20]	From OPAL	—	437.100 MHz	200 mW	814 km

Satellite / Launch date / Operating life	Launch Agency, Licensing Authority	Transponder input/output freq (bandwidth)	Beacon Frequencies	Transmitting Power (peak)	Apogee Height
Artemis Thelma Feb 12, 2000[19, 20]	From OPAL	See note 18	437.100 MHz	200 mW	814 km
Artemis Louise Feb 12, 2000[19, 20]	From OPAL	See note 18	437.100 MHz	200 mW	814 km
TiungSAT-1 (MO-46) Sept 26, 2000 operating (4/2003)	CIS/Malaysia	145.850, 145.925 MHz[7]	437.325 MHz	8 W	670 km
SaudiSat-1A (SO-41) Sept 26, 2000 operating (4/2003)	CIS/Saudi Arabia	145.850 MHz[7]	437.075 MHz	7 W	680 km
SaudiSat-1B (SO-42) Sept 26, 2000 operating (4/2003)	CIS/Saudi Arabia	2 meters [7, 18]	437.075 MHz	7 W	680 km
AMSAT-OSCAR 40 Nov 16, 2000 operating (4/2003)	ESA, Germany	Analog uplink bands (MHz) 21.230 (40 kHz), 24.940 (40 kHz) 145.915 (150 kHz), 435.675 (250 kHz), 1269.375 (250 kHz), 1268.450 (250 kHz), 2400.475 (250 kHz), 2446.575 (250 kHz), 5668.675 (250 kHz), Analog downlink bands (MHz) 145.880 (150 kHz), 435.600 (250 kHz), 2400.350 (250 kHz), 2401.350 (250 kHz) 10451.150 (250 kHz), 24048.150 (250 kHz) Digital uplink bands (MHz) 145.820 (40 kHz), 435.425 (250 kHz), 1269.125 (250 kHz), 1268.200 (250 kHz), 2400.225 (250 kHz), 2446.325 (250 kHz), 5668.425 (250 kHz) Digital downlink bands (MHz) 145.975 (40 kHz), 436.050 (300 kHz), 2400.800 (300 kHz), 2401.800 (300 kHz), 10451.600 (300 kHz), 24048.600 (300 kHz)	145.880 MHz 435.450, 435.850, 435,850 MHz 2400.200, 2400.350, 2400.600 MHz 2401.200, 2401.350, 2401.600 MHz 10451.000, 10451.150, 10451.400 MHz 24048.000, 24048.150, 24048.400 MHz	100 W	58950 km
Starshine 3 (SO-43) Sept 30, 2001 3.5 months[22]	USA/USA	—	145.825 MHz	1.2 W	481 km
PCsat (NO-44) Sept 30, 2001 operating (4/2003)	USA/USA	145.825, 435.250 MHz[7]	145.828, 144.390 MHz	2 W	806 km
Sapphire (NO-45) Sept 30, 2001 operating (4/2003)	USA/USA	145.945 MHz[7]	437.095 MHz	2 W	806 km

Satellite Launch date Operating life	Launch Agency, Licensing Authority	Transponder input/output freq (bandwidth)	Beacon Frequencies	Transmitting Power (peak)	Apogee Height
RS-21 (Kolibri-2000) Mar 19, 2002[23]	CIS/CIS	---	145.825, 145.850 MHz ? 435.335 MHz		404 km
BO-47/48 (IDEFIX) May 4, 2002 32 days	ESA/France	---	145.838, 435.278 MHz	1.2 W	814 km
RS-20 (Mozhayets) Nov 28, 2002 operating (4/2003)	CIS/CIS	---	145.825, 435.319 MHz ?		750 km
AO-49 (AATis-OSCAR) Dec 20, 2002 operating (4/2003)	CIS/Germany	435.275 MHz[7]	145.825 MHz	2 W	686 km
SaudiSat-1C (SO-50) Dec 20, 2002 operating (4/2003)	CIS/Saudi Arabia	145.850 MHz[7]	436.800 MHz	250 mW	697 km

Notes

[1]Never activated due to technical problems.
[2]Never activated due to regulatory constraints.
[3]Reentered Oct. 13, 1990.
[4]Autotransponder (ROBOT) uplink, downlink on beacon frequency.
[5]Withdrawn from service Nov. 5, 1990 due to deteriorating power budget.
[6]Reentered Dec. 5, 1996.
[7]Digital transponder, downlink on beacon frequency.
[8]Amateur operations shifted to UO-22 on Feb. 5 1992.
[9]Mother spacecraft turned off by CIS Sept. 16, 1994 due to maintenance costs.
[10]Checked out on amateur frequencies for several weeks in early 1994. Currently in commercial service.
[11]Also contains 70 W pulse transmitter at 41.997 MHz for scientific experiments.
[12]Transponder never activated due to technical problems. Reentered Oct 25, 1999.
[13]Reentered 21 May 1998.
[14]Transponders never activated due to command/control problems. Telemetry being received aperiodically as of 1/2003.
[15]This is a single band half-duplex spread-spectrum digital transponder.
[16]PANSAT is operational (1/2003). However, due to ground station equipment requirements, it is not in use (see **www.sp.nps.navy.mil/ pansat**/).
[17]Reentered Jan 11, 1999.
[18]Link is frequency agile or exact frequencies not yet announced
[19]Date released from OPAL
[20]No reception reports.
[21]Last confirmed operation. Current operational status not known.
[22]Reentered Jan 21, 2003.
[23]Date released from Progress M1-7
[24]Reentered May 3, 2002.

APPENDIX

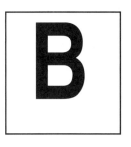

Radio Amateur Operation From Space

Table B.1
Radio Amateur Operation from Space: The First Decade

Spacecraft	Dates	Operator(s)	Notes
STS-9 Columbia	Nov 28-Dec 8, 1983	Owen Garriott (W5LFL)	Voice > 250 QSOs on 2 m
STS-51F Challenger	July 29-Aug 6, 1985	Tony England (W0ORE) John Bartoe (W4NYZ)	Voice, SSTV (space to Earth) Approximately 6000 students participated
STS-61A Columbia	Oct 30-Nov 6, 1985	Reinhard Furrer (DD6CF) Ernst Messerschmid (DG2KM) Wubbo Ockels (PE1LFO)	70 cm FM up, 2 m FM down Call sign used: DP0SL SPACELAB-D1
Mir	Nov 6- Dec 26, 1988	Vladimir Titov (U1MIR) Musa Manarov (U2MIR) Valery Polyakov (U3MIR)	2 m FM voice
Mir	Feb 9-Apr. 27, 1989	Alexander Volkov (U4MIR) Sergei Krikalev (U5MIR)	2 m FM voice
Mir	Continuous operation 1989-2001 (see Table B-2)		
STS-35 Columbia	Dec 2-Dec 11, 1990	Ron Parise (WA4SIR)	Voice, Packet
STS-37 Atlantis	April 1991	Ken Cameron (KB5AWP) Linda Godwin, N5RAX Jerry Ross, N5SCW Jay Apt, N5QWL Steve Nagel, N5RAW	Voice, Packet, ATV Uplink
STS-45 Atlantis	March 1992	Dave Leestma, N5WQC Dirk Frimout, ON1AFD Brian Duffy, N5WQW Kathy Sullivan, N5YYV	Voice
STS-50 Columbia	June 1992	Dick Richards, KB5SIW Ellen Baker, KB5SIX	Voice, Packet, SSTV, ATV Uplink
STS-47 Endeavour	Sep 1992	Jay Apt, N5QWL Mamoru Mohri, 7L2NJY	Voice, Packet
STS-56 Discovery	April 1993	Ken Cameron, KB5AWP Mike Foale, KB5UAC Steve Oswald, KB5YSR Ken Cockrell, KB5UAH Ellen Ochoa, KB5TZZ	Voice, Packet, SSTV, ATV Uplink

Spacecraft	Dates	Operator(s)	Notes
STS-55 Columbia	April 1993	Steve Nagel, N5RAW Charlie Precourt, KB5YSQ Ulrich Walter, DG1KIM Jerry Ross, N5SCW Hans Schlegel, DG1KIH	Voice, Packet
STS-57 Endeavour	June 1993	Brian Duffy, N5WQW Janice Voss, KC5BTK	Voice, Packet
STS-58 Columbia	Oct 1993	Bill McArthur, KC5ACR Rick Searfoss, KC5CKM Marty Fettman, KC5AXA	Voice, Packet

Table B.2

Summary: Radio Amateur Operation from Space

Year	Number of STS flights with Amateur Radio	Number of licensed operators on STS	Number of licensed operators on Mir
1983	1	1	0
1984	0	0	0
1985	2	5	0
1986	0	0	0
1987	0	0	0
1988	0	0	3
1989	0	0	4
1990	1	1	6
1991	1	5	5
1992	3	8	6
1993	4	15	5
1994	4	10	8
1995	4	15	8
1996	2	7	6

Table B.3

Comprehensive Information Resources on Amateur Operation From Space

INTERNET
- **www.marex-na.org**
- **www.marex-na.org/fileshtml/unprotopage.html**
- **www.issfanclub.com**

PUBLISHED (LISTED BY DATE)
- F. Bauer KA3HDO, L. McFadin W5DID, W. Marchant KC6ROL, C. Conley KD5SJO, "2001: an Amateur Radio Space Odyssey on the International Space Station," *Proceedings of the AMSAT-NA 19th Space Symposium*, 2001 pp 75-82.
- W. Marchant KC6ROL, F. Bauer KA3HDO, "Amateur Radio Operation On Board the International Space Station," *Proceedings of the AMSAT-NA 19th Space Symposium*, 2001 pp 83-87.
- F. Bauer KA3HDO, W. Marchant KC6ROL, "Amateur Radio on the International Space Station," *Proceedings of the AMSAT-NA 16th Space Symposium*, 1998, pp 124-128.
- F. Bauer KA3HDO, M. Bordelon KC5BTL, "Shuttle Amateur Radio Experiment Status 1995," *The AMSAT Journal*, Jan/Feb 1996, pp 19-30.
- G. Carpignano LW2DTZ, "Five Years of a Permanent Packet Radio Space Station," *Proceedings of the AMSAT-NA 14th Space Symposium*, 1996, pp 80-86.
- T. Kieselbach DL2MDE (Translated by J. Bubbers W1GYU), "The Amateur Radio Space Experiment SAFEX II: RR0DL – A New Amateur Radio Station on MIR," *The AMSAT Journal*, Nov/Dec 1995, pp 14-16.
- F. Bauer KA3HDO, L. McFadin W5DID, "Shuttle Amateur Radio Experiment (SAREX) Hardware Configurations and Flight Operations Support," *Proceedings of the AMSAT-NA 10th Space Symposium*, 1992, pp 100-110.
- V. Kondratko UV3DQE, J. Kasser G3ZCZ, "CQ Earth, This is MIR Calling," *The AMSAT Journal*, May 1990, pp 1, 4-7.

Table B.4

Operating Frequencies and Tracking Information: ISS, STS and *Mir*

ISS FREQUENCIES[1]

Voice (General QSO's)

Uplink Region 1:	145.200 MHz (includes Europe, Central Asia and Africa)
Uplink Region 2/3:	144.490 MHz (includes Americas and Pacific)
Downlink worldwide:	145.800 MHz (general QSO's and school contacts)

Packet

Uplink worldwide:	145.990 MHz
Downlink worldwide:	145.800 MHz

STS FREQUENCIES

STS amateur frequencies (not all frequencies used on all flights)
FM Voice Downlink (Worldwide): 145.55 MHz
FM Voice Uplink: 144.91, 144.93, 144.95, 144.97, 144.99 MHz
FM Packet Downlink: 145.55 MHz[2]
FM Packet Uplink: 144.49 MHz[2]

STS non-amateur frequencies of interest
259.7 MHz: EVA Packs to Shuttle[3]
279.0 MHz: EVA-EVA Packs & Shuttle[3]
296.8 MHz: Shuttle to EVA [3]
243.0 MHz: Emergency Shuttle and EVA beacons
—Not in normal use.[3]

MIR FREQUENCIES[4,5]

(Deorbited March 23, 2001)
Mir amateur frequencies

General
FM Voice Downlink: 145.800 MHz
FM Voice Uplink: 145.200 MHz
FM Packet Downlink: 145.800 MHz
FM Packet Uplink: 145.200 MHz

MIR SAFEX II
Mode 1 (General repeater, 2.2 MHz offset,141.3 Hz CTCSS tone required)
Downlink: 437.950 MHz
Uplink: 435.750 MHz

Mode 2 (Packet repeater, digipeating and mailbox, 9600 baud, 2.2 MHz offset, CTCSS not required)
Downlink: 437.975 MHz
Uplink: 435.775 MHz

Mode 3 (*Mir* Crew QSO, digital voice recorder broadcasts, 2.2 MHz offset,141.3 Hz CTCSS tone required)
Downlink: 437.925 MHz
Uplink: 435.725 MHz

Mir non-amateur frequencies of interest
143.625 MHz: *Mir* to ground; wideband FM (30 kHz)
130.165 MHz: *Mir* to STS during docking
121.750 MHz: *Mir* to Johnson Space Center

TRACKING DATA

Tracking data for ISS has to be updated almost daily and of course whenever maneuvers occur. Tracking data for STS must be updated several times per day due to the fact that maneuvers are very frequent. The best way to obtain this data is via the Internet. Two excellent sources are the AMSAT Web site at **www.amsat.org/amsat/keps/** and NASA's online tracker at: **www.spacefilght.nasa.gov/realdata/tracking/**.

Notes

[1]ARISS Amateur Radio operations began Nov 2000.
[2]Standard terrestrial 1200 baud packet
[3]AM modulated, not encrypted
[4]Although *Mir* is no longer in space, these frequencies may be used on Russian ISS modules
[5]Russian cosmonauts operate on Decreed Moscow Time (DMT) which is GMT + 3 hours. Their scheduled sleep time is 10 PM to 8 AM DMT. Radio operation frequently occurs near the start or end of this time period.

APPENDIX

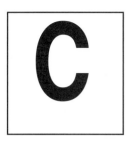

C Spacecraft Profiles

PHASE 2 SERIES
AMSAT-OSCAR 7

PHASE 3 SERIES
AMSAT-OSCAR 10
AMSAT-OSCAR 40

UOSAT SERIES
UoSAT-OSCAR 11
UoSAT-OSCAR 22
KITSAT-OSCAR 23
KITSAT-OSCAR 25
PoSAT-OSCAR 28
TMSAT-OSCAR 31
UoSAT-OSCAR 36
Malaysia-OSCAR 46

JAS SERIES
Fuji-OSCAR 20
Fuji-OSCAR 29

RS SERIES
RS-12/13
RS-15
RS-20
RS-21

MICROSAT SERIES
Pacsat-OSCAR 16
Lusat-OSCAR 19
ITAMSAT-OSCAR 26
AMRAD-OSCAR 27

UNIVERSITY AND INDEPENDENT

Gurwin-OSCAR 32	Artemis Louise
SEDSAT-OSCAR 33	Saudisat-1A (SO-41)
PANSAT-OSCAR 34	Saudisat-1B (SO-42)
SUNSAT-OSCAR 35	SaudiSat-OSCAR 50
JAWSAT (WO-39)	Starshine-OSCAR 43 (SO-43)
ASUSat-OSCAR 37	PCsat-NAV-OSCAR 44 (NO-44)
OPAL (OO-38)	Sapphire NAV-OSCAR 45
StenSat-OSCAR	(NO-45)
Artemis JAK	BreizhSat-OSCAR 47/48
Artemis Thelma	AATis-OSCAR 49 (AO-49)

Each section of this appendix contains a succinct description of a radio amateur satellite, or group of satellites, either currently in orbit and operational or soon to be launched. This information has been organized, insofar as possible, using the standard format outlined in Table C-1. Though detailed, the profiles contained here are by no means complete. Sources for additional information have been referenced when available.

Table C-1
Standard Format Used to Describe Satellites Listed in Appendix C

SPACECRAFT PRIMARY NAME

Note

GENERAL
1.1 Identification: international designation, NASA catalog number, prelaunch designation, also known as, radio license call sign
1.2 Launch: date, vehicle, agency, site
1.3 Orbital Parameters (as of date specified): general designation, period, apogee and perigee altitude (specified over mean radius of Earth [6371 km]), inclination, eccentricity, maximum access distance (see Eq 13.3), maximum access time, expected lifetime in orbit if less than 10 years, transfer orbit characteristics.
1.4 Ground Track Comments
1.5 Operations: Group(s) responsible for coordination and scheduling
1.6 Design/Construction Credits: project management, spacecraft subsystems
1.7 Primary References

SPACECRAFT DESCRIPTION
2.1 Physical Structure: shape, separation mass (mass of spacecraft released from rocket), thermal design
2.2 Subsystem Organization: block diagram

SUBSYSTEM DESCRIPTION
3.1 Beacons: frequency, power level
3.2 Telemetry
3.3 Telecommand System
3.4 Transponders: type, frequencies, output power, suggested uplink EIRP, translation equation
3.5 Attitude Control and Stabilization: primary control, secondary control, damping, sensors
3.6 Antennas: description, gain, polarization
3.7 Energy Supply and Power Conditioning: solar cell characteristics and configuration, storage battery, switching regulators, etc
3.8 Propulsion Systems
3.9 Integrated Housekeeping Unit (IHU) and On-Board Computers
3.10 Experimental Systems

SPACECRAFT NAME: AMSAT-OSCAR 7

In mid 1981, after providing 6.5 years of continuous service, AO-7 ceased operating. The cause was believed to be a shorted battery cell that prevented the solar panels from powering the electronic systems. In June 2002 Pat Gowen, G3IOR, reported hearing signals from AO-7. The spacecraft had revived after 21 years of sleep. Observations over the next several weeks revealed that (1) both the Mode A and Mode B transponders were operational, (2) the spacecraft only operated when in sunlight, and (3) the spacecraft responded to commands from the ground. See section 3.7 (Energy Supply and Power Conditioning) for additional information. This spacecraft is not being actively controlled, so potential users must check Mode A and Mode B downlinks when the spacecraft is in sunlight.

GENERAL

1.1   *Identification*

International designation: 1974-089B
NASA Catalog number: 07530
Prelaunch designation: A-O-B
Also known as: AO-7

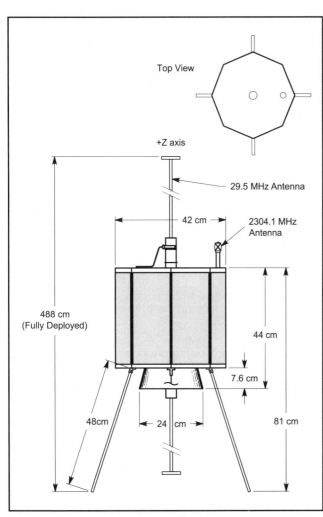

Figure 1—AMSAT-OSCAR 7 Structure

1.2 *Launch*

Date: 15 November 1974
Site: NASA Western Test Range; Lompoc, CA
(Vandenberg Air Force Base)
Launch Vehicle: Two-stage Delta 2310

1.3 *Orbital Parameters (1/2003)*

General designation: low altitude, circular, near polar, sun-synchronous
Period: 114.87
Apogee altitude: 1,466 km
Perigee altitude: 1,447 km
Eccentricity: 0.0012
Inclination: 101.8 degrees
Maximum access distance: 3,960 km

1.4 *Design/construction Credits*

Project management: AMSAT-US
Project manager: Jan King, W3GEY
Spacecraft subsystems: Designed and built by groups in Australia, Canada, US, (West) Germany

1.5 *Primary References:*

1. J. Kasser, G3ZCZ and J.A. King, W3GEY, "OSCAR 7 and Its Capabilities," *QST*, February 1974, pp. 56-60.

2. Jan King, W3GEY, "AMSAT-OSCAR 7 Final Telemetry Parameters and Equations," *AMSAT Newsletter*, Vol. VI, no. 4, Dec. 1974, pp. 4-12.

SPACECRAFT DESCRIPTION

2.1 *Physical Structure*

Shape: Right octahedral solid (see **Figure 1**).
Mass: 28.9 kg

2.2 *System Integration*

Block diagram of spacecraft electronics systems: See **Figure 2**.

Spacecraft Operation: The spacecraft has four primary operating modes, Modes A, B, C and D. These modes are discussed in section 3.3 (Command System) and should not be confused with the Mode A and Mode B transponders.

SUBSYSTEM DESCRIPTION

3.1 *Beacons*

AO-7 contains four beacons. These beacons can transmit: Morse code telemetry (at 10 or 20 WPM), RTTY telemetry or a dump of Codestore (see Chapter 5) memory.
Beacon 1 Frequency: 29.502 MHz
Power: 200 mW
Note: Generally on in conjunction with Spacecraft Mode A

Beacon 2 Frequency: 145.972 MHz
Power: 200 mW
Note: Generally on in conjunction with Spacecraft Modes B and C

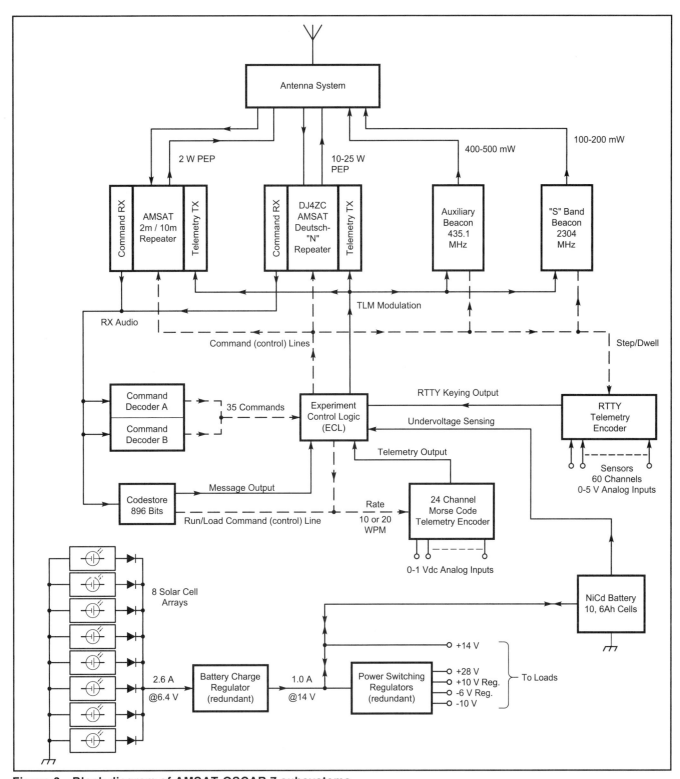

Figure 2—Block diagram of AMSAT-OSCAR 7 subsystems.

Beacon 3 Frequency: 435.100 MHz
Power: 10 mW (initially 400 mW but output dropped to 10 mW in early 1975)
Note: Spacecraft logic is designed to prevent this beacon from operating when satellite is in Spacecraft Modes B or C

Beacon 4 Frequency: 2304.1 MHz
Power: 40 mW
Note: Due to ITU frequency allocation changes in the early 1970s this beacon cannot be operated over the US without an STA from the FCC. An uplink command is required to turn this beacon on. A watchdog timer then turns it off after 14 minutes.

3.2 Telemetry

Formats available:
Morse code: 20 WPM (default) or 10 WPM. Contains 20 analog channels

Table 1

AMSAT-OSCAR 7 Spacecraft Operating Modes

Spacecraft Mode A
  2 meters/10 meters (Mode A) transponder on and/or 70 cm beacon on,
  70 cm/2 meters (Mode B) transponder off

Spacecraft Mode B
  70 cm/2 meters (Mode B) transponder on at full power
  2 meters/10 meters (Mode A) transponder off
  70 cm beacon off

Spacecraft Mode C
  70 cm/2 meters (Mode B) transponder on at 1/4 power
  2 meters/10 meters (Mode A) transponder off
  70 cm beacon off

Spacecraft Mode D (recharge)
  70 cm/2 meters (Mode B) transponder off
  2 meters/10 meters (Mode A) transponder off

RTTY: 45.5 bauds mark only format, contains 60 channels of analog data and 20 channels of status data
Codestore: See Transponder section.

3.3 Command System

The AO-7 spacecraft is designed to operate in one of four Spacecraft Modes. These modes are listed in **Table 1**.
The spacecraft command decoder is designed to recognize 35 commands (See **Table 2**). Experiments in 2002 have verified that at least 11 of these commands are still recognized.

3.4 Transponders

Transponder I: Mode A (2 meter/10 meter)
Type: linear, non-inverting
Uplink passband: 145.850-145.950 MHz
Downlink passband: 29.400-29.500 MHz
Translation equation: downlink (MHz) = uplink (MHz) – 116.450 MHz +/- Doppler
Power output: 1.3 W PEP
Uplink EIRP: a maximum of 100 watts is recommended
Note: A block diagram is shown in Chapter 14 (Figure 14.2).

Transponder II: Mode B (70cm/2 meters)
Type: linear, inverting
Uplink passband: 432.125 – 432.175 MHz
Downlink passband: 145.975 – 145.925 MHz
Translation equation: downlink (MHz) = 578.100 MHz – uplink (MHz) +/- Doppler
Power output: 8 W or 2.5 W PEP
Uplink EIRP: a maximum of 80 watts is recommended

Notes:
1. This transponder was designed by Karl Meinzer, DJ4ZC. It uses the Envelope Elimination and Restoration technique he developed (See Chapter 14 for additional information).

Table 2

AMSAT-OSCAR 7 Command States

Command #	Action
1	Select Spacecraft Mode A
2	Select Spacecraft Mode B
3	70 cm Beacon on (Spacecraft Mode A or D only)
4	70 cm Beacon off
5	Run Codestore
6	Load Codestore
7	Morse code TTY (20 WPM)
8	Morse code TTY (10 WPM)
9	2/10 transponder – full sensitivity
10	2/10 transponder – reduced sensitivity (-14dB)
11	Route Codestore to 70 cm beacon
12	Route Morse code TTY to 70 cm beacon
13	Route RTTY to 70 cm beacon
14	Route Morse code TTY to 10 meter and 2 meter beacons
15	Route Codestore to 10 meter and 2 meter beacons
16	Route RTTY to 10 meter and 2 meter beacons
17	Reset 24 clock
18	Select Spacecraft Mode C
19	Select Spacecraft Mode D
20	Select BCR 1
21	Select BCR 2
22	Set RTTY to dwell mode
23	Set RTTY to run mode
24	2304 MHz beacon on (14 minutes only)
25	2304 MHz beacon off
26	Set 2304 MHz beacon to internal keying
27	Route Morse code TTY to 2304 MHz beacon
28	Set RTTY to FSK mode
29	Set RTTY to AFSK mode
30	Same as 1
31	Same as 2
32	Same as 3
33	Same as 4
34	Same as 18
35	Same as 19

2. After AO-7 was designed, built, tested and ready for launch the regulations governing the Amateur Satellite Service (which is distinct from the Amateur Radio Service- see Appendix F) were changed. Two results of these changes were that the 70 cm uplink and the 13 cm downlink frequencies used by AO-7 were no longer available to the Amateur Satellite Service. AMSAT requested a special waiver for AO-7 because the changes could not be made before the scheduled launch date. The FCC responded by granting AMSAT permission to use the 70 cm uplink "on the condition that the Earth telecommand stations used in the OSCAR 7 project have the absolute capability to disable the space station from receiving 432.125-432.175 MHz uplink frequencies should disablement be necessary for any reason." The request to use the 13 cm downlink beacon was refused. For addition information, see **Figure 3**. Note that the FCC notice does not specify any termination date.

3.5 Attitude Stabilization and Control

AO-7 uses a passive attitude control system designed to provide a "controlled tumble." The system elements include:

Table 3

AMSAT-OSCAR 7 Antenna Polarization Chart

Note that when using circular polarization best results are obtained when the transmitting station polarization sense and the receiving station polarization sense match.

Link Polarization	Subsystem	Spacecraft Antenna
2 meters up	2 meters/10 meter transponder	left-hand circular[1]
10 meters down	2 meter/10 meter transponder	linear
70 cm up	70cm/2 meter transponder	right-hand circular[1]
2 meters down	70cm/2 meters transponder	right-hand circular[1]
70 cm down	beacon	left-hand circular[1]
13 cm down	beacon	right-hand circular[2]

Notes:

[1]Polarization sense referenced to spacecraft +Z axis. Ground stations off axis will observe elliptical polarization. Ground stations located north of the magnetic equator will generally obtain the best results by using an antenna matching the sense indicated in the table. Ground stations located south of the magnetic equator will generally obtain the best results using the opposite sense.

[2]The polarization remains nearly circular in the entire hemisphere seen by the +Z face of the spacecraft.

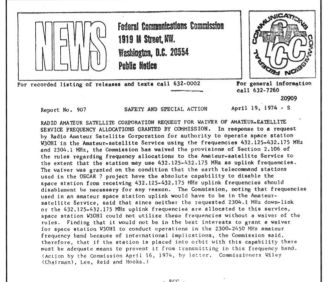

Figure 3—Letter of 19 April 1974 from FCC to AMSAT concerning use of 70 cm uplink and 13 cm downlink on AMSAT-OSCAR 7.

1. Four ALNICO-V bar magnets aligned parallel to the spacecraft Z-axis and located symmetrically with respect to it. Each magnet is a rectangular solid measuring 15 x 0.8 x 0.8 cm. The resulting far field is roughly equivalent to that which would be produced by a single 30,000 pole-cm magnet along the Z-axis. The +Z face (top) of the spacecraft points towards the Earth's north magnetic pole.

2. The four elements of the canted turnstile antenna are painted with reflective and non-reflective optical coatings so as to produce Radiometer induced spin.

3. Eight Allegheny Ludlum type 4750 permalloy hysterisis damping rods mounted perpendicular to the Z-axis dampen nutation and limit spin rate. Each rod is about 30 cm long, 0.32 cm in diameter, and bent in the center at a 135-degree angle.

4. AO-7 contains infrared phototransistors positioned to verify earth pointing.

3.6 Antennas

Antenna structures and placement can be seen in Figure 1. Antenna Polarization is listed in Table 3.

10 meters: half-wavelength dipole along z-axis

2 meters and 70 cm: A single antenna, known as a canted turnstile, mounted on the –Z face of the spacecraft is used for all 2 meter and 70 cm functions. It produces an elliptically polarized radiation field over a very large solid angle with some gain along the –Z-axis and some shadowing along the +Z-axis.

13 cm: A quadrifilar helix mounted on the top plate of the spacecraft is used in conjunction with the 2304 MHz beacon.

3.7 Energy Supply and Power Conditioning:

Solar cells
  Type: n on p silicon
  Size: 1 cm x 2 cm
  Total number: 1792
  Total surface area: 3,580 cm x cm
  Efficiency: 9% (beginning of life)
  Peak array output: 15 W

Batteries
  Cell type: NiCd
  Configuration: 10 cells in series

Note:

The initial failure of AO-7 in 1981, after 6.5 years of service, was believed to have resulted from one of the battery cells failing in a shorted mode. This is a relatively common failure scenario in NiCds that results from conductive filaments growing between the electrodes. The rebirth of AO-7, 21 years later is believed to be due to the disintegration of these filament(s) due to coexisting chemical processes with a different reaction rate. This is an interesting area for serious scientific inquiry.

SPACECRAFT NAME: AMSAT-OSCAR 10

Note: The main computer onboard OSCAR 10 failed in Dec 1986. As a result, ground command stations have no control over the orientation or operation of this spacecraft. However, the Mode B transponder remains on and operational and connected to the omnidirectional antenna. When the spacecraft orientation is favorable (with respect to the Earth *and* Sun) OSCAR 10 continues to provide good Mode B service. The transponder is open for use when available except when AMSAT requests that operation be temporarily suspended due to poor Sun angles or if FMing occurs on the downlink. If users cooperate OSCAR 10 may provide many more years of service. Because AMSAT has very limited control over this spacecraft and no telemetry is available, the following profile has been abbreviated.

GENERAL

1.1 Identification

International designation: 1983 058 B
NASA Catalog number: 14129
Prelaunch designation: AMSAT Phase IIIB, P3B
Also known as: AO-10

1.2 Launch

Date: Jun 16, 1983
Vehicle: Ariane-2
Agency: ESA
Site: Kourou, French Guiana

1.3 Orbital Parameters (Oct 1996)

General designation: high-altitude, elliptical, synchronous-transfer, Phase 3, Molniya
Period: 699.4 Minutes
Apogee altitude: 35,530 km
Perigee altitude: 3931 km
Eccentricity: 0.605
Inclination: 25.9°
Argument of Perigee: changing
  May 2003: 0°
  Rate of change: 0.27047°/day, 8.22°/month, 98.8°/year
Maximum access distance: 9035 km

1.4 Ground Track Data

The following information is useful for rough tracking. Given the time, latitude and longitude of a reference apogee, apogee *two* orbits later will 40.9 minutes earlier (next day) at a longitude 9.4° farther east at approximately the same latitude.

1.6 Design/Construction Credits

Project Management: AMSAT-NA (Jan King, W3GEY) and AMSAT-DL (Karl Meinzer, DJ4ZC)
Spacecraft subsystems: Contributed by groups in Canada, Hungary, Japan, United States, West Germany

1.7 Primary References

See references for Phase 3A and OSCAR 13.

Phase 3A. J. A. King, "Phase III: Toward the Ultimate Amateur Satellite," Part I, *QST*, Jun 1977, pp 11-14; Part II, *QST*, Jul 1977, pp 52-55; Part III, *QST*, Aug 1977, pp 11-13.

OSCAR 13. V. Riportella, "Introducing Phase 3C: A New, More Versatile OSCAR," *QST*, Jun 1988, pp 22-30; J. Miller, "A PSK Telemetry Demodulator for OSCAR 10," *Ham Radio*, Apr 1985, pp 50-51, 53-55, 57-62; also appeared in *Electronics and Wireless World*, Part 1, Oct 1984, pp 37-41, 59-60, Part 2, Nov 1984, pp 37-38. Be sure to see Miller's revisions: *OSCAR News*, #70, Apr 1988, p 13. "Phase 3C System Specifications," Part 1 and Part 2, *ASR*, no. 177, Jun 8, 1988, pp 3-4. P. Gulzow, DB2OS, "AMSAT OSCAR-13 Telemetry Block Format," *OSCAR News*, no. 73, Oct 1988, pp 8-14.

Also see: **www.cstone.net/~w4sm/AO-10.html**.

SPACECRAFT DESCRIPTION

2.1 Physical Structure

Shape: Tri-star as shown in Figure AO10-1
Mass: approximately 90 kg + fuel

SUBSYSTEM DESCRIPTION

3.4 Transponders

General
Design / Construction credits: K. Meinzer, DJ4ZC, Ulrich Mueller, DK4VW, and Werner Haas, DJ5KQ, University

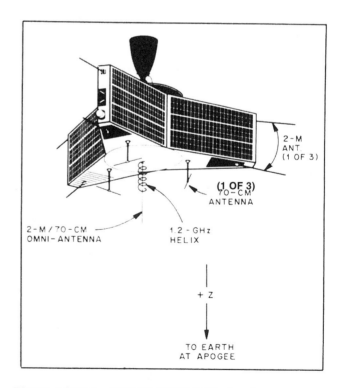

Figure AO10-1—AMSAT-OSCAR 10 structure.

of Marburg, West Germany

Transponder I: Mode B (70 cm/2 m) (only transponder operating)
  type: linear, inverting
  uplink passband: 435.027-435.179 MHz
  downlink passband: 145.825-145.977 MHz
  translation equation:
    downlink freq [MHz] =
      581.004 – uplink freq [MHz] ±Doppler
  maximum Doppler (at perigee): 5.0 kHz

SPACECRAFT NAME: AMSAT-OSCAR 40

A brief summary of the operational status of AO-40 follows. A "?" indicates that the system has not been thoroughly investigated.

OPERATING RECEIVERS

146 MHz (V-Rx)	
435 MHz (U-Rx)	
1.27 GHz (L1-Rx)	See Note 1
1.27 GHz (L2-Rx)	
2.4 GHZ (S1-Rx)	
2.4 GHZ (S2-Rx)	?
5.7 GHZ (C-Rx)	?

OPERATING TRANSMITTERS

2.4 GHz (S2-Tx)	
10 GHz (X-Tx)	?
24 GHz (K-Tx)	See Note 2

ANTENNAS

Directive	okay
Omni	not operational

EXPERIMENTS

YACE	okay
Scope A & Scope B	okay
CEDEX	okay
GPS	okay

SPACECRAFT

IF-Matrix	okay[3]
LEILA-1 & LEILA-2	okay
RUDAK-A & RUDAK-B	okay[4]
IHU-1 & IHU-2	okay
CAN Bus (SMrtNde)	okay
Earth & Sun Sensors	okay
Magnetorquing	okay
Reaction Wheels	okay
Solar Arrays (not deployed)	okay
Stabilization	spin stabilized

[1]The L1 Rx may be slightly more sensitive than the L2 Rx but it sometimes exhibits a slight gurgling distortion.

[2]Power output of the 24 GHz Tx decreased slightly on June 4, 2004.

[3]Due to interaction between the linear transponders and RUDAK they will not be scheduled simultaneously.

[4]Goal is to open one RUDAK for general operation in 2003.)

GENERAL

1.1 Identification

International designation: 2000 072 B
NASA Catalog number: 26,609
Prelaunch designation: P3D
Also known as: AO-40

1.2 Launch

Date: 16 Nov 2000
Vehicle: Ariane-5
Agency: ESA
Site: Kourou, French Guiana

1.3 Orbital Parameters as of July 2001(after all engine firings)

Projected range over next 20 years in [ ]
General designation: high-altitude, elliptical, synchronous-transfer, Phase 3, equatorial Molniya
Period: 1,146.4 minutes [1,144.9 min. to 1,149.5 min.]
Apogee altitude: 58,950 km
Perigee altitude: 870 km [810 km to 1,260 km]
Eccentricity: 0.800
Inclination: 5.3° [4.9° to 10.4°]
Argument of Perigee: 133° (1/2003)
Maximum access distance: 9,385 km

1.5 Operations

AO-40 operations and scheduling are coordinated by an informal international group representing the design and command team and organizations that provided support to the project. Schedules take into account the need to maintain spacecraft health and the desires of the user community and serious experimenters. The operating schedule is transmitted on the AO-40 beacon and widely reproduced on Web sites hosted by AMSAT-NA, AMSAT-DL, and AMSAT-UK. A typical schedule appears as follows:

```
N QST AMSAT AO-40    SCHEDULE   @=VARIABLE
2003-01-03

 MA    002 040 110@ 126 128 132 210 244 002

 ———7——1——3——2——6——4——5——0——7

S2/K-TX | S | S | S |S/K| S/K| S | S | S |

MB      | * | * |   | * | * | * | * |   |

RUDAK   |   |   | * |   |   |   |   |   |

V/U-RX  | U | U | V | U | U | U | U | V |

UPLINK  |   |  UL |   |   |  UL | UL |   |   |


    — W4SM for the AO-40 Command Team
```

To interpret the schedule note that one complete orbit of AO 40 is divided into 256 Mean Anomaly (MA) units, each one lasting about 4.8 minutes. An MA of 40 therefore occurs about 192 minutes after perigee. Most tracking programs designed for Radio Amateurs show MA in the range 0-256. However, some use, or have as an option, 0-360 so take note.

The first row of the table indicates the downlink (S2 or K or both) in operation during various segments of the orbit. The second row tells when the middle beacon (MB) is on. The third row shows when RUDAK is operating. The forth row indicates which spacecraft receiver can be accessed. And the fifth row indicates which uplinks are patched to the downlinks for transponder operation. For example, checking the table we see that from MA 40 to MA110 the U, L1 and L2 uplinks are connected to the S2 downlink.

1.6 Design/Construction Credits:

Project Management: AMSAT-DL
Project Director: Dr Karl Meinzer
P3D is an international satellite. Radio amateurs and scientists in the following countries have made major contributions to the subsystems mentioned.
Belgium: 2 meter and 70 cm receivers, 24 GHz Tx and antenna
Canada: component radiation testing, GPS system, IHU
Czech Republic: 23 cm receiver
Finland: 10 GHz Tx and antenna
Germany: system design, receivers, transmitters, IF matrix and LEILA, Arc-jet motor, IHU
Hungary: Battery Charge Regulators, communications experiment
Japan: camera experiment
Russia: propellant tanks
Slovenia: 2.4 GHz and 5.6 GHz receivers, IF matrix/LEILA
South Africa: 10 meter Tx

Table AO40-1
AO-40 Analog and Digital Transponder Frequencies

Uplink Frequencies

Band	Designator	Analog	Digital
15 m		21.210-21.250 MHz	none
12 m		24.920-24.960 MHz	none
2 m	V	145.840-145.990 MHz	145.800-145.840 MHz
70 cm	U	435.550-435.800 MHz	435.300-435.550 MHz
23 cm	L1	1269.250-1269.500 MHz	1269.000-1269.250 MHz
23 cm	L2	1268.325-1268.575 MHz	1268.075-1268.325 MHz
13 cm	S1	2400.350-2400.600 MHz	2400.100-2400.350 MHz
13 cm	S2	2446.450-2446.700 MHz	2446.200-2446.450 MHz
6 cm	C	5668.550-5668.800 MHz	5668.300-5668.550 MHz

Downlink Frequencies

Band	Designator	Analog	Digital
2 m	V	145.805-145.955 MHz	145.955-145.990 MHz
70 cm	U	435.475-435.725 MHz	435.900-436.200 MHz
13 cm	S1	2400.225-2400.475 MHz	2400.650-2400.950 MHz
13 cm	S2	2401.225-2401.475 MHz	2401.650-2401.950 MHz
3 cm	X	10451.025-10451.275 MHz	10451.450-10451.750 MHz
1.2 cm	K	24048.025-24048.275 MHz	24048.450-24048.750 MHz

UK: 2 meter Tx, IHU
US: spaceframe, launch vehicle adaptor, mechanical and thermal design, IHU, assembly and checkout, GPS system, antennas.

1.7 Primary References

1. Phase 3D Design Team (edited by D. Daniels), "Phase 3D Update," *Proceedings of the 14th AMSAT-NA Space Symposium, 1996,* pp 3-19.
2. "An Overview of the Electronics Modules on the AMSAT Phase 3D Satellite," Peter Guelzow, DB2OS, *AMSAT Journal,* Nov 2000, pp. 9-16.
3. Problems Encountered in Orbit Modification. K. Meinzer DJ4ZC et al. "AO-40 Log, 16 Nov 2000 – 01 Jan 2001," *The AMSAT Journal,* Jan/Feb 2001, pp. 16 – 22.
   R. Haighton, VE3FRH, "AO-40 News," *The AMSAT Journal,* Jan/Feb 2001, p. 2.
   S. Mills W4SM, P Guelzow DB2OS, "Letter," *The AMSAT Journal,* Sept/Oct 2001, pp 29, 30.
4. A. Friedman 4X4KX, J. White WDØE, M. Kingery KE4AZN, L. Johnson KK7P, H. Price NK6K, C. Green NØADI, "RUDAK DSP – Software Defined Radio in Space." *Proceedings of the AMSAT-NA 20th Space Symposium,* Nov. 2002, pp. 28-40.
5. J. White WDØE, H. Price NK6K, L. Johnson KK7P, "AO-40 RUDAK Description and Results," *Proceedings of the AMSAT-NA 20th Space Symposium,* Nov. 2002, pp. 41-59.

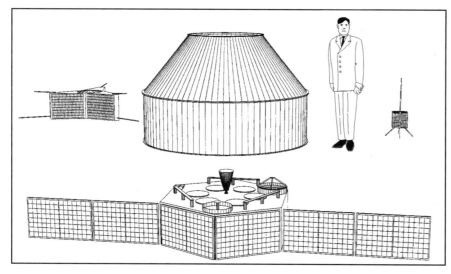

Figure AO-40-1—AO-40 structure with solar panels deployed. Reference: *AMSAT Journal,* Sep/Oct 1993, p 7.

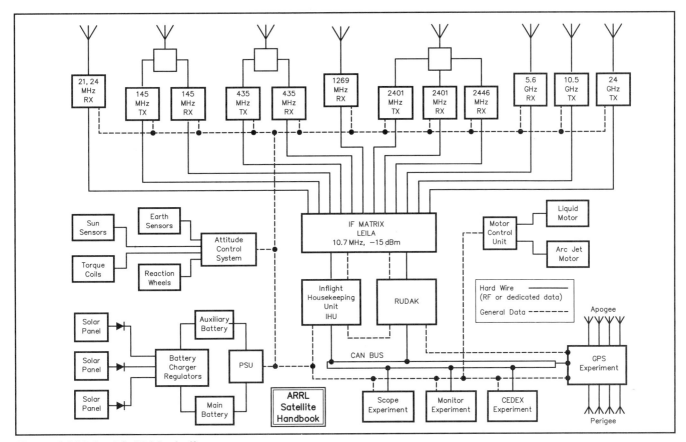

Figure AO40-2—AO-40 block diagram.

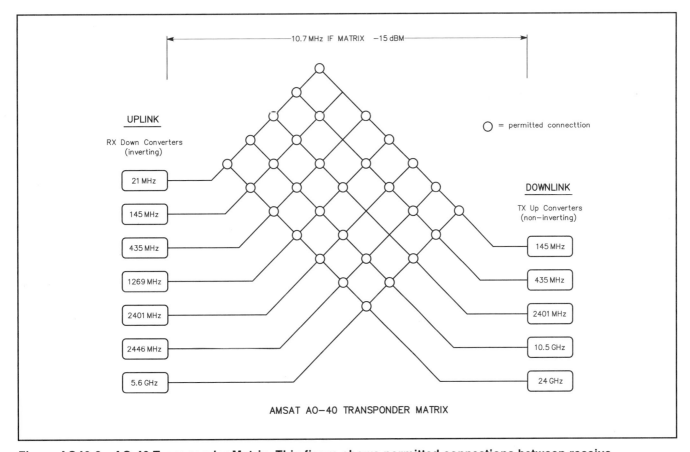

Figure AO40-3—AO-40 Transponder Matrix. This figure shows permitted connections between receive downconverters and transmit upconverters on AO-40. Links may be established using more than one receiver or transmitter.

Table AO40-2
AO-40 Analog Transponder Downlink Power Levels (Prelaunch Estimates)

145.880 (150 kHz)	100 W
435.600 (250 kHz)	120 W
2400.350 (250 kHz)	50 W
10451.150 (250 kHz)	60 W
24048.150 (250 kHz)	1 W

6. **www.amsat-dl.org/journal/adlj-p3d.htm**
7. S. Fraser, VK5ASF et al., Frequently Asked Questions
   www.amsat.org/amsat/sats/ao40/ao40-faq.html

SPACECRAFT DESCRIPTION

2.1 Physical Structure

Shape: Hexagonal cylinder measuring 2240 mm across at the corners and 675 mm in height. See Figure AO40-1. Each side panel measures approximately 1120 mm by 675 mm. After final orbit is reached four of the side panels will be extended as shown.

During launch the satellite is contained inside a cylindrical structure, called the Specific Bearing Structure (SBS), which acts as spacer between the two primary spacecraft. The SBS measures 2624 mm in diameter. It's designed to be able to handle the load forces imposed by a 4.7 metric ton load during launch.

Mass: The separation mass of AO-40 was approximately 630 kg. This includes approximately 244 kg of fuel (192 kg for bipropellant motor and 52 kg for the arc-jet motor) and 80 kg for the space frame.

AO-40 carries a novel thermal control subsystem suited to the three axis stabilization system adopted. The key elements are four open hexagonal ring shaped heat pipes extending around the perimeter of the spacecraft. These pipes move heat from one part of the spacecraft to other parts where it is ultimately radiated into space. (For a description of heat pipes, see section on thermal control in Chapter 14.)

A unique feature of the AO-40 design is that the pipes do not come in contact with space-facing panels. They depend upon indirect re-radiation of the heat from internal equipment to side panels that are deliberately allowed to become cold. The result is a very complex dynamic system whose behavior has been extensively studied by computer simulation. The design calls for the mean spacecraft temperatures to be between −5 and +20°C for the expected range of Sun angles from −80° to +80°.

For additional information see: D. Jansson, "Mechanical and Thermal Design of the Phase 3D Spacecraft," *The AMSAT Journal*, Jan/Feb 1996, pp 1, 4-7; D. Jansson, "Thermal Analytical Modeling of Phase 3D," *The AMSAT Journal*, Mar/Apr 1996, pp 10-11.

2.2 Subsystem Organization: See Figure AO40-2.

SUBSYSTEM DESCRIPTION

3.1 Beacons

Beacons are generally modulated with 400 bps BPSK

Table AO40-3
Suggested Uplink Station Configurations for Accessing AO-40 Transponders

These are highly tentative prelaunch estimates.

Possible Station Configuration

Uplink Band	TX Power	Antenna
146 MHz	10 W	7×7 crossed-Yagi
	50 W	Crossed dipoles over ground plane
435 MHz	10 W	10×10-el crossed-Yagi
	40 W	Crossed dipoles over ground plane
1.2 GHz	10 W	12 turn Helix
2.4 GHz	5 W	60 cm parabolic dish
5.6 GHz	10 W	60 cm parabolic dish

but other formulas may be used. Each downlink has one or more beacons available: General beacon (GB), Middle Beacon (MB) and Engineering Beacon (EB). Usually only one beacon is active at a given time. The S2 MB is 10 dB stronger than the S2 GB or EB.

Uplink signal levels should be adjusted to match GB or EB, i.e., 10 dB lower than MB!

Band	Frequency	Max. Doppler (at perigee)
2 m	145.898 MHz (MB)	2.5 kHz
70 cm	435.438 MHz (GB)	7.6 kHz
	435.588 MHz (MB)	
	435.838 MHz (MB)	
13 cm (S1)	2400.188 MHz (GB)	42 kHz

Table AO40-4
AO-40 Antennas (gains are approximate)

All circularly polarized antennas are right hand sense.
All high gain antennas are on "top" of spacecraft (+Z face).

Band	Antenna Type	Gain (Approx)
15 m	2 element deployed whip	0 dB$_i$
2 m	3 low profile folded dipoles	10 dB$_{ic}$
2 m	1/4 λ open sleeve	Omni
70 cm	6 element patch	13 dB$_{ic}$
70 cm	Pair of 1/4 λ whips	Omni
1.2 GHz	Short Back Fire, turnstile feed	15 dB$_{ic}$
2.4 GHz	Parabolic dish (S1)	18 dB$_{ic}$
2.4 GHz	5-turn Helix (S2)	10.5 dB$_{ic}$
5.7 GHz	Parabolic Dish	18-20 dB$_{ic}$
10.4 GHz	Dual Horn	20 dB$_{ic}$
24.0 GHz	Horn	26 dB$_i$
GPS (1.6 GHz)	4 patch ants (bottom, perigee use)	3 dB$_{ic}$
	4 patch ants (top, apogee use)	9 dB$_{ic}$

For additional information on antennas see: "Phase 3D Update," *Proceedings of the AMSAT-NA 14th Space Symposium, 1996*, pp 3-19, by P3D Design Team (compiled and edited by D. Daniels).

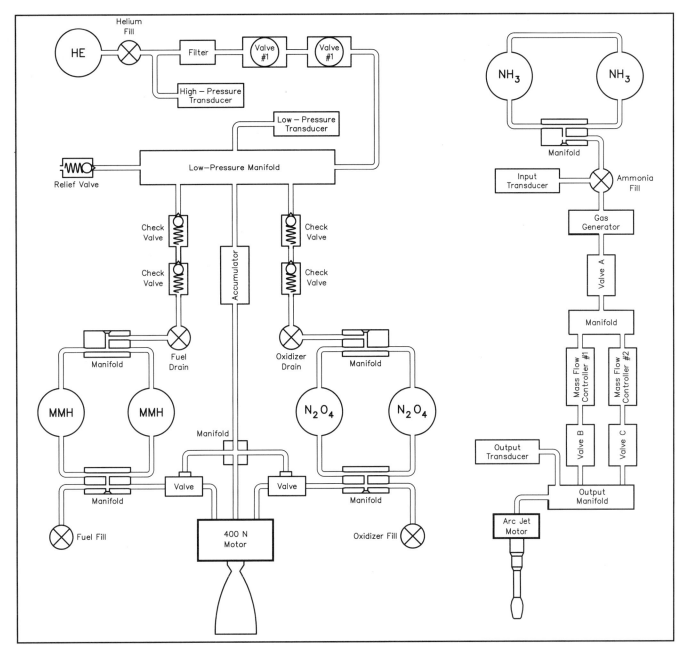

Figure AO40-4—AO-40 Propulsion Systems, block diagram. Reference: *Proceedings of AMSAT-NA Space Symposium*, p 63.

	2400.338 MHz (MB)	
	2400.588 MHz (EB)	
13 cm (S2)	2401.173 MHz (GB)	42 kHz
	2401.323 MHz (MB)	
	2401.573 MHz (EB)	
3 cm	10450.975 MHz (GB)	185 kHz
	10451.125 MHz (MB)	
	10451.375 MHz (EB)	
1.2 cm	24047.885 MHz (EB)	425 kHz
	24048.035 MHz (MB)	
	24048.285 MHz (EB)	

3.2 Telemetry

Telemetry will be provided on the beacons (generally 400 bps BPSK but CW and other modes possible) and via RUDAK. The spacecraft design allows for a great deal of flexibility and redundancy in the TTY system. A demodulator for 400 bps TTY can be found in: J. Miller, G3RUH, "A PSK Telemetry Demodulator for OSCAR 10," *Ham Radio*, Apr 1985, pp 50-51, 53-55, 57-62; Be sure to see Miller's revisions in *OSCAR News*, Apr 1988, p 13. Many of G3RUH's articles are archived at the AMSAT Web site.

3.4 Transponders

AO-40 departs from the traditional AMSAT approach of flying hardwired transponders. AO-40 carries a set of transmitter mixer/power amplifiers and a set of receiver front-ends that can be connected together through an IF matrix. See Figure AO40-3. Transponders can be dynamically configured via the IHU to use one or more uplinks and one or more downlinks. All configurations are inverting. The high power 70 cm and 13 cm power amplifiers employ HELAPS technology.

The IF matrix functions at 10.7 MHz with input and

output levels of –15 dBm. It operates in conjunction with a smart, multiple notching system, known as LEILA. LEILA is described in Chapter 14.

The RUDAK-U digital transponder shares the various receivers and transmitter power amplifiers used by the linear transponder. The DSP modulators can generate signals anywhere in the digital transponder passband. However, there are two frequencies fixed by hardware modems which will probably be used initially. These are;

RUDAK A: 2401.760 MHz
RUDAK B: 2401.882 MHz

For a description of RUDAK see References 3 and 4, section 1.7, and the text accompanying Figure 5.3 (Chapter 5).

Transponder frequencies are listed in Table AO40-1. Downlink powers (prelaunch estimates) are given in Table AO40-2.

3.5 Attitude Control and Stabilization

AO-40 has a complex attitude control subsystem. During the early orbit transfer stage of the mission AO-40 will be spin stabilized. During the operational stage of the mission it will be three axis stabilized with the spacecraft +Z axis continually pointed at the center of the Earth.

The attitude control hardware on the spacecraft consists of a set of three reaction wheels, two rings of electromagnets and six nutation dampers. Attitude information is obtained from a complement of Earth and Sun sensors. Control is via the IHU. The feasibility of using the GPS system as a back up attitude control system will be tested on AO-40.

The reaction wheels are orthogonally mounted and suspended using magnetic bearings. The suspension eliminates problems inherent with frictional wear and the use of lubricants in space. The bearings, which require a total of 15 W to operate, are designed to outlive the 10 to 15 year design lifetime of the spacecraft. They were a joint project of the University of Darmstadt and the University of Marburg. Additional information is available on the Web at **www.amsat.org/amsat/sats/phase3d/wheels/index.html**.

The magnetic torquing system consists of two hexagonal rings, each consisting of six 6000-turn solenoids. The two solenoids on each face are connected together and to the solenoids on the opposite face. This provides three groupings that can be pulsed in either direction. When operating the total power dissipation is about 10.7 W with the solenoids producing a field of about 1.2 T. This will be used during both the spin stabilized phase (operation similar to torquing coils on AO-10 and AO-13) and during the three axis stabilized phase (momentum dumping).

Six tube-shaped nutation dampers containing glycerin and water (about 50/50) have been included for the spin stabilized stages of the mission.

3.6 Antennas: See Figure AO40-1 and Table AO40-4

3.7 Energy-Supply and Power Conditioning

Solar Arrays: AO-40 is the first amateur satellite to employ deployable solar panels. Rectangular solar panels cover the six faces of the spacecraft. Two are permanently mounted. The other four are deployed as shown in Figure AO-40-1 using cabaret hinges (the type used on old North American western saloon doors) designed to operate in space. The total solar panel area is 4.46m². The cells are BSFR Silicon having a beginning of life efficiency of 14.3%. They will initially provide about 620 W when optimally illuminated (about 435 W at 45º Sun angle). After 10 years in orbit the power available will drop to about 500 W (350 W at 45º sun angle).

Batteries: The Main Battery, composed of 20 cells, is divided in three subassemblies of 7, 7 and 6 cells. The battery provides 22-28 volts and has a capacity of 40 Ah. The Auxiliary Battery is composed of 40 cells and has a capacity of 10 Ah. Both batteries employ nickel-cadmium technology.

Battery Control Regulators similar to those flown on earlier Phase 3 missions are again being supplied by the Hungarian group led by Dr Bandi Gschwindt, HA5WH, of the Technical University of Budapest.

3.8 Propulsion Systems

See Figure AO40-4 for a block diagram of the propulsion systems. For a detailed description see D. Daniels, "Phase 3D Propulsion System," *Proceedings of the AMSAT-NA 13th Space Symposium, 1995*, pp 61-63.

High thrust propulsion system
  Type: high thrust liquid-fuel, bi-propellant rocket engine similar to unit used on OSCARs 10 and 13.
  Thrust: 400 Newton
  Fuel: Mono-Methyl-Hydrozine (MMH) (60+ kg)
  Oxidizer: Nitrogen tetroxide (N_2O_4) (130 kg)
  Ignition system: none (fuel is self-igniting [hypergolic])
  Pressurization: Helium
  Fuel/oxidizer storage: Six spherical 50 liter propellant tanks fabricated in Russia (measured bursting pressure = 63 bar).
Low thrust propulsion system
  Type: Arc-jet thruster designed and constructed at Institute for Space Systems, University of Stuttgart. Development funded by German Space Agency (DARA)
  Thrust: 115 milli-Newton
  Fuel: anhydrous ammonia (about 80 liters)
  Ignition system: about 750 W electrical power required to initiate and maintain arc.
  Maximum burn time: about 450 hours
  Reference: **www.amsat.org/amsat/sats/phase3d/ATOS.html**

3.9 Integrated Housekeeping Unit

AO-40 carries a primary and several secondary computers. The primary computer, which is the heart of the IHU, is similar to the one flown on OSCAR 13. The IHU incorporates a networking adapter called the Controller Area Network (CAN) Bus to connect the IHU to the other spacecraft computer systems. The CAN bus is an automotive standard widely used in Europe, Japan and the US.

The RUDAK-U system contains two computers (NEC V53 CPUs) and 32 Mbyte of EDAC memory. All data from Experimental systems is routed to RUDAK.

Primary computer
  CPU: 1802 COSMAC (radiation hardened)
  Memory: 64 kbytes of error detecting and correcting
      (EDAC) memory
  Operating System: Multitasking using IPS language

3.10a Experimental Systems: GPS

It is believed that AO-40 is the first satellite in a highly elliptical orbit utilizing the GPS (Global Positioning Satellite) system. As a result, it will be able to map the antenna patterns of the GPS satellites over a very large range of altitudes of interest to potential users.

The AO-40 GPS system is designed to provide information on satellite position to within 10-20 meters accuracy. Another goal of the GPS experiment is to determine whether the GPS system can provide accurate information on spacecraft attitude.

The GPS subsystem consists of two commercial Trimble TANS VECTOR receivers donated by NASA. One receiver (perigee experiment) is connected to four standard 1.6 GHz patch antennas (donated by Bell Aerospace) and four Trimble preamps (donated by NASA). The other receiver (apogee experiment) is connected to four high-gain air loaded patch antennas (also donated by Bell) and four specially constructed high gain preamps. The GPS unit communicates with the rest of the spacecraft via the CAN bus and a dedicated 9.6 kbaud RS-422 serial link to RUDAK. Plans are to have the GPS system downlink <UI> packets containing onboard derived Keplerian elements through RUDAK.

3.10b Experimental Systems: SCOPE

The SCOPE Camera experiment, designed and built by the Japanese AMSAT group (JAMSAT) will provide color images of Earth. The SCOPE experiment consists of two cameras, one a wide angle unit and the other having a narrow field of view. The cameras are commercial camcorder CCD units modified for the space environment.

Images will be downlinked using the RUDAK system. Software programs will be made available to translate the images into formats commonly used by desktop computers.

3.10c Experimental Systems: Monitor

AO-40 carries an RF spectrum analyzer covering 0.5–30 MHz provided by Dr Bandi Gschwindt, HA5WH, of the Technical University of Budapest.

3.10d Experimental Systems: CEDEX

AO-40 carries a radiation monitor provided by Dr Craig Underwood of the University of Surrey.

SPACECRAFT NAME: UOSAT-OSCAR 11

GENERAL

1.1 Identification

International designation: 84-021B
NASA Catalog number: 14781

Prelaunch designation: UoSAT-B
Also known as: UoSAT-2, UO-11

1.2 Launch

Date: March 1, 1984
Vehicle: Delta 3920
Agency: NASA (U.S.)
Site: Western Test Range, Lompoc, CA (Vandenberg
  Air Force Base)

1.3 Orbital Parameters (Jan 1996)

General designation: low-altitude, circular, sun-
  synchronous, near polar
Period: 98.0 minutes
Apogee Altitude: 678 km
Perigee Altitude: 662 km
Eccentricity: 0.0011 (nominally circular)
Inclination: 97.8°
Maximum access distance: 2820 km

1.5 Operations

Coordinating Group: UoSAT Project; Dr. Martin Sweeting, G3YJO, Centre for Satellite Engineering Research; University of Surrey; Guildford, Surrey GU2 5XH, England

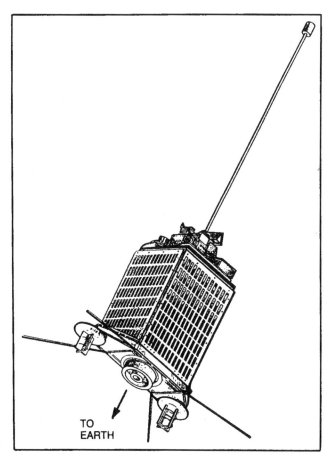

Figure UO11-1—Pictorial view of UoSAT-OSCAR 11.

1.6 Design/Construction Credits

Project manager: Dr. Martin Sweeting, G3YJO
Construction: Built at University of Surrey, England

1.7 Primary References

1) UoSAT-2 Project Summary, UoSAT Datasheet, Sheet 5, UoSAT Spacecraft Engineering Research Unit, Department of Electronic and Electrical Engineering, University of Surrey;
2) M. Sweeting, "The UoSAT-B Experimental Amateur Spacecraft," *Orbit*, Vol. 5, no. 1, Jan/Feb 1984, pp 12-16;
3) C. Wallis, "OSCAR 11 Report," ongoing series of reports posted on AMSAT-BB web site. Contact **g3cwv@amsat.org** or **clivew@zetnet.co.uk** for location of archives.

SPACECRAFT DESCRIPTION

2.1 Physical Structure

Shape: Rectangular solid core approximately 58.5 cm (height) × 35.5 cm × 35.5 cm. See Fig UO11-1. The base (the side with the launch fitting) has a "wing" extending about 16 cm, which holds two SHF helical antennas (bottom side) and the Navigation Magnetometer and Space Dust experiments (top side).
Mass: just over 60 kg

SUBSYSTEM DESCRIPTION

3.1 Beacons

Beacon 1
  Frequency: 145.826 MHz
  Power output: 400 mW (nominal) (TTY channel no. 35)
  Modulation: NBFM (AFSK) ±kHz
  Total RF/dc efficiency: 45%
  Maximum Doppler: 3.6 kHz

Beacon 2 (employs phase-locked synthesizer)
  Frequency: 435.025 MHz
  Power output: 600 mW (nominal) (TTY channel no. 45)
  Modulation: NBFM (AFSK) ±5 kHz
  Total RF/dc efficiency: greater than 40%
  Maximum Doppler: 10.5 kHz

Beacon 3 (design by Colin Smithers, G4CWH)
  Frequency: 2401.5 MHz
  Power output: 500 mW (nominal) (TTY channel no. 55)
  Modulation: NBFM (AFSK) ±10 kHz
  Total RF/dc efficiency: 20%
  Maximum Doppler: 57.9 kHz

3.2 Telemetry

The telemetry system, under control of the main spacecraft computer, has been designed to provide a high degree of flexibility with respect to what is measured and the downlink data format. Provisions for monitoring 60 analog and 96 digital status points are included. For information on decoding TTY content see:

(1) R. Diersing, "Processing UoSAT Whole-Orbit Telemetry Data," *Proceedings of the 4th Annual AMSAT Space Symposium, 1986*, ARRL, pp 55-76;
(2) R. Diersing, "Microcomputer Processing of UoSat OSCAR 9 Telemetry," *The ARRL Satellite Anthology*, 1988, ARRL, pp 46-51.

Several methods for decoding UoSAT 11 telemetry have been employed. A detailed description of an excellent demodulator can be found in: J. Miller, "Data Decoder for UoSAT," *Wireless World*, May 1983, pp. 28-33. This article contains tutorial information that is of help in understanding the operation of the UO-11 TTY systems. UO-11 TTY can also be demodulated using a BELL 202 compatible 1200 baud modem. (Note: the 1200 baud modems in common use for computer access via telephone are *not* BELL 202). The article by Diersing in *The ARRL Satellite Anthology* (see references above) includes directions for a simple demodulator that provides good reception when signal strength is high and QRM is low.

3.3 Telecommand System

The telecommand system consists of three redundant uplink receivers and demodulators operating in the 2 meter, 70 cm and 23 cm amateur bands.

3.4 Transponders

The spacecraft does not contain any open access transponders. However, it does include an experiment that has been used to develop transponders for Pacsat. (See Digital Communications Experiment.)

3.5 Attitude Stabilization and Control

Navigation Magnetometer: three-axis flux gate device with 14-bit resolution.
Magnetorquers: three-axis; six coils, one around edge of each face of spacecraft.
Sun Sensors: 6 sensors utilizing grey-code masking provide 360° of coverage.
Horizon Sensor: edge detector using two photodetectors mounted at ends of narrow tubes. Capable of responding to Earth, Moon, or Sun.

3.7 Energy Supply and Power Conditioning

Solar Arrays:
  The spacecraft contains four arrays attached to the four faces of the main framework. The arrays, manufactured by Solarex, each measure 49.5 × 29.5 cm.

Storage Battery:
  Consists of 10 "F" size commercial Ni-Cd cells in series. These cells are from a group space qualified by AMSAT (see Chapter 14). Provides 12 V at 6.4 Ah.

Power Conditioning
  Two redundant Battery Charge Regulators (BCR) accept 28 V supplied by solar arrays and provide proper voltage and current to charge battery. Power Conditioning Module (PCM) accepts poorly regulated 12-14 V from

battery/BCR bus and provides regulated 10 V, 5 V, and –10 V to spacecraft systems. Power Distribution Module (PDM): Controls and monitors power distributed to various spacecraft systems and experiments. Safety latch thresholds under ground control via telecommand system.

3.9 Integrated Housekeeping Unit

CPU: 1802 COSMAC
RAM: 36 K Using Error Detection and Correction (Hamming code)
Digitalker speech synthesizer with more than 550 words in ROM

3.10a Digital Communications Experiment (DCE)

The DCE was designed and built by AMSAT and VITA groups in the USA and Canada. It consists of an NSC-800 CPU and nearly 128 K of CMOS RAM. Communication with the IHU 1802 is via two serial ports. The DCE is being used to investigate various packet radio protocols for use with future digital store-and-forward radio amateur satellites. In addition, the DCE interfaces with the navigation magnetometer and the telemetry system to provide mass long-term data storage. Since use of the DCE requires knowledge of the spacecraft command system and codes access is restricted. The DCE is the forerunner of today's open access packet systems.

3.10b Space Dust Experiment

Detectors employing dielectric diaphragm (for large particles) and piezo crystal microphone (for small particles) provide information on number of impacts and particle momentum.

3.10c CCD Camera

This camera is an improved version of the unit flown on OSCAR 9. It contains an active area of 384×256 pixels with each pixel having 128 grey levels. Image is stored in 96 K of RAM in DSR experiment.

3.10d Particle Detectors and Wave Correlator Experiment

Sensors include three Geiger counter tubes with different electron energy detection thresholds and a multi-channel electron spectrometer running under the control of an NSC-800 CPU. Electron flux spectrum is measured at eight energy levels. The wave correlator experiment is designed to help identify (1) wave-modes responsible for accelerating electrons into the auroral beam and (2) wave-modes that limit the further growth of the auroral beam.

3.10e Digital Store and Readout Experiment (DSR)

The DSR contains two banks of 96 k CMOS RAM that can be used in conjunction with CCD Camera and other experiments.

3.10f Digitalker

The Digitalker speech synthesizer contains more than 550 words in ROM. Operating under the control of the IHU

it's principally used to announce telemetry for educational demonstrations.

SPACECRAFT NAME: UOSAT-OSCAR 22

Note: All amateur operation was moved from UO-14 to UO-22 on Feb 5, 1992. UO-14 returned to amateur use as single channel FM repeater 2/2000.

GENERAL

1.1 Identification

International designation: 91-050B
NASA Catalog number: 21575
Prelaunch designation: UoSAT-F
Also known as: UoSAT-5, UO-22

1.2 Launch

Date: July 17, 1991
Time: 01:35:31 UTC
Vehicle: Ariane

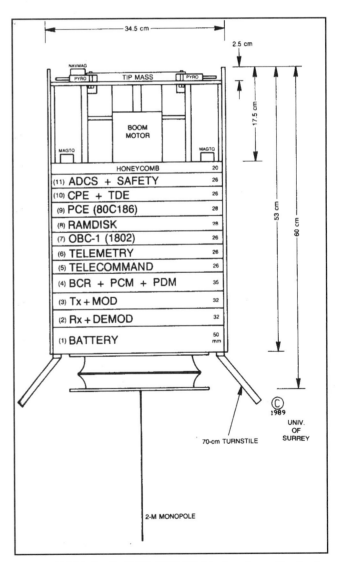

Figure UO22-1—UoSAT-OSCAR 14 structure. Typical of UoSAT MicroSat space platform.

Agency: ESA
Site: Kourou, French Guiana

1.3 Orbital Parameters (Jan 1997)

General Designation: low-altitude, circular, sun-
   synchronous, near polar
Period: 100.2 minutes
Apogee altitude: 781 km
Perigee altitude: 769 km
Eccentricity: 0.00085
Inclination: 98.3°
Maximum access distance: 3006 km

1.5 Operations

Coordinating Group: UoSAT Project; Dr. Martin
Sweeting, G3YJO, Centre for Satellite Engineering Re-
search; University of Surrey; Guildford, Surrey
GU2 5XH, England

1.6 Design/Construction Credits

Project manager: Dr. Martin Sweeting
Construction: Built at University of Surrey

1.7 Primary References

1) J. Magliacane, "Spotlight On: UoSAT-OSCAR-22,"
   The AMSAT Journal, May/Jun 1992, p 17-18.
2) J. Ward, "The UO-22 Earth Imaging System," The
   AMSAT Journal, Nov/Dec 1991, pp 1, 4-7.

SPACECRAFT DESCRIPTION

2.1 Physical Structure

Shape: Rectangular solid similar to UO-11 and UO-14. (See
Figure UO22-1.)
Dimensions: Measures 350×350×650 mm.
Mass: 48.4 kg

SUBSYSTEM DESCRIPTION

3.1 Beacons

Frequency: 435.120 MHz

3.4 Transponders

UoSAT-OSCAR 22 carries a 9600 baud Mode JD digital
   transponder known as the PACSAT Communications
   System (PCS). See Chapter 5 for operation
Uplink frequencies:
   145.900 MHz   (intermittent)
   145.975 MHz
Downlink frequency: 435.120 MHz

3.5 Attitude Stabilization and Control

Five meter gravity gradient boom with 3 kg tip mass.
Magnetorquers: six coils provide three-axis control.

3.10a Earth Imaging Experiment

UO-22 carries a monochrome CCD imager optimized
for meteorological scale imaging. The camera produces a
CCIR video image having a resolution of 578×576 pixels
(aspect ratio is 4:3). The earth surface resolution of the

system is on the order of 2-3 km, with a field of view of
approximately 1000 km². Images are comparable in detail
to those produced by NOAA spacecraft.

The camera uses a Fairchild charge-coupled-device
(CCD) detector similar to those found in home video-cam-
eras. Video from the CCD is digitized by a flash analog-to-
digital converter and stored in low power static RAM. The
96 kbyte raw image is sent to the TDPE where it is compressed before transmission. The data compression will
amount to a 50% to 90% reduction in the amount of memory
required to store an image and a similar reduction in the
transmission time.

Digitized images are stored in RAM for later processing
and transmission using the Pacsat Broadcast Protocol. This
system has been very successful. See Reference 2 and
D. Walter, "Computer Processing of UO-22 and KO-23
Images," The AMSAT Journal, Jan/Feb 1993, pp 8-10.

SPACECRAFT NAME: KITSAT-OSCAR 23

GENERAL

1.1 Identification

International designation: 92-052B
NASA Catalog number: 22077
Prelaunch designation: KITSAT-A
Also known as: Uribyol (our star), KITSAT-1, KO-23

1.2 Launch

Date: Aug 10, 1992
Time: 23:08 GMT
Vehicle: Ariane
Agency: ESA
Site: Kourou, French Guiana

1.3 Orbital Parameters (Jan 1997)

General Designation: low-altitude, circular, sun-
   synchronous, near polar
Period: 111.9 minutes
Apogee altitude: 1334 km
Perigee altitude: 1312 km
Eccentricity: 0.00148
Inclination: 66.08°
Maximum access distance: 3806 km

1.5 Operations

Coordinating Group: Operated from the Satellite Technology Research Center (SaTReC) in South Korea.

1.6 Design/Construction Credits

Construction: Built by a team of faculty and students
from the Korean Advanced Institute of Science and Technology (KAIST) and UoSAT engineers under a technology
transfer program at the University of Surrey's Center for
Spacecraft Engineering Research.

1.7 Primary References

1) J. Magliacane, "Spotlight On: KITSAT-OSCAR-23,"
   The AMSAT Journal, Mar/Apr 1993, p 17-18.

2) "The KITSAT-1 Mission Overview," Fact sheet (in English)
   issued by Satellite Technology Research Center, Korea Advanced Institute of Science and Technology, 1992. SaTReC,KAIST, 373-1, Kusung-dong, Yusung-gu, Taejon, 305-701, Korea.

SPACECRAFT DESCRIPTION

2.1 Physical Structure

Shape: Rectangular solid similar to UoSATs 11, 14, 22.
Dimensions: 350×350×650 mm.
Mass: 48.6 kg

SUBSYSTEM DESCRIPTION

3.1 Beacons

Frequency: 435.175 MHz

3.4 Transponders

KITSAT-OSCAR 23 carries a 9600 baud Mode JD digital transponder known as the PACSAT Communications System (PCS) identical to the one on UO-22. KITSAT's PCS contains 13 Mbytes of CMOS RAM.
Uplink frequencies: 145.850 MHz, 145.900 MHz
Downlink frequency: 435.175 MHz
Call signs: HL01-11 (Broadcast), HL01-12 (BBS)

3.5 Attitude Stabilization and Control

Five meter gravity gradient boom with 3 kg tip mass.
Magnetorquers: six coils provide three-axis control.

3.10a Earth Imaging System (EIS)

KO-23 carries two monochrome CCD imagers. One, with a wide angle lens having a resolution of 3500 meters, acts as a "spotting camera." The second, with a telephoto lens, has a resolution of 400 meters. The experimental package includes a transputer Image Processor. KO-23 has returned excellent images.

3.10b Digital Signal Processing Experiment (DSPE)

The DSPE uses Texas Instruments TMS320C30 and TMS320C25 DSP chips for several experiments including high speed TTY, stored speech, spoken TTY, etc. Broadcast voice messages have been observed on the downlink on several occasions.

3.10c Cosmic Ray Experiment (CRE)

The CRE includes a Total Dose Experiment (TDE) and a Cosmic Particle Experiment (CPE). Since KO-23 is in a somewhat different orbit from other UoSAT spacecraft the information is of special interest.

SPACECRAFT NAME: KITSAT-OSCAR 25

GENERAL

1.1 Identification

International designation: 93-061C
NASA Catalog number: 22828

Prelaunch designation: KITSAT-b
Also known as: KITSAT-2, KO-25

1.2 Launch

Date: Sept 26 1993
Vehicle: Ariane
Agency: ESA
Site: Kourou, French Guiana

1.3 Orbital Parameters (Jan 1997)

General Designation: low-altitude, circular, sun-synchronous, near polar
Period: 100.8 minutes
Apogee altitude: 813 km
Perigee altitude: 797 km
Eccentricity: 0.0011
Inclination: 98.56°
Maximum access distance: 3060 km

1.5 Operations

Coordinating Group: Operated from the Satellite Technology Research Center (SaTReC) in South Korea.

1.6 Design/Construction Credits

Construction: Built by faculty and students of the Korean Advanced Institute of Science and Technology (KAIST) in South Korea based on the standard UoSAT MicroSat platform.

1.7 Primary Reference

1) Try **http://www.ee.surrey.ac.uk/CSER/UOSAT/missions/kitsat2.html**
When last checked, this site was under construction. Although the UoSAT small satellite home page on the Web maintains a link to the KAIST home page, the KAIST site was also under construction when last checked.

SPACECRAFT DESCRIPTION

2.1 Physical Structure

Shape: Rectangular solid similar to UoSATs 11, 14, 22.
Dimensions: 350×350×650 mm.
Mass: 48.7 kg

SUBSYSTEM DESCRIPTION

3.1 Beacons

Frequency: 436.500 MHz, 435.175 MHz

3.4 Transponders

KITSAT-OSCAR 25 carries a 9600 baud Mode JD digital transponder known as the PACSAT Communications System (PCS) similar to the one on KO-23.
Uplink frequencies: 145.980 MHz, 145.870 MHz
Downlink frequency: 436.500 MHz, 435.175 MHz
Call signs: HL02-11 (Broadcast), HL02-12 (BBS)

3.5 Attitude Stabilization and Control

Five meter gravity gradient boom with 3 kg tip mass.
Magnetorquers: six coils provide three-axis control.

3.10a Earth Imaging Experiment

KO-25 carries an imaging system substantially different from the one on KO-23. The system uses two CCD images. The wide angle lens, which has a resolution of 4000 meters, takes color images. The monochrome telephoto lens has a resolution of 200 meters. KO-23 has returned excellent images. KO-25 is returning excellent images. For additional information see: Sang-Keun Yoo, "KITSAT-2 Imaging System," *The AMSAT Journal*, May/June 1994, p 27.

3.10b Digital Signal Processing Experiment (DSPE)

3.10c Infra Red Sensor Experiment (IREX)

3.10d Low Energy Electron Detector (LEED) Experiment.

SPACECRAFT NAME: PoSAT-OSCAR 28

Note: PoSAT-OSCAR 28 is a commercial/scientific satellite with amateur capabilities. It was in amateur service for several weeks in early 1994 but has not been on the amateur bands since that time (as of early 1997). It is in good operating condition but its future with respect to the amateur service is not currently known.

GENERAL

1.1 Identification

International designation: 93-061D
NASA Catalog number: 22829
Prelaunch designation: PoSAT-1, PO-28
Also known as: PO-28

1.2 Launch

Date: Sept 26 1993
Vehicle: Ariane
Agency: ESA
Site: Kourou, French Guiana

1.3 Orbital Parameters (Jan 1997)

General Designation: low-altitude, circular, sun-synchronous, near polar
Period: 100.8 minutes
Apogee altitude: 812 km
Perigee altitude: 798 km
Eccentricity: 0.0010
Inclination: 98.56°
Maximum access distance: 3060 km

1.5 Operations

Coordinating Group: Portuguese consortium consisting of representatives of the academic and industrial communities of Portugal.

1.6 Design/Construction Credits

Construction: Built at the University of Surrey by a team consisting of seven Portuguese engineers and the UoSAT staff under a technology transfer program.

1.7 Primary Reference

1) See **http://www.ee.surrey.ac.uk/CSER/UOSAT/ missions/posat1.html**
2) P. Carvalho, "Letter from AMSAT-PO," *OSCAR News*, Feb 1994, p 35.

SPACECRAFT DESCRIPTION

2.1 Physical Structure

Shape: Rectangular solid similar to UoSATs 11, 14, 22.
Dimensions: 350×350×650 mm.

SUBSYSTEM DESCRIPTION

3.1 Beacons

Frequency: 435.250 MHz, 435.275 MHz

3.4 Transponders

PoSAT-OSCAR 28 carries a 9600 baud Mode JD digital transponder known as the PACSAT Communications System (PCS) similar to the one on UO-22.

Uplink frequencies: 145.975 MHz, 145.925 MHz
Downlink frequency: 435.250 MHz, 435.275 MHz

3.5 Attitude Stabilization and Control

Five meter gravity gradient boom with 3 kg tip mass.
Magnetorquers: six coils provide three-axis control.

3.10a Earth Imaging Experiment

PO-28 carries an imaging system consisting of two CCD images. The wide angle lens has a resolution of 2000 meters. The telephoto lens has a resolution of 200 meters. PO-28 has returned excellent images.

3.10b GPS Navigation Experiment

PO-28 carries a GPS receiver based on the Trimble TANS-II receiver. The onboard transputer (DSPE) provides satellite position and velocity and an onboard time reference. Radio amateurs did not take part in preparing this experiment.

3.10c Digital Signal Processing Experiment (DSPE)

Spacecraft contains two Texas Instruments TMS320 series DSP units for experimenting with modulation of downlink data.

3.10d Cosmic Ray Experiment

Spacecraft contains large area PIN diode and multi-channel analyser capable of detecting energetic particles over a wide range of energies. The unit also contains special RADFETs to monitor accumulated ionizing dose.

SPACECRAFT NAME: TMSAT-OSCAR 31

GENERAL

The primary function of this spacecraft is to test new imaging systems. The satellite contains five cameras, a complex attitude control system for camera aiming, a high speed downlink capable of handling large image files, and extensive onboard data handling and storage capabilities.

The worldwide radio amateur community is deeply indebted to the owner/operator, the Thai Microsatellite Company Ltd, which, working in conjunction with University of Surrey, UK, has demonstrated a serious commitment to disseminating information about the imaging experiments and radio links. The early years of this mission will focus on testing the imaging and data processing systems. In later years the focus may switch to radio amateur store-and-forward communications.

1.1 Identification

International designation: 1998-043C
NASA Catalog number: 25,396 (early orbits listed as 25,395)
Also known as: TO-31, TMSAT-1, *Thai-MicroSAT-OSCAR 31*, Thai Phutt

1.2 Launch

Date: July 10, 1998 (launched with Gurwin-OSCAR 32)
Time: 0630 UTC
Vehicle: Ukrainian Zenit Rocket
Agency: RKA (Russian Space Agency)
Site: Baikonur Cosmodrome, Kazakhstan

1.3 Orbital Parameters

General designation: low-altitude, circular, sun synchronous, near polar
Period: 101.2 minutes
Apogee altitude: 826 km
Perigee altitude: 824 km
Eccentricity: 0.00011 (nominally circular)
Inclination: 98.8 degrees
Maximum access distance: 3,082 km

1.5 Operations

The primary command station for TMSAT is HS0AM in Bangkok. Scheduling is at the discretion of the owner, Thai Microsatellite Company Ltd (TMSC) which is part of Mahanakorn University of Technology (MUT), Bangkok, Thailand. Following commissioning TMSAT was opened to the worldwide radio amateur community for store and forward communications and image downloading in late November 1998.

1.6 Design/Construction Credits

TMSAT is owned and operated by TMSC. It was constructed at Surrey Satellite Technology Limited (SSTL), University of Surrey, UK under the direction of SSTL engineers. Packaging is similar to KITSAT-OSCAR 23.

1.7 Primary References

1) C. Jackson, "TMSAT-1 Successfully Launched into Orbit", *AMSAT Journal*, Jul/Aug 1998, pp. 1, 4-6.
2) J. Paffett, C. Jackson, Z. Wahl "38k4 Receiver Requirements", *AMSAT Journal*, Nov/Dec 1997, pp. 9-11.
3) **www.sstl.co.uk/missions/subpage_missions.html**

SPACECRAFT DESCRIPTION

2.1 Physical Structure

Shape: Rectangular solid similar to UoSATs 11, 14, 22 and KITSATs.

Dimensions:: 35 cm×35 cm×65 cm. (core)
External features: 146 MHz canted turnstile antenna earth facing. Gravity gradient boom and 435 MHz turnstile facing out from earth.
Mass: 48.7 kg

SUBSYSTEM DESCRIPTION

3.1 Beacons

Frequency: 436.925 (Primary), 436.900, 436.950, 436.975 MHz
Power output: 2.0 W (nominal), (redundant transmitters)
Modulation: 9,600 bit/s FSK or 38,400 bit/s FSK (referred to as 38k4 baud)
Throughput: Using the 38k4 baud rate throughputs of 1.5 MB have been reported on nearby passes.
Maximum Doppler: 10.3 kHz
Broadcast Call sign: TMSAT1-11 (uploading disabled)
BBS Call sign: TMSAT1-12 (uploading enabled)

3.2 Telemetry

Ground stations can decode telemetry using the DTLM program in WiSP32. Early samples were posted on AMSAT-BB by M. Wakita (**JE9PEL@jamsat.or.jp**). The data consists of 70 clearly labeled analog channels and 16 unlabeled status channels. Additional information is available at **www.ne.jp/asahi/hamradio/je9pel/**

3.4 Transponder

TO-31 carries a mode JD digital transponder using the PACSAT AX.25 Protocol communications system
uplink: 145.925 (Primary), 145.975 MHz
Modulation: 9,600 bit/s
downlink: on beacon frequency
Note: Receiver is frequency agile and capable of scanning. Amateurs are asked not to transmit to TMSAT when the secondary Onboard computer (OBC 186) is controlling the spacecraft. When this occurs the call sign TMSATS will be in use. Please do *NOT* program this call sign into your uplink software.

3.5 Attitude Stabilization and Control

Gravity gradient boom
Magnetorquer: six coils
Momentum Wheel
Magnetometer: three-axis flux-gate

3.9 Onboard Computers

Computer 1: OBC386, 128 MB RAM
Computer 2: OBC186, 16 MB RAM
Computer 3: Transputer (Parallel processing system for on-board image processing)

3.10a Imaging Experiment

TMSAT contains 5 cameras: a Wide Angle Camera (WAC) similar to the imager used on UO-22, three Narrow Angle Cameras (NAC), and a Video Camera.
Wide Angle Camera
Sensor: CCD, 568×560 pixels, made by EEV Ltd.

Lens: ultra wide angle, focal length = 4.8 mm
Ground Coverage (from 820 km): 1500 km×1500 km (about 2 km per pixel)
Filter: 810-890 nm (near-IR), chosen to provide strong contrast between land, sea and clouds.
Memory required: 330 kB per image
Narrow Angle Cameras (three identical units except for filters)
Sensor: CCD, 1020×1020 pixels, made by Eastman-Kodak
Lens: focal length = 75 mm
Ground Coverage (from 820 km): 100 km×100 km (about 100 m per pixel)
Filter 0 (NAC0): 810-890 nm (near-IR)
Filter 1 (NAC1): 610-690 nm (red)
Filter 2 (NAC2): 510-590 nm (green)
Memory required: 1 MB per image, 3 MB for full multispectral (false-color) image
Video Camera
Sensor: CMOS, 382 × 287 pixels
Lens: focal length = 25 mm, f/8
Field of view: 10.5 × 7.8 degrees
Optical band: 350-750 nm
Exposure: on chip automatic — 25,000:1 dynamic range
Memory required: 135 kB per image, 4 MB for series of 30 images
Use: Still picture or series of still pictures
Image Processing/Handling

To see the excellent quality of TO-31 images download a JPEG file from **www.ee.surrey.ac.uk/CSER/UOSAT/amateur/tmsat/index.html**

These files can be easily viewed on a standard JPEG viewer.

Raw images from TO-31 are also available if you wish to experiment with image processing. Check **www.sstl.co.uk/amsat/rawdata**

TMSAT raw image files are named as follows:

file name	camera	width×height
TM00xxxx.IMI	wide angle camera	611 × 576 pixels
TM01xxxx.IMI	wide angle camera (low resolution)	141×156 pixels
TM10xxxx.IMI	narrow angle IR	1020×1020 pixels
TM20xxxx.IMI	narrow angle red filter	1020×1020 pixels
TM30xxxx.IMI	narrow angle green filter	1020×1020 pixels
TM50xxxx.IMI	video camera (8 bit gray scale)	141×141 pixels

Files with the extension .IMC are compressed. To view these you also need the accompanying thumbnail file (same name with IMT extension).

Images can be decoded using an image viewer that works with raw data and lets you specify number of pixels for width and height. See, for example, VK5HI's software for *Win95/NT* available at **ftp://ftp.amsat.org/amsat/software/win32/display/ccddsp97-119.zip**

Image viewers designed for Landsat satellites will also work. For an excellent tutorial on processing images check G. Ratcliff (VK5AGR), "Amateur Radio Satellite Imaging — The Past, Present and Future," Proceedings of the AMSAT-NA 15th Space Symposium, Toronto, Oct 1997, pp 119-137.

Many amateurs enjoy working with raw data files so that they can experiment with: false color assignments, overlay positioning, geometric distortion compensation, etc. Specific TMSAT cameras also require special processing. For example, the Wide Angle Camera transmits even scan lines first and then odd scan lines. As a result it produces two images which should be combined for full resolution. And, when combining Narrow Angle Camera images, one has to compensate for offsets. The following values are suggested by John Melton, N6LYT/G0ORX:

NAC0:	left 1 pixel	up 1 pixel
NAC1:	left 2 pixels	down 6 pixels
		(rotated 180 degrees)
NAC2:	right 11 pixels	up 33 pixels

Don't forget that the imaging, and image processing system aboard the spacecraft, are serious ongoing experiments. As the mission progresses it's likely that the characteristics of the downlink data will change as the software team tests various processing approaches aboard the spacecraft.

3.10b Other Experiments

1) Digital Signal Processing
2) GPS

SPACECRAFT NAME: UoSAT-OSCAR 36

GENERAL

UoSAT-OSCAR 36 is the first minisatellite built at the University of Surrey. It is significantly larger than earlier UoSAT microsatellites. This allows for a high power budget which permits a greatly expanded range of missions.

1.1 Identification

International designation: 1999-021A
NASA Catalog number: 25,693 (early orbits listed as 25,694)
Also known as: UoSAT-12, UO-36

1.2 Launch

Date: 21 April 1999
Time: 0500 UTC
Vehicle: Converted SS-18 ICBM (Dnepr Launcher)
Agency: Kosmotras (Russian-Ukrainian International Space Company)
Site: Baikonur Cosmodrome, Kazakhstan

1.3 Orbital Parameters

Note: Those tracking this mission may need to update orbital elements frequently due to the fact that this spacecraft has a propulsion system and small burns have a significant effect on tracking.

General designation: low-altitude, circular
Period: 97.7 minutes
Apogee altitude: 666 km
Perigee altitude: 649 km
Eccentricity: 0.00125 (nominally circular)
Inclination: 64.6 degrees
Maximum access distance: 2,795 km

1.5 Operations

UO-36 operations are controlled by the owner, Surrey Satellite Technology Ltd and the University of Surrey, UK. The primary command station is located at the University of Surrey, Guildford, UK. Tentative plans are to open the Merlion communications transponder for radio amateur operation on a regular basis once the spacecraft is fully checked out. This is likely to occur outside of normal working hours in England and Singapore. UO-36 is a very complex spacecraft so checkout may require an extended period of time. However, since recent UoSAT spacecraft have often operated for more than a decade the amateur radio community may have access to this satellite for many years.

1.6 Design/Construction Credits

The spacecraft is a research and development project funded by SSTL and UoSAT with invited payloads from Nanyang Technological University (NTU), Singapore, and the European Space Agency.

1.7 Primary References

1) C. Jackson (G7UPN), "UoSAT-12/OSCAR-36 Successfully in Orbit!," *AMSAT Journal*, May/June 1999, pp 8, 9.
2) R. A. da Silva Curie (G7GLY), E. Seumahu (9V1WTI), T. S. Hie, C. T. Wei, "The UoSAT-12 MERLION Payload," *OSCAR NEWS*, Dec 1996, pp 41-43.
3) **www.sstl.co.uk/missions/mn_uosat_12_extra_tech1. html**

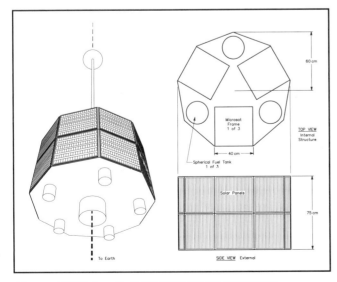

Figure UO36-1— UoSAT-OSCAR 36 structure.

SPACECRAFT DESCRIPTION

2.1 Physical Structure

Surrey Satellite Technologies new MiniBus platform used on UO-36 is shown in Figure UO36-1. The unusual nine sided structure is roughly cylindrical in shape with a height of about 0.8 m, a diameter of about 1.2 m. and a mass of approximately 325 kg. The nine rectangular facets of the spacecraft, each measuring approximately 40×80 cm, are used to support solar panels. The "top" and "bottom" plates support antennas, cameras, propulsion nozzles, attach fixtures, etc.

The structure is built on three short microsat frames (roughly cubes) with three spherical propellant tanks placed as shown. The spacecraft design uses the enclosed volume efficiently, provides desired rotational symmetry and produces a sturdy structure.

The satellite is divided into two main regions — a Payload Frame and a section built around the three microsat frames. The Payload Frame is located between the earth facing facet of the spacecraft and a plate of similar dimensions bolted to the microsat structures. Payloads can be carried in one or more standard SSTL Microbus module trays in the microsat module stacks or in the Payload Frame.

SUBSYSTEM DESCRIPTION

3.1 Beacons

Beacon I
    Frequency: 437.025, 437.400 MHz
    Power: 10 W (a 50 W amplifier can be switched in if desired)
    Modulation: 9,600 baud FSK, 38,400 baud (primary); 76,800 baud (experimental)
Beacon II
    Frequency: 2401.0 MHz
    Power: 1 W (7 W optional)
    Modulation: NBFM (when linear transponder operating),
    1 Mbit/s BPSK with optional Viterbi encoding in conjunction with digital mode.
    Antenna: left hand circular polarization

3.4 Transponders

Transponder I
    This is a relatively standard UoSAT digital store-and-forward transponder incorporating four 2-m Receiver modules, three 70-cm transmit modules, and a 50 watt amplifier that can be switched on line if desired.
    Uplink frequency: frequency agile
    Uplink modulation: 9,600 bit/s FSK
    Downlink: see beacons
Transponder II (NTU/SSTL Merlion Transponder)
    This is a new L-band uplink, S-band downlink transponder developed jointly by Nanyang Technical University (Singapore) and SSTL. It supports analog, digital-DSP and digital-regenerative communications modes and can serve as a high speed (1 M bit/s) downlink for image and other

spacecraft generated files. The transponder can operate in either a digital or analog mode. It consists of two (redundant) L-band receive down converters, a complex IF/processing unit, and two (redundant) S-band transmit up converters. When operating In the analog mode the transponder is non-inverting. In the digital mode the receiver is frequency agile, can support 256k 512k and 1M bit/s with square root raised cosine shaping. Also included is an experimental spread spectrum mode that can use lower data rates for small ground stations.

Uplink center frequency:1265 MHz
Downlink center frequency:2420 MHz
Bandwidth: 1.6 MHz
Power: 7 W

3.5 Attitude Control and Stabilization

Spacecraft is three-axis stabilized and designed to be earth pointing.
Earth pointing accuracy: 0.5 degrees
Target earth pointing accuracy using experimental systems: 0.1 degree
Sensors

Sensor	Accuracy	Note
magnetometer	1.0 degree	
sun azimuth	1.0 degree	
sun elevation	1.0 degree	
earth horizon	0.1 degree	infrared, two-axis
CCD star field camera	0.005 degree	
GPS	0.1 degree	interferometric mode using 4 antennas

Actuators
Gravity Gradient Boom
Cold gas thruster system
fuel compressed nitrogen gas
total impulse: 4000 N
angular impulse: 2000 Nm
delta v capability: 17.8 m/s
magnetorquers
offset momentum wheel system
Processors: 80C186, 80C386, TSM320C32, T805

3.6 Antennas

L- and S-band antennas are designed to equalize power flux density across the satellite footprint.

S-band	Quadrifilar Helix 1	Merlion Transponder
S-Band	Quadrifilar Helix 2	Merlion Transponder
L-band	Quadrifilar Helix 1	Merlion Transponder
L-band	Quadrifilar Helix 2	Merlion Transponder
70 cm	Helix	
2 m	turnstile	
2 m	omni	

3.7 Energy Supply and Power Conditioning

The spacecraft supports nine rectangular solar panels measuring approximately 35×75 cm. Each panel uses highly efficient GaAs cells and has its own battery charge regulator. UO-36 contains three 6 Ah 28 V NiCd battery packs.

3.8 Propulsion Systems

UO-36 contains an experimental electric propulsion system using Nitrous Oxide as a fuel.

Nitrous Oxide (laughing gas) fluid is relatively environmentally friendly and is easy to control.

The "Resistojet" thruster can be used for precise orbit adjustment. This permits constellation phasing, minor orbit adjustments, drag compensation and momentum dumping. The propulsion system can be connected to Microcosm's Orbit Control Kit and the GPS system discussed in section 3.10b.

Fuel: Nitrous Oxide
Fuel Mass: 2.5 kg (provides 14 hours running time)
Thrust: 93 mN
Input power: 90 watts (provided by spacecraft batteries)
Total delta V: 10.4 m/s

3.9 On-Board Computers and Bus System

The spacecraft contains four independent computers including an 80C186, 80C386, TMS320C32 and a T805. It also contains several DSP units and dedicated CPU's in various subsystems. Subsystems and On-board computers are interconnected by Ethernet and CAN local area networks.

3.10a Imaging System

UO-36 contains four imaging systems: a high resolution camera, a multispectral medium resolution system (two cameras), a wide-angle color CCD imager, and a star-field system (two cameras). The high and medium resolution systems are designed for earth imaging, the wide-angle camera for meteorological cloud cover monitoring, and the star-field cameras are for spacecraft attitude control. See comments under TMSAT-OSCAR 31 for information on image processing.

Surrey High Resolution Earth Imaging System
This system uses commercial off-the-shelf optics. It can be programmed to capture a series of time delayed images.
Lens: Leica, f5.6
Focal length: 560 mm
Sensor: Kodak 1024×1024 pixel
Spectral response: haze penetration panchromatic
Ground coverage: 10 km×10 km
Ground resolution: 10 m

Surrey Multi-spectral Medium Resolution Earth Imaging System
This system consists of two identical multispectral cameras. Each camera uses a rotating filter wheel to image in 4 spectral bands.
Lens: Leica, f3.4
Focal length: 180 mm
Spectral response: 4 bands (the standard LANDSAT-4 blue, green, red, near IR)
Ground coverage: 60 km×30 km (using both cameras)
Ground resolution: 30 m

Star-Field Imager

UO-36 carries two star-field cameras employing CCD sensors. The cameras provide information to a precision of 0.005 degrees which can be used by the attitude control system.

3.10b GPS Receiver

This is a new **S**pace **G**PS **R**eceiver (SGR) specially developed for satellite applications by Surrey and ESA/ESTEC. The SGR uses the MITEL (formally GEC Plessey) chipset and an ARM60 32 bit RISC microprocessor. Special attention has been paid to radiation tolerance.

The SGR has 5 antennas, 4 of which can be used at one time. This makes it possible to accurately calculate spacecraft attitude by applying interferometry techniques to phase difference measurements. The SGR can also, of course, be used to continually generate accurate updated orbital elements during operation of the onboard propulsion system. This permits autonomous orbit keeping in conjunction with patented software provided by Microcosm (Microcosm Orbit Control Kit).

SPACECRAFT NAME:
Malaysia-OSCAR 46

1.1 Identification

International designation: 2000 057D
NASA Catalog number: 26,548
Also known as: TiungSAT-1, MO-46

1.2 Launch

Date: 26 September 2000
Time: 10:05 UTC
Vehicle: DNEPR
Agency: RKA (Russian Space Agency)
Site: Baikonur Cosmodrome, Kazakhstan

1.3 Orbital parameters (8/2001)

General Designation: low-altitude, circular
Period: 97.5 minutes
Apogee altitude: 672 km
Perigee altitude: 619 km
Eccentricity: 0.0038
Inclination: 64.6°
Maximum access distance: 2,806 km

1.5 Operations

Primary ground station, 9M2MCS, located at Universiti Kebangsaan Malaysia (UKM).

1.6 Design/Construction Credits

TiungSAT-1 is a non-commercial project under the auspices of Astronautic Technology Sdn Bhd (ATSB) of Kuala Lumpur, Malaysia. Construction took place at the Surrey Space Centre (University of Surrey, England) as a collaborative venture between ATSB and Surrey Satellite Technology Ltd. (SSTL).

1.7 Primary References

1)**www.sstl.co.uk/missions/mn_tiungsat_1.html**
click on "further information" (pdf reader required)

SPACECRAFT DESCRIPTION

2.1 Physical Structure

TiungSAT-1 is based on SSTL modular microsatellite bus (see Figure UO22-1).
Shape: Rectangular solid
Dimensions: 360 × 360 × 690 nm
Mass: 50 kg

SUBSYSTEM DESCRIPTION

3.1 Beacons

Frequencies:	437.325 MHz (primary)
	435.300 MHz (secondary)
	435.350 MHz (secondary)
	435.375 MHz (secondary)

Modulation: Standard PACSAT Digital System

Data rates:	9.6 kbps (commissioning)
	38.4 kbps (general operations)
	76.8 kbps (experimental)

Call signs
Broadcast: MYSAT3-11
BBS: MYSAT3-12
NUP: MYSAT3-10
Tx Power: 2.5 – 8.0 W adjustable

3.4 Transponders

Type: Standard PACSAT digital store and forward, 9.6 kbps
Uplink frequencies: 144.460 MHz
145.850 MHz (use to initiate downlink)
145.925 MHz (use to initiate downlink)

Note: At present, the primary goal of this mission is to gather and downlink earth images. Uplinking is therefore confined to command stations. However, as with UO-36, any ground station may initiate downlink broadcasts when spacecraft power budget allows. See WiSP help files for information.

Downlink frequency: (see Beacons)

3.5 Attitude Stabilization and Control

Gravity Gradient Boom: standard UoSAT
Magnetorquers: standard UoSAT
Momentum Wheel: employs 1 kg mass, 5 mN-m torque, 0.22 nms storage

3.10a Experimental Systems: Earth Imaging

Wide Angle Camera
   Field of view: 1200 × 1200 km
      Ground resolution: ~ 1 km
Three Narrow Angle Cameras (R, G. B)
   Field of view: 80 × 80 km
      Ground resolution: ~ 70 m
Viewing software: CCD Display 97 by VK5HI available from AMSAT-NA.

(See TMSAT-OSCAR 31 for details)

3.10b. Experimental Systems: CEDEX

CEDEX is a cosmic radiation monitor. It's an advanced model of unit flown on AO-40

3.10c. Experimental Systems: GPS

This system uses a single Rx and two patch antennas for on-board orbit determination.

SPACECRAFT NAME: FUJI-OSCAR 20

Note: In late 1996 the FO-20 control team announced that FO-20 would be operated only in the analog mode for the foreseeable future.

GENERAL

1.1 Identification

International designation: 1990-013C
NASA Catalog number: 20480
Prelaunch designation: JAS-1B
Also known as: FO-20, Fuji-2
Call letters: 8J1JBS

1.2 Launch

Date: Feb 7, 1990 (01:25 UTC)
Vehicle: H1
Agency: NASDA (Japanese National Space Agency)
Site: Tanegashima Space Center, Japan

1.3 Orbital Parameters (Jan 1997)

General designation: low-altitude, elliptical, non-sun-synchronous
Period: 112.2 minutes
Apogee altitude: 1752 km
Perigee altitude: 918 km
Eccentricity: 0.0541
Inclination: 99.02°
Maximum access distance: 4264 km

1.5 Operations

Coordinating Group: JAMSAT (Japanese AMSAT)

1.6 Design/Construction Credits

JARL (Japan Amateur Radio League)
NASDA (Japanese National Space Agency)
NEC (Nippon Electric Company): space frame, power supply, etc.
JAMSAT (Japanese AMSAT): transponders, telemetry/command, IHU, ground-support systems.

1.7 Primary References

Note: Except for the orbit, Fuji-OSCAR 20 is very similar to Fuji-OSCAR 12 (aka JAS-1 and Fuji-1).
1) J. Magliacane, "Spotlight On: Fuji-2/OSCAR-20,"

The AMSAT Journal, Nov/Dec 1992, pp 17-19.
2) "Introduction of JAS-1b," by JARL, *QEX*, Sep 1989, pp 8-11.

SPACECRAFT DESCRIPTION

2.1 Physical Structure

Shape: Polyhedron of 26 faces, 25 covered in solar cells.
Overall size: 470 (height) × 440 × 440 mm
Mass: 50 kg
Thermal control: Passive using solar cell cover glass and coatings.
See Figure FO20-1

2.2 Subsystem Organization: See FO20-2

SUBSYSTEM DESCRIPTION

3.1 Beacons

Frequency: 435.795 MHz
Modulation: CW (primary) or PSK (secondary)
Power: 60 mW
Maximum Doppler: 10.1 MHz

Frequency: 435.910 MHz (digital transponder downlink)
Modulation: PSK
Power: 1.0 W
Maximum Doppler: 10.1 MHz

3.2 Telemetry

FO-20 has both CW and packet TTY systems. CW telemetry is sent on the 435.795 MHz beacon at 20 WPM. A CW TTY frame contains 20 channels, which may be thought of as forming a 5 row by 4 column array. The frame marker is the standard HI.

The telemetry system sends two types of information:

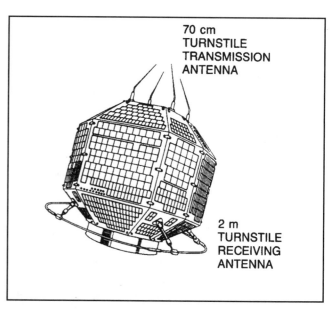

Figure FO20-1 —Drawing of Fuji-OSCAR 20 (from *OSCAR News***, Dec 1989, p 36).**

Table FO20-1
Fuji-OSCAR 20 CW Telemetry

(Reference: JR1NVU, ''The Telemetry Formats of JAS-1B/Fuji-OSCAR 20,'' *The AMSAT Journal*, Sep 1990, pp 20-21.

Channel identification

HI	1A	1B	1C	1C	
	2A	2B	2C	2D	
	3A	3B	3C	3D	
	4A	4B	4C	4C	
	5A	5B	5C	5D	HI

Channel contents

HI	1nn	1nn	1nn	1nn	
	2nn	2nn	2nn	2nn	
	3nn	3nn	3nn	3nn	
	4jj	4jj	4jj	4jj	
	5jj	5jj	5jj	5jj	HI

Decoding equations for analog channels (1A-3D)

1A	Total solar panel current	$I = 19(nn + 0.4)$ mA
1B	Batter charge/discharge	$I = -38(nn - 50)$ mA
1C	Battery terminal voltage	$V = 0.22(nn + 4)$ V
1D	Battery center tap	$V = 0.1(nn + 4)$ V
2A	Bus voltage	$V = 0.20(nn + 4)$ V
2B	+5 V regulator output	$V = 0.062(nn + 4)$ V
2C	Mode JA power output	$P = 2.0(nn + 4)^{1.618}$ mW
2D	Calibration voltage #1	$V = (nn + 4)/50$ V
3A	Battery temperature	$T = 1.4(67 - nn)$ °C
3B	Structure temperature #1	$T = 1.4(67 - nn)$ °C
3C	Structure temperature #2	$T = 1.4(67 - nn)$ °C
3D	Structure temperature #3	$T = 1.4(67 - nn)$ °C

Decoding information for status channels (4A-5D)

CH	BIT	DESCRIPTION	STATE 1	STATE 0
4A	0	JTA Power	ON	OFF
4A	1	JTD Power	ON	OFF
4A	2	Eng. data #1	——	——
4A	3	Eng. data #3	——	——
4A	4	Beacon	PSK	CW
4B	0	UVC	ON	OFF
4B	1	UVC level	1	2
4B	2	Battery	tric	full
4B	3	Battery logic	tric	full
4B	4	Main relay	ON	OFF

Decoding information for status channels (4A-5D con't)

CH	BIT	DESCRIPTION	STATE	
4C	0	PCU	bit 1	(LSB)
4C	1	PCU	bit 2	(LSB)
4C	2	PCU	manual	auto
4C	3	Eng. data #3	——	——
4C	4	Eng. data #4	——	——
4D	0	Memory bank #0	ON	OFF
4D	1	Memory bank #1	ON	OFF
4D	2	Memory bank #2	ON	OFF
4D	3	Memory bank #3	ON	OFF
4D	4	Computer power	ON	OFF
5A	0	Memory select	bit 1	(LSB)
5A	1	Memory select	bit 2	(MSB)
5A	2	Eng. data #5	——	——
5A	3	Eng. data #6	——	——
5A	4	Eng. data #7	——	——
5B	0	Solar panel #1	lit	dark
5B	1	Solar panel #2	lit	dark
5B	2	Solar panel #3	lit	dark
5B	3	Solar panel #4	lit	dark
5B	4	Solar panel #5	lit	dark
5C	0	JTA CW beacon	CPU	TLM
5C	1	Eng. data #8	——	——
5C	2	Eng. data #9	——	——
5C	3	Eng. data #10	——	——
5C	4	Eng. data #11	——	——
5D	0	Eng. data #12	——	——
5D	1	Eng. data #13	——	——
5D	2	Eng. data #14	——	——
5D	3	Eng. data #15	——	——
5D	4	Eng. data #16	——	——

status data from two state (on/off or other) devices and analog data relating to voltages, currents and temperatures. The first 12 channels contain analog data as per Table FO20-1. Each channel consists of three digits. The first digit is a row marker. The remaining two digits per channel contain the raw data. The spacecraft has sensors placed at 29 analog test points and 33 status points. Decoding information is in Table FO20-1.

PSK telemetry is sent on 435.910 MHz in the form of AX.25 packets. Three types of frames are used: real-time TTY (ASCII or binary), stored TTY (ASCII or binary) and messages (numbered 0 to 9). The real-time and stored ASCII frames contain information on all 29 analog data points and 33 status points.

3.3 Telecommand System

The telecommand system recognizes five operating modes. Numbers in parentheses refer to operating power required.

Mode D. All loads off except command receiver. (2.5 W)
Mode JA on. (5.3 W)
Mode JD on with from 1 to 4 256 k memory banks activated. (JD-1 [6.2 W], JD-2 [6.7 W], JD-3 [7.0 W], JD-4 [7.3 W])
Mode DI. All loads off except command receiver, CPU, and memory.
Mode JAD. Both JA and JD on. (10.2 W)

3.4 Transponders

Transponder 1: Mode JA
type: linear, inverting
Uplink passband: 145.900 - 146.000 MHz
Downlink passband: 435.800 - 435.900 MHz
Translation equation:
Downlink freq [MHz] =
581.800 – uplink freq [MHz] ±Doppler
Power output: 2-W PEP
Recommended uplink EIRP: 100 W
Bandwidth: 100 kHz
Maximum Doppler: 6.7 kHz

Transponder 2: Mode JD
Type: digital
Uplink channels:
#1 145.850 MHz
#2 145.870 MHz
#3 145.890 MHz
#4 145.910 MHz
Downlink channel: 435.910 MHz
Power output: 1-W RMS

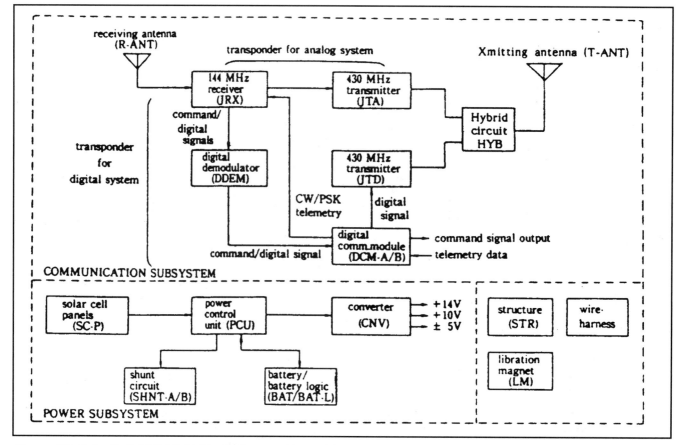

Figure FO20-2—Fuji-OSCAR 20 block diagram (from *OSCAR News*, June 1989, p 11).

Recommended uplink EIRP: 100 W
Comments: Uplink must be Manchester coded FM. Data rate is 1200 baud. The downlink is 1200 baud BPSK. For information on Modems see Chapter 5.

3.5 Attitude stabilization

Two 1 TAm² permanent magnets mounted parallel to spacecraft Z axis align along Earth's local magnetic field.

3.6 Antennas

2-m receive: turnstile mounted on bottom of spacecraft. 70-cm transmit (Mode JA and JD): canted turnstile on top of spacecraft. A circulator and phase shifter enables the use of a single antenna for both links.

3.7 Energy Supply and Power Conditioning

Power Subsystem: See Figure FO20-2. Battery control logic monitors voltage, current and temperature of storage battery. Software will attempt to utilize spacecraft systems to minimize activation of over-voltage control (OVC) and under-voltage control (UVC) functions.

Solar cells: Gallium Arsenide. Spacecraft contains approximately 1530 cells, 900 measuring 1×2 cm and 630 measuring 2×2 cm. The total cell surface area is about 4320 cm². When first launched these cells generated about 13 W (optimum satellite orientation) and about 11

watts average when spacecraft is in sunlight. Compared to Fuji-1 these figures represent an increase of 9% in cell area and 70% in available power.

Bus voltage: +11 to 18 (14 V average)
Battery: 11 NiCd cells providing about 14 V at 6 Ah.
Instrument Switching Regulators are used to provide +10 V, +5 V and –5 V for spacecraft systems. Efficiency >70%.

3.9 IHU

CPU: NSC-800 (Controls spacecraft and digital transponder)
RAM: 48 256-kbit NMOS DRAMs. These are configured using a hardware-based error detection and correction scheme to provide 1 Mbyte of EDAC 8-bit memory. The operating system resides in approximately 32 k, the rest is used for message storage.

SPACECRAFT NAME: Fuji-OSCAR 29

GENERAL

1.1 Identification

International designation: 1996-046B
NASA Catalog number: 24278
Prelaunch designation: JAS-2

Also known as: FO-29, Fuji-3

1.2 Launch

Date: Aug 17, 1996 (01:29 UTC)
Vehicle: H2
Agency: NASDA (Japanese National Space Agency)
Site: Tanegashima Space Center, Japan

1.3 Orbital Parameters (Jan 1997)

General designation: low-altitude, elliptical, non-sunsynchronous
Period: 106.5 minutes
Apogee altitude: 1330 km
Perigee altitude: 808 km
Eccentricity: 0.0351
Inclination: 98.56°
Maximum access distance: 3801 km

1.5 Operations

Coordinating Group: JAMSAT (Japanese AMSAT)

1.6 Design/Construction Credits

JARL (Japan Amateur Radio League)
NASDA (Japanese National Space Agency)
NEC (Nippon Electric Company): space frame, power supply, etc.
JAMSAT (Japanese AMSAT): transponders, telemetry/command, IHU, ground-support systems.

1.7 Primary References

1) F. Yamashita, "JAS-2 Now Under Preparation," *The AMSAT Journal*, Sep/Oct 1995, pp 24-29.
2) NASDA Press kit, "H-II Launch Vehicle No. 4, Launch and Tracking & Control of the Advanced Earth Observing Satellite (ADEOS), (BBD-000089 JSF9682T).
3) **www.jarl.or.jp/English/5_Fuji/ejasmenu.htm**

SPACECRAFT DESCRIPTION

2.1 Physical Structure

Shape: Polyhedron of 26 faces, 25 covered in solar cells.
Overall size: 470 (height)×440×440 mm
Mass: 50 kg
Thermal control: Passive using solar cell cover glass and coatings. See Fig FO29-1

2.2 Subsystem Organization: See Figure FO29-2

SUBSYSTEM DESCRIPTION

3.1 Beacons

Frequency: 435.795 MHz
Modulation: CW 12 WPM
Maximum Doppler: 10.1 MHz
Power: 100 mW

Frequency: 435.910 MHz (digital transponder [1200 and 9600 bauds] and digitalker downlink)
Modulation: PSK

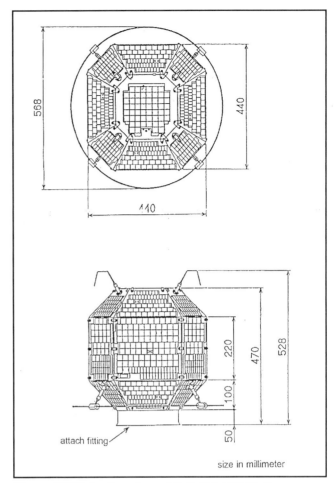

Figure FO29-1—Drawing of Fuji-OSCAR 29 (from AMSAT Journal, Sep/Oct 95 p 26).

Power: 1.0 W
Maximum Doppler: 10.1 MHz

3.2 Telemetry

FO-29 has both CW and packet TTY systems. CW telemetry is sent on the 435.795 MHz beacon at 12 WPM. A CW TTY frame contains 24 channels that may be thought of as forming a 6 row by 4 column array. The frame marker is the standard HI.

The telemetry system sends two types of information: status data from two state (on/off or other) devices (channels 1A through 2A) and analog data relating to voltages, currents and temperatures (channels 2B through 6D). Each channel consists of three digits. The first digit is a row marker. Decoding information is in Table FO29-1.

PSK telemetry is sent on 435.910 MHz in the form of AX.25 packets. Three types of frames are used: real-time TTY (ASCII or binary), stored TTY (ASCII or binary) and messages (numbered 0 to 9). The real-time and stored ASCII frames contain information on all 29 analog data points and 33 status points.

3.3 Telecommand System

The telecommand system recognizes five operating modes. Numbers in parentheses refer to operating power required.

Mode D. All loads off except command receiver. (2.5 W)

Mode JA on. (5.3 W)

Mode JD on with from 1 to 4 256 k memory banks activated.
(JD-1 [6.2 W], JD-2 [6.7 W], JD-3 [7.0 W], JD 4 [7.3 W])

Mode DI. All loads off except command receiver, CPU, and
memory.

Mode JAD. Both JA and JD on. (10.2 W)

3.4 Transponders

Transponder 1: Mode JA
    type: linear, inverting
    uplink passband: 145.900 - 146.000 MHz
    downlink passband: 435.800 - 435.900 MHz
    translation equation:
        downlink freq [MHz] =
            581.800 – uplink freq [MHz] ±Doppler
    power output: 900 mW RMS
    recommended uplink EIRP: 100 W
    bandwidth: 100 kHz
    maximum Doppler: 6.7 kHz

Transponder 2: Mode JD 1200 bps packet
    type: digital
    uplink channels:
        #1 145.850 MHz
        #2 145.870 MHz
        #3 145.890 MHz
        #4 145.910 MHz
    downlink channel: 435.910 MHz
    power output: 1-W RMS
    recommended uplink EIRP: 100 W

Comments: Uplink must be Manchester coded FM. The protocol is AX.25 Level 2 Version 2. Data rate is 1200 baud. The downlink is 1200 baud BPSK. For additional information see Table FO29-2 and Chapter 5.

Transponder 3: Mode JD 9600 bps packet
    type: digital
    uplink channels: 145.870 MHz
    downlink channel: 435.910 MHz
    power output: 1 W RMS
    recommended uplink EIRP: 100 W
    downlink channel: 435.910 MHz
    power output: 1-W RMS
    recommended uplink EIRP: 100 W

Comments: Uplink must be Manchester coded FM. The protocol is AX.25 Level 2 Version 2. Data rate is 1200 baud. The downlink is 1200 baud BPSK. For additional information see Table FO29-2 and Chapter 5.

Transponder 3: Mode JD 9600 bps packet
    type: digital
    uplink channels: 145.870 MHz
    downlink channel: 435.910 MHz
    power output: 1 W RMS
    recommended uplink EIRP: 100 W

Comments: UoSAT compatible 9600 bps packet. See Chapter 5 for additional information. The two digital transponders cannot be operated at the same time.

3.5 Attitude stabilization

FO-29 employs a new attitude control system using two torquing coils and solar and geomagnetic sensors. The spacecraft will be spin stabilized about its symmetry axis. This axis will be set perpendicular to the orbit plane (wheel mode).

3.6 Antennas

2-m receive: ring shaped turnstile mounted on bottom of spacecraft. The antenna produces right hand circular polarization *only* in the direction of the top of the spacecraft.

70-cm transmit: turnstile on top of spacecraft. A combiner allows this antenna to be used by the analog and digital transponders.

3.7 Energy Supply and Power Conditioning

Power Subsystem: Battery control logic monitors voltage, current and temperature of storage battery. Software will attempt to utilize spacecraft systems to minimize activation of over-voltage control (OVC) and under-voltage control (UVC) functions.

Solar cells: Gallium Arsenide. Spacecraft contains approximately 1448 cells, 748 measuring 1×2 cm and 700 measuring 2×2 cm. The total cell surface area is about 4296 cm^2. When first launched these cells will have an efficiency of about 17%.

Bus voltage: +11 to 18 (14 V average)
Battery: 11 NiCd cells providing about 14 V at 6 Ah.
Instrument Switching Regulators are used to provide +10 V,
    +5 V and –5 V for spacecraft systems. Efficiency >70%.

3.9 IHU

CPU: NEC V50 (Controls spacecraft and digital transponder)
RAM: 2 Mbyte SRAM

Table FO29-1

FO-29 Telemetry

System Status Data

Bit	Status Item	1	0	
1A				
0	main relay	on	off	MSB of 1st 4 bits
1	DCM	on	off	
2	SRAM	on	off	
3	packet 1200	1200	9600 or off	LSB of 1st 4 bits
4	packet 9600	9600	1200 or off	MSB of 2nd 4 bits
5	JTA	on	off	
6	JTD	on	off	
7	geomagnetic sensor	on	off	LSB of 2nd 4 bits
1B				
0	solar sensor	on	off	
1	UVC control	on	off	
2	UVC level	2	1	
3	mode of PCU	manual	auto	
4	PCU level 1/2	2	1 or 3	
5	PCU level 3	3	1 or 2	
6	battery charging mode	trickle	full	
7	battery logic	full	trickle	
1C				
0				
1				
2				
3				
4	digitalker	on	off	
5				
6	mode of UVC	on	off	
7	CPU run/reset	on	off	

[1D and 2A are not assigned.]

Measured Analog Data

Bit	Item	Reduction Formula[1]
2B		
2C	spinning rate	
2D	spinning rate	
3A	status of attitude	
3B	solar angle	
3C	geomagnetic sensor Y	
3D	geomagnetic sensor Z	
4A	solar panel current	$I=-0.009765*N$ A
4B	charging/discharging current	$I=-(2-0.01953*N$ A
4C	terminal voltage of battery	$V=0.10761*N$ V
4D	middle point voltage of battery	$V=0.04814*N$ V
5A	bus voltage	$V=0.09843*N$ V
5B	JTA transmitting power	$P=-4.66+2.13e-1*N$ dBm
5C	temperature of body 1	$T=(1.95321-N*19.53e-3)/(0.02039$ Celsius deg)
5D	temperature of body 2	$T=(1.95321-N*19.53e-3)/(0.02039$ Celsius deg)
6A	temperature of body 3	$T=(1.95321-N*19.53e-3)/(0.02039$ Celsius deg)
6B	temperature of body 4	$T=(1.95321-N*19.53e-3)/(0.02039$ Celsius deg)
6C	temperature of battery	$T=(1.95321-N*19.53e-3)/(0.02039$ Celsius deg)
6D	—	

[1]These are preliminary descriptions. Final reduction formulae will be announced later including digital telemetry reading.

Fuji-OSCAR 29 CW TTY Decoding Information

HI	1A	1B	1C	1D	
	2A	2B	2C	2D	
	3A	3B	3C	3D	
	4A	4B	4C	4D	
	5A	5B	5C	5D	HI

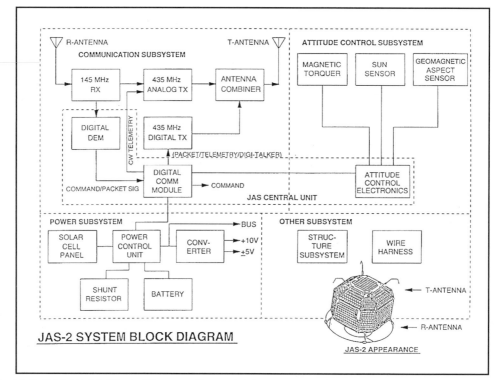

JAS-2 SYSTEM BLOCK DIAGRAM

JAS-2 APPEARANCE

Figure FO29-2—Fuji-OSCAR 29 Block Diagram (from *AMSAT Journal* Sep/Oct 95 p 27).

Table FO29-2

FO-29 Digital Transponder User Commands and TNC Settings

Command	Description
A	User's command
B	Bulletin; lists file headers addressed to all.
F	Lists the latest file header and those in reverse order of time.
FDD <MM/DD>	Lists file headers in reverse order of time from MM/DD.
H	Help, shows list of commands and their explanation.
K <nnn>	Deletes file, possible by posted and addressed station only.
M	Lists file headers addressed to user.
R <nnn>	Shows message of file.
U	Lists current users.
W	Writes messages, sending is requested address and title of message, after that messages are sent, and termination of message should be pressed 14, return at the line head.
Y	Requests more display for B and F commands.
Q	Requests disconnection of current link.

FO-29 TNC Settings

Item	Setting
FULLDUP	ON
MAXFRAMES	4
PACLEN	128 or less

If there is a *SOFTDCD* command, turn it OFF.

SPACECRAFT NAME: RS-12/13

Note: COSMOS 2123 carries RS-12 and RS-13 as secondary payloads. Spacecraft on this launch were designed to operate independently but remain attached to a common space platform.

High energy particles emitted during a solar storm in the summer of 2002 appear to have destroyed key electronic systems on COSMOS 2123. RS-12/13 has not been heard since. This section is being retained here because there is reason to believe that RS spacecraft with similar systems may be launched in the future.

GENERAL

1.1 Identification

International designation: 1991 007A
NASA Catalog number: 21089

1.2 Launch

Date: Feb 5, 1991
Site: Plesetsk
Launch Vehicle: COSMOS Rocket

1.3 Orbital Parameters (Jan 1997)

General designation: low-altitude, circular, near polar, non sun-synchronous
Period: 104.8 minutes
Apogee altitude: 1014 km
Perigee altitude: 969 km
Eccentricity: 0.0030
Inclination: 82.9°

Table RS12/13-1
RS-12 Frequency Chart

	Uplink Band (MHz)	Downlink Band (MHz)	Translation Constant (MHz)
Mode K	21.210-21.250	29.410-29.450	8.200
Mode T	21.210-21.250	145.910-145.950	124.700
Mode A	145.910-145.950	29.410-29.450	−116.500
Mode KT	21.210-21.250	29.410-29.450 & 145.910-145.950	8.200 124.700
Mode KA	21.210-21.250 & 145.910-146.950	29.410-29.450	8.200 −116.500

Translation Eq: downlink freq [MHz] =
translation constant + uplink freq [MHz] ±Doppler
Beacon frequencies: 29.4081, 29.4543, 145.9125 and
145.9587 MHz
Robot uplink frequencies: 21.1291 and 145.8308 MHz

Table RS12/13-2
RS-13 Frequency Chart

	Uplink Band (MHz)	Downlink Band (MHz)	Translation Constant (MHz)
Mode K	21.260-21.300	29.460-29.500	8.200
Mode T	21.260-21.300	145.960-146.000	124.700
Mode A	145.960-146.000	29.460-29.500	−116.500
Mode KT	21.260-21.300	29.460-29.500 & 145.960-146.000	8.200 124.700
Mode KA	21.260-21.300 & 145.960-146.000	29.460-29.500	8.200, −116.500

Translation Eq: downlink freq [MHz] =
translation constant-uplink freq [MHz] ±Doppler
Beacon frequencies: 29.4582, 29.5043, 145.8622 and
145.9083 MHz
ROBOT uplink frequencies: 21.1385 and 145.8403 MHz

Maximum access distance: 3379 km

1.5 Operations

The primary control station is RS3A in Moscow. Although both spacecraft can operate concurrently, the usual practice is for only one spacecraft to be on at any given time.

1.6 Design/Construction Credits

Built at the Tsiolkovskiy Museum for the History of Cosmonautics in Kaluga (about 180 km southwest of Moscow). The project managers for the spacecraft were Aleksandr Papkov and Viktor Samkov.

SPACECRAFT DESCRIPTION

2.1 Physical Structure

RS-12/13 is integrated into a COSMOS maritime navigation spacecraft from which it receives power.

2.2 Subsystem Organization

RS-12/13 contains several linear transponders which can be interconnected. The spacecraft also contains a ROBOT and several beacons.

SUBSYSTEM DESCRIPTION

3.1 Beacons: See Table RS12/13-1

Power output: 0.45 W or 1.2 W (low/high option)

3.4 Transponders: See Table RS12/13-2

Power output: 8 W PEP

3.7 Energy-Supply and Power Conditioning

The following power requirements have been listed
RS-12 all systems off: 4.6 W
RS-12 all systems on: 35 W
RS-13 all systems off: 3.5 W
RS-13 all systems on: 25 W

SPACECRAFT NAME: RS-15

GENERAL

1.1 Identification

International designation: 1994 085A
NASA Catalog number: 23439
Prelaunch designation: Radio-ROSTO

1.2 Launch

Date: Dec 26, 1994 (03:00 UTC)
Site: Baikonur
Launch Vehicle: Rokot (stages 1 and 2: SS-19,
stage 3: Briz)

1.3 Orbital Parameters (Jan 1997)

General designation: low-altitude, circular, near polar,
non sun-synchronous
Period: 127.7 minutes
Apogee altitude: 2159 km
Perigee altitude: 1900 km
Eccentricity: 0.0154
Inclination: 64.8°
Maximum access distance: 4635 km

1.5 Operations:

The primary control station is RS3A in Moscow.

1.6 Design/Construction Credits

Project Manager: Alexandr Papkov, UA3XBU and Viktor Samkov of the Tsiolkovskiy Museum for the History of Cosmonautics in Kaluga (180 km southwest of Moscow).

SPACECRAFT DESCRIPTION

2.1 Physical Structure

Shape: Spherical like unit about 1 meter in diameter. Similar to RS-3 to RS-8 series.

Table RS15-1
RS-15 CW Telemetry Decoding Information

1. II U,K,W,O - Voltage of the onboard power supply less than normal
   S,D,R,G - Voltage of the onboard power supply is normal
   $n \times 0.4$ = real voltage in volts

2. IN U,K,W,O - Sensitivity transponder rx is maximum
   S,D,R,G - Sensitivity transponder rx is minimum
   $n/10$ = TX 29 MHz output power.

3. IA U,K,W,O - Beacon-1 output is nominal
   S,D,R,G - Beacon-1 output is maximum
   $n \times 0.2$ = IFA-1 power supply voltage

4. IM U,K,W,O - Beacon-2 output is nominal
   S,D,R,G - Beacon-2 output is maximum
   $n \times 0.2$ = IFA-2 power supply voltage

5. NI U,K,W,O - Service info
   S,D,R,G - Service info
   $n \times 0.2$ = Stabilizer +5 V (Volts)

6. NN U,K,W,O - Service info
   S,D,R,G - Service info
   $n \times 0.4$ = Solar battery voltage (volts)

7. NA U,K,W,O - Service info
   S,D,R,G - Service info
   $n \times 20$ = Solar battery current (mA)

8. NM U,K,W,O - Service info
   S,D,R,G - Service info
   $n \times 20$ = the consumption current (mA)

9. AI U,K,W,O - TLM sampling period = 60 min
   S,D,R,G - TLM sampling period = 15 min
   $n - 10$ = 10m TX temperature in C

10. AN U,K,W,O - Transmission of TLM = 600 Baud
    S,D,R,G - Transmission of TLM = 1200 Baud
    $n - 10$ = 2m RX temperature

11. AA U,K,W,O - Transmission from board memory = 600 Baud
    S,D,R,G - Transmission from board memory = 1200 Baud
    $n - 10$ = stabilizer temperature in C

12. AM U,K,W,O - Receiving of board memory = 600 Baud
    S,D,R,G - Receiving of board memory = 1200 Baud
    $n - 10$ = temp of charger block in C

13. MI U,K,W,O - Transmission of TLM info is ON
    S,D,R,G - Transmission of TLM Info Is OFF
    n - temp., solar battery block 1 (identified by a table)

14. MN U,K,W,O - Transmission from board memory is ON
    S,D,R,G - Transmission from board memory is OFF
    n - temp., solar battery block 2 in C (identified by a table)

15. MA U,K,W,O - No use
    S,D,W,O - No use
    n - temp., solar battery block 3 in C (identified by a table)

16. MM U,K,W,O - Accumulator is OFF
    S,D,W,O - Accumulator is ON
    n - pressure in the hermetic container (identified by a table)

This should assist our scientific use of RS-15 and to explore some of the anomalies of variable spin fading, signal strength, etc. Note that there is no positive indication of a Mode "K" or "T" transponder system unless it is resident within the vectors labeled "Service Info."—*Pat, G3IOR*

Mass: About 70 kg.

SUBSYSTEM DESCRIPTION

3.1 Beacons

Beacon 1: 29.3525 MHz, 0.4 or 1.2 W
Beacon 2: 29.3987 MHz, 0.4 or 1.2 W

3.2 Telemetry

Telemetry is sent in CW at 20 WPM on the beacon frequencies. A frame consists of 16 channels. For TTY decoding information see Table RS15-1.

3.4 Transponders

Type: linear, noninverting
Power output: 0.4 or 1.2 W PEP
Uplink: 145.858-145.898 MHz
Downlink: 29.354-29.394 MHz (weak)

SPACECRAFT NAME: RS-20

Note: RS-20 is a Radio Amateur payload on the Russian Mozhayets spacecraft which is being used to test and develop navigation equipment for the GLONASS and Navstart navigation systems.

GENERAL

1.1 Identification

International designation: 2002-054B
NASA Catalog number: 27,560
    Also known as: Mozhayets

1.2 Launch

Date: 28 November 2002 (06:07 UTC)
Site: Plesetsk Cosmodrome
Launch Vehicle: lightweight Kosmos-3M rocket

1.3 Orbital Parameters (Jan. 2003)

General designation: low altitude, circular, near polar, sun-synchronous
Period: 99.0 minutes
Apogee altitude: 750 km
Perigee altitude: 689 km
Eccentricity: 0.0043
Inclination: 98.2 degrees
Maximum access distance: 2,950 km

1.4 Operations

The RS-20 module is designed to train students in spacecraft operating methods and telemetry analysis. Students

Table RS20-1

Telemetry decoding information for RS-20

Label	Normal Min:Max N range	Decoding Formula	Parameter	Units
RS 20				
UBS	100:170	N / 10	Main bus voltage	volts
IBS	10:250	N / 100	Main bus current	amps
USUN	0:180	N / 10	Solar panel charge voltage	volts
ISUN	0:180	N / 100	Solar panel charge current	amps
ITXA	0:170	N / 100	435 MHz Tx current	amps
PTXA	0:70	N / 10	435 MHz Tx output power	watts
TTXA	50:190	N − 100	435 MHz Tx temperature	deg. C
ITXB	0:150	N / 100	145 MHz Tx current	amps
PTXB	0:70	N / 10	145 MHz Tx output power	watts
TTXB	50:190	N − 100	145 MHz Tx temperature	deg. C
TEXT	30:250	N − 100	Outer case temperature	deg. C
TINT	30:190	N − 100	Inner case temperature	deg. C
TOR	10:250	N − 100	Earth sensor temperature	deg. C
UOR	0:100	N / 10	Sun sensor voltage	volts
MTX	0:255	—	Housekeeping data	
MRX	0:255	—	Housekeeping data	
RS 20				

and personnel of the Mozhaisky Military space Academy in St. Petersburg were involved in its construction.

SPACECRAFT DESCRIPTION

2.1 Physical Structure

Mass: 90 kg (Mozhayets)

SUBSYSTEM DESCRIPTION

3.1 Beacons

Beacon 1: 145.828 MHz
Beacon 2: 435.319 MHz

3.2 Telemetry

RS-20 transmits CW telemetry. Each frame contains 16 parameters and begins and ends with "RS-20". Decoding information is contained in Table RS20-1

3.3 Transponders

RS-20 does not carry a transponder.

SPACECRAFT NAME: Kolibri-2000 (RS-21)

Note: Kolibri-1 is the first in a series of Research/Educational Microsats. Current plans are for a total of five spacecraft by 2010. Amateur Radio equipment is an integral part of the command/control/telemetry design.

Several options are being considered to extend mission duration. These include raising the initial altitude, improving aerodynamic shape, adding an on-board propulsion system.

GENERAL

1.1 Identification

International designation: 2001-051C

NASA Catalog number: 27,394
Also known as: Kolibri-1, Kollibry, SRSS-1
Formal name: Russian/Australian Research and Educational Microsatellite Kolibri-2000 Mission

1.2 Launch

Date: 19 March 2002 (Released from M1-7 at 22:00 UTC)
Reentry date: 3 May 2002
Launch Vehicle: Progress M1-7 supply vehicle as it departed ISS

1.3 Orbital Parameters (at deployment)

General designation: low altitude, circular, high inclination
Period: 92.4 minutes
Apogee altitude: 404 km
Perigee altitude: 398 km
Eccentricity: 0.00038
Inclination: 51.6 degrees
Maximum access distance: 2,210 km

1.4 Operations

Ground Control Stations

Primary: NILAKT ROSTO base in Kaluga
Secondary: SKB KP IKI in Tarusa, Spacecraft Control Center at Krasnoznamensk,

1.5 Design/construction Credits

RS-21 construction was directed by the Space Research Institute (IKI) of the Russian Academy of Sciences with assistance from several Russian agencies and a grant from the International Astronautic Federation of the United Nations.Radio systems were developed by a team long involved with amateur RS projects headed by Alexander Papkov, UA3XBU.

1.6 Primary References

Alexander Zaitsev, RW3DZ, Director of IKI Microsat office, has provided timely information throughout the project. See:
www.iki.rssi.ru/kollibri/otch_e.htm and
www.iki.rssi.ru/kollibri/mission1_e.htm.
Note: the previous URL's spell Kolibri as "kollibri."
tarusa.ru/kolibri2000
www.kolibri2000.ru/main/index.phtml (Text in Russian but excellent **photos**)

SPACECRAFT DESCRIPTION

2.1 Physical Structure

Shape: Rectangular solid. See Figure RS21-1
Height: 52 cm
Base: 26 cm x 26 cm
Four solar panels, each 26 cm x 52 cm, hinged at base are
  deployed after spacecraft is in orbit.
Mass: 20.5 kg

SUBSYSTEM DESCRIPTION

3.1 Beacons

Frequencies: 435.335 MHz, 145.825 MHz, 145.850 MHz

3.2 Telemetry

CW or 1200 baud AX.25 AFSK or FM voice message
CW telemetry similar to RS-20. See **www.marex-na.org/fileshtml/rs21sat.htm**l.

3.3 Transponders

RS-21 did not contain a transponder but it did contain a 70-cm command system. System documentation mentions ground station use of RS-12/13 on several occasions possibly suggesting that future Kolibri missions will contain transponders.

3.4 Attitude Stabilization and Control

The system is designed to provide 3-axis control and support photo imaging It includes a gravity gradient boom and torquing coils. Sensors include a 3-axis flux-gate magnetometer and a sun tracker.

3.5 Energy Supply and Power Conditioning

Solar Panels: 4 deployed (each 26 cm x 52 cm)
Power Provided: 60 W Max (0.5 m^2)
Battery System designed so that spacecraft could survive four months of in space "cold storage" (vacuum, no-charging) aboard M1-7 before release.

3.6 Experimental Systems

1. The spacecraft itself was the primary mission experiment. It had to verify that the design/construction consortium could build and arrange for integration and certification of a component of the Russian Segment of the International Space Station. The microsatellite structure, scientific hardware and service equipment (onboard systems, radio equipment, electric power suppliers) received certification. A Flight Safety Certificate for the satellite as a whole, and for the separation procedures from the Progress M1-7 transport cargo vehicle, was received.

2. The spacecraft verified the feasibility of Tracking of Kolibri-1 from the NILAKT ROSTO ground control complex using NORAD data received via Internet.

3. The spacecraft included the following scientific sensors chosen to collect information on the interaction between the earth's magnetosphere and plasma clouds ejected from the sun's surface.

  a) 3-axis flux-gate magnetometer (range +/- 64000 nT). One axis tuned to 50-60 Hz
  b) Particle analyzer responding to:
  electrons with energies > 100 KeV
  protons with energies > 50 eV
  neutrons with energies between 0.1 eV and 1.0 eV
  Gamma radiation with energy > 300 KeV
  c) Electric Field analyzerinduced quasi-static fields in range +/- 2560 V/m spectral fluctuation density in 50-60 Hz frequency band (earth based power transmission lines)

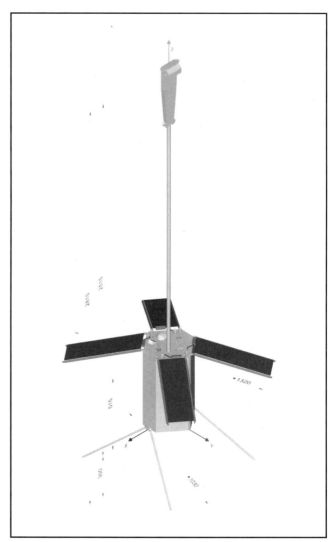

Figure RS21-1—RS-21 "Kolibri-2000" Spacecraft

SPACECRAFT SERIES: MicroSat

Includes: OSCARs 16-19, 26, 27, 30

Note: This section includes data common to all seven spacecraft unless noted otherwise. It is followed by sections containing information specific to each satellite. For additional information on MicroSat systems see Chapter 14.

GENERAL

1.7 Primary References:

1) T. Clark, C. Duncan, J. King, B. McGwier "The First Flock of MicroSats," *The AMSAT Journal*, May 1989, pp 3-10.

2) D. Loughmiller and B. McGwier "MicroSat: The Next generation of OSCAR Satellites," Part 1, *QST*, May 1989 pp 37-40; Part 2, *QST*, June 1989, pp 53-54.

3) T. Clark "AMSAT's MicroSat/Pacsat Program," *Proceedings of the AMSAT-NA Sixth Space Symposium*, Atlanta, Nov 1988, ARRL.

SPACECRAFT DESCRIPTION

2.1 Physical Structure

Shape: cube approximately 23 cm on edge.
See Figure MSat-1
Mass: approximately 9 kg

Thermal design: passive; spacecraft coatings are designed to minimize heat input from the Sun and Earth. The objective is to keep the spacecraft temperature between –5°C and +5°C to promote as high an efficiency from the solar cells as is possible and to extend the life of the NiCd storage batteries.

Note: A MicroSat spacecraft is composed of five aluminum trays formed into a stack held together with stainless steel tie bolts. The frame stack assembly measures 230×230×213 mm. Tray slots are numbered from 1 to 5 starting at the –Z face (bottom) of the spacecraft. Honeycombed side panels manufactured from 4.8 mm thick aluminum stock hold antennas and solar cells. This structure has been flight qualified to standards meeting the requirements of all the world's currently available launchers.

2.2 Subsystem Organization

Table MSat-1 lists the standard functions of the various MicroSat trays.

Subsystem organization is based on a bus structure. Each module mates to a wiring harness consisting of a 25 conductor ribbon cable. The ribbon cable carries dc power (40% of conductors), digital data or control signals (40%) and analog voltages for telemetry sensors and direct CPU control of modules. Each module (other than the main computer) contains a Motorola MC14469 AART (Addressable Asynchronous Receiver/Transmitter). The AART provides a standardized computer to module interface for commands and data. The AART uses ordinary ASCII communications at 4800 bps over what is essentially a 6-inch-long Local Area Network (LAN).

SUBSYSTEM DESCRIPTION

3.2 Telemetry

With MicroSat spacecraft the concept of a fixed telemetry frame is obsolete. Telemetry functions are managed by the onboard computer. Telemetry is downlinked over regular beacon or transponder downlink channels in the form of packets. Unconnected packets contain basic telemetry and bulletins. Users can connect to the satellite via the transponder and request additional telemetry information. A transmitted telemetry channel contains a unique identifier and a data value. The identifier references the module of origin and the module's multiplexer address. If spare computing power exists (and if someone is willing to develop

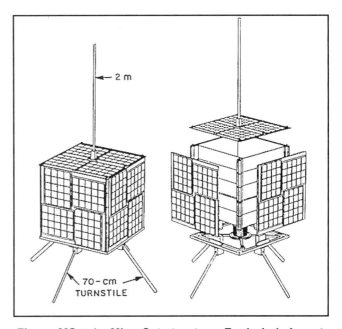

Figure MSat-1—MicroSat structure. Exploded view at right. (*drawings courtesy WD4FAB*)

Table MSat-1

MicroSat Module Functions (listed from top to bottom tray)

Module No.	Pacsat and Lusat	Dove	Webersat
+Z facet	(top)		
05	FSK Packet Rx	Command Rx	TSFR
04	TSFR	Flight Computer	Flight Computer
03	Power Module	Power Module	Power Module
02	Flight Computer	TSFR	FSK Packet Rx
01	BPSK Packet Tx	FM Voice Tx	BPSK Packet Tx
–Z facet	(bottom)		

TSFR (This Space For Rent):
    Pacsat: 13 cm transmitter
    Lusat: 70-cm beacon with dedicated microcomputer
       control
    DOVE: D/A Buffer/Converter, 13 cm transmitter
    Webersat: Camera, multiple experiments

software) it should be possible to initiate on board data processing so that telemetry may be downlinked in the form of plain text packets that identify the parameter being measured and provide a value. The telemetry system allows for up to 200 telemetry points. Sensor identification and decoding equations are shown in Table MSat-2. Updated telemetry decoding information is available on disk for IBM compatible computers from AMSAT.

3.4 Transponder (AO-16, LU-19, IO-26 only)

The standard pacsat transponder consists of a receive unit and a transmit unit operating under the control of the on-board computer. The design is optimized for file transfer operation and uses the same ground and space software as the UoSAT 9600 bps system.

The standard transponder configuration consists of 5 uplinks (4 for users and 1 for commanding) in the 2-m band and one downlink at 70 cm. A block diagram of the transponder FM receiver may be found in Chapter 14 (Figure 14-3). It simultaneously monitors 4 16-kHz wide channels, spaced at intervals of 20 kHz, and a command channel. When a properly formatted AX.25 packet is received it sends a connect acknowledgment. Uplink signals must be Manchester encoded FM (AFSK) using ±3 kHz deviation. To receive signals from the spacecraft the ground station must use a special PSK modem and an SSB receiver. A description of the equipment needed to transmit to, and receive signals from, this transponder is included in Chapter 5. The downlink is BPSK. Uplink and downlink operate at 1200 bps. Transmissions are digital, NRZ-I, BPSK, HDLC and compatible with AX.25 Level Two protocol.

The 437 MHz transmitter section of the transponder

Table MSat-2

Microsat Telemetry

All decoding equations are of the form

Parameter = $An^2 + Bn + C$
where n is the telemetry count.
   Sample coefficients (A, B, C) are given for DOVE. These are early prelaunch values (1/7/90). Updated values and telemetry-decoding software is available on IBM-compatible disks from AMSAT.

Channel hex	dec	Description	C	B	A	Units
		All Microsats except as noted below				
0	0	RX D Disc				kHz
1	1	RX D S meter				counts
2	2	RX C Disc				kHz
3	3	RX C S meter				counts
4	4	RX B Disc				kHz
5	5	RX B S meter				counts
6	6	RX A Disc	+10.472	−0.09274	0.000	kHz
7	7	RX A S meter	+0.000	+1.000	0.000	counts
8	8	RX E/F Disc	+9.6234	−0.09911	0.000	kHz
9	9	RX E/F S meter	+0.000	+1.000	0.000	counts
A	10	+5-V Bus	+0.000	+0.0305	0.000	Volts
B	11	+5-V Rx current	+0.000	+0.000100	0.000	Amps
C	12	+2.5-V Ref	+0.000	+0.0108	0.000	Volts
D	13	+8.5-V Bus	+0.000	+0.0391	0.000	Volts
E	14	IR detector	+0.000	+1.000	0.000	counts
F	15	LO monitor I	+0.000	+0.000037	0.000	Amps
10	16	+10-V bus	+0.000	+0.05075	0.000	Volts
11	17	GASFET Bias I	+0.000	+0.000026	0.000	Amps
12	18	Ground Ref	+0.000	+0.0100	0.000	Volts
13	19	+Z Array V	+0.000	+0.1023	0.000	Volts
14	20	RX Temp	+101.05	−0.6051	0.000	°C
15	21	+X (RX) Temp	+101.05	−0.6051	0.000	°C
16	22	Bat 1 V	+1.7932	−0.0034084	0.000	Volts
17	23	Bat 2 V	+1.7978	−0.0035316	0.000	Volts
18	24	Bat 3 V	+1.8046	−0.0035723	0.000	Volts
19	25	Bat 4 V	+1.7782	−0.0034590	0.000	Volts
1A	26	Bat 5 V	+1.8410	−0.0038355	0.000	Volts
1B	27	Bat 6 V	+1.8381	−0.0038450	0.000	Volts
1C	28	Bat 7 V	+1.8568	−0.0037757	0.000	Volts
1D	29	Bat 8 V	+1.7868	−0.0034068	0.000	Volts
1E	30	Array V	+7.205	+0.07200	0.000	Volts
1F	31	+5-V Bus	+1.932	+0.0312	0.000	Volts
20	32	+8.5-V Bus	+5.265	+0.0173	0.000	Volts

contains two units for redundancy. Only one operates at a time. Each unit can be set to 1 of 16 power levels producing up to 4 W output. One transmitter operates with straight PSK modulation while the other uses raised-cosine modulation, which is compatible but has lower level out-of-band modulation products. (Second harmonic subcarriers from the straight PSK transmitter are only down 14 dB from the main lobe; those from the raised-cosine transmitter are down 38 dB). The 70-cm raised-cosine transmitters use HELAPS techniques producing up to 9 W PEP. At high power settings each transmitter achieves an RF/dc efficiency of about 65% (BPSK) and 56% (raised cosine). Efficiency falls off slowly at lower power settings.

Maximum values for Doppler shift on the various MicroSat links are as follows:

2 m: 3.5 kHz
70 cm: 10.3 kHz
23 cm: 30.1 kHz
13 cm: 56.7 kHz

3.5 Attitude Stabilization and Control

Passive magnetic stabilization is used. Each spacecraft contain four small permanent magnets aligned along the Z axis. With this type of stabilization and the near polar inclination the satellite Z axis will rotate twice per orbit (see Chapter 14). In order to minimize the buildup of thermal gradients the spacecraft is spun slowly about its Z axis using the 2-m antenna as a radiometer (one side of each element is painted black and the other side is painted white). This method was used very successfully on both AMSAT-

Channel hex	dec	Description	C	B	A	Units
21	33	+10-V Bus	+7.469	+0.021765	0.000	Volts
22	34	BCR Set Point	-8.762	+1.1590	0.000	Counts
23	35	BCR Load Cur	-0.0871	+0.00698	0.000	Amps
24	36	+8.5-V Bus Cur	-0.00920	+0.001899	0.000	Amps
25	37	+5-V Bus Cur	+0.00502	+0.00431	0.000	Amps
26	38	-X Array Cur	-0.01075	+0.00215	0.000	Amps
27	39	+X Array Cur	-0.01349	+0.00270	0.000	Amps
28	40	-Y Array Cur	-0.01196	+0.00239	0.000	Amps
29	41	+Y Array Cur	-0.01141	+0.00228	0.000	Amps
2A	42	-Z Array Cur	-0.01653	+0.00245	0.000	Amps
2B	43	+Z Array Cur	-0.01137	+0.00228	0.000	Amps
2C	44	Ext Power Cur	-0.02000	+0.00250	0.000	Amps
2D	45	BCR Input Cur	+0.06122	+0.00317	0.000	Amps
2E	46	BCR Output Cur	-0.01724	+0.00345	0.000	Amps
2F	47	Bat 1 Temp	+101.05	-0.6051	0.000	°C
30	48	Bat 2 Temp	+101.05	-0.6051	0.000	°C
31	49	Baseplate Temp	+101.05	-0.6051	0.000	°C
32	50	PSK TX RF Out				Watts
33	51	RC TX RF Out				Watts
34	52	PSK TX HPA Temp	+101.05	-0.6051	0.000	°C
35	53	+Y Array Temp	+101.05	-0.6051	0.000	°C
36	54	RC PSK HPA Temp	+101.05	-0.6051	0.000	°C
37	55	RC PSK BP Temp	+101.05	-0.6051	0.000	°C
38	56	+Z Array Temp	+101.05	-0.6051	0.000	°C
39	57	S-Band HPA Temp	+101.05	-0.6051	0.000	°C
3A	58	S-Band TX RF Out	-0.0451	+0.00403	0.000	Watts
DOVE						
0	0	E/F Audio (Wide)	+0.000	+0.0246	0.000	V (P-P)
1	1	E/F Audio (Nar)	+0.000	+0.0246	0.000	V (P-P)
2	2	Mixer Bias V	+0.000	+0.0102	0.000	Volts
3	3	Osc Bias V	+0.000	+0.0102	0.000	Volts
4	4	RX A Audio (W)	+0.000	+0.0246	0.000	V (P-P)
5	5	RX A Audio (N)	+0.000	+0.0246	0.000	V (P-P)
32	50	FM TX #1 RF Out	+0.0256	-0.000884	+0.0000836	Watts
33	51	FM TX #2 RF Out	-0.0027	+0.001257	+0.0000730	Watts
Lusat						
39	57	Lu Beacon Temp A				°C
3A	58	Lu Beacon Temp D				°C
3B	59	Coax Relay Status				Counts
3C	60	Coax Relay Status				Counts
Webersat						
39	57	Not available				
3A	58	Not available				

OSCAR 7 and AMSAT-OSCAR 8. The spin rate is expected to be between 0.25 and 1.0 rpm. Hysteresis damping rods are used to limit the spin rate and to minimize oscillations of the Z axis about the local magnetic field.

3.6 Antennas

The following antennas are used on Pacsat, Lusat, Webersat and ITAMSAT. Each spacecraft includes additional antennas described under section for specific satellite.

70-cm antenna: The 70-cm transmit antenna is a canted turnstile consisting of four radiating elements mounted on the –Z surface (bottom) of the spacecraft. The signal is circularly polarized along the Z axis only. Antenna elements are made of flexible, springy, semi-cylindrical metal approximately 1.0 cm in width.

2-m antenna: The 2-m receive antenna is a stub slightly shorter than $1/4$ wavelength mounted on the +Z face of the spacecraft. It is made of the same material used for the 70-cm antenna elements. This antenna produces a linearly polarized signal and a torroidal pattern.

3.7 Energy Supply and Power Conditioning

Solar Cell Characteristics
    type: silicon using back-surface reflective technology
    efficiency: 15%+ at beginning of life (OSCARs 16-19)
    size: 20×20 mm
    total area: 1760 cm^2
    peak output: 15.7 W (optimal orientation)
    minimal output: 6 W (poorest orientation, averaged over orbit with 34% eclipse time)

Solar Cell Configuration: (slight differences in Webersat)
    basic unit: a "clip" of 20 cells arranged in a 4×5 pattern
    total number of modules: 20 clips+4 half clips
    location: –Z face contains 4 half clips. The other five surfaces each contain 4 clips.

Storage Battery

Consists of 8 6-Ah commercial aviation NiCd cells manufactured by GE/Gates and space qualified by AMSAT (see Chapter 14).
    Battery bus voltage at 100% charge: 11.7 V
    Battery bus voltage at 30% charge (maximum safe discharge level): 9.2 V

Power Module

The power module is a slightly oversize tray containing storage battery, battery charging regulator (BCR) and instrument switching regulators (ISRs). It is the only module designed to fit in a specific slot (slot 3). The BCR downconverts the nominal 22 V output of the solar array to the battery bus voltage of about 10 V. Two IRSs supply 8.5 V and 5.0 V. Switching regulators using pulse width modulation provide an efficiency of about 88%. The power module is heavily instrumented with telemetry sensors for measuring voltages, currents, and temperatures. Current sensing technology is based on the highly efficient method developed for Phase 3 which uses toroids biased into saturation by an ac signal (see Chapter 15).

Software continuously monitors power module operation and control transmitter power level so as to optimize use of available power and prolong battery lifetime. This is a new method of power management for AMSAT and it is expected that software will have to be refined over the life of the mission.

3.9 On-Board Computer (OBC)

The OBC is the primary payload on all MicroSats. It controls, and forms an essential component of, the packet transponder, telemetry system, power system and other mission specific modules. The OBC module also contains an 8-bit analog to digital converter with a measurement range of 0-2.55 V and a resolution of 10 mV. This A/D converter monitors the analog bus lines for telemetry sensor data. A watchdog timer guards against problems that could cause the OBC to "lock up."
    CPU: NEC V40 (similar to 80C188)
    ROM: 2 k for restart
    RAM (area #1): 256 k static RAM. Employs error detection and correction (Hamming code with 12-bits per 8-bit byte). Used for operating system and program storage. To reduce power consumption EDAC circuitry does not run continuously in background.
    RAM (area #2): 2 M static RAM. Used for message storage. Divided into four 0.5-M bank switched regions that may be individually powered down.
    RAM (area #3): 8 M static RAM. Organized as serial-interface mass storage that operates like a RAM disk.
    Operating System: Quadron multi-tasking (appears similar to MS-DOS to each application). (Donated by Quadron, Inc.) This allows ground stations to develop software on standard IBM type PCs.
    Languages (on-board applications): assembler and Microsoft C linked with Microsoft LINK.
    Power requirements: 1.5 W peak, 0.5 W average (expected)

SPACECRAFT NAME: Pacsat-OSCAR 16

MISSION OBJECTIVE

To provide the worldwide community of radio amateurs with a satellite based digital store-and-forward message system.

1.1 Identification

International designation: 90-005D
NASA Catalog number: 20439
Prelaunch designation: Pacsat, MicroSat-A

1.2 Launch

Date: Feb 22, 1990
Time: 01:35:31 UTC
Vehicle: Ariane (version: 40, family: 4, mission: V35)
Agency: ESA
Site: Kourou, French Guiana

1.3 Orbital Parameters (Jan 1997)

General Designation: low-altitude, circular, sun
  synchronous, near polar
Period: 100.7 minutes
Apogee altitude: 807 km
Perigee altitude: 791 km
Eccentricity: 0.0011
Inclination: 98.5°
Maximum access distance: 3050 km

1.5 Operations

Coordinating Group: AMSAT-NA

1.6 Design/Construction Credits

Project manager: J. King, W3GEY
Accomplishing a task of this magnitude requires major efforts by a large number of people, many of whom are credited in the references. Space doesn't permit repeating the list here but it would be remiss not to mention the immense contributions of Tom Clark, Dick Jansson, Lyle Johnson and Bob McGwier.

SPACECRAFT DESCRIPTION

2.2 Subsystem description: See Table MSat-1

SUBSYSTEM DESCRIPTION

3.4 Transponder

uplink frequencies:
  145.900 MHz
  145.920 MHz
  145.940 MHz
  145.960 MHz

downlink frequencies:
  437.051 MHz (primary, raised cosine)
  437.026 MHz (secondary, BPSK)
  2401.143 MHz (secondary, BPSK, 1 W)
Connect address: Pacsat-1

3.5 Attitude Stabilization and Control

OSCAR 16 contains the standard MicroSat stabilization system. In addition is has an infrared sensor mounted on the +Z facet of the spacecraft which is connected to the module containing the 2-m receiver. This sensor can provide information relating to spacecraft attitude. Its field of view is about 8° and its sensitivity is adjustable in 16 steps. Whole orbit data collected from this sensor will be used to study spacecraft dynamics of the MicroSat structure.

3.6 Antennas

The 13 cm transmit antenna is a bifilar helix (volute).

3.10 TSFR Module

The TSFR module on OSCAR 16 contains a 13-cm transmitter based on the 70-cm pacsat design with a chain of 4 multipliers added to the local oscillator strip. The final

amplifier is an Avantek AV-8140. Check current periodicals for an operating schedule.
  downlink frequency: 2401.143 MHz BPSK
  power: 1 W
  RF/dc efficiency: 32%

SPACECRAFT NAME: Lusat-OSCAR 19

MISSION OBJECTIVE

To provide the worldwide community of radio amateurs with a satellite based digital store-and-forward message system.

1.1 Identification

International designation: 90-005G
NASA Catalog number: 20442
Prelaunch designation: MicroSat-D

1.2 Launch

Date: Feb 22, 1990
Time: 01:35:31 UTC
Vehicle: Ariane (version: 40, family: 4, mission: V35)
Agency: ESA
Site: Kourou, French Guiana

1.3 Orbital Parameters (Jan 1997)

General Designation: low-altitude, circular, sun-
  synchronous, near polar
Period: 100.7 minutes
Apogee altitude: 807 km
Perigee altitude: 790
Eccentricity: 0.0012
Inclination: 98.6°
Maximum access distance: 3050 km

1.5 Operations

Coordinating Group: AMSAT-LU (Argentina) under direction of Arturo Caru, LU1AHC, and Carlos Huertas, LU4ENQ

1.6 Design/Construction Credits

Project manager: J. King, W3GEY
Accomplishing a task of this magnitude requires major efforts by a large number of people, many of whom are credited in the references. Space doesn't permit repeating the list here but it would be remiss not to mention the immense contributions of Tom Clark, Dick Jansson, Lyle Johnson and Bob McGwier.

SPACECRAFT DESCRIPTION

2.2 Subsystem description: See Table MSat-1

SUBSYSTEM DESCRIPTION

3.4 Transponder

Uplink frequencies:

145.840 MHz
145.860 MHz
145.880 MHz
145.900 MHz
Downlink frequencies:
    437.153 MHz (primary, BPSK)
    437.125 MHz (secondary, raised cosine)
connect address: Lusat-1

3.5 Attitude Stabilization and Control

An infrared sensor mounted on the +Z facet of the spacecraft is connected to the module containing the 2-m receiver. This sensor can provide information relating to spacecraft attitude. Its field of view is about 8° and its sensitivity is adjustable in 16 steps.

The four permanent bar magnets mounted parallel to the Z axis have their poles oriented opposite to the direction used on OSCARs 16-18. This orientation should slightly favor Southern Hemisphere users.

3.10 70-cm CW beacon

The experimental module on OSCAR 17 contains a 70-cm CW data beacon built by AMSAT-LU. This transmitter is controlled by a dedicated microprocessor and it's designed to provide telemetry and bulletins to stations who do not have packet radio capabilities. Morse telemetry is sent in an abbreviated format where multiple dashes in numeric data are sent as a single dash (•- = 1, ••- = 2, -• = 6, etc.).

Frequency: 437.127 MHz
Power: 750 mW

SPACECRAFT NAME: ITAMSAT-OSCAR 26

MISSION OBJECTIVE

To provide the worldwide community of radio amateurs with a satellite based digital store-and-forward message system.

1.1 Identification

International designation: 93 061F
NASA Catalog number: 22826
Call sign: ITMSAT

1.2 Launch

Date: Sept 26, 1993
Vehicle: Ariane 4
Agency: ESA
Site: Kourou, French Guiana

1.3 Orbital Parameters (Jan 1997)

General Designation: low-altitude, circular, sun
    synchronous, near polar

Period: 100.8 minutes
Apogee altitude: 813 km
Perigee altitude: 799 km
Eccentricity: 0.0010
Inclination: 98.6°
Maximum access distance: 3061 km

1.5 Operations

Coordinating Group: AMSAT-Italy

1.6 Design/Construction Credits

Project manager: Alberto Zagni, I2KBD and Luca Bertagnolio, IK2OVV with the assistance of AMSAT-NA.

SPACECRAFT DESCRIPTION

2.2 Subsystem description: See Table MSat-1

SUBSYSTEM DESCRIPTION

3.4 Transponder

  Uplink frequencies:
    145.875 MHz
    145.900 MHz
    145.925 MHz
    145.950 MHz

  Downlink frequencies:
    437.822 MHz (primary, raised cosine)
    435.867 MHz (secondary, BPSK)

SPACECRAFT NAME: AMRAD-OSCAR 27

MISSION OBJECTIVE

AO-27 is an experiment aboard the commercial satellite EYESAT-1 built by Interferometrics Inc. The spacecraft contains a single channel FM repeater with a very sensitive receiver.

1.1 Identification

International designation: 93 061 G
NASA Catalog number: 22829

1.2 Launch

Date: Sept 26, 1993
Vehicle: Ariane 4
Agency: ESA
Site: Kourou, French Guiana

1.3 Orbital Parameters (Jan 1997)

General Designation: low-altitude, circular, sun-
    synchronous, near polar
Period: 100.9 minutes
Apogee altitude: 813 km
Perigee altitude: 800 km
Eccentricity: 0.0009

Inclination: 98.6°
Maximum access distance: 3060 km

1.5 Operations

Coordinating Group: AMRAD

1.6 Design/Construction Credits

The amateur equipment aboard AO-27 was built by AMRAD, a technically-oriented organization of radio amateurs located near Washington, DC.

1.7 Primary References

1. Official AO-27 Web site: **www.ao27.org**
2. AO-27 TEPR States Explained: **www.ao27.org/ao27/tepr.html**
3. FAQ page by W2RS: **www.amsat.org/amsat/intro/ao27/ao27faq.html**

SPACECRAFT DESCRIPTION

2.2 Subsystem description: See Table MSat-1

SUBSYSTEM DESCRIPTION

3.4 Transponder

Single channel crossband FM repeater
Uplink: 145.850 MHz
Downlink: 436.800 MHz (target)
436.797 MHz (measured)

The repeater has a very sensitive receiver. When the channel is free it's possible to put a signal through with a couple of watts to an H-T. Due to power budget constraints the spacecraft cannot operate continuously. The operating schedule is controlled by an onboard timer that turns on for a prescribed time interval (generally about 20 minutes) after the spacecraft enters daylight.

The AO-27 operating schedule is designed to prolong battery life. The method employed, called Timed Eclipse Power Regulation (TEPR), directs the spacecraft to use the times when it enters sunlight and eclipse as reference points for turning the transponder on and off. The result is that the transponder is generally turned on for a fixed time interval (TEPR 5) shortly after the spacecraft enters sunlight. In early 2003 AO-27 entered a period of continuous sunlight and TEPR scheduling was not modified. Full details are contained in reference 1 and 2 of section 1.7.

UNIVERSITY AND INDEPENDENT

SPACECRAFT NAME: Gurwin-OSCAR 32

1.1 Identification

International designation: 1998-043D

NASA Catalog number: 25,397
Also known as: GO-32, Techsat-1B, Gurwin-II (Techsat-II is a **different** spacecraft)

1.2 Launch

Date: July 10, 1998 (launched with TMSAT-OSCAR 31)
Time: 0630 UTC
Vehicle: Ukrainian Zenit Rocket
Agency: RKA (Russian Space Agency)
Site: Baikonur Cosmodrome, Kazakhstan

1.3 Orbital Parameters

General designation: low-altitude, circular, sun synchronous, near polar
Period: 101.3 minutes
Apogee altitude: 826 km
Perigee altitude: 823 km
Eccentricity: 0.00016 (nominally circular)
Inclination: 98.8 degrees
Maximum access distance: 3,082 km

1.5 Operations

Gurwin-OSCAR 32 operations are directed by the Israel Institute of Technology (Technion) in response to the requirements of the scientific/engineering groups involved. Since this is the Technions first successful satellite, testing and commissioning will take an extended period of time. Reports on the Techsat WEB site indicate that this spacecraft is being used extensively and that most systems are functioning. Communications from the operations staff indicate that attention will be directed to placing the amateur payloads in service as soon as the primary investigators obtain preliminary results.

1.6 Design/Construction Credits

The Gurwin-OSCAR 32 spacecraft was designed and constructed at the Technion (Israel Institute of Technology) under the direction of the Asher Space Research Institute in cooperation with several industrial partners. It is part of an ongoing program of satellite construction which included Techsat 1A, lost 28 March 1995 when the launch vehicle failed to attain orbit.

1.7 Primary References

1) **www.iarc.org/techsat/techsat.html**
2) **www.technion.ac.il/ASRI/techsat/index.htm**

SPACECRAFT DESCRIPTION

2.1 Physical Structure

Shape: GO-32 is a rectangular solid. See Figure GO32-1.
Mass: 48 kg.

Note: The spacecraft is 3-axis stabilized. Solar cells are mounted on four faces. The earth facing panel is used for antennas, camera, retro reflector and an UV spectra radiometer. The remaining face includes an attach fitting.
Dimensions: approximately 40 cm×40 cm×40 cm.

SUBSYSTEM DESCRIPTION

3.1 Beacon

Frequency: 435.225 MHz (primary), 435.325 MHz
Power (two transmitters for redundancy)
   Transmitter 1: 1.0 W
   Transmitter 2: 3.0 W (optional)
Modulation (See transponder comments)
   9,600 bit/s FM
   1,200 bit/s FM or BPSK

3.4 Transponder

This spacecraft contains a single digital store-and-forward transponder that is also employed for downlinking telemetry. Downlink frequencies listed have been in service. Uplink frequencies listed are preflight specifications. They have not yet (2/2000) been observed in operation.
   VHF Uplink:145.850, 145.890, 145.930 MHz
   L-band uplink: 1269.700, 1269.800, 1269.900 MHz
Modulation
   Primary: 9,600 bit/s standard UoSAT AX.25 protocol
   Emergency: 1,200 bit/s FM
   Optional: 1,200 bit/s BPSK (downlink only)
Downlink: On beacon frequencies

3.5 Attitude Control and Stabilization

One of the primary goals of the GO-32 mission was to develop, test and refine the platforms attitude control system. The operators have already demonstrated Techsats ability to provide 3-axis stabilization to an accuracy of better than 3 degrees. This is accomplished with a relatively simple, robust active system that does not require a gravity gradient boom.
Sensors
   Static Horizon Sensor
   32 Detectors: 4 units at 90 degrees each with 8 detectors
   Accuracy: 0.1 degree, 0.05 degree (goal using signal processing)
Magnetometer
   Primarily used for backup but can produce a pointing accuracy of better than 10 degrees as a standalone system.
Actuators
   Momentum Wheel
   Magnetorquer

3.6 Antennas

VHF: monopole (linear polarization)
L-band: monopole (linear polarization)
UHF: canted turnstile (circular polarization along main axis, sense not specified)
   Note: The monopole antennas are likely to have nulls in certain directions. However, because this is a 3-axis stabilized spacecraft, the conditions under which nulls occur should be predictable.

3.7 Energy Supply and Power Conditioning

Battery: NiCd
Bus: 12 V
Solar Panels: 4

Power Budget: Telemetric data from the early days of the mission show that total solar panel output consistently averaged more than 20 W per orbit. Satellite housekeeping requirements (including downlink beacon) are less than 10 W.

3.9 On-Board Computers

Dual (redundant) 80C186EC and 12 MB CMOS RAM

3.10 Experimental Systems

The Techsat 3-axis stabilization system, modular platform, and ten watt payload power budget allow the spacecraft to handle a diverse complement of experiments in addition to those directly related to platform design and operation. GO-32 carries the following payloads:

1. UV spectra radiometer designed for measuring atmospheric ozone concentration. The radiometer uses a photometer which measures solar back scattered ultra-violet radiance.

2. Panchromatic CCD camera for earth imaging. The footprint of this camera covers 25 km×30 km with a resolution of approximately 55 m.

3. Spectrometer for detection of X-Ray and gamma emissions

4. Proton and Heavy Particle Detector.

5. Technology Experiment involving high temperature superconductivity and cryocooler design. The cryocooler has reached 80 K in orbit

6. Passive Laser Retro reflector.

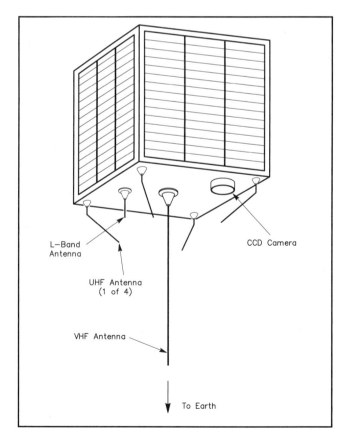

Figure GO32-1—Gurwin-OSCAR 32 spacecraft

SPACECRAFT NAME: SEDSAT-OSCAR 33

This spacecraft is currently in orbit but the operations group has not been able to activate the communications payloads. Prospects for recovery do not appear good. However, since useful telemetry describing the operation of the onboard systems is being aperiodically received from this spacecraft an abbreviated profile follows.

1.1 Identification

International designation: 1998-061B
NASA Catalog number: 25,509
Also known as: SO-33, SEDSAT-1

1.2 Launch

Date: 24 Oct 1998
Time: 12:08 UTC
Vehicle: Delta II
Agency: NASA
Site: Vandenberg AFB, CA, US

1.3 Orbital Parameters

General designation: low-altitude
Period: 101.1 minutes
Apogee altitude: 1,085 km
Perigee altitude: 554 km
Eccentricity: 0.03690
Inclination: 31.4 degrees
Maximum access distance: 3,480 km

1.6 Design/Construction Credits

SEDSAT (**S**tudents for the **E**xploration and **D**evelopment of space **Sat**ellite) is essentially an educational project developed at the University of Alabama in Huntsville. The spacecraft design had to undergo major revisions on several occasions as prospective launches were offered and canceled.

1.7 Primary References

1. **www.seds.org/pub/seds/sedsat/updates**
2. R. A. Hillman and M. W. Maier, "Design of a Space Image Processing System," Proceedings of the 15th AMSAT-NA Space Symposium, 1997, Toronto.

SUBSYSTEM DESCRIPTION

3.1 Beacon

Frequency: 437.914 MHz
Modulation: 9,600 bit/s FSK
Power: 3 W (average)

3.4 Transponders

Transponder I
    Type: Linear
    uplink: 145.915 - 145.975 MHz
    downlink: 29.350 to 29.420 MHz
Transponder II
    Type: Digital, FM

Uplink: data available is inconsistent (± 10 kHz deviation required)
    1,266.684 - 1,266.690 MHz or
    1,268.110 - 1,268.250 MHz
Downlink: 437.914 MHz (observed center)

SPACECRAFT NAME: PANSAT-OSCAR 34

This spacecraft is believed to be operational but it is not being used at the present time. Ground stations need special equipment to use the primary mission subsystem, the spread spectrum transponder. This equipment is described in the PANSAT web site. Experimenters (especially educational institutions) willing to commit the resources required to work with this spacecraft should contact the construction group (see web site).

1.1 Identification

International designation: 1998-064B
NASA Catalog number: 25,520
Also known as: PO-34

1.2 Launch

Date: 30 Oct 1998 (date deployed from Shuttle)
Time: 12:08 UTC
Vehicle: Released from Shuttle Discovery on second day of STS-95 mission
Agency: NASA

1.3 Orbital Parameters

General designation: low-altitude, circular
Period: 95.8 minutes
Apogee altitude: 570 km
Perigee altitude: 559 km
Estimated Lifetime in Orbit: > 10 years
Eccentricity: 0.00079 (nominally circular)
Inclination: 28.5 degrees
Maximum access distance: 2,600 km

1.6 Design/Construction Credits

PANSAT (**P**etite **A**mateur **N**avy **Sat**ellite) is a small satellite designed and built by students, faculty, and staff at the US Naval Postgraduate School, Monterey, CA. The spacecraft is primarily an educational project. The primary radio amateur payload is a digital spread-spectrum transponder optimized for store-and-forward communications.

1.7 Primary References

1. **www.sp.nps.navy.mil/pansat/**
2. S. Bible (N7HPR), D. Sakoda (KD6DRA) "PANSAT — The Petite Amateur Navy Satellite," *The AMSAT Journal*, July/August 1999, pp 1, 4-6.

SUBSYSTEM DESCRIPTION

3.4 Transponder

PANSAT carries an experimental transponder using

direct-sequence spread-spectrum modulation. The center frequency is 436.5 MHz and operation is half-duplex. The bit rate is 9842 bits/s and the spacecraft has 9MB of message area.

SPACECRAFT NAME: SUNSAT-OSCAR 35

Sunsat-OSCAR 35 ceased operating in January 2001. The construction group is working on a new spacecraft. This section will be retained until details on the new satellite become available.

GENERAL

1.1 Identification

International designation: 1999-008C
NASA Catalog number: 25,636
Also known as: SO-35, Kleinsat, SUNSAT 1

1.2 Launch

Date: 23 Feb 1999
Time: 09:29 UTC
Vehicle: Delta II
Agency: NASA
Site: Vandenberg Air Force Base, CA, US

1.3 Orbital Parameters

General designation: low-altitude, near polar
Period: 99.9 minutes
Apogee altitude: 871 km
Perigee altitude: 654 km
Eccentricity: 0.01525
Inclination: 96.5 degrees
Maximum access distance: 3,158 km

1.5 Operations

SUNSAT operations are directed by the University of Stellenbosch, South Africa. Educational activities are central to the SUNSAT project and Amateur Radio was viewed as an important component when these activities were first planned. As a result, amateur operations are likely to be a primary activity on UO-35.

Due to the wide variety of payloads carried and a varying power budget the SUNSAT operating plans can be expected to change frequently. SA-AMSAT has been making the operating schedule available in advance via the SUNSAT Web site and the usual HF and Internet channels. These include the AMSAT-BB and AMSAT News Service (free subscriptions to AMSAT-BB and ANS can be obtained at **http://www.amsat.org**).

1.6 Design/Construction Credits

SUNSAT (**S**tellenbosch **Un**iversity **Sat**ellite) was designed and constructed by students, faculty, and staff at the University of Stellenbosch in South Africa. Funding was provided by Stellenbosch University, by grants from the government and South African industries, and by contributions from radio amateurs around the world. AMSAT South Africa has been represented on the Advisory Board for the SUNSAT project since its inception in 1989 and involved in the entire design process. As a result, amateur radio payloads play an important role in the mission. Faculty members involved in SUNSAT design have studied at the University of Surrey and are sensitive to compatibility issues, so many functional similarities to UoSAT spacecraft can be seen.

1.7 Primary References

1) H. Van De Groenendaal (ZS5AKV), "SUNSAT: South Africa's First Satellite," *AMSAT Journal*, Sep/Oct 1998, pp 1, 4-7.
2) **sunsat.ee.sun.ac.za** (SUNSAT main page)
3) **sunsat.ee.sun.ac.za/pub1.htm** [For clarification: "pub1" ends in "one"]
This page contains a list of SUNSAT technical publications which are available on the Internet. See especially:
a) A. Schoonwinkel, G. W. Milne, S. Mostert, W. H. Steyn and K. van der Westhuizen, "Pre-Flight Performance of SUNSAT, South Africa's First Remote Sensing and Packet Communications Microsatellite."
b) S. Mostert, A. Schoonwinkel and G.W. Milne, "Pre-flight Performance of the Communication Payloads on SUNSAT, South Africa's First Microsatellite."

SPACECRAFT DESCRIPTION

2.1 Physical Structure

Shape: Rectangular Solid with solar panels on the four sides. See Figure SO35-1.
Dimensions: 45×45×62 cm
Mass: 60 kg
Note: The top and bottom are used for antennas, launcher attachment ring, camera, attitude sensors, gravity gradient boom mount, etc..

SUBSYSTEM DESCRIPTION

3.1 Beacons

Frequencies
Crystal controlled (as follows) but a redundant synthesized system with 12.5 kHz steps is available to operate on nearby frequencies.
145.825 MHz
436.300 MHz
436.250 MHz (The was the primary telemetry frequency early in mission)
13 cm: frequency not specified. (This transmitter appears to have failed early into the mission).
Modulation:
1,200 baud AFSK-FM compatible with terrestrial packet systems
1,200 baud Bell 202 format used for initial telemetry
9,600 baud UoSAT compatible.
voice synthesized
1 MB/s (13 cm only)

3.4 Transponders

SUNSAT contains several transmitters and receivers that

can be configured to operate as digital or FM voice transponders in response to ground command. This provides great operational flexibility. Primary frequency control is via crystal but a redundant synthesized mode with 12.5 kHz steps exists.

Transmitters
    2-m (2 units) Frequencies: 145.825 MHz (1 W or 4 W)
    70 cm (2 units) Frequencies: 436.250 MHz, 436.300 MHz (1.5 W or 10 W)
    13 cm Frequency not specified (5 W). Failed early in mission.

Receivers
    2-m (2 units) Frequencies: 145.825, 145.850, 145.900, 145.950 MHz
    70-cm (2 units) Frequencies: 436.291, 436.250 MHz
    24 cm Frequency not specified

Modulation: See Beacons

Some typical transponder configurations follow but other arrangements are possible

Mode B configuration for FM voice operation
        uplink: 436.291 MHz (18 kHz bandwidth)
        downlink: 145.825 MHz

Mode J configuration for command/control, telemetry, store and forward messaging
        uplink: 145.825 MHz, 145.850, 145.900, 145.950 MHz
        downlink: 436.250, 436.300 MHz

Parrot repeater for FM voice operation
        This mode employs time sharing of the links.
        Typical operation consists of a tone burst on down link indicating the start of a ten second recording period. This is followed by a double tone burst and a ten second replay. The cycle is then repeated.
        up/down links: 145.825 MHz

3.5 Attitude Control and Stabilization

The SO-35 attitude determination/control system is designed to point the onboard imager to within one kilometer on the surface of the earth from an altitude of 850 km. It consists of:

Sensors	*approximate accuracy*
Solar cells mounted on each facet	5 degree
CCD star camera	0.05 degree
3-axis magnetometer	1.0 degree
sun sensor	1.0 degree
horizon sensors	1.0 degree

SUNSAT has provided a similar magnetometer to be flown on the German SAFIR-2 satellite. The horizon sensors, which consist of two orthogonal linear CCD devices and lens assemblies, use visible wavelengths.

Actuators

Gravity gradient boom (coarse pointing control). Deployed 27 Feb 1999

Magnetorqueing (pointing to within 1 degree). Used to damp slow oscillations and to dump momentum from reaction wheels.

Servo-motor reaction wheels (fine pointing control). Four units carried on spacecraft.

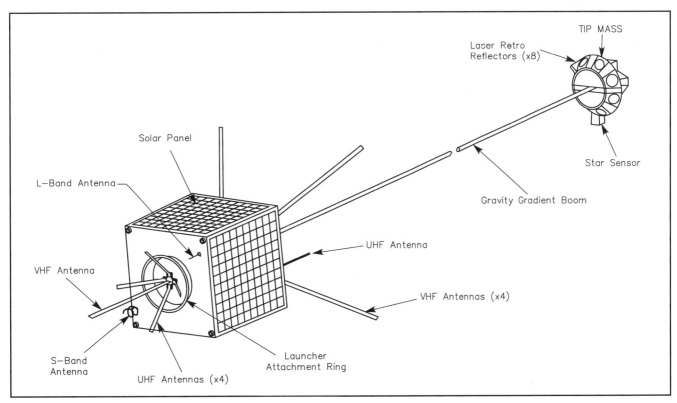

Figure SO35-1—External structure of SUNSAT-OSCAR 35

3.6 Antennas

See Figure UO35-1 for placement
  2-m: monopole
  2-m: canted turnstile
  70 cm: monopole
  70 cm: canted turnstile; circular polarization specified
    as RHCP
  23 cm: monopole
  13 cm: monopole

3.7 Energy Supply and Power Conditioning

Solar panels employing GaAs cells mounted on a carbon fiber substrate are positioned on the four sides of the spacecraft. The battery uses a 14 V bus.

3.9 On-Board Computers and Bus System

The spacecraft contains two control processors, an 80C188EC and a 386-SL. A T800 transputer is dedicated to fine attitude control. The 386-SL can also be used to manage attitude control. The spacecraft also has three 80C31 embedded microcontrollers. 64 MB of RAM disk storage is available for image and message files.

3.10 Experimental Systems

1) High Resolution Imager
   Detector: Silicon CCD
   Spectral Region: operates in visual and near IR. Three
     color system (bands similar to SPOT 4)
   Ground Resolution: 15 m
   Ground Coverage: 50×50 km
   Note: SUNSAT has provided a similar imager for
     KITSAT-3
2) Precision Attitude Control (See 3.5)
3) Experiment to monitor the effect of radiation on small
   electronic components. Developed at Rhenish Girls High
   School, Stellenbosch, South Africa.
4) Microphone experiment to monitor sounds (vibrations)
   generated on spacecraft (including reaction wheels). Developed at George Campbell Technical High School,
   Durban, South Africa.
5) Laser retro-reflectors for NASA

SPACECRAFT NAME:
JAWSAT Multi-Payload Adaptor including Artemis (3), ASUSAT-1, FALCONSAT, OPAL, STENSAT, WEBER-2, Etc

The JAWSAT Multi-Payload Adaptor (MPA) spacecraft included a number of named subsystems permanently attached to the space frame and several independent satellites which were deployed from the MPA. One of the deployed spacecraft, OPAL, carried a group of very small independent satellites, called picosats, which were later released to orbit on their own.

In the following outline of the JAWSAT mission communications capabilities are shown thus:

[****] single channel FM voice repeater & digital transponder capabilities
[***] digital transponder,
  [**] no transponder but digital telemetry on amateur frequencies,
  [*] digital telemetry compatible with amateur systems but operating on commercial frequencies

JAWSAT MPA (Multi-Payload Adaptor)
  Attached Subsystems
    PEST (Plasma Experiment Satellite Test)
    ACP (Attitude Controlled Platform)
    Weber-2 (Communications System) [****]
    Deployment Imaging (Six digital cameras)
  Deployed Satellites
    ASUSat-1 [****]
    FalconSat [*]
    OCS (Optical Calibration Sphere)
    OPAL (Orbiting Picosat Automatic Launcher) [***]
      StenSat [****]
      DARPA/Aerospace (Two tethered spacecraft)
      Artemis JAK [**]
      Artemis Thelma [**]
      Artemis Louise [**]

Status Update

ASUSAT-1 failed after approximately one day in orbit due to discharge of the primary battery. The problem is attributed to a fault between the solar panels and the battery. Once the battery pack was depleted the spacecraft ceased operating. JAWSAT and OPAL are marginally operable. Control stations are having a difficult time commanding these spacecraft. Prognosis is indeterminate.

All picosats were successfully deployed from OPAL. However, there have not been any confirmed reception reports attributable to either StenSat or the Artemis trio. This may be a result of the fact that the spacecraft received an unexpectedly rough ride into space or that they were exposed to extreme temperatures during the two weeks they remained aboard OPAL.

1.1 Identification

Artemis JAK
  International designation: 2000-004 J or K ?
  NASA Catalog number: 26,091 or 26,092 ?

Artemis Thelma & Louise
  International designation: 2000-004L/M
  NASA Catalog number: 26,093; 26,094
  Also known as: Thunder & Lightning

ASUSat-1
  International designation: 2000-004E
  NASA Catalog number: 26,065
  Also known as: ASUSat-OSCAR

FalconSat
  International designation: 2000-004D

NASA Catalog number: 26,064

JAWSAT
    International designation: 2000-004A
    NASA Catalog number: 26,061
    Also known as: JAWSAT MPA, Weber 2

OPAL
    International designation: 2000-004C
    NASA Catalog number: 26,063

StenSat
    International designation: 2000-004 J or K ?
    NASA Catalog number: 26,091 or 26,092 ?
    Also known as: StenSat-OSCAR

Weber-2 (Part of JAWSAT)

1.2 Launch

Date: 27 January 2000
Time: 03:03 UTC
Vehicle: Orbital Sciences Minotaur rocket (modified Minuteman II ICBM with Pegasus XL upper stage)
Agency: US Air Force
Site: Commercial Spaceport Complex at Vandenberg Air Force Base, California

1.3 Orbital Parameters

General designation: Low altitude, nominally circular, near polar
Period: 100.4 minutes
Apogee altitude: 814 km
Perigee altitude: 758 km
Eccentricity: 0.0039
Inclination: 100.2 degrees
Maximum access distance: 3,061 km

1.6 & 1.7 Design/Construction Credits, References

ACP (Attitude Controlled Platform)

The ACP is a low cost, lightweight, 3-axis stabilization experiment sponsored by the Center for Aerospace Technology (CAST) at Weber State University, Ogden, Utah. It consists of reaction wheel canisters and a magnetometer. The ACP was used to orient JAWSAT during the deployment of its payloads. See **cast.weber.edu/jawsat/jawsat.html** for additional information.

Artemis

The Artemis project operates out of the **S**anta **C**lara **R**emote **E**xtreme **E**nvironment **M**echanism (SCREEM) laboratory at Santa Clara University in California. Engineering students in the SCREEM program produced three of the picosats released by OPAL: Artemis JAK, Artemis Thelma and Artemis Louise. Thelma and Louise carry instruments to measure the EM energy generated in the VLF band by lightning storms. They occupy two of OPALs 8-inch trays. JAK, a beacon experiment, shares an 8-inch tray with StenSat. The Artemis spacecraft use radio amateur

frequencies and radio amateur digital protocols to downlink data. It's believed that all three use batteries as a primary power source. As a result, their operation will be limited to less than one month in space. The communications systems on the Artemis satellites are discussed in section 3. For information on the design of these picosats, each weighing less than 1 kg, see: **screem.engr.scu.edu/artemis/**

ASUSat-1

The ASUSat-1 program began in 1993 at Arizona State University as part of a NASA Space Grant educational project. Students have played a central role in the design and fabrication of this sophistical 6 kg spacecraft. The satellite contains several communications payloads of interest to radio amateurs and the project mission statement assigns radio amateur activities a primary function.

During early orbits telemetry from ASUSat-1 indicated that the spacecrafts internal batteries were not being recharged by the solar panels. After approximately one day in orbit, when the batteries were depleted, the spacecraft ceased to function. Hopes for recovery are slim.

For information on the ASUSat-1 project see: S. Ferring, J. Rademacher, H. Reed, J. Puig-Suari, "ASUSAT 1: A Low-Cost AMSAT Nanosatellite," *1996 AMSAT-NA Conference Proceedings*, pp 58-65; "JAWSAT, ASUSat1, OPAL, and StenSat Ready for Launch, *AMSAT Journal*, pp 1, 4-10, Sep/Oct 1999; **nasa.asu.edu/asusat/**

DARPA/Aerospace

This project involves two tethered picosats released from OPAL. The spacecraft do not use radio amateur frequencies or protocols. However, they use communications links employing digital cordless telephone technology that may be of interest to radio amateurs. The spacecraft are powered by lithium thionyl chloride batteries. For information see **www.aero.org/news/current/picosat.html**

FalconSat

FalconSat-1, the primary payload on the JAWSAT MPA, was sponsored by US Air Force Academy in Colorado Springs, CO. Although it does not carry any amateur radio payloads FalconSat-1 employs digital communications links (primary downlink is 400.475 MHz, secondary at 400.680 MHz) that use 9,600 bit/s and are compatible with amateur protocols.

At present the downlink has been tested and is operating but it is only commanded on when the spacecraft is in view of Colorado Springs. The group's web site, formerly located at **www.usafa.af.mil/dfas/falcon.html**, is no longer accessible but a new site has been promised.

JAWSAT

JAWSAT is the name generally used to describe the Joint Air Force Academy Weber State University Satellite/ Spaceframe. The spacecraft is also known as the JAWSAT **M**ulti-**P**ayload **A**dapter or JAWSAT MPA. The JAWSAT MPA was developed by the Center for Aerospace Technology (CAST) at Weber State University and One Stop Satellite Solutions of Ogden, Utah (**www.osss.com/**).

JAWSAT carries four subsystems: ACP, PEST, Imaging and Communications System (Weber-2). ACP and PEST are discussed elsewhere in this section. The imaging system consists of six digital cameras for observing deployment of the payloads released by JAWSAT. The Communications component is the system of greatest interest to radio amateurs. During the early stages of the mission it will be used for down linking telemetry which will include information on operation of the MPA, ACP, PEST, and imaging system files. Later in the mission it will be devoted to amateur activities. Details of the communication system are in Section 3.

For additional information on JAWSAT see: "JAWSAT, ASUSat1, OPAL, and StenSat Ready for Launch," *AMSAT Journal*, pp 1, 4-10, Sep/Oct 1999;
> **cast.weber.edu/jawsat/**

OCS

The Optical Calibration Sphere is a 3.5 m diameter kapton/aluminum balloon deployed from JAWSAT. Under optimal conditions it may be visible to the naked eye. The sphere was built by L'Garde, Inc. for the Air Force Research Laboratory. This experiment does not carry any radio links. Additional information on the OCS is available at the L'Garde web site **www.lgarde.com/programs/ocse.html**

OPAL

OPAL, the **O**rbiting **P**icosat **A**utomatic **L**auncher, was designed and constructed at the Space Sciences Development Laboratory at Stanford University. It is Stanford University's second **S**atellite **QUI**ck **R**esearch **T**estbed (SQUIRT) spacecraft. The SQUIRT project is designed to enable students, engineers and scientists to place experiments in orbit quickly and inexpensively. OPAL has four launch trays each capable of holding two small (1"×3"×4") picosats or a single large (1"×3"×8") picosat. On this flight OPALs primary mission was to launch six picosats — StenSat, three Artemis spacecraft, and the DARPA/Aerospace pair. Its secondary mission involved testing accelerometer and magnetometer components. OPALs picosat payloads are discussed elsewhere in this section.

The 24 kg OPAL mothership employs a telemetry system and a transponder both operating on amateur frequencies. Transponder details are contained in Section 3.

For additional information see: R. Twiggs (KE6QMD), J. Cutler, G. Hutchinson, J. Williams, "OPAL: A First Generation Microsatellite That Provides Picosat Communications for the Amateur Radio Community," *AMSAT-NA Conference Proceedings*, Oct 1999, pp 40-47; "JAWSAT, ASUSat1, OPAL, and StenSat Ready for Launch," *AMSAT Journal*, pp 1, 4-10, Sep/Oct 1999; **ssdl.stanford.edu/opal/**

PEST (Plasma Experiment Satellite Test)

The PEST project is designed to validate a new method of studying electrified gases in space. It's sponsored by Space Sciences Laboratory at NASA's Marshall Space Flight Center. Telemetry from PEST will be available on the JAWSAT downlink. For information on PEST see **www.ssl.msfc.nasa.gov/newhome/headlines/ast22mar99_1.htm**

StenSat

StenSat is a small (1"×3"×4") picosatellite deployed from OPAL. Its primary mission is to provide satellite communications (single channel FM voice) to the Radio Amateur community. StenSat was designed and built by a small group of radio amateurs and electronics/computer enthusiasts residing in the Washington, DC area. The entire project took place over the course of about 5 months and cost about $2,000 in out-of-pocket expenses. The key team members were Hank Heidt (N4AFL), Kevin Doherty, Carl Wick (N3MIM), Jim McGuire, David Niemi, Dan Schultz (N8FGV), Chris Rogers and Steve Lim. The StenSat transponder is discussed in Section 3.

For additional information see: H. Heidt (N4AFL) & K. Doherty, "StenSat Journal: Our Experience Building a Picosatellite," *AMSAT Journal*, pp 14-16, Nov/Dec 1999; **www.stensat.org**

Weber-2

The communications package affixed to the JAWSAT MPA is sometimes referred to as Weber-2. It provides communications for the ACP, PEST, the Imaging experiment and other JAWSAT subsystems on amateur frequencies. Once the MPA is checked out it's expected that the communications systems will be opened for use by radio amateurs on a regular basis. For transponder information see the JAWSAT entry in Section 3.

SUBSYSTEM DESCRIPTIONS

3.1/3.4 Beacons/Transponders:

JAWSAT MPA (Weber-2)
    Transponder I (digital mode or FM voice mode))
        Operating modes: digital (9,600 bit/s FSK, UoSAT compatible);
        FM voice; linear
        uplink: 145.860 MHz
        downlink: 437.070 (1.6 W), 437.175 MHz (0 - 8W)
    Beacon Frequencies: 437.070; 437.175; 2,403.2 MHz
    Modulation: 9,600 bit/s FSK; 38,400 bit/s FSK (option on 13 cm downlink). All UoSAT compatible

Artemis: JAK/Thelma/Louise
    Note: These three spacecraft do not carry transponders
    Beacon Frequency: 437.100 MHz (used on all three spacecraft)
    Modulation:
        Thelma/Louise: 1,200 bit/s AFSK
        JAK: CW
    Command Uplink: 2 m using DTMF encoding

ASUSat-1

Note: ASUSat-1 carries two receivers and one transponder. These can be configured as two transponders but only one can operate at any time.

Transponder I (digital mode)
Uplink 145.820 MHz
Downlink: 436.700, 436.500 MHz (2 W)
Modulation: 9,600 bit/s FSK, UoSAT compatible

Transponder II (FM Voice and digital backup)
Uplink: 145.990 MHz
Downlink: 436.700, 436.500 MHz (2W)

OPAL

Transponder I (digital only)
Uplink: not announced
Downlink: 437.100 MHz
Modulation: 9,600 bit/s FSK, UoSAT compatible

StenSat

Note: StenSat carries a Mode J single channel FM transponder with DTMF control and provides AX.25 packet telemetry on the downlink.

Transponder (Single channel FM repeater)
Uplink: 145.840 MHz
Downlink: 436.625 MHz
TX power: 100 mW (low), 250 mW (high) (high/low can be set by ground command)

Beacon
Frequency: 436.625 MHz (shared with Transponder)
Modulation: 1,200 bit/s AFSK AX.25 telemetry,
Morse Code ID: STENSAT DE N4AFL/1
Telemetry timing: one packet every 5 or 120 seconds, (switchable by ground command);
Can be initiated by transmitting "ping" on uplink
Morse Code: once every 240 seconds.

Commanding: StenSat recognizes the following uplink DTMF commands (Pings)
#7464464 Send single telemetry packet
#7370563 Send extended telemetry packet
#6676326 Switch into FM voice repeater mode

2 m Antenna: dipole constructed from spring steel measuring tape
70 cm Antenna: dipole constructed from spring steel measuring tape

SPACECRAFT NAME: SaudiSat-OSCAR 41

1.1 Identification

International designation: 2000 057A
NASA Catalog number: 26,545
Prelaunch designation: SaudiSat-1A

1.2 Launch

Date: 26 September 2000
Time: 10:05 UTC

Vehicle: DNEPR
Agency: RKA (Russian Space Agency)
Site: Baikonur Cosmodrome, Kazakhstan

1.3 Orbital parameters (8/2001)

General Designation: low-altitude, circular
Period: 97.6 minutes
Apogee altitude: 678 km
Perigee altitude: 622 km
Eccentricity: 0.0040
Inclination: 64.6°
Maximum access distance: 2,817 km

1.6 Design/Construction Credits

Saudisat-1 was designed and built by the Space Research Institute at the King Abdulaziz City for Science and Technology, Riyadh, Kingdom of Saudi Arabia.

1.7 Primary References:

1) **saudisat.kacst.edu.sa/**
2) *The AMSAT Journal*, Sept/Oct 2000, p30.

SPACECRAFT DESCRIPTION

2.1 Physical Structure

Shape: Cube
Dimensions: 23 x 23 x 23 cm
Mass: 10 kg

SUBSYSTEM DESCRIPTION

3.1 Beacons

Frequency: 436.775 MHz
Modulation: Standard PACSAT Digital System
Data rates: 9600 baud
Call signs
  Broadcast: sasat1-11
  BBS: sasat1-12
Tx Power: 1 W (7W option)

3.4 Transponder

Type: 9600 baud store-and-forward (PACSAT Broadcast Protocol compatible) or FM repeater
Downlink frequency: 436.775 MHz
Uplink frequency: 145.850 MHz

3.5 Attitude Stabilization and Control

Passive magnetic

3.6 Antennas

70 cm: 4-element trunstile on bottom of spacecraft. Left-hand circular polarization along axis.

2 meters: Single whip on top of spacecraft. Linear polarization.

3.7 Energy Supply and Power Conditioning

Solar cells: all six spacecraft faces
Peak power gathering: 18 W

Experimental system: Autonomous self-healing battery charger and regulator.

SPACECRAFT NAME: SaudiSat-OSCAR 42

Note: SO-42 is nearly identical to SO-41. Only the differences are listed here.

1.1 Identification

International designation: 2000 057E
NASA Catalog number: 26,549
Prelaunch designation: Saudisat-1B

1.2 Launch

Date: 26 September 2000
Time: 10:05 UTC
Vehicle: DNEPR
Agency: RKA (Russian Space Agency)
Site: Baikonur Cosmodrome, Kazakhstan

1.3 Orbital parameters (8/2001)

General Designation: low-altitude, circular
Period: 97.6 minutes
Apogee altitude: 682 km
Perigee altitude: 624 km
Eccentricity: 0.0041
Inclination: 64.6°
Maximum access distance: 2,825 km

1.6 Design/Construction Credits

Saudisat-2 was designed and built by the Space Research Institute at the King Abdulaziz City for Science and Technology, Riyadh, Kingdom of Saudi Arabia.

1.7 Primary References:

1) **saudisat.kacst.edu.sa/**
2) *The AMSAT Journal*, Sept/Oct 2000, p30.

SPACECRAFT DESCRIPTION

Mass: 10 kg

SUBSYSTEM DESCRIPTION

3.1 Beacons

Frequencies: 437.775 MHz
Modulation: Standard PACSAT Digital System
Data rates: 9.6 kbps
Call signs
  Broadcast: sasat2-11
  BBS: sasat2-11
Tx Power: 7 W (can only be operated for limited time)

3.4 Transponders

Type: 9.6 kbps store and forward (can operate in FM bent pipe mode for voice)
  downlink frequency: 437.775 MHz
  uplink frequency: to be announced

SPACECRAFT NAME: SaudiSat-OSCAR 50

GENERAL

1.1 Identification

International designation: 2002 058C
NASA Catalog number: 27607
Also known as SaudiSat-1C, SO-50

1.2 Launch

Date: 20 Dec. 2002 (17:00 UTC)
Site: Baikonur Cosmodrome, Kazakhstan
Launch Vehicle: DNEPR 1 (converted SS-18)

1.3 Orbital Parameters (Jan. 2003)

General designation: low altitude, circular, high inclination
Period: 98.0 minutes
Apogee altitude: 697 km
Perigee altitude: 641 km
Eccentricity: 0.0040
Inclination: 64.6 degrees
Maximum access distance: 2,853 km

1.4 Design/Construction Credits

Constructed at Space Research Institute of KACST, Riyadh, Saudi Arabia; Turki Al Saud, Director.

SUBSYSTEM DESCRIPTION

3.1 Beacons

Frequency: 436.800 MHz
Power Level: 250 mW

3.2 Transponders

Type: single-channel FM voice
Uplink: 145.850 MHz
Downlink: 436.800 MHz
  Same link frequencies as AO-27.
Power: 250 mW
Notes: A 67.0-Hz subaudible tone is required on the uplink to switch on the transponder. In addition, a command station must enable the transponder (reset a timeout timer) several times per orbit to maintain accessibility.

3.3 Antennas

70 cm transmit: quarter wavelength whip on bottom (-Z face) of spacecraft
2-meter receive: quarter wavelength whip on top (+Z face) of spacecraft

SPACECRAFT NAME:
Starshine-OSCAR 43

Re-entered: 21 Jan. 2003. Last transmission: 9 Jan. 2002

GENERAL

1.1 Identification

International designation: 2001-043A
NASA Catalog number: 26,929
Also known as: SO-43, Starshine-3

1.2 Launch

Date: 30 Sept. 2001 (02:40:02 UTC)
Site: Kodiak Launch Complex, Alaska
Launch Vehicle: Athena-I (Lockheed Martin)

1.3 Orbital Parameters (as of 1 Oct. 2001)

General designation: low altitude, circular, near polar
Period: 94.0 minutes
Apogee altitude: 481 km
Perigee altitude: 475 km
Eccentricity: 0.00049
Inclination: 67.05 degrees
Maximum access distance: 2,403 km

1.4 Design/Construction Credits

Starshine 3 is part of a series of small optically reflective satellites built as part of an educational program designed to involve K-12 students in space related activities. It was built by an informal, volunteer coalition of organizations and individuals known as "Project Starshine" headquartered in Monument, Colorado.
Design: Naval Research Laboratory
Project Director: Gill Moore N7YTK
Launch: Sponsored by NASA

1.5 Primary References:

1. **www.azinet.com/starshine**

SPACECRAFT DESCRIPTION

2.1 Physical Structure

Shape: Sphere
Dimensions: diameter = 95 cm
Mass: 91 kg

SUBSYSTEM DESCRIPTION

3.1 Beacon

Frequency: 145.825 MHz
Power Level: 1.25 W
(Transmitter built by Cynetics Corp.)

3.2 Telemetry

9600 baud AX.25 FSK
Packets sent at 30s or 120s intervals
Identifying data header: STRSHN3 N7YTK
APRS packet compatible

3.3 Transponders

This spacecraft does not contain a transponder. However, spacecraft contains command receiver operating half duplex.

3.4 Antennas

Pair of 1/4-wavelength monopoles fed 180 degree out of phase.

3.5 Experimental Systems

Starshine-3 has a spherical surface covered with 1500 polished aluminum mirrors, 31 laser retro-reflectors and seven clusters of solar cells (used to power the radio amateur beacon).

Students in more than 1000 schools in over 30 countries polished the 1500 mirrors on the spacecraft. Each reflector consisted of a very accurately machined front-surface aluminum mirror coated with a scratch-resistant, anti-oxidizing layer of silicon dioxide. Under appropriate conditions, it could be seen with the naked eye.

SPACECRAFT NAME: NAV-OSCAR 44

The objective of the NO-44 APRS (Automatic Position Reporting System) Satellite Mission is to provide students majoring in aerospace at the US Naval Academy hands on experience in satellite design and operations. PCsat is open to radio amateurs worldwide and everyone is welcome to use it. However, users are asked to read and follow the operating guidelines (see **www.ew.usna.edu/pcsat**) that allow this resource to be efficiently shared to maximize its utility to all.

GENERAL

1.1 Identification

International designation: 2001-043C
NASA Catalog number: 26,931
Also known as: PCsat (Prototype Communications Satellite), NO-44, USNA-1

1.2 Launch

Date: 30 Sept. 2001 (02:40:02 UTC)
Site: Kodiak Launch Complex, Alaska
Launch Vehicle: Athena-I (Lockheed Martin)

1.3 Orbital Parameters (1/2003)

General designation: low altitude, circular, near polar
Period: 100.76 minutes
Apogee altitude: 806 km
Perigee altitude: 798 km
Eccentricity: 0.00055
Inclination: 67.05 degrees
Maximum access distance: 3,048 km

Figure NO44-1—PCsat. The +X panel, with four 19-inch whips, is forward facing.

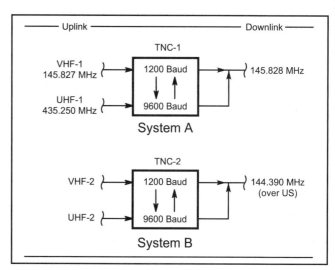

Figure NO44-2—PCsat Transponder Input/Output Architecture

1.4 Design/construction Credits

Funded by: U.S. Naval Academy (USNA) and Boeing Corporation

Launch sponsored by: U.S. Department of Defense Space

Test Program in cooperation with NASA.

Note: This is the first spacecraft produced by the USNA Small Satellite program under direction of Lt Col Billy Smith. Spacecraft design and construction were coordinated by USNA Satellite Laboratory Chief Engineer, Bob Bruninga, WB4APR.

1.5 Primary References:

1. Bob Bruninga, WB4APR, "An APRS Satellite for Mobile/Handheld Communications," *QEX*, Jan/Feb 2002, pp. 47-53.

2. Bob Bruninga has provided extensive PCsat documentation on the Internet. For general information see

(i) the PCsat Operations and Communications Plan at **www.ew.usna.edu/~bruninga/PCSAT/opsplan.html**

(ii) PCsat at **www.ew.usna.edu/~bruninga/pcsat.html**

(iii) the PCsat User Service Agreement at **www.ew.usna.edu/~bruninga/pcsat/contract.txt**

Additional references to specific areas of interest are contained in the following sections.

SPACECRAFT DESCRIPTION

2.1 Physical Structure

Shape: The core of the spaceframe is a cube. See Figure NO44-1

Dimensions: 25 x 25 x 25 cm

Mass: 12 kg

SUBSYSTEM DESCRIPTION

3.1 Beacons

Beacon 1: 145.828 MHz (world wide) as measured with spacecraft in orbit. Target was 145.825 MHz

Beacon 2: 144.390 MHz (activated over US only). May be operated over other regions upon request if ITU regula-

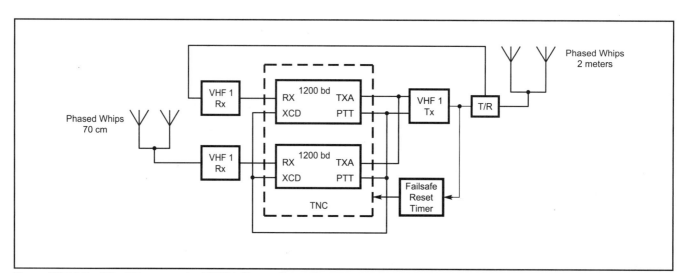

Figure NO44-3—PCsat Transponder TNC/Tx/Rx configuration

tions and IARU guidelines permit.

Power Level: 2 W

Format: 1200 baud AFSK and 9600 baud FSK, AX.25 packets

3.2 Telemetry

PCsat telemetry packets are interleaved with user UI packets on the downlink and are transmitted at least once every 60 seconds. Each packet contains five analog values. By using a multiplexer in conjunction with the TNC, the spacecraft can downlink 20 telemetry channels in four sequential packets. See **www.ew.usna.edu/~bruninga/ pcsat/tlm-eqns.htm** for detailed information.

3.3 Telecommand

The design of NO-44 is unique. It uses the TNC as the core of each digital transponder to handle all spacecraft command, control and telemetry functions. As a result, the spacecraft does not require a separate computer for command, control, telemetry or housekeeping functions. This design approach greatly reduces satellite complexity, shortens the design cycle and contributes to spacecraft reliability.

The TNC used on NO-44 is a modified Kantronics KPC-9612Plus. In essence, the spacecraft is a digipeater with support systems (power supplies and radio links) designed for the space environment. The TNC is the brains and core.

3.4 Transponders

PCsat contains two interconnected digital transponders that are identical except for input/output frequencies. Each consists of a hardware TNC designed for UI (unnumbered information) frame digipeating of user APRS messages and an accompanying receiver and transmitter. Spacecraft transponder architecture is shown in Figures NO44-2 and NO44-3.

Transponder I (System A, W3ADO)
Uplink VHF1: 145.825 MHz
Uplink UHF1: 435.250 MHz
Downlink: 145.828 MHz
Transponder II (System B, PCsat)
Uplink VHF2: unpublished[1]
Uplink UHF2: unpublished[1]
Downlink: 144.390 MHz (activated over US only)

[1]These uplinks are unpublished. However, they are available to Amateur Radio operators traveling in remote areas who desire to get status packets back to the world of APRS.

Also, the spacecraft has a limited store-and-forward capability. This feature is for users operating from isolated areas such as Antarctica where the probability of another ground station being inside the spacecraft footprint is very low. To use it the "wilderness traveler" directs his TH-D7 or TMD-700 (or other APRS compatible radio) to select a "Priority" or "Special" or "Custom" flag in the position/ status packet and to set a beacon repetition rate of once every 3 minutes. Once captured by PCsat, the last three

such packets are repeated once every three minutes around the world until replaced by new ones. Contact **WB4APR@ amsat.org** for additional information.

The dual-port design of the transponder TNC permits each uplink (VHF or UHF, 1200 baud or 9600 baud) to be directed to the VHF downlink as either a 1200 baud or 9600 baud signal. Routing (choice of output frequency and baud rate) is controlled by the use of digipeater call signs. For example, a user with a low power handheld transceiver (under 5 W) listening to the 1200 baud 145.825 MHz downlink can transmit a 1200-baud packet to transponder I on 145.825 MHz. If the path VIA APRSAT is used, the downlink will be at 1200 baud. If the path VIA XBAUD is used the downlink will be at 9600 baud. The path chosen depends on the capabilities of the receiving station. To make it easier for users working with other APRS systems the spacecraft will accept several aliases in place of APRSAT. For an up-to-date review, see the PCsat Operations and Communications Document at **www.ew.usna.edu/ ~bruninga/pcsat/opsplan.html**.

3.5 Attitude Control

PCsat uses a minimal attitude control system consisting of a single magnetized bolt along the spacecraft Z-axis. The North-seeking pole is at the –Z face.

3.6 Antennas

See Figure NO44-1

70 cm: four 6.5-inch whips. Each whip is mounted at midpoint of spacecraft –X panel edge.

2 meters: Four 19-inch whips. Each whip is mounted at midpoint of spacecraft +X panel edge

3.7 Energy Supply and Power Conditioning

Solar panels: All six faces of the satellite cube contain solar panels.

+X, -X, +Y, -Y Panels: terrestrial rated 1 W Teflon coated.

+Z Panel: Four space rated high efficiency glass-covered cells, 70% more efficient than terrestrial panels.

-Z Panel: custom built, 40% more efficient than terrestrial panels, (Not operational)

Batteries: Two strings, each string consisting of 12 NiCd cells (AA size), producing ~14.4 V.

Subsystem power requirements (* means always on)

module	power
TNC-1 *	0.25 W
TNC-2 *	0.25 W
VHF Rx-1 *	0.3 W
VHF Rx-2 *	0.3 W
UHF Rx-1	0.5 W
UHF Rx-2	0.5 W
GPS Rx	2 W
Tx-1	4 W
Tx-2	4 W

Cooling: Radiator, 3 W

3.8 Experimental Systems

1. PCsat itself is an experimental system dedicated to exploring the feasibility of using multiple LEO satellites in conjunction with terrestrial APRS systems to provide worldwide real-time message and position/status data exchange, especially between low power handheld and mobile ground stations. This is in contrast to earlier amateur satellite experiments with digital transponders that were optimized for message store-and-forward communications.

2. PCsat serves as a focal point for ongoing experiments involving low-power GPS tracking of travelers (especially to remote locations), buoys, telemetry devices, wildlife, etc.

3. PCsat serves as a focal point for stimulating ongoing experiments with APRS related activities involving the International Space Station, STS and other amateur satellites.

4. PCsat serves as a focal point for development activities involving automatic spacecraft/Internet message linking to provide worldwide real-time position/status reporting via an LEO spacecraft.

5. PCsat includes a GPS receiver developed by German space Operations Center for NASA. When this receiver is active, PCsat reports its position on the downlink using the APRS format.

SPACECRAFT NAME: NAV-OSCAR 45

GENERAL

1.1 Identification

International designation: 2001-043D
NASA Catalog number: 26,932
Also known as: NO-45, Sapphire

1.2 Launch

Date: 30 Sept. 2001 (02:40:02 UTC)
Site: Kodiak Launch Complex, Alaska
Launch Vehicle: Athena-I (Lockheed Martin)

1.3 Orbital Parameters (Jan. 2003)

General designation: low altitude, circular, near polar
Period: 100.8 minutes
Apogee altitude: 806 km
Perigee altitude: 796 km
Eccentricity: 0.00067
Inclination: 67.06 degrees
Maximum access distance: 3,048 km

1.4 Design/Construction Credits

Constructed at Stanford University 1994 – 1998 under direction of R. Twiggs, KE6QND.

Launch Operations under direction of M. Swartwout, KE6YNJ, Washington University, St Louis.

Launch sponsored by US Department of Defense Space

Test Program and the Naval Academy Satellite Program

1.5 Primary References

1. "Sapphire – Stanford's First Amateur Satellite," R. Twiggs, KE6QND, M. Swartwout, KE6YNJ, *AMSAT-NA 16th Space Symposium*, Vicksburg, MS, Oct. 1998, pp. 89-104.

2.   **students.cec.wustl.edu/~sapphire/sapphire_overview.html**

SPACECRAFT DESCRIPTION

2.1 Physical Structure

Shape: Hexagonal cylinder (See Figure NO45-1)
Dimensions: 6 square sides of 24 x 24 cm, hexagonal top and bottom plates
Mass: 18.2 kg

SUBSYSTEM DESCRIPTION

3.1 Beacon

Frequency: 437.095 MHz
Power Level: 2 W (modified Hamtronics transmitter kit)

Figure NO45-1—A drawing of NAV-OSCAR 45 (Sapphire)

3.2 Telemetry

1200 baud AX.25 AFSK

3.3 Transponders

Type: Digital (Generally operating as APRS UI digipeater)
Uplink: 145.945 MHz
Downlink: 437.095 MHz (beacon)
TNC: modified Kantronics

3.4 Attitude Stabilization and Control

Uses system similar to AMSAT-OSCAR 7 designed to provide a "controlled tumble." System elements:

Four ALNICO-V bar magnets aligned along spacecraft Z-axis.

Radiometer induced spin resulting from coating 435 MHz antenna elements with reflective and non-reflective paints.

Hysterisis rods perpendicular to Z-axis to dampen nutation and limit spin rate.

Infrared phototransistors positioned to verify earth pointing.

3.5 Antennas

70 cm: turnstile
2 meters: 1/4 wavelength whip (omni)

3.6 Energy Supply and Power Conditioning:

Solar cells: GaAs, 24 strings, 20 cells per string
Batteries: 10 space-rated NiCd "D" cells in two strings of 5

3.7 Experimental Systems

1. The primary goal of the NO-45 mission is to space-qualify micro-machined infrared sensors (Tunneling Horizon Detectors) that operate at room temperature.

2. Secondary goals include obtaining earth photos using a modified B/W Logitech "Photoman Plus" digital camera having an estimated resolution of 1 km at Earth surface and testing a modified RC Systems voice synthesizer.

SPACECRAFT NAME: IDEFIX
BreizhSat-OSCAR 47/48

The goal of the short lifetime IDEFIX mission is to determine whether the last stage of the Ariane launch vehicle, which is often abandoned in a stable orbit, could be used to support a long lifetime amateur payload. The project addresses serious concerns related to thermal behavior, solar illumination and available power, and antenna shielding and pattern.

GENERAL

1.1 Identification

International designation: 2002-021B
NASA Catalog number: 27,422
Also known as: IDEFIX, BO-47/48

1.2 Launch

Date: 4 May 2002 (01:31 UTC)
Site: ESA launch complex, Kourou, French Guiana
Launch Vehicle: Ariane 4 flight V151 (remains attached to third stage)

1.3 Orbital Parameters (May 10)

General designation: low altitude, circular, sun-synchronous?
Period: 100.9 minutes
Apogee altitude: 814 km
Perigee altitude: 799 km
Eccentricity: 0.0011
Inclination: 98.7 degrees
Maximum access distance: 3,063 km

1.4 Design/Construction Credits

IDEFIX was designed, constructed and funded by AMSAT-France. The core construction crew consisted of:
Project Director: Ghislain Ruy, F1HDD
Software: Christophe Mercier
Hardware: Jeff Boivin, F6CWN
Guiana Operations: Norbert Sayou, FY1DW
Coordination: Jean-Louis Rault, F6AGR

The name BreizhSat was selected to acknowledge the efforts of several volunteer with roots in the region of western France known as Bretagne. "Breizh" means Bretagne in the Breton language

The actual project evolved over an extremely short time span. The Initial Project Proposal was submitted Jan 28, 2002. Integration on Ariane third stage occurred on April 8/9, 2002. This was made possible by the use of equipment previously developed for Russian RS-19 spacecraft and French SATEDU projects.

1.5 Primary References

1. G. Ruy, F1HDD/ON1RG, "The IDEFIX Project," *The AMSAT Journal*, Sept/Oct 2002, pp 10-14. (Originally presented at AMSAT-UK Colloquium, July/Aug 2002.)

2. **idefix-france.net**. For information in English, click on US flag.

3. A special issue of *Journal de AMSAT-France*, (édition spécial IDEFIX), was devoted to this project. A CD (CD-ROM IDEFIX) with detailed information and photos was also produced. Both are available from AMSAT-France, 14bis, rue des Gourlis, 92500 RUEIL-MALMAISON, France. Contact AMSAT-France as to cost. See **idefix-france.net**.

SPACECRAFT DESCRIPTION

2.1 Physical Structure

The IDEFIX mission includes two autonomous but similar spacecraft known as:
CU1 = Payload 1 = Idefix-1 = BO-47
CU2 = Payload 2 = Idefix-2 = BO-48
…where "CU" stands for "charge utile" or, payload.

See Figure BO47/48-1.

Mechanical: rectangular box, approximately 10 x 18 x 30 cm (Standard Weidmuller k61 die cast AlSi alloy case) bolted to 5-mm thick Al plate mounted on shock absorbers (Hutchison Vibrachoc silicon dampers) attached to Ariane third stage.

Mass: 6 kg

Thermal: Expected range: -20 to +70 C. Observed range: -22 to +40 C

SUBSYSTEM DESCRIPTION

3.1 Beacons

The beacons were switched on by a timer on 7 May 2002 and operated until battery depletion.

CU1
Frequency: 145.838 MHz
Power level: 160 mW
Operational lifetime: 32 days

CU2
Frequency: 435.278 MHz
Power level: 1.2 W
Operational lifetime: 14 days

3.2 Telemetry

Format 1: similar to AO-40 (400 bps BPSK Manchester encoding)

Format 2: voice (NBFM), prerecorded messages in several languages

Format 3: Payload temperature transmitted as analog tone (~1800 Hz) superposed on voice message.

CU1 transmission sequence (~ 40 s total):
voice: < 15 s
silence: 12 s
TLM: 3 s
silence: 12 s

CU2 transmission sequence (~ 110 s total)
TLM: 3 s
silence: 22 s
TLM: 3 s
silence: 22 s
TLM: 3 s
silence: 22 s
TLM: 3 s
silence: 22 s
voice: 6 s
silence: 7 s

The CU1 TLM frame consisted of 8 channels of data. The CU2 TLM frame consisted of 16 channels of data. Complete information on decoding and channel content is available on the IDEFIX website (**idefix-france.net**). Software is available that enables a ground station to connect their receiver audio output to a computer soundcard (via "line in" connector) to automatically display decoded telemetry. See, for example, *WDECPSK* that runs under *Windows* and allows one to display AO-40 telemetry. Instructions, in English, for using *WDECPSK* are available at

Figure BO47/48-1— A sketch of BO-48 showing 70 cm whips, case and shock absorbers.

perso.club-internet.fr/fa1rtp/idefix/e-telecharg.htm. A complete description of IDEFIX telemetry encoding is available in French at **perso.club-internet.fr/fa1rtp/idefix/telemesure.htm**.

3.3 Transponders

IDEFIX did not include transponders. Mission results indicate that it is feasible to include transponders on future long lifetime missions.

3.4 Attitude Stabilization

AMSAT France has no control over the Ariane third stage stabilization. However, once in orbit, AMSAT can use ESA data to manage payload subsystems in the most efficient and effective manor.

3.5 Antennas

2 meters (CU1): two monopoles mounted on Ariane third stage

70 cm (CU2): two monopoles mounted on CU2 case (see Figure BO47/48-1).

3.6 Energy Supply and Power Conditioning

Both IDEFIX payloads were powered entirely by primary cells. No solar cells were used to power electronic systems. Each payload used 12 space-rated lithium (Li Thyonile LSH20) cells manufactured by SAFT. Each battery consisted of 3 strings of 4 cells providing a bus voltage of 14.6 V and having a capacity at launch of 600 Wh.

3.7 IHU

CU1 and CU2 used the 80c32X2 microprocessor running at 6.144 MHz.
CU1: 32K ROM
CU2: 32K ROM and 32k RAM

3.8 Experimental Systems

1. The primary goal of this mission was to demonstrate the feasibility of using the Ariane rockets final stage as a carrier for radio amateur payloads despite the totally uncontrolled and unfavorable thermal and illumination con-

ditions expected. The results suggest that using the third stage as a platform for long lifetime communications payloads is possible and that doing so can reduce mission design and integration time and costs.

2. The Li cells used on IDEFIX were being tested for the CNES/ESA Rosetta interplanetary probe.

SPACECRAFT NAME: AATis-OSCAR 49

GENERAL

1.1 Identification

International designation: 2002 058A
NASA Catalog number: 27,605
Also known as: SAFIR-M, AO-49 (SAFIR-M is a communications payload aboard the RUBIN-2 Spacecraft)

1.2 Launch

Date: 20 Dec. 2002 (17:00 UTC)
Site: Baikonur Cosmodrome, Kazakhstan
Launch Vehicle: DNEPR 1 (converted SS-18)

1.3 Orbital Parameters (Jan. 2003)

General designation: low altitude, circular,
high inclination
Period: 97.9 minutes
Apogee altitude: 686 km
Perigee altitude: 642 km
Eccentricity: 0.0032
Inclination: 64.6 degrees
Maximum access distance: 2,833 km

1.6 Design/Construction Credits

The SAFIR-M project is directed by the German group "Arbeitskreis Amateurfunk & Telekomunikation in der Schule e.V." (AATiS), in English, Working Group for Amateur Radio and Telecommunications in Schools. The payload was designed and built at the University of Applied Sciences, Pforzheim Germany.
Project Coordinator: Oliver Amend, DG6BCE, AATiS e.V.
Director of Development: Dr. Wolf-Henning Rech, DF9IC, Fachhochschule Pforzheim

1.7 Primary References

1. **amend.gmxhome.de**
2. **www.aatis.de**

SPACECRAFT DESCRIPTION

2.1 Physical Structure (Rubin-2 Spacecraft)

Shape: core is rectangular solid
Dimensions: 34 x 34 x 30 cm
Mass: 30 kg

SUBSYSTEM DESCRIPTION

The SAFIR-M payload is a subsystem aboard the RUBIN-2 spacecraft. Its primary connections to the main spacecraft are through Rubin-2's ORBCOMM Communicaton-4 module and data/command bus.

3.1 Beacons

Frequency: 145.825 MHz
Primary Format: 9600 baud FSK AX.25
Secondary Format: Digital voice messages up to
2 minutes in length uplinked from command station.
Power Level: 2W

3.2 Telemetry

Sent as AX.25 message blocks on beacon

3.3 Transponder

Type: Digital
Characteristics: digipeater optimized for AX.25 UI-frames. When an AX.25 frame is received correctly, it is echoed on the downlink along with several previously received packets
Uplink: 435.275 MHz, 1200 baud AFSK
Downlink: 145.825 MHz, 9600 baud FSK
Spacecraft ID: DP0AIS
Default Settings:
Transponder is only on when RUBIN-2 is in sunlight
All Beacon messages are 54.6 seconds in length
Beacon message types: INFO, DATA0, DATA1, MH0, MH1. Examples may be seen at **amend.gmxhome.de/funktionen.htm.**
After eclipse, all onboard counters are rest to default values

3.4 Attitude Stabilization and Control

All spacecraft station-keeping activities are handled by RUBIN-2 that contains:
Magnetometer
Magnetorquers (3)
Solar sensors (6)

3.5 Energy Supply and Power Conditioning

These functions are handled by the solar powered RUBIN-2 spacecraft. NiCd cells, configured as 4 strings, 10 cells per string are used for energy storage. Because of power budget considerations, SAFIR-M is generally operated only when spacecraft is in sunlight.

3.6 Experimental Systems

The RUBIN-2 spacecraft contains several experimental systems of interest to the Radio Amateur Satellite community. These include:
1. Ion Drive thruster (FEEP) provided by Carlo Gavazzi Space, Milan Italy.
2. GPS Receiver optimized for mini-satellite use (Carlo Gavazzi Space)
3. Space testing of Lithium Cells (Eagle Pitcher, US) designed for terrestrial mobile use. See **www.ohb-system.de/News/presse/2012_02.htm**l for additional information.

APPENDIX

Internet Sites of Interest

In the last few years, the Internet has changed from a specialized information resource shared by a small number of research scientists into a vast store of data used by large numbers of people. The Internet (aka the World Wide Web, Web, WWW) contains a great deal of material of interest to those engaged in amateur satellite activities. Three examples of the type of information available follow. The examples were chosen to give readers who have never used the Web some idea of its power.

If you're interested in the details of a new amateur satellite being built in the Technion in Israel you can go directly to the Web site maintained by the group building the spacecraft and find hundreds of pages of detailed information, much of which has never appeared in printed media.

In the past if you wanted to find out where a particular satellite would be at particular time you had to acquire and install tracking software and hunt down up-to-date orbital elements. Now you can go directly to a Web site that provides on line tracking information for hundreds of satellites and get the information you need in seconds.

Acquiring a catalog for small electronics parts used to involve mailing a request and waiting a week or two to receive a catalog that was probably printed six months ago. Now you can obtain the data immediately at the manufacturers or distributors Web site. And, additional specifications, if needed are often easily accessible.

The Web, however, does have shortcomings. The very characteristics that allow it to grow so rapidly can hamper its effective use. While there's a great deal of very valuable information on the Web, the gems are often buried under mountains of garbage (poorly organized, error riddled data), which makes it hard to find what you need. And, it seems that everything is being changed on a daily basis. Sites change names and move; a database that provided accurate, up-to-date information for a year may be suddenly abandoned, and so on. Despite these minor problems it's clear that the Web is going to become more and more important as a source of information to those interested in the amateur satellite program.

The following list contains a sampling of key Web sites that are likely to be of interest to amateur satellite operators. There's no need to provide a comprehensive list since the best sites have up-to-date links to related sites. Chances are that by the time you read this some of the sites will have changed addresses or become inactive. But as long as some are still in operation, you'll have a starting point to build your own address book.

One of the best web sites for finding addresses for satellites, and satellite-related information, is known as Google. It can be accessed at **www.google.com**. This site will also perform machine translations into English for sites in other major languages.

MAJOR ORGANIZATIONS
American Radio Relay League (ARRL)
www.arrl.org

AMSAT France (AMSAT-Fr)
www.ccr.jussieu.fr/physio/amsat-france/

AMSAT Germany (AMSAT-DL)
www.amsat.org/amsat-dl/adl-engl.html

AMSAT North America (AMSAT-NA)
www.amsat.org/

AMSAT United Kingdom (AMSAT-UK)
www.uk.amsat.org/

Surrey Satellite Technology Laboratories Ltd. (SSTL)
www.sstl.co.uk/

Surrey Space Center (SSC)
www.ee.surrey.ac.uk/SSC/

RECENT and FUTURE RADIO AMATEUR SATELLITE PROJECTS
Small Satellite Home Page sponsored by Surrey Space Center, UK
www.SmallSatellites.org

AMSAT-NA Current Satellite Summary
www.amsat.org/amsat/sats/n7hpr/satsum.html

AMSAT-NA Future Satellite Summary
www.amsat.org/amsat/sats/n7hpr/future.html

Specific Spacecraft: See Appendix C for each satellite

TRACKING: GENERAL
AMSAT-NA Software list
www.amsat.org/amsat/catalog/software.html

Northern Lights Software Associates (Program: Nova)
www.nlsa.com/

TRACKING: ONLINE
Marshall Space Flight Center
liftoff.msfc.nasa.gov/realtime/JTrack/

Bester Tracking Systems
www.bester.com/satpasses.html

Heavens Above
www.heavens-above.com/

International Space Station and STS
www.spaceflight.nasa.gov/realdata/tracking/

TRACKING: ORBITAL ELEMENTS
AMSAT-NA
www.amsat.org/amsat/keps/menu.html

Kelso
www.celestrak.com/

GSFC (requires registration)
oig1.gsfc.nasa.gov/

TRACKING: REFERENCE DATA
National Space Science Data Center
nssdc.gsfc.nasa.gov/

SPACEWARN Bulletin
nssdc.gsfc.nasa.gov/about/about_spacewarn.html

AMATEUR RADIO OPERATORS IN SPACE
Amateur Radio on the International Space Station (ARISS)
ariss.gsfc.nasa.gov/

ARISS Radio Amateur Activities
spaceflight.nasa.gov/station/reference/radio/

STS and International Space Station
Spaceflight.nasa.gov/

Space Station News (Mark Curtiss)
www.cosmicimages.com/iss/index.html

NASA SPACE EDUCATION PROGRAMS
edspace.nasa.gov/

education.nasa.gov/

spacelink.msfc.nasa.gov/

ESA SPACE EDUCATION PROGRAMS
www.esa.int/export/esaMl/Education/

GENERAL INTEREST
Apollo Lunar Surface Journal
www.hq.nasa.gov/office/pao/History/alsj/

EME
www.nitehawk.com/rasmit/

Central States VHF Society
www.tc.umn.edu/nlhome/m042/liebe009/

GJ4ICD's Amateur Radio Information
urer.itl.net/~equinox

HF-FAX Home Page
www.hffax.de/

High altitude ballooning
www.amsat.org/amsat/balloons/balloon.htm

Hubble Telescope
oposite.stsci.edu/

Ionospheric Heating Facility, Gakona Alaska
www.haarp.alaska.edu

Mars Missions (Government)
mars.jpl.nasa.gov/missions/

National Radio Astronomy Observatory
www.nrao.edu/

National Polar-orbiting Operational Environmental Satellite System
www.ipo.noaa.gov/

NOAA/NESDIS Center for Satellite Applications and Research
orbit-net.nesdis.noaa.gov/arad/fpdt/

Orbitsserra (N2WWD Satellite Page)
www.mindspring.com/~n2wwd/body_index.html

San Bernardino Microwave Society
www.ham-radio.com/sbms/

SETI (Search for Extraterrestrial Intelligence) League
www.setileague.org/

SETI@home
setiathome.ssl.berkeley.edu/

SETI Institute
www.seti-inst.edu/

Space Environment Laboratory current solar forecast
www.sel.noaa.gov/forecast.html

Spacewarn Bulletin
nssdc.gsfc.nasa.gov/about/about_spacewarn.html

Space Weather Now (National Oceanic and Atmospheric Administration)
www.sec.noaa.gov/SWN/

Suppliers/Manufacturers Amateur Satellite Ground Station Equipment
www.amsat.org/amsat/suppliers.html

Tucson Amateur Packet Radio (TAPR)
www.tapr.org/

VHF Communications Magazine (Great Britain)
www.clearlight.com/~vhfcomm

WB5OTD Amateur Satellite Information
www.sirinet.net/~acagle

Weather Satellites (Dallas Remote Imaging Group)
www.drig.com/

W4SM AO-40/AO-10 Info & Links
www.cstone.net/~w4sm/ham1.html

GOVERNMENT RELATED
European Space Agency (ESA) Home Page
www.esrin.esa.it/

FCC Home Page
www.fcc.gov/

National Aeronautics and Space Administration (NASA)
www.nasa.gov/

Jet Propulsion Laboratory
www.jpl.nasa.gov/

Johnson Space Center
www.jsc.nasa.gov/

Kennedy Space Center
www.ksc.nasa.gov/

Goddard Space Flight Center
www.gsfc.nasa.gov/

National Oceanic and Atmospheric Administration (NOAA)
www.sec.noaa.gov/

National Environmental Satellite, Data, and Information Service (NOAA/NESDIS)
www.nesdis.noaa.gov/

APPENDIX

Conversion Factors, Constants and Derived Quantities

CONVERSION FACTORS

The following values have been established by international agreement and are exact as shown. There is no round-off or truncation error.

1 foot = 0.3048 meter
1 statute mile = 1609.344 meters
1 nautical mile = 1852 meters

Some additional conversion factors:

Length: $1.000°$ of arc at surface of Earth
  = 60.00 nautical miles
  = 111.2 km
  = 69.10 statute miles

Mass: $1.000 \text{ kg} = 6.852 \times 10^{-2}$ slugs

Force: $1.000 \text{ N} = 0.2248$ pounds
  1.000 kg (force) = 2.205 pounds (at surface of Earth)

SELECTED CONVERSION PROCEDURES

(to four significant digits unless indicated otherwise)

1) To convert from statute miles to kilometers, multiply by 1.609
2) To convert from kilometers to statute miles, multiply by 0.6214
3) To convert from inches to meters, multiply by 0.0254 (exact)
4) To convert from meters to inches, multiply by 39.37

CONSTANTS

Flattening factor for the Earth:
  f = 1/298.257

Geocentric gravitational constant:
  $GM = 3.986005 \times 10^{14} \dfrac{m^3}{s^2}$

Mass of Earth:
  $M = 5.976 \times 10^{24}$ kg
  $= 4.095 \times 10^{23}$ slugs

Mean Earth-Sun distance:
  $1 \text{ AU} = 1.49600 \times 10^{11}$ m

Mean equatorial radius of earth:
  R_{eq} = 6378.140 km = 3963.376 statute miles

Mean radius of Earth:
  R = 6371 km = 3959 statute miles

Mean solar year = 365.24219870 mean solar days
π = 3.1415926535898
Solar day = 1440 minutes (exact)
Sidereal day = 1436.07 minutes
  = 23:56:45 (HH:MM:SS)
  = 23.9344 hours

Solar constant:
  P_o = 1380 W/m^2

Speed of light in vacuum:
  c = 299,792.458 km/s

Stefan-Boltzmann constant

  $\sigma = 5.67 \times 10^{-8} \dfrac{\text{joules}}{K^4 m^2 s}$

Universal gravitational constant:

  $G = 6.672 \times 10^{-11} \dfrac{m^3}{kg-s^2}$

  $= 3.439 \times 10^{-8} \dfrac{ft^3}{slug-s^2}$

ABBREVIATIONS

K = kelvin

kg = kilogram

m = meter

N = Newton $\left(kg\dfrac{m}{s^2} \right)$

s = second

W = watt

Sources
[1] *The Astronomical Almanac For The Year 1989*, issued by the Nautical Almanac Office, United States Naval Observatory, US Government Printing Office.
[2] *The CRC Handbook of Physics and Chemistry*, 68th Ed., Chemical Rubber Co, 1987/88, Cleveland, Ohio.
[3] For a more extensive collection of values, see W. Larson and J. Wertz (eds.), *Space Mission Analysis and Design*, 2nd Ed., Kluwer Academic Publishers, 1992.

APPENDIX

Rules and Regulations Governing the Amateur Satellite Service

The amateur service, of which the amateur-satellite service is a part, is governed by a complex hierarchy of rules. At the top of the pyramid lies the International Telecommunication Union (ITU), with headquarters in Geneva. Member nations of the ITU (most countries) are obligated to see that radio services under their jurisdiction operate in compliance with ITU regulations. ITU member nations meet aperiodically at World Radio Conferences (WRCs) to consider changes to the existing regulations.

The US agency responsible for administering the radio spectrum is the Federal Communications Commission. The rules governing the amateur service are known as Part 97. In Part 97 the FCC delegates certain frequency management and coordination tasks to the amateur service. In the US (and possibly in other countries) the band plans adopted by the amateur service therefore constitute an informally recognized adjunct to the rules governing the amateur service. This latter authority is based on an FCC letter (April 27, 1983) which stated that ". . .we [FCC] conclude that any amateur who selects a station transmitting frequency not in harmony with those plans [IARU Region 2 band plans] is not operating in accord with good amateur practice."

This appendix contains selected rules and regulations specifically directed at the amateur-satellite service. Keep in mind that this list is in no way complete and that, in addition to the regulations quoted here, amateur-satellite service operations must comply with all regulations governing the amateur service unless specific mention is made otherwise. The rules and regulations presented in the remainder of this appendix are divided into three categories: those attributed to the ITU, which are international in nature; those attributed to the FCC, which affect amateurs operating under its jurisdiction; and those attributed to International Amateur Radio Union (IARU) Region 2 band plans.

ITU INTERNATIONAL RADIO REGULATIONS

Article 1—Terms and Definitions

Section III. Radio Services

§3.34 Amateur Service:

A radiocommunication service for the purpose of self-

training, intercommunication and technical investigations carried out by amateurs, this is, by duly authorized persons interested in radio technique solely with a personal aim and without pecuniary interest.

§3.35 Amateur-Satellite Service:

A radiocommunication service using space stations on earth satellites for the same purposes as those of the amateur service.

Article 32—Amateur Service and Amateur-Satellite Service

Section II. Amateur-Satellite Service

Sec. 6. The provisions of Section I of this Article [Amateur Service] shall apply equally, as appropriate, to the Amateur-Satellite Service.

Sec. 7. Space stations in the Amateur-Satellite Service operating in bands shared with other services shall be fitted with appropriate devices for controlling emissions in the event that harmful interference is reported in accordance with the procedure laid down in Article 22. Administrations authorizing such space stations shall inform the IFRB[International Frequency Registration Board] and shall ensure that sufficient earth command stations are established before launch to guarantee that any harmful interference which might be reported can be terminated by the authorizing administration.

Resolution No. 642

Relating to the Bringing into Use of Earth Stations in the Amateur-Satellite Service.

Recognizing

that the procedures of Articles 11 and 13 are applicable to the amateur-satellite service.

Recognizing Further

a) that the characteristics of each station in the Amateur-Satellite Service vary widely.

b) that space stations in the Amateur-Satellite Service are intended for multiple access by amateur earth stations in all countries.

c) that coordination among stations in the amateur and Amateur-Satellite Services is accomplished without the need for formal procedures.

d) that the burden of terminating any harmful interference

is placed upon the administration authorizing a space station in the Amateur-Satellite Service pursuant to the provisions of No. 2741 of the Radio Regulations.

Notes

that certain information specified in Appendices 3 and 4 cannot reasonably be provided for earth stations in the Amateur-Satellite Service.

Resolves

1. that when an administration (or one acting on behalf of a group of named administrations) intends to establish a satellite system in the Amateur-Satellite Service and wishes to publish information with respect to earth stations in the system it may:

1.1 communicate to the IFRB all or part of the information listed in Appendix 3; the IFRB shall publish such information in a special section of its weekly circular requesting comments to be communicated within a period of four months after the date of publication;

1.2 notify under Nos. 1488 to 1491 all or part of the information listed in Appendix 3; the IFRB shall record it in a special list;

2. that this information shall include at least the characteristics of a typical amateur earth station in the amateur-satellite service having the facility to transmit signals to the space station to initiate, modify, or terminate the functions of the space station.

FCC RULES AND REGULATIONS

Part 97—Amateur Radio Service (Adopted December 20, 1994)

Subpart A—General Provisions

§97.3 Definitions.

(a) The definitions of terms used in Part 97 are:

(3) *Amateur-satellite service.* A radiocommunication service using stations on Earth satellites for the same purpose as those of the amateur service.

(15) *Earth station.* An amateur station located on, or within 50 km of the Earth's surface intended for communications with space stations or with other Earth stations by means of one or more other objects in space.

(34) *Radio Regulations.* The latest ITU *Radio Regulations* to which the United States is a party.

(38) *Space station.* An amateur station located more than 50 km above the Earth's surface.

(39) *Space telemetry.* A one-way transmission from a space station of measurements made from the measuring instruments in a spacecraft, including those relating to the functioning of the spacecraft.

(41) *Telecommand.* A one-way transmission to initiate, modify, or terminate functions of a device at a distance.

(42) *Telecommand station.* An amateur station that transmits communications to initiate, modify or terminate functions of a space station.

(43) *Telemetry.* A one-way transmission of measurements at a distance from the measuring instrument.

§97.5 Station license required.

(a) The person having physical control of the station apparatus must have been granted a station license of the type listed in paragraph (b), or hold an unexpired document of the type listed in paragraph (c), before the station may transmit on any amateur service frequency from any place that is:

(1) Within 50 km of the Earth's surface and at a place where the amateur service is regulated by the FCC;

(2) Within 50 km of the Earth's surface and aboard any vessel or craft that is documented or registered in the United States; or

(3) More than 50 km above the Earth's surface aboard any craft that is documented or registered in the United States.

Subpart B—Station Operation Standards

§97.113 Prohibited transmissions.

(e) No station shall retransmit programs or signals emanating from any type of radio station other than an amateur station, except propagation and weather forecast information intended for use by the general public and originated from United States Government stations and communications originating on United States Government frequencies between a space shuttle and its associated Earth stations. Prior approval for such retransmissions must be obtained from the National Aeronautics and Space Administration. Such retransmissions must be for the exclusive use of amateur operators. Propagation, weather forecasts, and shuttle retransmissions may not be conducted on a regular basis, but only occasionally, as an incident of normal amateur radio communications.

Subpart C—Special Operations

§97.207 Space station.

(a) Any amateur station may be a space station. A holder of any class operator license may be the control operator of a space station, subject to the privileges of the class of operator license held by the control operator.

(b) A space station must be capable of effecting cessation of transmissions by telecommand whenever such cessation is ordered by the FCC.

(c) The following frequency bands and segments are authorized to space stations:

(1) The 17 m, 15 m, 12 m and 10 m bands, 6 mm, 4 mm, 2 mm and 1 mm bands; and

(2) The 7.01-7.1 MHz, 14.00-14.25 MHz, 144-146 MHz, 435-438 MHz, 1260-1270 MHz and 2400-2450 MHz, 3.40-3.41 GHz, 5.83-5.85 GHz, 10.45-10.50 GHz and 24.00-24.05 GHz segments.

(d) A space station may automatically retransmit the radio signals of Earth stations and other space stations.

(e) A space station may transmit one-way communications.

(f) Space telemetry transmissions may consist of specially coded messages intended to facilitate communications or related to the function of the spacecraft.

(g) The licensee of each space station must give two written, pre-space station notifications to the Wireless Telecommunications Bureau, FCC, Washington, DC 20554. Each notification must be in accord with the provisions of Articles 11 and 13 of the Radio Regulations.

   (1) The first notification is required no less than 27 months prior to initiating space station transmissions and must specify the information required by Appendix 4 and Resolution No. 642 of the Radio Regulations.

   (2) The second notification is required no less than 5 months prior to initiating space station transmissions and must specify the information required by Appendix 3 and Resolution No. 642 of the Radio Regulations.

(h) The licensee of each space station must give a written, in-space station notification to the Wireless Telecommunications Bureau, FCC, Washington, DC 20554, no later than 7 days following initiation of space station transmissions. The notification must update the information contained in the pre-space notification.

(i) The licensee of each space station must give a written, post-space station notification to the Wireless Telecommunications Bureau, FCC, Washington, DC 20554, no later than 3 months after termination of the space station transmissions. When the termination is ordered by the FCC, notification is required no later than 24 hours after termination.

§97.209 Earth station.

(a) Any amateur station may be an Earth station. A holder of any class operator license may be the control operator of an Earth station, subject to the privileges of the class of operator license held by the control operator.

(b) The following frequency bands and segments are authorized to Earth stations:

   (1) The 17 m, 15 m, 12 m and 10 m bands, 6 mm, 4 mm, 2 mm and 1mm bands; and

   (2) The 7.0-7.1 MHz, 14.00-14.25 MHz, 144-146 MHz, 435-438 MHz, 1260-1270 MHz and 2400-2450 MHz, 3.40-3.41 GHz, 5.83-5.85 GHz, 10.45-10.50 GHz and 24.00-24.05 GHz segments.

§97.211 Space Telecommand station.

(a) Any amateur station designated by the licensee of a space station is eligible to transmit as a telecommand station for that space station, subject to the privileges of the class of operator license held by the control operator.

(b) A telecommand station may transmit special codes intended to obscure the meaning of telecommand messages to the station in space operation.

(c) The following frequency bands and segments are authorized to telecommand stations:

   (1) The 17 m, 15 m, 12 m and 10 m bands, 6 mm, 4 mm, 2 mm, and 1mm bands; and

   (2) The 7.0-7.1 MHz, 14.00-14.25 MHz, 144-146 MHz, 435-438 MHz, 1260-1270 MHz and 2400-2450 MHz, 3.40-3.41 GHz, 5.65-5.67 GHz, 10.45-10.50 GHz and 24.00-24.05 GHz segments.

(d) A telecommand station may transmit one-way communications.

§97.217 Telemetry

Telemetry transmitted by an amateur station on or within 50 km of the Earth's surface is not considered to be codes and ciphers intended to obscure the meaning of communications.

§97.303 Frequency sharing requirements.

[Numerous entries in this section pertain to frequencies allocated to the Amateur-Satellite Service. Due to space limitations only two prominent ones will be listed.]

(f) In the 70 cm band:

   (3) The 430-440 MHz segment is allocated to the amateur service on a secondary basis in ITU Regions 2 and 3. No amateur station transmitting in its band in ITU Regions 2 and 3 shall cause harmful interference to, nor is protected from interference due to the operation of, stations authorized by other nations in the radiolocation service. In ITU Region 1, the 430-440 MHz segment is allocated to the amateur service on a co-primary basis with the radiolocation service. As between these two services in this band in ITU Region 1, the basic principle that applies is the equality of right to operate. Amateur stations authorized by the United States and radiolocation stations authorized by other nations in ITU Region 1 shall operate so as not to cause harmful interference to each other.

(h) No amateur station transmitting in the 23 cm band, the 3 cm band, the 24.05-25.25 GHz segment, the 76-81 GHz segment, the 144-149 GHz segment and the 241-248 GHz segment shall cause harmful interference to, nor is protected from interference due to the operation of, stations authorized by other nations in the radiolocation service.

§97.313 Transmitter power standards.

(a) An amateur station must use the minimum transmitter power necessary to carry out the desired communications.

APPENDIX

G | Satellite Tracking- Graphic Aids

Figure H.1 is a full-size OSCARLOCATOR map board; Figure H.2 is a spiderweb for use with the map. Figure H.3 is a chart used to determine where to point an antenna toward a geostationary satellite. Details on using the OSCARLOCATOR appear in Chapter 7.

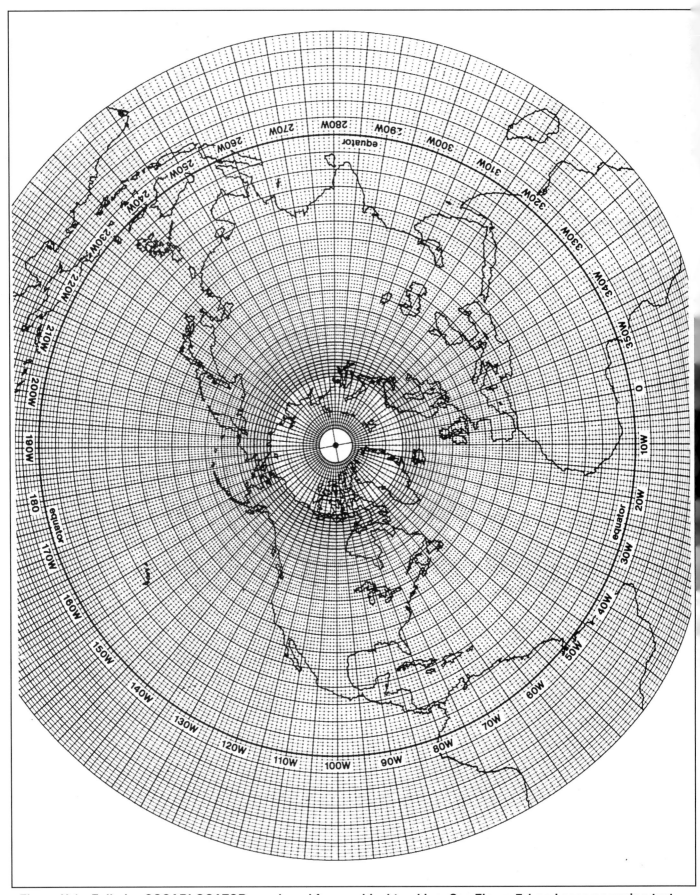

Figure H.1—Full-size OSCARLOCATOR map board for graphical tracking. See Figure 7.1 and accompanying text.

2

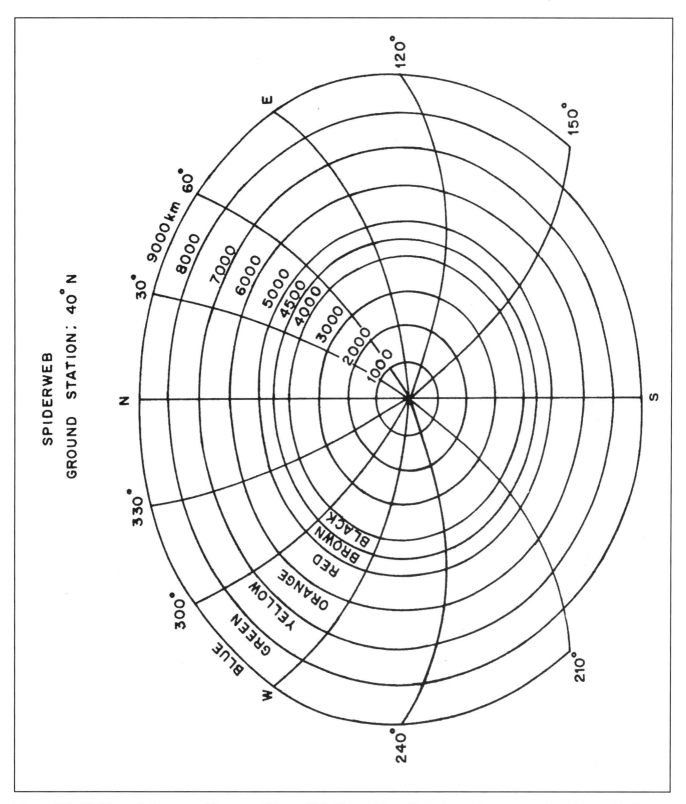

Figure H.2—Spiderweb for use with map of Figure H.1. The spiderweb is drawn for a ground station at 40° N latitude. It will provide reasonable results at nearby latitudes. Appendix D contains a computer program that enables the user to prepare spiderwebs using any distances for a ground station at any latitude.

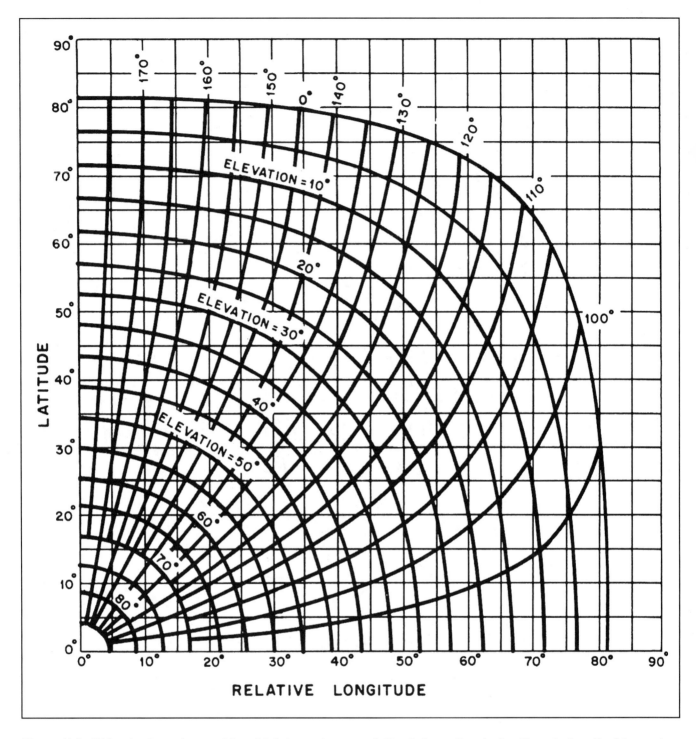

Figure H.3—This chart can be used for obtaining antenna pointing information (azimuth and elevation) toward a geostationary satellite from your ground station. See Figure 7.6 and accompanying text.

Glossary

Note: All terms are defined as they apply to space satellites.

access range: See acquisition distance.

acquisition circle: "Circle" drawn about a ground station and keyed to a specific satellite. When the subsatellite point is inside the circle, the satellite is in range.

acquisition distance: Maximum distance between sub-satellite point and ground station at which access to spacecraft is possible.

alligator: Ground station with high-power transmitter and poor receiver.

altitude: The distance between a satellite and the point on the Earth directly below it. Same as height.

AMSAT: Registered trademark of Radio Amateur Satellite Corporation, PO Box 27, Washington, DC 20044. Also known as AMSAT-NA (North America).

anomalistic period: The elapsed time between two successive perigees of a satellite.

AOS (acquisition of signal): The time at which a particular ground station begins to receive radio signals from a satellite. For calculations, AOS is generally assumed to occur at an elevation angle of 0°.

apogee: Point on orbit where satellite-geocenter distance is maximum.

argument of perigee: The polar angle locating the perigee point of a satellite in the orbital plane; drawn between the ascending node, geocenter and perigee; and measured from the ascending node in direction of satellite motion. When the argument of perigee is between 0 and 180°, perigee is over the Northern Hemisphere. When the argument of perigee is between 180 and 360°, the perigee is over the Southern Hemisphere.

ARISS: Amateur Radio on the International Space Station.

ARRL (American Radio Relay League): Membership organization of radio amateurs in the US. 225 Main St, Newington, CT 06111.

ascending node (EQX): Point on satellite orbit (or ground track) where subsatellite point crosses equator with satellite headed north.

ascending pass: With respect to a particular ground station, a satellite pass during which spacecraft is headed in a northerly direction while in range.

AU (Astronomical Unit): Mean sun-earth distance = 1.49×10^{11} m.

autotransponder: A computer-like device aboard a spacecraft designed to receive and respond to uplink signals directed to it. Several RS spacecraft have carried autotransponders. Also known as a ROBOT.

azimuth: Angle in the horizontal plane measured clockwise with respect to north (north = 0°).

Bahn latitude and longitude (ALAT and ALON): Angles that describe the orientation of a spin stabilized satellite in its orbital plane. When Bahn latitude is 0° and Bahn longitude is 180°, the directional antennas on the satellite will be pointing directly at the SSP when the spacecraft is at apogee.

BCR (battery charge regulator): Electronic control unit on satellite placed between solar cells and battery.

bird: Slang for satellite.

BOL (beginning of life): Usually used in reference to a satellite parameter that changes over time, such as solar-cell efficiency.

boresight: The direction of maximum gain of a spacecraft antenna. Also refers to point on earth where spacecraft antenna produces maximum signal level.

BRAMSAT: AMSAT Brazil.

classical orbital elements: A set of orbital elements, usually including an epoch time specified at perigee, right ascension of ascending node (RAAN), inclination, eccentricity, argument of perigee and period. Because these parameters are Earth-referenced and based on geometrical properties, they're especially useful for intuitively picturing an orbit.

Codestore: A digital memory system aboard early AMSAT spacecraft that could be loaded with data by ground stations for later rebroadcast in Morse or other codes.

coverage circle: (With respect to a particular ground station) the region of Earth that is eventually accessible for communication via a specific satellite; (With respect to a particular satellite) the region around the instantaneous SSP that is in view of the satellite.

DBS (direct broadcast satellite): Commercial satellite designed to transmit TV programming directly to the home; (Direct Broadcast Service): Environmental satellite service designed to be received directly by end user.

decay rate: Short name for rate of change of mean motion. A parameter specifying how atmospheric drag affects a satellite's motion.

delay time: (transponder delay time)—The elapsed time between the instant a signal enters a transponder and the instant it leaves; (path delay time)—the elapsed time between the transmission of an uplink signal and the instant it is received.

descending node: Point on satellite orbit (or ground track) where subsatellite point crosses equator with satellite headed south.

descending pass: With respect to a particular ground station, a satellite pass during which satellite is headed in a southerly direction while in range.

digital transponder: A device that receives a digitally encoded signal, demodulates it and then retransmits it in a digital format. The retransmitted signal may be on the same frequency or a different frequency; may occur after a short time interval or may be on demand; may use the same or different modulation and encoding scheme.

Doppler shift: The observed frequency difference between the transmitted signal and the received signal on a link where the transmitter and receiver are in relative motion.

downlink: A radio link originating at a spacecraft and terminating at one or more ground stations.

eccentricity: A parameter used to describe the shape of the ellipse constituting a satellite orbit.

EIRP: Effective isotropic radiated power.

elevation: Angle above the horizontal plane.

elevation circle: On a map or globe, the set of all points about a ground station where the elevation angle to a specified satellite is a fixed value.

EME (Earth-Moon-Earth): Communication mode that involves bouncing signals off the Moon.

epoch (epoch time): A reference time at which orbital elements are specified.

equatorial plane: An imaginary plane, extending throughout space, that contains the equator of the primary body (often the Earth).

EQX: Ascending node.

ESA (European Space Agency): A consortium of European governmental groups pooling resources for space exploration and development.

footprint: A set of signal-level contours, drawn on map or globe, showing the performance of a high-gain satellite antenna. Usually applied to geostationary satellites.

geocenter: Center of the oblate spheroid used to represent the Earth.

geostationary satellite: A satellite that appears to hang motionless over a fixed point on the equator.

GPS (Global Positioning System): A series of satellites designed to be used for position determination on the surface of the Earth. Experiments on P3D use signals from the GPS for position and attitude determination.

ground station: A radio station, on or near the surface of the Earth, designed to receive signals from, or transmit signals to, a spacecraft.

ground track (subsatellite path): Path on surface of Earth traced out by SSP as satellite moves through space.

HELAPS: A technique for producing high-efficiency linear transponders. Developed by Dr Karl Meinzer, DJ4ZC.

IARU: International Amateur Radio Union.

IHU (Integrated Housekeeping Unit): The onboard computer and associated electronics used to control a spacecraft.

inclination: The angle between the orbital plane of a satellite and the equatorial plane of the Earth.

increment: See longitudinal increment.

IPS (Interpreter for Process Structures): A high-level, FORTH-like language employed as an operating system on the computers aboard several OSCAR satellites. Developed by Dr Karl Meinzer, DJ4ZC.

ITU (International Telecommunication Union): International organization responsible for coordinating use of radio spectrum.

JAMSAT: AMSAT Japan.

JARL: Japan Amateur Radio League

Keplerian orbital elements: A set of *orbital elements* specified at an arbitrary epoch time, that include mean anomaly, right ascension of ascending node (RAAN), inclination, eccentricity, argument of perigee and mean motion (or period or semi-major axis). Closely related to classical orbital elements.

LEO (Low Earth Orbit): Generally refers to heights between 200 and 3000 km.

linear transponder: A device that receives radio signals in one segment of the spectrum, amplifies them linearly, translates (shifts) their frequency to another segment of the spectrum and retransmits them.

line of nodes: The line of intersection of a satellite's orbital plane and the Earth's equatorial plane.

LNA (low-noise amplifier): Term sometimes used for the device that radio amateurs generally refer to as a low-noise preamp.

longitudinal increment: Change in longitude of ascending node between two successive passes of specified satellite. Measured in degrees west per orbit (°W/orbit).

LOS (loss of signal): The time at which a particular ground station loses radio signals from a satellite. For calculations, LOS is generally assumed to occur at an elevation angle of 0°.

maximum access distance: The maximum distance, measured along the surface of the Earth, between a ground station and the subsatellite point at which the satellite enters one's range circle. (Corresponds to a 0° elevation angle.)

mean anomaly (MA): A number that increases uniformly with time, used to locate satellite position on orbital ellipse. For OSCAR satellites, MA varies from 0 to 256. When MA is 0 or 256, satellite is at perigee. When MA is 128, satellite is at apogee. When MA is between 0 and 128, satellite is headed up toward apogee. When MA is between 128 and 256, satellite is headed down toward perigee. Astronomers usually work with an MA that varies from 0 to 360.

mean motion: Number of revolutions (perigee to perigee) completed by satellite in a solar day (1440 minutes).

microsat: Small satellite, generally in the range of 10 to 100 kg.

minisat: Small satellite, generally in the range of 100 to 500 kg.

Mir: Russian Space Station.

Molniya: Series of communications satellites produced by USSR. Orbits selected for AMSAT Phase 3 satellites were patterned after the Molniya series.

NASA: US National Aeronautics and Space Administration.

NASDA: Japanese National Space Development Agency.

nodal period: The elapsed time between two successive ascending nodes of a satellite.

node: Point where satellite ground track crosses the equator.

OBC (onboard computer): The central computer that controls spacecraft functions.

orbital elements: Set of six numbers, specified at a particular time (epoch), that completely describe size, shape and orientation of satellite orbit.

orbital plane: An imaginary plane, extending throughout space, that contains a satellite's orbital track.

OSCAR: Orbiting Satellite Carrying Amateur Radio.

OSCARLOCATOR: A tracking device designed for satellites in circular orbits.

pass: See satellite pass.

PCA (point of closest approach): Point on segment of satellite orbit, or ground track, at which satellite is closest to specific ground station.

perigee: Point on orbit where satellite-geocenter distance is a minimum.

period: The amount of time it takes a satellite to complete one revolution about the earth. See anomalistic period and nodal period.

phase: See mean anomaly.

Phase 3 Tracker: A tracking device related to the OSCARLOCATOR that is designed to be used with a satellite in an elliptical orbit.

picosat: small satellite, generally under 10 kg.

point of closest approach: See PCA.

RAAN (right ascension of ascending node): An angle that specifies the orientation of a satellite's orbital plane with respect to the fixed stars. The angular distance, measured eastward along the celestial equator, between the vernal equinox and the hour circle of the ascending node of the spacecraft.

range circle: On a map or globe, "circle" of specific radius centered about ground station.

reference orbit: First orbit of UTC day for satellite specified.

Satellabe: A tracking device for circular orbits. Similar to OSCARLOCATOR, but with added features.

satellite pass: Segment of orbit during which satellite passes in range of particular ground station.

s/c: Informal abbreviation for spacecraft.

semi-major axis (SMA): Half the long axis of an ellipse. Can be used to describe the size of an elliptical orbit in place of the orbital element mean motion.

sidereal day: The amount of time it takes the Earth to rotate exactly 360° about its axis with respect to the "fixed" stars. The sidereal day contains approximately 1436.07 minutes (see solar day).

slant range: Distance between satellite and a particular ground station at time specified.

SMA: See semi-major axis.

solar constant: Incident energy 1 AU from the sun falling on a plane surface of unit area oriented perpendicular to the direction of radiation. Value is approximately 1.38 kW/m².

solar day: The solar day, by definition, contains exactly 24 hours (1440 minutes). During the solar day, the Earth rotates slightly more than 360° with respect to "fixed" stars (see sidereal day).

spiderweb: On a map or globe, set of azimuth curves radiating outward from, and concentric elevation "circles" about, a particular terrestrial location.

squint angle: Angle between primary axis of satellite antenna and line between satellite and ground station. The size of the squint angle depends on the location of the ground station. With P3D, ground stations at the SSP will see a squint angle of zero.

SSP: Subsatellite point.

stationary satellite: See geostationary satellite.

subsatellite path: See ground track.

subsatellite point (SSP): Point on surface of Earth directly below satellite.

telemetry: Radio signals, originating at a satellite, that convey information on the performance or status of onboard subsystems. Also refers to the information itself.

TCA (time of closest approach): Time at which satellite passes closest to a specific ground station during orbit of interest.

TLM: Short for telemetry.

transponder: See linear transponder and digital transponder.

true anomaly: The polar angle that locates a satellite in the orbital plane. Drawn between the perigee, geocenter and current satellite position, and measured from perigee in direction of satellite motion.

TVRO (TV receive only): A TVRO terminal is a ground station set up to receive downlink signals from 4-GHz or 12-GHz commercial satellites carrying TV programming.

uplink: A radio link originating at a ground station and directed to a spacecraft.

WARC: World Administrative Radio Conference organized by ITU. Now called WRC.

WRC: World Radio Conference organized by ITU.

window: For a specific satellite, the overlap region between acquisition "circles" of two ground stations. Communication between the two stations via the specified satellite is possible when SSP passes through window.

ZRO test: Contest that involves ground stations attempting to receive very weak reference signals being retransmitted through a satellite transponder. Named in memory of K2ZRO for his important contributions to the OSCAR program.

About the ARRL

The seed for Amateur Radio was planted in the 1890s, when Guglielmo Marconi began his experiments in wireless telegraphy. Soon he was joined by dozens, then hundreds, of others who were enthusiastic about sending and receiving messages through the air—some with a commercial interest, but others solely out of a love for this new communications medium. The United States government began licensing Amateur Radio operators in 1912.

By 1914, there were thousands of Amateur Radio operators—hams—in the United States. Hiram Percy Maxim, a leading Hartford, Connecticut, inventor and industrialist, saw the need for an organization to band together this fledgling group of radio experimenters. In May 1914 he founded the American Radio Relay League (ARRL) to meet that need.

Today ARRL, with approximately 170,000 members, is the largest organization of radio amateurs in the United States. The ARRL is a not-for-profit organization that:

• promotes interest in Amateur Radio communications and experimentation

• represents US radio amateurs in legislative matters, and

• maintains fraternalism and a high standard of conduct among Amateur Radio operators.

At ARRL headquarters in the Hartford suburb of Newington, the staff helps serve the needs of members. ARRL is also International Secretariat for the International Amateur Radio Union, which is made up of similar societies in 150 countries around the world.

ARRL publishes the monthly journal *QST*, as well as newsletters and many publications covering all aspects of Amateur Radio. Its headquarters station, W1AW, transmits bulletins of interest to radio amateurs and Morse code practice sessions. The ARRL also coordinates an extensive field organization, which includes volunteers who provide technical information and other support for radio amateurs as well as communications for public-service activities. ARRL also represents US amateurs with the Federal Communications Commission and other government agencies in the US and abroad.

Membership in ARRL means much more than receiving *QST* each month. In addition to the services already described, ARRL offers membership services on a personal level, such as the ARRL Volunteer Examiner Coordinator Program and a QSL bureau.

Full ARRL membership (available only to licensed radio amateurs) gives you a voice in how the affairs of the organization are governed. ARRL policy is set by a Board of Directors (one from each of 15 Divisions). Each year, one-third of the ARRL Board of Directors stands for election by the full members they represent. The day-to-day operation of ARRL HQ is managed by an Executive Vice President and a Chief Financial Officer.

No matter what aspect of Amateur Radio attracts you, ARRL membership is relevant and important. There would be no Amateur Radio as we know it today were it not for the ARRL. We would be happy to welcome you as a member! (An Amateur Radio license is not required for Associate Membership.) For more information about ARRL and answers to any questions you may have about Amateur Radio, write or call:

ARRL—The national association for Amateur Radio
New Ham Desk
225 Main Street
Newington CT 06111-1494
860-594-0200

Prospective new amateurs call:
800-32-NEW HAM (800-326-3942)
You can also contact us via e-mail at **newham@arrl.org**
or check out *ARRLWeb* at **http://www.arrl.org/**

Index

FEEDBACK

Please use this form to give us your comments on this book and what you'd like to see in future editions, or e-mail us at **pubsfdbk@arrl.org** (publications feedback). If you use e-mail, please include your name, call, e-mail address and the book title, edition and printing in the body of your message. Also indicate whether or not you are an ARRL member.

Where did you purchase this book?
☐ From ARRL directly ☐ From an ARRL dealer

Is there a dealer who carries ARRL publications within:
☐ 5 miles ☐ 15 miles ☐ 30 miles of your location? ☐ Not sure.

License class:
☐ Novice ☐ Technician ☐ Technician Plus ☐ General ☐ Advanced ☐ Amateur Extra

---

Name _____ ARRL member? ☐ Yes ☐ No

_____ Call Sign _____

Daytime Phone ( ) _____ Age _____

Address _____

City, State/Province, ZIP/Postal Code _____

If licensed, how long? _____ E-mail _____

Other hobbies_____

_____

Occupation _____

For ARRL use only	SAT HB
Edition	1 2 3 4 5 6 7 8 9 10 11 12
Printing	4 5 6 7 8 9 10 11 12

From _____

_____

_____

EDITOR, SATELLITE HANDBOOK
AMERICAN RADIO RELAY LEAGUE
225 MAIN STREET
NEWINGTON CT 06111-1494

— — — — — — — — — — — — — — — — — please fold and tape — — — — — — — — — — — — — — — — — —